2020

The ARRL
HANDBOOK
FOR RADIO COMMUNICATIONS

NINETY-SEVENTH EDITION

Volume 1: Introduction and Fundamental Theory — Ch. 1-4

Volume 2: Practical Design and Principles Part 1 — Ch. 5-11

Volume 3: Practical Design and Principles Part 2 — Ch. 12-18

Volume 4: Antenna Systems and Radio Propagation — Ch. 19-21

Volume 5: Equipment Construction and Station Accessories — Ch. 22-24

▶ **Volume 6:** Test Equipment, Troubleshooting, RFI, and Index — Ch. 25-28

Editor
H. Ward Silver, NØAX

Contributing Editors
Steven R. Ford, WB8IMY
Mark J. Wilson, K1RO

Editorial Assistant
Maty Weinberg, KB1EIB

Technical Consultants
Bob Allison, WB1GCM
Edward F. Hare, Jr., W1RFI
Zachary H.J. Lau, W1VT

Cover Design
Sue Fagan, KB1OKW
Bob Inderbitzen, NQ1R

Production
Michelle Bloom, WB1ENT
Jodi Morin, KA1JPA
David F. Pingree, N1NAS

Additional Contributors to the 2020 Edition
John Brooks, N9ZL
Jim Brown, K9YC
Glen Brown, W6GJB
Ralph Crumrine, NØKC

Don Daso, K4ZA
Joel Hallas, W1ZR
Bill Koch, W2RMA
Rick Lindquist, WW1ME
Glenn Loake, GØGBI
Helmut Berka, DL2MAJ
Oliver Micic, DG7XO
Carl Luetzelschwab, K9LA
Phil Salas, AD5X
Rob Sherwood, NCØB
Cory Sickles, WA3UVV
George Steber, WB9LVI
Jim Tonne, W4ENE
Paul Wade, W1GHZ

Published by:
ARRL The national association for AMATEUR RADIO®
225 Main Street, Newington, CT 06111-1400 USA
www.arrl.org

Copyright © 2019 by
The American Radio Relay League, Inc.

Copyright secured under the Pan-American Convention

International Copyright secured

All rights reserved. No part of this work may be reproduced in any form except by written permission of the publisher. All rights of translation are reserved.

Printed in the USA

Quedan reservados todos los derechos

ISBN: 978-1-62595-107-6 Softcover
ISBN: 978-1-62595-113-7 Six-Volume Set

Kindle eBook Editions
 ISBN: 978-1-62595-091-8 — Volume 1
 ISBN: 978-1-62595-092-5 — Volume 2
 ISBN: 978-1-62595-093-2 — Volume 3
 ISBN: 978-1-62595-094-9 — Volume 4
 ISBN: 978-1-62595-095-6 — Volume 5
 ISBN: 978-1-62595-096-3 — Volume 6

Ninety-Seventh Edition

About the cover:
The collection of components comprises the HF Packer miniHFPA2 amplifier kit. Although the kit is not featured in this 2020 edition of the ARRL Handbook, its components represent the spirit of project design and craftsmanship that has been part of Amateur Radio from the beginning.

Contents

A more detailed Table of Contents is included at the beginning of each chapter.

VOLUME 1

INTRODUCTION AND FUNDAMENTAL THEORY

1 **What is Amateur (Ham) Radio?**
1.1 Do-It-Yourself Wireless
1.2 Joining the Ham Radio Community
1.3 Your Ham Radio Station
1.4 Getting on the Air
1.5 Your Ham Radio "Lifestyle"
1.6 Public Service
1.7 Ham Radio in the Classroom
1.8 Resources
1.9 Glossary

2 **Electrical Fundamentals**
2.1 Introduction to Electricity
2.2 Resistance and Conductance
2.3 Basic Circuit Principles
2.4 Power and Energy
2.5 Circuit Control Components
2.6 Capacitance and Capacitors
2.7 Inductance and Inductors
2.8 Semiconductor Devices
2.9 References and Bibliography

3 **Radio Fundamentals**
3.1 AC Waveforms
3.2 Measuring AC Voltage, Current and Power
3.3 Effective Radiated Power
3.4 AC in Capacitors and Inductors
3.5 Working with Reactance
3.6 Impedance
3.7 Quality Factor (Q) of Components
3.8 Resonant Circuits
3.9 Analog Signal Processing
3.10 Electromagnetic Waves
3.11 References and Bibliography

4 **Circuits and Components**
4.1 Practical Resistors
4.2 Practical Capacitors
4.3 Practical Inductors
4.4 Transformers
4.5 Practical Semiconductors
4.6 Amplifiers
4.7 Operational Amplifiers
4.8 Miscellaneous Analog ICs
4.9 Analog-Digital Interfacing
4.10 Analog Device and Circuits Glossary
4.11 Heat Management
4.12 References and Bibliography

VOLUME 2

PRACTICAL DESIGN AND PRINCIPLES — PART 1

5   RF Techniques
5.1 Introduction
5.2 Lumped-Element versus Distributed Characteristics
5.3 Effects of Parasitic (Stray) Characteristics
5.4 Semiconductor Circuits at RF
5.5 Ferrite Materials
5.6 Impedance Matching Networks
5.7 RF Transformers
5.8 Noise
5.9 Two-Port Networks
5.10 RF Design Techniques Glossary
5.11 References and Bibliography

6   Computer-Aided Circuit Design
6.1 Circuit Simulation Overview
6.2 Simulation Basics
6.3 Limitations of Simulation at RF
6.4 Electromagnetic Analysis of RF Circuits
6.5 References and Bibliography

7   Power Sources
7.1 Power Processing
7.2 AC-AC Power Conversion
7.3 Power Transformers
7.4 AC-DC Power Conversion
7.5 Voltage Multipliers
7.6 Current Multipliers
7.7 Rectifier Types
7.8 Power Filtering
7.9 Power Supply Regulation
7.10 "Crowbar" Protective Circuits
7.11 DC-DC Switchmode Power Conversion
7.12 High-Voltage Techniques
7.13 Batteries
7.14 Glossary of Power Source Terms
7.15 References and Bibliography
7.16 Power Supply Projects

8   DSP and SDR Fundamentals
8.1 Introduction to DSP
8.2 Introduction to SDR
8.3 Analog-Digital Conversion
8.4 Data Converters for SDR and DSP
8.5 Digital Signal Processors
8.6 Digital (Discrete-time) Signals
8.7 The Fourier Transform
8.8 Glossary of DSP and SDR Terms
8.9 References and Bibliography

9   Oscillators and Synthesizers
9.1 How Oscillators Work
9.2 LC Variable Frequency Oscillator (VFO) Circuits
9.3 Building an Oscillator
9.4 Crystal Oscillators
9.5 Oscillators at UHF and Above
9.6 Frequency Synthesizers
9.7 Phase Noise
9.8 Glossary of Oscillator and Synthesizer Terms
9.9 References and Bibliography

10   Analog and Digital Filtering
10.1 Introduction
10.2 Filter Basics
10.3 Passive LC Filters
10.4 Active Audio Filters
10.5 Digital Filters
10.6 Quartz Crystal Filters
10.7 SAW Filters
10.8 Transmission Line VHF/UHF/Microwave Filters
10.9 Helical Resonators
10.11 Filter Projects
10.12 Glossary of Filter Terms
10.13 References and Bibliography

11   Modulation
11.1 Introduction
11.2 Amplitude Modulation (AM)
11.3 Angle Modulation
11.4 FSK and PSK
11.5 Quadrature Modulation
11.6 Analytic Signals and Modulation
11.7 Image Modulation
11.8 Spread Spectrum Modulation
11.9 Pulse Modulation
11.10 Modulation Bandwidth and Impairments
11.11 Glossary of Modulation Terms
11.12 References and Further Reading

VOLUME 3

PRACTICAL DESIGN AND PRINCIPLES — PART 2

12 Receiving
12.1 Characterizing Receivers
12.2 Heterodyne Receivers
12.3 SDR Receivers
12.4 Mixing and Mixers
12.5 Demodulation and Detection
12.6 Automatic Gain Control (AGC)
12.7 Noise Management
12.8 References and Bibliography

13 Transmitting
13.1 Characterizing Transmitters
13.2 Transmitter Architecture
13.3 Modulators
13.4 Transmitting CW
13.5 Transmitting AM and SSB
13.6 Transmitting Angle Modulation
13.7 Effects of Transmitted Noise
13.8 Microphones and Speech Processing
13.9 Voice Operation
13.10 Transmitter Power Stages
13.11 References and Bibliography

14 Transceiver Design Topics
14.1 Signal Chains in SDR Transceivers
14.2 User Interfaces
14.3 Configuration and Control Interfaces
14.4 SDR Design Tools

15 Digital Protocols and Modes
15.1 Digital "Modes"
15.2 Unstructured Digital Modes
15.3 Fuzzy Modes
15.4 Structured Digital Modes
15.5 Networking Modes
15.6 Digital Mode Table
15.7 Glossary of Digital Protocol and Mode Terms
15.8 References and Bibliography

16 Amateur Radio Data Platforms
16.1 Platform Overview
16.2 Sensors
16.3 Navigation Data and Telemetry
16.4 Payloads
16.5 High Altitude Balloon Platforms
16.6 Unmanned Aerial Vehicles (UAVs)
16.7 Rockets
16.8 Robotics
16.9 Fixed Stations
16.10 References and Bibliography

17 RF Power Amplifiers
17.1 High Power, Who Needs It?
17.2 Types of Power Amplifiers
17.3 Vacuum Tube Basics
17.4 Tank Circuits
17.5 Transmitting Tube Ratings
17.6 Sources of Operating Voltages
17.7 Tube Amplifier Cooling
17.8 Vacuum Tube Amplifier Stabilization
17.9 MOSFET Design for RF Amplifiers
17.10 Solid-State RF Amplifiers
17.11 Solid State Amplifier Projects
17.12 Tube Amplifier Projects
17.13 References and Bibliography

18 Repeaters
18.1 A Brief History
18.2 Repeater Overview
18.3 FM Voice Repeaters
18.4 D-STAR Repeater Systems
18.5 System Fusion Repeater Systems
18.6 Digital Mobile Radio (DMR)
18.7 Other Digital Voice Repeater Technologies
18.8 Glossary of FM and Repeater Terminology
18.9 References and Bibliography

VOLUME 4

ANTENNA SYSTEMS AND RADIO PROPAGATION

19 Propagation of Radio Signals
19.1 Fundamentals of Radio Waves
19.2 Sky-Wave Propagation and the Sun
19.3 MUF Predictions
19.4 Propagation in the Troposphere
19.5 VHF/UHF Mobile Propagation
19.6 Propagation for Space Communications
19.7 Noise and Propagation
19.8 Propagation Below the AM Broadcast Band
19.9 Glossary of Radio Propagation Terms
19.10 References and Bibliography

20 Transmission Lines
20.1 Transmission Line Basics
20.2 Choosing a Transmission Line
20.3 The Transmission Line as Impedance Transformer
20.4 Matching Impedances in the Antenna System
20.5 Baluns and Transmission-Line Transformers
20.6 PC Transmission Lines
20.7 Waveguides
20.8 Glossary of Transmission Line Terms
20.9 References and Bibliography

21 Antennas
21.1 Antenna Basics
21.2 Dipoles and the Half-Wave Antenna
21.3 Vertical (Ground-Plane) Antennas
21.4 T and Inverted-L Antennas
21.5 Slopers and Vertical Dipoles
21.6 Yagi Antennas
21.7 Quad and Loop Antennas
21.8 HF Mobile Antennas
21.9 VHF/UHF Mobile Antennas
21.10 VHF/UHF Antennas
21.11 VHF/UHF Beams
21.12 Radio Direction Finding Antennas
21.13 Rotators
21.13 Glossary
21.14 References and Bibliography

VOLUME 5

EQUIPMENT CONSTRUCTION AND STATION ACCESSORIES

22 Component Data and References
22.1 Component Data
22.2 Resistors
22.3 Capacitors
22.4 Inductors
22.5 Transformers
22.6 Semiconductors
22.7 Tubes, Wire, Materials, Attenuators, Miscellaneous
22.8 Computer Connectors
22.9 RF Connectors and Transmission Lines
22.10 Reference Tables

23 Construction Techniques
23.1 Electronic Shop Safety
23.2 Tools and Their Use
23.3 Soldering Tools and Techniques
23.4 Surface Mount Technology (SMT)
23.5 Constructing Electronic Circuits
23.6 CAD for PCB Design
23.7 Microwave Construction
23.8 Mechanical Fabrication

24 Assembling a Station
24.1 Fixed Stations
24.2 Mobile Installations
24.3 Portable Installations
24.4 Remote Stations

VOLUME 6

TEST EQUIPMENT, TROUBLESHOOTING, RFI, AND INDEX

25 Test Equipment and Measurements
25.1 Introduction
25.2 DC Measurements
25.3 AC Measurements
25.4 RF Measurements
25.5 Receiver Measurements
25.6 Transmitter Measurements
25.7 Antenna System Measurements
25.8 Miscellaneous Measurements
25.9 Construction Projects
25.10 References and Further Reading
25.11 Glossary of Test Equipment and Measurement Terms

26 Troubleshooting and Maintenance
26.1 Test Equipment
26.2 Components
26.3 Getting Started
26.4 Inside the Equipment
26.5 Testing at the Circuit Level
26.6 After the Repairs
26.7 Professional Repairs
26.8 Typical Symptoms and Faults
26.9 Radio Troubleshooting Hints
26.10 Antenna Systems
26.11 Repair and Restoration of Vintage Equipment
26.12 References and Bibliography

27 RF Interference
27.1 Managing Radio Frequency Interference
27.2 FCC Rules and Regulations
27.3 Elements of RFI
27.4 Identifying the Type of RFI Source
27.5 Locating Sources of RFI
27.6 Power-Line Noise
27.7 Elements of RFI Control
27.8 Troubleshooting RFI
27.9 Automotive RFI
27.10 RFI Projects
27.11 Glossary of RFI Terms
27.12 References and Bibliography

28 Safety
28.1 Electrical Safety
28.2 Antenna and Tower Safety
28.3 RF Safety

Advertiser's Index
Index
Project Index
Author's Index

DOWNLOADABLE CONTENT AND TOOLS
Space Communications
Digital Communications
Image Communications
Digital Basics
Station Accessories and Projects
2020 HF Transceiver Survey
Radio Mathematics

Contents

25.1 Introduction
    25.1.1 Measurement Standards
    25.1.2 Measurement Accuracy
25.2 DC Measurements
    25.2.1 Basic Vocabulary and Units
    25.2.2 Multimeters
    25.2.3 Panel Meters
25.3 AC Measurements
    25.3.1 Basic Vocabulary and Units
    25.3.2 Using Multimeters for AC Measurements
    25.3.3 Measuring Frequency and Time
    25.3.4 Oscilloscopes
    25.3.5 Audio-Frequency Oscillators and Function Generators
    25.3.6 Measuring Inductance and Capacitance
25.4 RF Measurements
    25.4.1 Measuring RF Voltage and Current
    25.4.2 Measuring RF Power
    25.4.3 Spectrum Analyzers
    25.4.4 Measuring RF Impedance
    25.4.5 Network Analyzers
    25.4.6 RF Signal Generators
    25.4.7 Using Noise Sources
    25.4.8 RF and Microwave Test Accessories
25.5 Receiver Measurements
    25.5.1 Standard ARRL Lab Tests
    25.5.2 Other Common Receiver Measurements
25.6 Transmitter Measurements
    25.6.1 Standard ARRL Lab Tests
    25.6.2 Other Common Transmitter Measurements
25.7 Antenna System Measurements
    25.7.1 Field Strength Measurements
    25.7.2 SWR Meters
    25.7.3 Noise Bridges
    25.7.4 Antenna Analyzers
    25.7.5 Time-Domain Reflectometry
25.8 Miscellaneous Measurements
    25.8.1 Testing Digital Circuitry
    25.8.2 Service Monitors
    25.8.3 Testing Digital Modulation
    25.8.4 Software-based Test Equipment
25.9 Construction Projects
    25.9.1 Bipolar Transistor Tester
    25.9.2 Logic Probe
    25.9.3 Inductance Tester
    25.9.4 Fixed-Frequency Audio Oscillator
    25.9.5 Wide-Range Audio Oscillator
    25.9.6 Two-Tone Audio Generator
    25.9.7 RF Current Meter
    25.9.8 RF Ammeters
    25.9.9 RF Step Attenuator
    25.9.10 High-Power RF Samplers
    25.9.11 RF Oscillators for Circuit Alignment
    25.9.12 Hybrid Combiners for Signal Generators
    25.9.13 Gate-Dip Oscillator (GDO)
    25.9.14 RF Power Meter
    25.9.15 RF Voltmeter
    25.9.16 A Low-Frequency VNA Adapter
25.10 References and Further Reading
    25.10.1 References
    25.10.2 Further Reading
25.11 Test and Measurement Glossary

Chapter 25 — Downloadable Supplemental Content

Supplemental Files
- Test and Measurement Bibliography
- Papers on Receiver Testing and Performance by Rob Sherwood, NC0B
  - "Receiver Noise Floor and Band Noise"
  - "Reciprocal Mixing Test Procedure"
  - "Sherwood Lab Setup for Dynamic Range Measurements"
  - "Terms Explained for the Sherwood Table of Receiver Performance"
- "Antenna Analyzer Pet Tricks" by Paul Wade, W1GHZ

Project Files
- Gate Dip Oscillator articles and PCB artwork — Alan Bloom, N1AL
- Build a Return Loss Bridge — James Ford, N6JF
- Logic Probe — supporting photos and graphics — Alan Bloom, N1AL
- RF Power Meter — supporting files — William Kaune, W7IEQ
- Compensated RF Voltmeter articles — Sidney Cooper, K2QHE
- "Noise Instrumentation and Measurement" by Paul Wade W1GHZ
- RF Sampler Construction details — Thomas Thompson, W0IVJ
- RF Step Attenuator — Denton Bramwell, K7OWJ
- Tandem Match articles — John Grebenkemper, KI6WX
- Transistor Tester — PCB artwork and layout graphics — Alan Bloom, N1AL
- Two-Tone Oscillator — PCB artwork and layout graphics — ARRL Lab
- "A Low Frequency Adapter for your Vector Network Analyzer (VNA)" by Jacques Audet, VE2AZX
- "No-Fibbin'" RF Field Strength Meter," by John Noakes, VE7NI
- "Apparatus for RF Measurements" by Bruce Pontius, N0ADL, and Kai Siwiak, KE4PT

Chapter 25

Test Equipment and Measurements

This chapter, originally written by Alan Bloom, N1AL, covers test equipment and measurement techniques common to Amateur Radio. Along with the 2018 edition's new section on Antenna System Measurements, the downloadable supplemental information includes four new papers by Rob Sherwood, NC0B, on receiver testing and performance, and a paper by Paul Wade, W1GHZ on antenna analyzer applications.

The initial sections discuss ac, dc, and RF measurements and describe what to look for in commercially available test equipment. The concluding sections discuss transmitter and receiver performance testing, including the standard tests performed by the ARRL Lab. A selection of simple test equipment construction projects is presented as well.

25.1 Introduction

According to the great physicist Sir William Thomson, Lord Kelvin, (1824-1907) "When you can measure what you are speaking about, and express it in numbers, you know something about it; but when you cannot measure it, when you cannot express it in numbers, your knowledge is of a meager and unsatisfactory kind." This is the purpose of electronic test and measurement, to express the characteristics and performance of electronic devices in numbers that can be observed, recorded and compared.

The amateur should undertake to master basic electronic and test instruments: the multimeter, oscilloscope, signal generator, RF power meter and SWR and impedance analyzers. This chapter, written by Alan Bloom, N1AL is the reader's guide to these instruments and the physical parameters they measure. The chapter goes beyond basic instrumentation to advanced instruments and measurements that are often encountered by amateurs. The material does not attempt to be complete in covering all available instruments and measurements. The goal of the chapter is to instruct and educate, present useful projects, and encourage the reader to understand more about these important facets of the radio art.

25.1.1 Measurement Standards

The measurement process involves evaluating the characteristic being tested using a *standard*, which is a rule for determining the proper numbers to assign to the measurement. In the past, instruments were calibrated to standards represented by physical objects. For example, the reference standard for length was a platinum bar, exactly 1.0 meters long, stored in an environmentally-controlled vault in Paris, France. In the latter part of the 20th century, most measurements were redefined based on fundamental physical constants. In 1983 the meter was defined as the distance traveled by light in free space in 1/299,792,458 second.

While most common everyday measurements in the United States still use the old Imperial system (feet, inches, pounds, gallons, and so on), electronic measurements are based on the international system of units, called *SI* after the French name *Système International d'Unités*, which is the modern, revised version of the metric system. The SI defines seven base units, which are length (meter, m), time (second, s), mass (kilogram, kg), temperature (kelvin, K), amount of substance (mole, mol), current (ampere, A), and light intensity (candela, cd). All other units are derived from those seven. For example, the unit of electric charge, the coulomb, is proportional to s × A and the volt has the dimensions $m^2 \times kg \times s^{-3} \times A^{-1}$.

In the United States, measurement standards are managed by the *National Institute of Standards and Technology* (NIST), a non-regulatory agency of the federal government which until 1988 was called the National Bureau of Standards (NBS).[1] (Notes may be found in the References section.) NIST's services include calibration of *transfer standards*. The transfer standards in turn are used to calibrate *working standards* which are used by companies to calibrate and measure their products. Such products are said to be *NIST traceable* if the rules and procedures specified by NIST have been followed. Most low-cost instruments used by hobbyists are another level down in accuracy, being calibrated by instruments that themselves may or may not be NIST traceable.

25.1.2 Measurement Accuracy

Accuracy and resolution are different specifications that are often confused. *Resolution* is the smallest distinguishable difference in a measured value. *Accuracy* is the maximum expected error in the measurement. For example an 8-digit frequency counter can measure the frequency of a 100 MHz signal to a resolution of 1 Hz, which is 0.01 ppm (parts per million). However, accuracy is determined by the time-base oscillator used as a reference, which typically would be significantly less accurate than 0.01 ppm in a low-cost instrument. Similarly, many digital voltmeters can display measurements to more digits of resolution than their accuracy permits. The extra resolution can be useful when comparing two or more values that differ only slightly because closely-spaced measurements tend to have nearly the same error. The difference can then be measured more accurately than the individual values.

An instrument's accuracy can be specified in absolute or relative terms or sometimes in both. An example of an absolute specification is an RF power meter with an accuracy of "5% of full scale." If the full-scale reading is 100 W, then the accuracy is plus or minus 5 W at all power levels. Theoretically a reading of 10 W could represent an actual power of 5 W to 15 W.

An example of a relative accuracy specification is an analog voltmeter with an accuracy of 3%. That means a voltage of 1.000 V can be measured to an accuracy of plus or minus 0.030 V. A voltage of 10.000 V can be measured to an accuracy of plus or minus 0.3 V. An example of a combined absolute and relative accuracy specification is a frequency counter with an accuracy of "1 ppm plus one count." When measuring a 100 kHz signal with 1 Hz resolution, one count is 10 ppm of the 100 kHz signal. The total accuracy is 1 + 10 = 11 ppm, or ±1.1 Hz.

An important point is that measurement error is not a mistake but rather a natural result of the imperfections inherent in any measurement. The sources of error can be sorted into several general classes. *Systematic error* is repeatable; it is always the same when the measurement is taken in the same way. An example is the inaccuracy of the voltage reference in a digital voltmeter that causes all measurements to be off by the same percentage in the same direction. *Random error* is caused by noise and results in a different measured value each time it is measured. Receiver sensitivity measurements involve measuring the signal-to-noise ratio of the audio output which varies due to the random fluctuations of the noise level.

Dynamic error results when the value being measured changes with time. The peak-envelope power (PEP) of a single-sideband transmitter varies with the modulation that is present at the particular time the measurement is taken. *Instrument insertion error* (also called *loading error*) is an often-overlooked factor. For example, a voltmeter must draw at least a little current from the circuit under test in order to perform the measurement, which can affect circuit operation. When performing high-frequency measurements, the capacitance of the measurement probe often can be significant.

25.2 DC Measurements

In discussions of instruments and measurements, the abbreviation *dc* generally refers to currents and voltages that remain stable during the measurement. If the dc current or voltage changes rapidly, it is said to have an *ac component* that may be measured separately.

25.2.1 Basic Vocabulary and Units

The **Electrical Fundamentals** chapter introduces basic electrical units of measurement and how they relate to circuit operation. The following material discusses additional points of particular relevance to test and measurement.

VOLTAGE

Another name for voltage is *potential difference*, because it is a measure of the difference in electrical potential between two points in a circuit. That is a very important point that is widely misunderstood among radio amateurs, technicians and even many engineers. It makes no sense to speak of the voltage "at" a particular point in a circuit unless you specify the reference point to which you are measuring the difference in potential. Normally the reference point is understood to be the chassis or circuit common. However, it is worth remembering that if the other lead of your voltmeter is connected to some other point in the circuit the readings will likely be different. Voltage is not a property of only a single circuit node, but rather is a measure of the *difference* in potential between two points. This is why voltmeters have two leads.

Unfortunately, the circuit common connection is conventionally called the "ground" which leads people to believe that it must be connected to the Earth for proper operation. In fact, the voltage with respect to Earth has no effect on the circuit as long as all the differences of potential within the circuit are correct. For example, a low-pass filter may need to be "grounded" to the chassis or circuit common connection for proper operation but it does not need to be "grounded" to the Earth.

The simplest way to calibrate an inexpensive meter is simply to use a more accurate meter. For example, when constructing a home-built power supply, the analog panel meter may be calibrated with a digital voltmeter (DVM) because most DVMs have better accuracy than an analog meter. Perhaps the most practical voltage reference for the home workshop is an integrated circuit voltage reference. Special circuit techniques in the IC are used to generate a very stable, low-temperature-coefficient reference based on the band-gap voltage of silicon, approximately 1.25 V, on the chip. Inexpensive devices with specified accuracy of 0.1% and better are available from companies such as Analog Devices, Linear Technology, Maxim and National Semiconductor.

CURRENT

Conventional current is the flow of positive charge and is considered to flow in the direction of positive to negative voltage, or from the higher voltage point in a circuit toward the lower voltage point. The flow of negatively-charged electrons in the opposite direction from negative to positive voltage is sometimes called *electronic current*. Electronic and conventional current are equivalent, but flow in opposite directions. Conventional current is used in most circuit design and is reflected in the direction of the arrow in the symbol for diodes and bipolar transistors. An *ammeter* is an instrument for measuring current. An ammeter may be calibrated by measuring the attractive force between two electromagnets carrying the current to be tested, but in practice it is easier to place a known resistor in series, measure the voltage drop across the resistor, and calculate the current using Ohm's law. Resistance and voltage can both be calibrated accurately, so that method gives good accuracy.

The most common analog ammeter type is the *D'Arsonval galvanometer* in which the pointer is attached to a rotating electromagnet mounted between the poles of a fixed permanent magnet. The modern form of this meter was invented by Edward Weston and uses two spiral springs to provide the restoring force for the pointer, providing good scale linearity and accuracy. Most commonly-available meter movements of this type have a full-scale deflection between about 50 µA and several mA.

Digital ammeters use an analog-to-digital converter to measure the voltage drop across a low-value resistor and scale the result to display as a value of current. They are generally more accurate than analog meters and are more rugged due to the lack of delicate moving parts.

RESISTANCE

Measuring resistance requires one or more precision resistors to use as a reference, either in a bridge circuit or as part of an ohmmeter as described below. Resistors with a 1% rating cost only a few pennies and are readily available in a wide variety of values from many suppliers. *Precision* resistors are generally considered to be those with a tolerance of 0.1% or less and are typically available for less than a dollar or so in small quantities. Expect to pay a few dollars each for parts with a 0.01% tolerance.

An *ohmmeter* is a meter designed for measuring resistance. Various circuits can be used, but most are variations of the simplified schematics in **Figure 25.1**. In the circuit at A, the battery is in series with the resistor under test. If the resistance is zero (the test leads are shorted) then the battery is in parallel with the voltmeter and it reads a maximum value. If the resistance is infinite (test leads not connected) the meter reads zero. If the resistor equals R, the internal reference resistance, the meter reads half-scale.

In the circuit at B, the resistor under test is in parallel with the voltmeter. The meter indication is reversed from the series-connected circuit, that is, the meter reads zero for zero resistance, full-scale for infinite resistance, and mid-scale when the resistor equals R. In both circuits, an adjustment is normally provided to set the meter to full scale with the test leads shorted or open, as appropriate. In addition, a switch selects different values of the internal resistance R for measuring high or low-valued resistances.

A *Wheatstone bridge* is a method of measuring resistance that does not depend on the accuracy of the meter. Each arm of the bridge ($R_1 - R_S$ and $R_2 - R_X$) forms a voltage divider. In **Figure 25.2**, the meter is a zero-center type so that it can read both positive and negative voltages between the center connections of the two voltage dividers. When variable resistor R_S in Figure 25.2B is adjusted for a zero reading on the meter, then the two arms of the bridge have the same ratio,

$$\frac{R_1}{R_S} = \frac{R_2}{R_X}$$

The resistor under test, R_X, can be calculated from

$$R_X = R_S \frac{R_2}{R_1}$$

Nowadays, the Wheatstone bridge is rarely used for measuring resistance since it is not as convenient as an ohmmeter, but the concept is important for several other types of measurement circuits that will be covered later.

25.2.2 Multimeters

A *multimeter* is probably the single most useful test equipment for an electronics experimenter. Besides measuring dc voltage and current, most also measure resistance and low-frequency ac voltage as well. Another common feature is a tone that sounds whenever the test leads are shorted, which is useful as a quick continuity tester. With most modern multimeters, the voltage they use for the resistance measurement is too low to forward-bias the junction of a silicon diode or transistor, which is a desirable characteristic for measuring in-circuit resistance. Many multimeters also have a special "diode" mode with a higher test voltage so that diodes and transistors can be tested as well. It is increasingly common for even low-cost digital multimeters to include functions such as frequency and capacitance measurement.

ANALOG MULTIMETERS

Nearly all analog multimeters use a D'Arsonval meter for the display. Compared to a digital display, analog meters have the advantage that it is easier to see whether the reading is increasing or decreasing as adjustments are made to the circuit under test. The experimenter may want to consider owning an inexpensive analog multimeter for that kind of testing as well as a higher-quality digital instrument for more precise measurements.

A *volt-ohm meter* (VOM) is a basic analog instrument that includes no electronic circuitry other than a switch and resistors to set the scale, a battery for the resistance-measuring circuit, and perhaps a diode to convert ac voltage to dc. Despite the name, most can also measure current as well as voltage and resistance.

A disadvantage of the VOM is that, when measuring voltage, the current to operate the meter must be drawn from the circuit under test. A figure of merit for a VOM it its *ohms-per-volt* (Ω/V) rating, which is just the reciprocal of the full-scale current of the meter movement. For example, if the VOM uses a meter that reads 50 µA full-scale then it has $1 / 50 \times 10^{-6} = 20,000$ ohms per volt. On the 1-V scale the meter has a resistance of 20 kΩ and on the 10-V scale, it is 200 kΩ.

Depending on the circuit being tested, drawing 50 µA may be enough to disrupt the measurement or the operation of the circuit. To solve that problem, some analog meters include a built-in amplifier with high input impedance. In the days of vacuum tubes, such meters were called *vacuum-tube voltmeters*

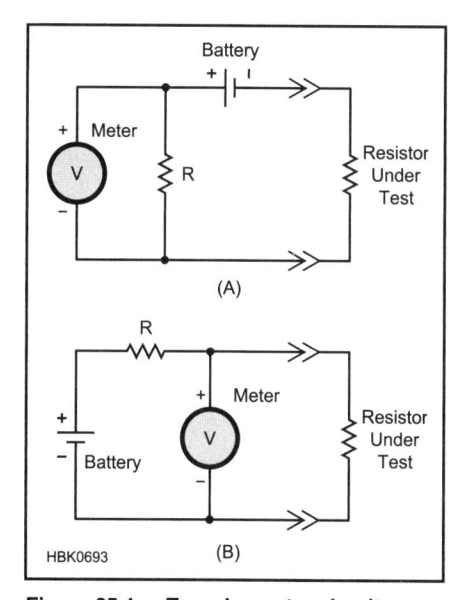

Figure 25.1 — Two ohmmeter circuits. At A, the meter reads full scale with a zero-ohm resistor and reads zero with no resistor connected. The circuit at B is the opposite; the meter reads full scale with no resistor connected (infinite resistance) and reads zero with zero resistance.

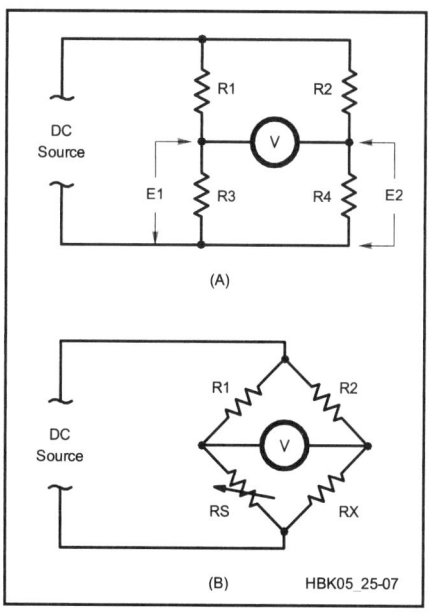

Figure 25.2 — A Wheatstone bridge circuit. A bridge circuit is actually a pair of voltage dividers (A). B shows how bridges are normally drawn.

(VTVM). An example is shown in **Figure 25.3**. The modern equivalent is called an *electronic voltmeter* and generally uses an amplifier with field-effect transistors at the input. Again, despite the name, VTVMs and electronic voltmeters usually can measure current and resistance as well.

DIGITAL MULTIMETERS

Instead of using an analog meter to display its measurements, a *digital multimeter* (DMM) has a digital readout, usually an LCD display. A microprocessor controls the measurement process and the display. (See **Figure 25.4**.) To convert the analog voltage or current being measured to a digital number requires an analog-to-digital converter (ADC) controlled by a microprocessor. Most use a dual-slope type of ADC, which trades off a relatively slow measuring speed for excellent accuracy and low cost. (Analog-to-digital conversion is discussed in the **Analog Basics** chapter.)

A digital voltmeter is constructed as shown in **Figure 25.5**. The input section is the same as in an analog electronic voltmeter. A range

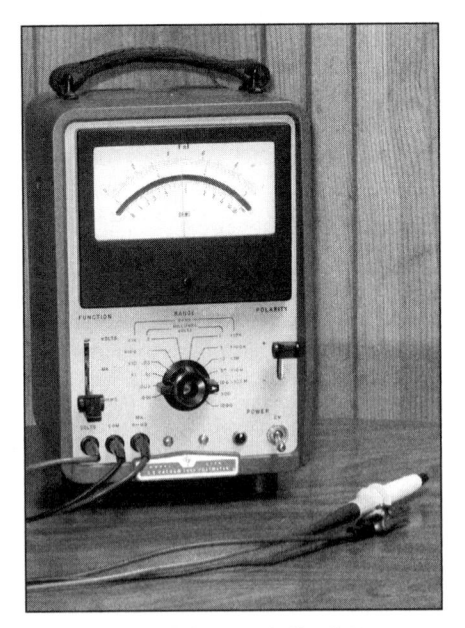

Figure 25.3 — This classic Hewlett-Packard HP412A vacuum-tube voltmeter (VTVM) has specifications that put many modern solid-state multimeters to shame.

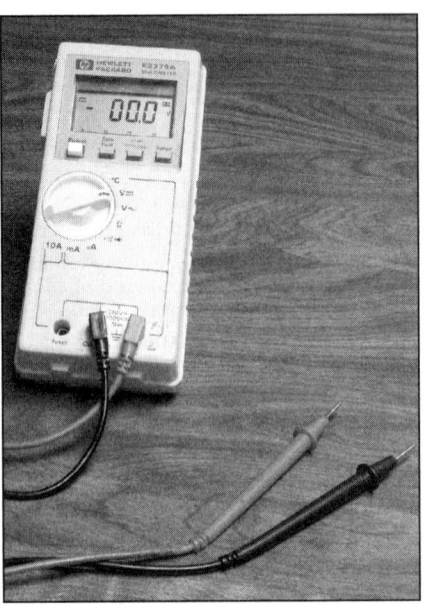

Figure 25.4 — A modern digital multimeter typically has a liquid crystal display readout.

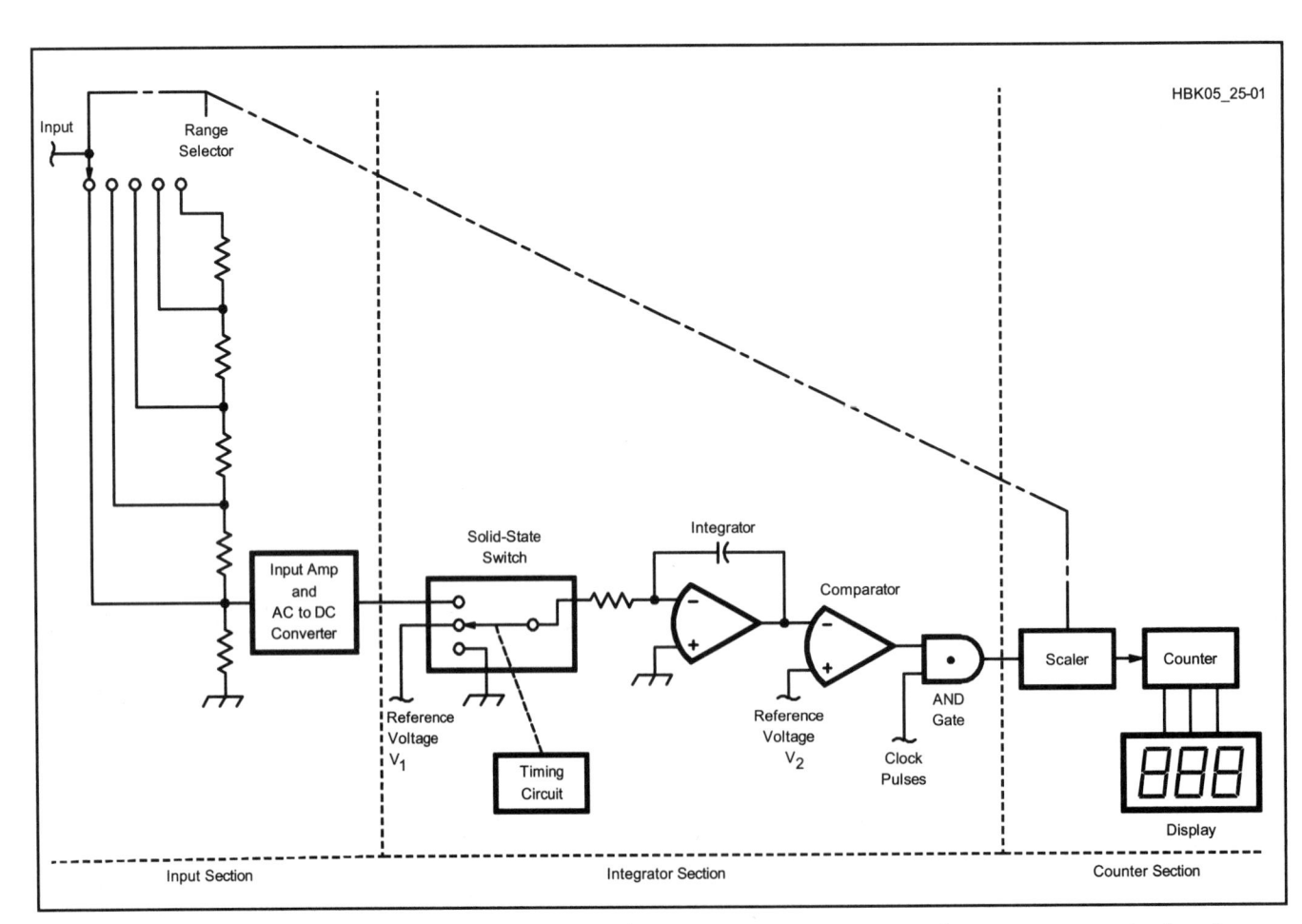

Figure 25.5 — A typical digital voltmeter consists of three parts: an input section for scaling, an integrator to convert voltage to a pulse whose width varies with voltage, and a counter to measure the width of the pulse and display the measured voltage.

selector switch scales the input signal appropriately for amplification by an input preamplifier, which also includes a rectifier circuit that is used when in ac mode to convert the ac signal into dc, suitable for conversion by the ADC.

An additional feature that becomes possible with digital multimeters is *autoranging*. The selector switch is used only to choose between voltage, current, resistance and any other available functions. The scale or range is selected automatically based on the amplitude of the signal being measured, which is a nice convenience. If the signal is fluctuating such that it causes frequent range changes, there is usually a way to turn off auto-ranging and select the range manually.

Digital multimeters that feature a serial data interface can also act as a *data logger*, taking and storing measurements for use by a PC or under the control of a PC.[2] This is a very useful feature for experimenters.

HOW TO USE A MULTIMETER

When preparing to make a measurement, the first thing to do is to select the proper function on the multimeter — voltage, current, resistance or some other function. If the meter is not an auto-ranging type, set the range to the lowest value that does not over-range the meter. If you're not sure of the voltage or current being measured, start with a high range, connect the test probes then switch the range down until a good reading can be obtained. Choosing the correct function and range may involve connecting the test leads to specific connectors on the meter.

When measuring high voltage, special precautions must be taken. As little as 35 V should be considered dangerous because it can produce lethal current in the human body under some conditions. Grasp the test probes by the insulated handles, being careful to keep fingers away from the metal probe tips. Pay attention to the multimeter manufacturer's maximum voltage ratings. Special test probes are generally available for measuring high voltage. Do not exceed the meter's rated maximum voltage.

High current can be dangerous as well. If a probe accidentally shorts a power supply to ground, sparks can fly, damaging the equipment and endangering the operator. Be careful of metal jewelry such as rings and bracelets. If connected across a high-current circuit you could get a nasty burn. Most meters have a fuse to protect the instrument from an over-current condition in current-measuring mode. If the multimeter turns on but always reads zero, consult the manual on how to replace the fuse.

To measure a current, the meter must be inserted in series with the circuit. In a series-connected circuit, all components carry the same current, so it doesn't matter which component is disconnected to allow inserting the ammeter. Select the one that is most convenient, or the one that is at a low-voltage point if you're measuring a high-voltage circuit. For measuring ac power circuits without disconnecting them, clamp-on current probes are used.

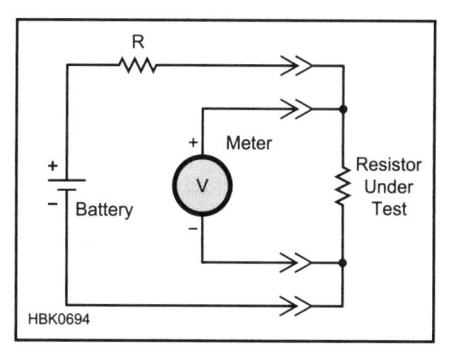

Figure 25.6 — The four-wire technique for measuring low-value resistors. By connecting the current source and the meter separately to the leads of the device under test, the error due to lead resistance is reduced.

It can be difficult to measure low-value resistors accurately because of the resistance of the meter leads, typically one or two tenths of an ohm. With the series-connected ohmmeter circuit described in the previous section, the calibration procedure compensates for that and some digital meters may have a means to compensate as well. However, accurate low-resistance measurement requires the *four-wire* technique, as illustrated in **Figure 25.6**. Two wires are connected to each end of the resistor, one to carry the test current and one to read the voltage with a high-input impedance voltmeter. In that way the resistance of the wires does not affect the measurement.

A similar technique can be used to measure high currents. Most inexpensive meters do not have a high-enough current range to measure the 20 A or so that is drawn from a 12-V power supply by a typical 100 W transceiver. The solution is to use an external *meter shunt*, which is a low value resistor placed in series with the current. See **Figure 25.7**. The multimeter reads the voltage, E, across the shunt, and then the current is calculated from Ohm's Law, $I = E/R_S$, where R_S is the resistance of the shunt. Resistors designed for this service may have four leads rather than two to allow a true four-wire measurement. The clamp-on current probes mentioned earlier may also be used.

There are several issues that apply specifically to analog multimeters. An analog meter movement is a rather delicate device. It can be damaged if the case is dropped or mechanically shocked. When transporting the instrument, it is a good idea to place a low resistance or short in parallel with the terminals of the meter movement, which increases damping and reduces the amount of pointer movement as the case is bounced around. Some multimeters have a special OFF position on the selector switch for that purpose. On others, switching to the highest current range accomplishes the same thing.

Most D'Arsonval meters have an adjustment screw located near the pointer's pivot point that may be accessed from the front of the meter. It should be adjusted so that the meter reads zero with no signal applied.

Some older VOMs include a high-voltage battery that is used on the highest resistance ranges. When testing solid-state devices, that voltage can be high enough to cause damage. If there is any doubt, use another high-impedance multimeter to test the voltage on the test leads of the VOM when it is set to the highest resistance ranges.

MULTIMETER CRITICAL SPECIFICATIONS

The first decision when selecting a multimeter is whether you want an analog or digital type. That is largely a matter of personal taste. Digital meters are generally more accurate but analog meters may make it easier to tune a circuit for a specific voltage or current. The next decision is between a hand-held or bench-type instrument. The latter tend to have more features and better specifications, but obviously are less portable and usually are more expensive.

The most obvious selection criteria are the features provided. Nearly all multimeters measure dc voltage, current and resistance and most also measure low-frequency ac voltage. Other common features on digital meters include autoranging and automatic turn-off to

Figure 25.7 — This 50-A, 50-mV current shunt has a resistance of 0.05 / 50 = 0.001 Ω. The two large terminals are for connecting to the circuit under test and the two small terminals are for connecting to a voltmeter.

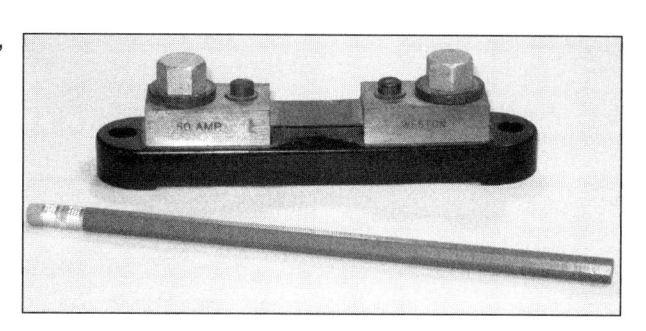

Probe Adapters for Multimeters

Multimeters come with test probes intended for precise contact with terminals, components, wires, and so forth. They work well if the item to be probed is easily exposed or otherwise available to the probe. Measuring signals on connector pins, however, is often a challenge. Inserting a probe into the miniature sockets on many connectors is often not possible and if the connector has exposed pins, trying to insure the probe does not slip to or between adjacent pins is nearly impossible. The solution is to build an adapter as shown in Figure 25.A's three examples.

Figure 25.A1 provides a convenient way to hold probes steady in a spring-loaded, push-button, two-wire speaker connector connected to a pair of Powerpole connectors. Keep the colors of the wires, buttons, and connectors consistent to prevent confusion. An enclosure such as an inexpensive plastic box protects the exposed terminals.

Figure 25.A2 shows how to adapt an automotive-style fuse to make a current-measuring adapter for your multimeter. First, remove the back of the fuseholder and the fuse element and pry the fuseholder open. Solder leads to the exposed terminals then glue or snap the fuseholder back together. Be sure to include the external in-line fuseholder — available in auto parts stores — so that the circuit is protected and you don't blow an expensive multimeter fuse. (Note — multimeter fuses are rated at the full voltage limits of the meter for your safety. Do not replace them with low-voltage fuses.)

Figure 25.A3 is a typical adapter for a multi-pin connector using a terminal strip. Take care to arrange the terminals in order of pin number and label them so you don't have to guess when using the adapter. Make an adapter for the common connectors in your station and you'll never regret it!

These are just three types of adapters — you will no doubt think of many more that will help you with your particular needs. Remember to protect yourself against exposed voltages and short-circuits when constructing and using the adapters. (Thanks to W4QO and KG4VHV and the *QRP Quarterly* for the suggestions.)

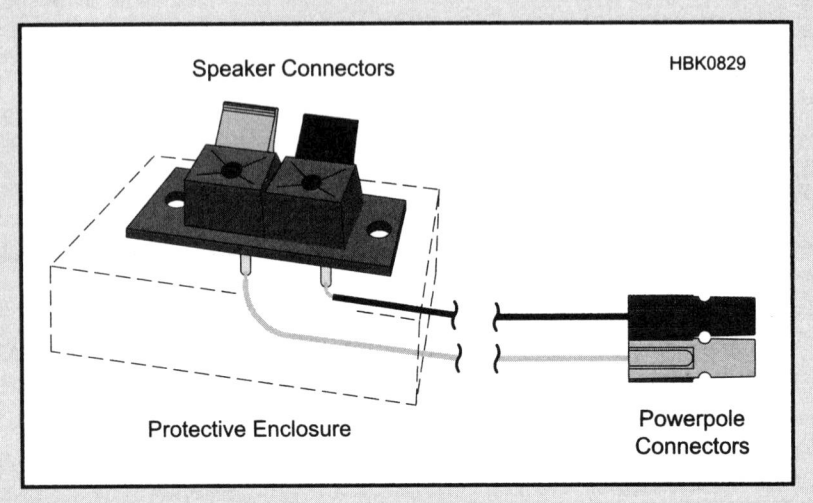

Figure 25.A1 — A convenient way to hold probes steady

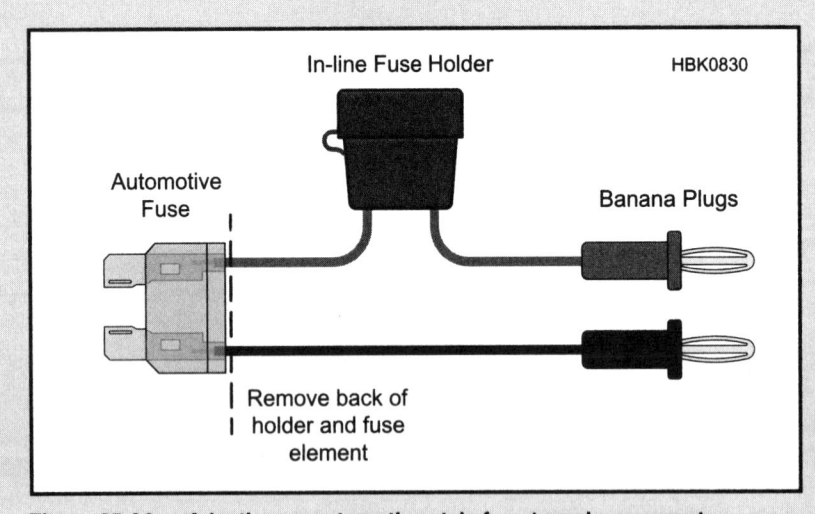

Figure 25.A2 — Adapting an automotive-style fuse to make a current-measuring adapter.

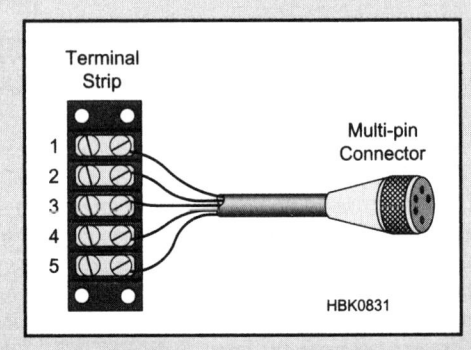

Figure 25.A3 — A typical adapter for a multi-pin connector.

save the battery. More capable meters include features such as data hold, peak voltage, true RMS voltage, 4-wire resistance, capacitor tester, inductor tester, diode and transistor tester, logic tester, frequency counter, computer data logging and a graphical display.

One important feature that is often not specified is over-voltage and over-current protection. On analog meters, there may be internal back-to-back diodes across the meter movement to protect it from over-voltage. Most digital meters include autoranging which should prevent damage from any voltage below the specified maximum. The current-measuring input on both types is normally protected with a fuse.

The next most critical specification is the available measurement ranges of the voltage, current, resistance and any other functions provided. Analog meters tend to space the voltage and current ranges by a factor of three. For example, the full-scale voltage readings might be 3 V, 10 V, 30 V, 100 V, 300 V or perhaps 5 V, 15 V, 50 V, 150 V, 500 V. The latter is a particularly good choice since two voltages that are commonly measured, 12 V dc and 120 V ac, are near the top of a range where accuracy is best. The more range selections provided, the greater the span of values that can be measured. With auto-ranging instruments the measurement minimum and maximum range may not be obvious without consulting the manual.

The input impedance is important in minimizing the effect of the multimeter on the circuit under test. Impedance should be high for voltage measurements and low for current measurements. For VOMs the figure of merit for voltage measurements is the ohms-per-volt rating. Multiply the full-scale voltage range by ohms-per-volt to get the input resistance. Both digital and analog electronic voltmeters usually have the same input impedance on all voltage ranges, typically between 1 and 11 MΩ. The input resistance for current measurements is often specified by the *burden voltage*, which is the voltage drop across the test leads with a full-scale signal. Typical values vary widely, from a few millivolts to more than a volt. The voltage drop can often be reduced by switching to a higher current range, at the expense of measurement resolution.

Measurement accuracy can be an important specification for some applications. An inexpensive analog meter may have voltage and current accuracy of 3% or so. The best analog meters have accuracy specifications in the range of 1%. At that level, accuracy may be limited by *parallax*, which causes the meter reading to appear to change as you change the angle of view. To mitigate that, some high-end analog meters have a *mirror scale*. The reflection of the pointer in the mirror has a parallax error equal and opposite to the unreflected pointer so that the correct reading is half way between the two.

You can't necessarily tell the accuracy of a digital meter from the number of digits in the display. Usually the accuracy is limited by the analog circuitry. However, the number of digits defines the resolution, which can be important when comparing two nearly-equal readings or when tuning a circuit for a peak or minimum value. A typical DMM might have a specified accuracy of 0.1% to 1% for dc measurements and perhaps 1% to 3% for ac voltage. (See the section on ac measurements.) Many inexpensive digital multimeters do not have published specifications and may not be very accurate.

Many bench-type multimeters and some hand-held units can be connected to a computer. That allows the computer to control the instrument to take automated readings and store the results in a computer file. Some older test equipment may have a GPIB (general purpose interface bus) interface, also known as IEEE-488 (HPIB on Hewlett-Packard equipment). GPIB-to-USB converters are available to allow connection to a PC.[3] Modern instruments typically have a USB or RS-232 interface.

USED AND SURPLUS MULTIMETERS

Figure 25.3 shows a typical multimeter that might show up at a ham flea market or on the Internet, a Hewlett-Packard model 412A VTVM. While obsolete, it is still a very useful instrument with capabilities that are rare in modern units. For example, it can measure dc voltage down to 1 mV (0.001 V) full scale and the burden voltage for current measurements is only 1 mV for currents up to 10 mA, rising to 100 mV at 1 A. The highest resistance range is 100 MΩ center scale, which allows reasonably-accurate resistance measurements up to about 1 GΩ. Don't overlook surplus equipment just because it is old. Some of it is a real bargain.

When buying a used analog multimeter, the most important thing to check is the meter movement itself. D'Arsonval meters are rather delicate and easy to damage. For a VOM or battery-operated multimeter, put the instrument in resistance-measuring mode then short and un-short the test leads. The needle should move smoothly between zero and full scale. If you can't do that test, at least make sure that the needle rests close to zero. Rotate the instrument back and forth to make the needle move and observe whether it appears to bind. It is difficult or impossible to repair a damaged meter movement.

Digital multimeters are less delicate than analog meters and many of their failures are electronic in nature so they sometimes can be repaired using normal troubleshooting techniques. Of course it is always a good idea to test used equipment before buying, if possible. If at all possible, measure voltage and resistance with the meter to be sure it is fundamentally sound.

25.2.3 Panel Meters

Analog panel meters are quite expensive to buy new so many experimenters keep an eye open for flea-market bargains. You often can find old "boat anchor" equipment with good salvageable panel meters selling for less than the value of the meters.

The scale markings on surplus meters often represent what the meter was measuring in the equipment rather than the actual current flowing through the meter itself. Sometimes the full-scale current of the meter movement will be shown in small text at the bottom of the scale. However, that may not be the same as the current measured at the meter terminals because some meters include an internal shunt.

The only sure way to know the full-scale current and resistance of a surplus meter is to measure it. The resistance can be measured with the ohmmeter function of a multimeter, but be careful. On the lowest resistance ranges, the multimeter may output enough voltage and current to damage the meter under test. If the multimeter is an auto-ranging type you have no way to control test current unless you can turn auto-ranging off. With a non-autoranging ohmmeter, start the measurement at the highest resistance scale and then reduce the scale one step at a time until a valid reading is obtained, while keeping an eye on the meter under test to be sure it is not over-ranged.

A safer way to measure both the full-scale current and resistance of a panel meter is to place a high-value resistor in series with it and connect the combination to a dc power supply, perhaps a battery. A 1.5-V battery in series with a 100 kΩ resistor (15 μA of current) is a good starting point. Keep trying smaller and smaller resistance values until a good reading is obtained on the meter. Assuming the scale that is marked on the meter's scale face is linear, the full-scale current is

$$I_{FS} = I_{TEST} \frac{D_{FS}}{D_{TEST}}$$

where I_{FS} is the full-scale meter current, D_{FS} is the scale's full-scale marking, D_{TEST} is the needle indication measured with the test current, and I_{TEST} is the test current, which is equal to the voltage across the resistor divided by the resistance. The meter's resistance is the voltage across the meter divided by I_{TEST}.

USING PANEL METERS

Whether surplus or new, it is rare that a panel meter measures exactly what you need for a particular application. Usually you must change the current or voltage sensitivity.

To increase the full-scale current, place a *current shunt* in parallel with the meter. This is simply a resistor whose value is

$$R_{SHUNT} = R_M \frac{I_M}{I_{FS} - I_M}$$

where R_M is the meter resistance, I_M is the meter full-scale current and I_{FS} is the desired full-scale current reading. The shunt resistance is very small for high-current shunts, such that the resistance of the wires or circuit traces can cause a significant error. To reduce that error, connect the meter directly to the leads of the shunt, with no wires or circuit traces in common with the high-current path.

You can make a low-value shunt by wrapping a length of copper wire around a resistor or other component used as a form. Unfortunately, however, the resistance of copper has a poor temperature coefficient, typically around 0.4 percent per degree C. That means the meter reading can change more than 10% between a warm and a cold day. As the wire self-heats from the high current flowing through, the meter reading can easily be in error by 20% or more. Commercial shunts are made from a metal with a low temperature coefficient such as nichrome. Copper-wire shunts should only be used where accuracy is not important. (A table of wire resistance in ohms per foot (Ω/ft) is available in the **Component Data and References** chapter.)

If the panel meter is to be used to measure voltage, a *voltage multiplier* resistor is inserted in series with the meter. The value is

$$R_{MULT} = \frac{V_{FS}}{I_M} R_M$$

where V_{FS} is the desired full-scale voltage, I_M is the meter full-scale current and R_M is the meter resistance. If the meter has an internal current shunt, it should normally be removed to maximize the value of the multiplier resistor. For high-voltage applications, be aware that in addition to a power rating a resistor also has a working voltage specification, perhaps 200 to 250 V or so for a typical ¼ W, through-hole resistor. Applying voltages higher than the rating — even if the rated power dissipation is not exceeded — can result in arcing across the body of the resistor. If you need to measure a voltage higher than the voltage rating,

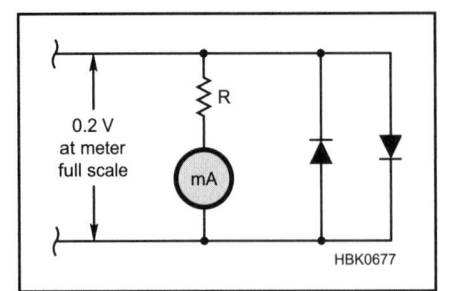

Figure 25.8 — Back-to-back silicon diodes protect the meter by limiting the maximum voltage. See the text for a discussion of how to select the value of R.

use several resistors in series. For example, to measure a 2000-V power supply, ten ¼ W resistors in series, each with a value of one-tenth the desired resistance, would be suitable.

If you intend to use the same panel meter for several different purposes in your project, be sure to use a *break-before-make* switch to make the selection. That protects the meter by making sure it is never connected to two circuits at the same time, even for an instant.

Analog D'Arsonval meters are easily damaged if subjected to excessive current. A standard technique to protect them is to wire back-to-back diodes in parallel with the meter. Silicon junction diodes have the property that they act like an open circuit for low voltages and start to conduct when the forward voltage reaches about 0.4 V. Most meters can withstand up to two times the full-scale current without damage. So choose resistor R in **Figure 25.8** such that the voltage across the diodes is about 0.2 V when the meter current is at full scale, that is

$$R = \frac{0.2 \text{ V}}{I_M} - R_M$$

where I_M is the full-scale meter current and R_M is the meter resistance. If that equation results in a negative value for R, replace each diode with two diodes in series and recalculate using 0.4 V instead of 0.2 V in the equation.

MAKING NEW PANEL SCALES

It seems like the scale that is printed on the meter scale is never what you need for your project. You can usually disassemble the meter to remove the scale plate to modify the scale. Be sure you are working in a clean environment and temporarily reassemble the meter while you are working on the scale to prevent any dust or other contaminant from entering the delicate mechanism. Take particular care that magnetic metal debris cannot get into the meter movement where it is attracted by the permanent magnets.

There are several methods for modifying the scale markings for your own purposes. If only the labels are wrong and the tick marks are spaced appropriately, you can add new labels with a permanent marker or dry-transfer labels. If the old labels are not useful, sometimes they can be removed with a pencil eraser. If you need a completely new meter scale, one old trick is to turn the scale plate over and draw the new scale on the back. However, software is available to design and print custom scales. An Internet search will quickly find dozens of low-cost and free programs, such as *Meter Basic* by Jim Tonne, W4ENE, which is included with the downloadable supplemental content.

DIGITAL PANEL METERS

Digital panel meters (DPMs) are available as preassembled modules that are almost as easy to use as analog meters. The displays are generally of the liquid crystal type, with or without a backlight, and typically have 3 to 4½ digits. A "½" digit is one that can display only a 1 or a blank. Displays with a half-digit usually have a full-scale input voltage of either 2 V or 200 mV minus one count, so that the full-scale voltage is 199.9 mV, for example. Most have programmable decimal points after each digit and some have indicators to indicate the units, such as µ, m, V, A and so forth. DPMs have a high input impedance so there is minimal loading on the circuit under test.

The required power supply voltage varies by model. Some require a floating supply, so if the power supply and the voltage being measured need a common ground connection, be sure the meter is capable of that.

Accuracy is typically 0.1% or better. The total accuracy is usually limited by the external circuitry that drives the meter, such as the amplifier, current shunt or attenuator that is required to get the signal within the input voltage range of the DPM.

25.3 AC Measurements

This section covers issues that affect all ac signals, while the following section on RF measurements concentrates on aspects of ac measurements that are particular to the higher frequencies.

25.3.1 Basic Vocabulary and Units

The **Electrical Fundamentals** chapter includes an introduction to basic electrical units of ac waveforms. The following material emphasizes some additional points that have particular relevance to test and measurement.

AC WAVEFORM VALUES

With ac signals, the voltage and current change periodically with time so, as you might expect, there are several ways to express their value. See **Figure 25.9**. The *average* voltage or current is the value averaged over one period and is equal to the *dc component* of the signal. For a symmetric, periodic ac signal with no dc component, the average is always zero. Non-periodic signals must be averaged over a long period of time to obtain a valid average.

The *peak* value of an ac signal is just as its name implies, the maximum value that the signal ever achieves. The *peak-to-peak* value is the difference between the positive and negative peaks. For a symmetrical-ac waveform such as a sine or square wave, the peak-to-peak is twice the peak.

The *RMS* (*root-mean-square*) value of voltage or current is that which would produce the same heating in a resistor as a dc voltage or current of the same value. For a sine wave, it is

$$V_{RMS} = \frac{1}{\sqrt{2}} V_{PK} \approx 0.707 \times V_{PK}$$

where V_{RMS} is the RMS voltage and V_{PK} is the peak voltage. A similar equation applies for RMS current. Don't forget that the equation only applies for sine waves. For example, the RMS voltage of a square wave is 1.0 times the peak. See **Figure 25.10**. Also be aware that the RMS value includes the effect of any dc component. If you wish to refer to the RMS value of the ac component only, be sure to state that explicitly.

The formulas for power apply for RMS voltage and current as well as for dc, $P = E_{RMS} I_{RMS}$, $P = E_{RMS}^2 / R$ and $P = I_{RMS}^2 R$, where P is power in watts, E_{RMS} is RMS potential difference in volts and I_{RMS} is RMS current in amperes. However, that assumes that the voltage and current are in phase, as in a resistor or an antenna at resonance. If they are not in phase, then the power in the above equations must be corrected by multiplying it by the *power factor*,

$$PF = \cos \theta$$

where θ = arctan (X / R), the phase angle caused by the reactance, X, and the resistance, R, of the circuit.

25.3.2 Using Multimeters for AC Measurements

Most multimeters can indicate the RMS value of ac voltage and current, but many do not measure the RMS value directly. Instead they measure the rectified average or peak voltage and then apply a correction factor so that the display reads RMS, assuming a sine wave. Unfortunately, that means that the RMS values are not accurate if the ac signal being measured does not have a sinusoidal waveform.

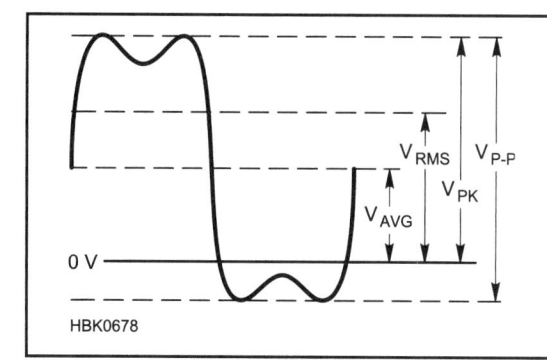

Figure 25.9 — Various methods to express the voltage or current of an ac signal. The average value, V_{AVG}, is the dc component. V_{RMS} is the root-mean-square, V_{PK} is the peak and V_{P-P} is the peak-to-peak value.

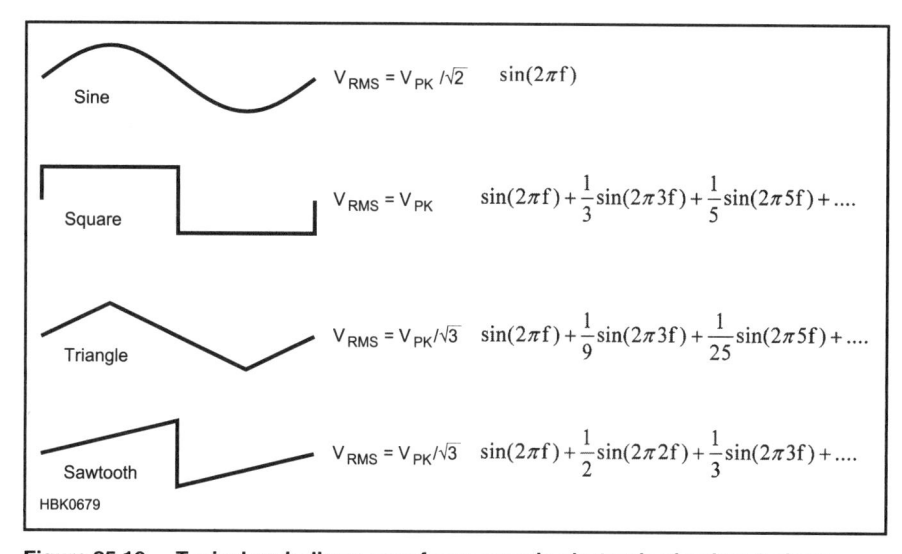

Figure 25.10 — Typical periodic ac waveforms seen in electronic circuitry. A single cycle of each example is shown. At the center are listed the relationships between V_{RMS}, the root-mean-square, and V_{PK}, the peak value, assuming the waveform has no dc component. Periodic waveforms are composed of sine waves at the fundamental and harmonic frequencies. At the right are the relative amplitudes of the various frequency components.

Sine: $V_{RMS} = V_{PK}/\sqrt{2}$ $\quad \sin(2\pi f)$

Square: $V_{RMS} = V_{PK}$ $\quad \sin(2\pi f) + \frac{1}{3}\sin(2\pi 3f) + \frac{1}{5}\sin(2\pi 5f) + ...$

Triangle: $V_{RMS} = V_{PK}/\sqrt{3}$ $\quad \sin(2\pi f) + \frac{1}{9}\sin(2\pi 3f) + \frac{1}{25}\sin(2\pi 5f) + ...$

Sawtooth: $V_{RMS} = V_{PK}/\sqrt{3}$ $\quad \sin(2\pi f) + \frac{1}{2}\sin(2\pi 2f) + \frac{1}{3}\sin(2\pi 3f) + ...$

Some meters full-wave rectify the ac signal and then measure the average of that, internally correcting for the difference between the average of a rectified sine wave

$$V_{AVG} = \frac{2}{\pi} V_{PK} = 0.637 \times V_{PK}$$

and the RMS value

$$V_{RMS} = \frac{}{\sqrt{}} V_{PK} \approx 0.707 \times V_{PK}$$

so that the reading is in RMS. Very inexpensive analog meters may only use a half-wave rectifier which causes RMS readings for asymmetric waveforms to vary with the orientation of the test connections.

Additional considerations may apply to RMS readings. For example, the accuracy of the RMS reading for most meters varies with frequency of the applied signal. Check the specifications of the multimeter for the frequency range over which it may be used to measure RMS values.

The only way to accurately measure RMS values of non-sinusoidal signals is with a meter that has *true RMS* capability. Such a meter uses circuitry or software to compute the RMS value of the signal. Note that the measurement bandwidth of the meter must include the significant harmonics of the signal as well as the fundamental in order to give accurate RMS readings.

An example of a measurement that requires a true RMS voltmeter is receiver sensitivity. For that, you need to measure signal and noise levels at the receiver audio output. Standard multimeters using a rectifier and averaging circuit give inaccurate results when measuring noise because noise and sine waves have different peak-to-RMS ratios. Another advantage of true RMS meters is that they tend to have better scale linearity, even for sinusoidal signals. A diode detector is nonlinear, especially at the low end of the scale.

Frequency response is another limitation when making ac measurements with a multimeter. Most are specified from below 50 or 60 Hz, to cover power-line frequencies, up to a few hundred Hz. Many receiver measurements use a 1 kHz test frequency, so a meter specified up to at least that frequency is especially useful.

For all of these and other reasons, the ac accuracy is usually significantly worse than the dc accuracy. Generally, an oscilloscope makes more accurate ac measurements than a multimeter. Modern digital oscilloscopes often have built-in capability to indicate peak, average and true RMS voltage.

One final issue with multimeters is the ac impedance of the probes. While the dc input resistance of a modern electronic multimeter is typically over 1 MΩ, the capacitive reactance can be a significant factor at radio frequencies. Even if all you care about is the dc voltage, if ac signals are present, reactance of the probe can affect the circuit's operation.

25.3.3 Measuring Frequency and Time

FREQUENCY COUNTERS

The basic instrument for measuring frequency is the *frequency counter*. A block diagram of a very basic design is shown in **Figure 25.11**. Three digits are shown, but typically there are more. The signal to be measured is routed through three cascaded decade counters. For 1 Hz frequency resolution, the counters count for 1 second. For 10 Hz resolution, they count for ¹⁄₁₀ second, and so on. The count time is determined by a high-stability crystal oscillator, whose frequency is divided down to 1 Hz, ¹⁄₁₀ Hz, or whatever resolution is desired. At the end of each count time, control circuitry stores the final count in latches that drive the digit displays and at the same time resets the counters for the next count period.

With this scheme, the displays are updated once per second when 1 second resolution is chosen, 10 times per second with 10 Hz resolution, and so on. One issue is that if the frequency is part-way between two adjacent displayed values, the least-significant digit will flicker back and forth between the two values on successive counts. Sometimes the designer chooses not to show the least-significant digit for that reason, even though that slows down the display update rate by a factor of 10 for any given display resolution.

Some frequency counters include the ability to measure time as well. In the block diagram, the connections to the first divide-by-10 stage input and the control circuit input are swapped. In that way the signal being measured controls the count time, and the reference oscillator provides the signal being counted. If the divided-down reference oscillator has a frequency of 1 kHz, for example, then the period can be measured to a resolution of 1 ms. This same technique can be used to measure low-frequency signals as well. For example, when measuring the frequency of a subaudible tone encoder, you need at least 0.1 Hz measurement resolution. Normally, that would require a 10-second count time which can be inconvenient. Some counters are able to measure the period, calculate the reciprocal, and display the resulting frequency. Since the count time is only one cycle of the measured signal, the display updates in real time.

Many frequency counters include a *prescaler*, a frequency divider between the input and the main part of the circuitry, to allow

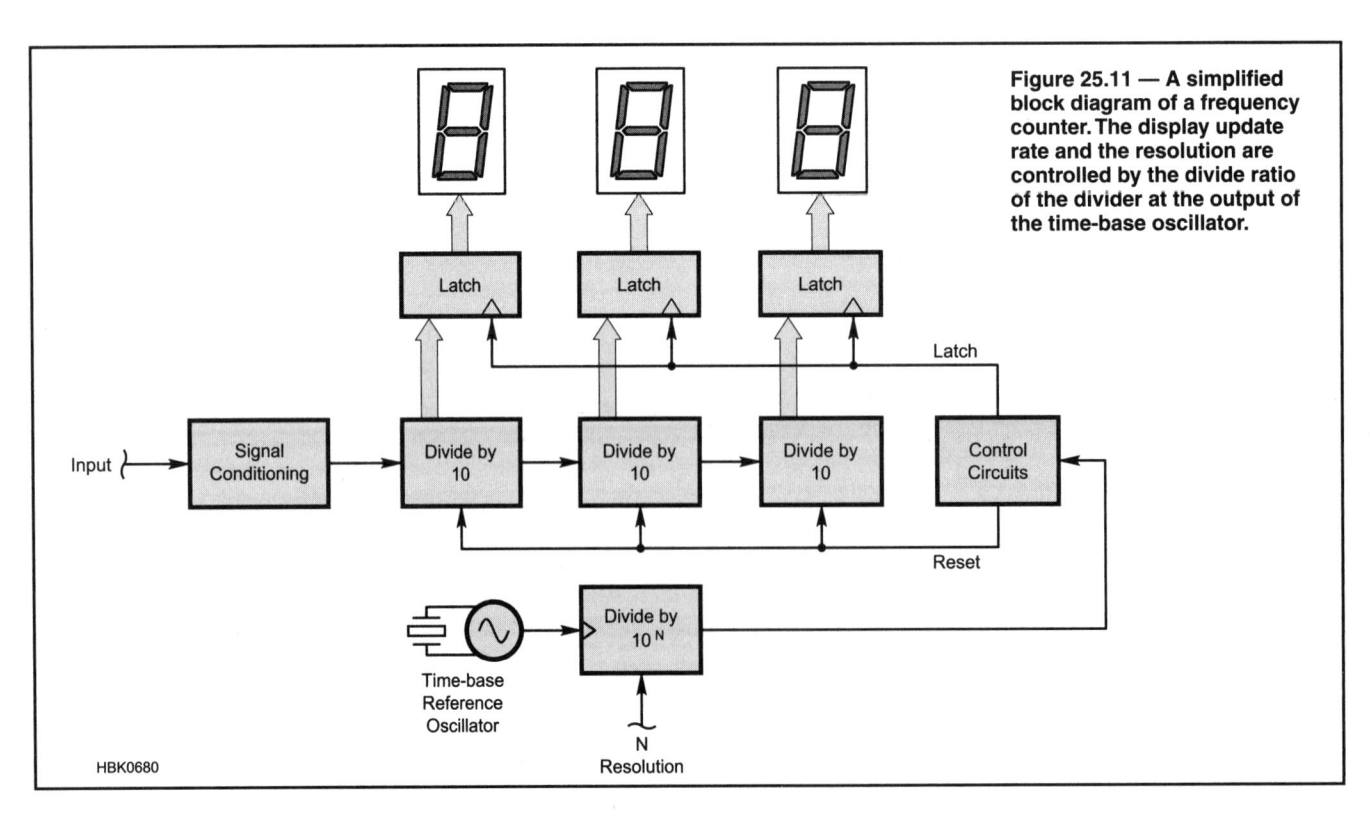

Figure 25.11 — A simplified block diagram of a frequency counter. The display update rate and the resolution are controlled by the divide ratio of the divider at the output of the time-base oscillator.

operation at higher frequencies. Usually the prescaler has a 50-Ω input. For low frequencies, there is a separate high-impedance input, typically 1 MΩ, that bypasses the prescaler. A switch selects between the two inputs.

It is important to realize that the so-called high-impedance input only has a high impedance at low frequencies. For example, if the stray input capacitance is 30 pF, then the impedance is only 177 Ω at 30 MHz. If you try to measure the frequency of an oscillator by connecting the frequency counter's input directly to the circuitry, it likely will alter the oscillator tuning enough to invalidate the measurement. If possible, connect the counter to the output of a buffer amplifier or at some other point in the circuitry that won't be adversely affected. If that isn't possible, another trick is to use a pickup coil placed near the oscillator. The coil could be a few turns of insulated wire soldered between the center conductor and shield of a coaxial cable that connects to the frequency counter input. Hold the coil just close enough to get a stable reading.

When connecting a frequency counter to a circuit, observe the maximum voltage and power ratings, both for dc and ac. An oscilloscope probe with a 10:1 attenuation ratio connected to the high-impedance input is a good method to reduce both the signal level as well as the capacitive loading.

Frequency counters tend to have sensitive inputs. Only a small fraction of a volt is typically enough for valid readings. It is quite practical to measure the frequency of a nearby transmitter off the air with a small whip antenna. The transmitter should not be modulated while measuring its frequency. SSB transmitters should be measured in CW mode.

The principle figure of merit for a frequency counter is its frequency accuracy, which is primarily determined by the reference oscillator, also known as the *time base*. The time base accuracy is affected by the temperature, power supply voltage, crystal aging and quality of calibration. For a temperature-compensated crystal oscillator (TCXO), the total accuracy is typically a few parts per million (ppm). If it is 10 ppm, for example, then the error at 144 MHz is 1.44 kHz.

Normally temperature is the factor with the greatest effect on the short-term stability. For best accuracy, calibrate the reference oscillator at the same temperature at which measurements will be taken.

Other important specifications are the number of digits in the display, frequency resolution, display update time, frequency range, input sensitivity, input impedance and, for portable units, power supply voltage and current. In choosing a frequency counter you'll need to decide if you want a desktop model or a portable handheld unit. Additional features to consider include the size and visibility of the display, the ability to measure period, a data hold feature, an external time base input, adjustable trigger level and polarity, input attenuator, switchable low-pass filter, and frequency ratio measurement.

Commercial frequency counters have become so common that it hardly pays to construct your own from scratch. Units with a wide range of prices, feature sets and performance levels are available both on-line and from local electronics distributors. Older used and surplus frequency counters tend to be less of a bargain than other types of test equipment because advances in solid-state electronics have made modern instruments inexpensive, lightweight and packed with features and performance.

FREQUENCY MARKER GENERATORS

Before the advent of digital frequency synthesizers, most shortwave amateur receivers and transceivers included a crystal calibrator, which is a low-frequency (typically 25 or 100 kHz) oscillator with strong harmonics throughout the HF spectrum, used to calibrate the analog dial on the radio. Early units used an actual 100 kHz crystal in the oscillator, but modern units use a higher-frequency crystal and a frequency divider to obtain the low-frequency signal.[4]

Most modern Amateur Radio equipment uses a crystal-controlled synthesizer or digital frequency display, so no crystal calibrator is needed. However, the idea can still be useful for testing homebrew gear. If the low-frequency signal consists of a series of narrow pulses rather than a square wave, then all the harmonics are of the same amplitude up to the point where the pulse width is a significant portion of a cycle. This can be approximated by placing a small-value capacitor in series with the output. The harmonics should have constant amplitude for frequencies below

$$f \ll \frac{1}{2\pi RC}$$

where f is the frequency in MHz, C is the capacitance in μF and R is the load resistance, usually 50 Ω.

WAVEMETERS

An *absorption wavemeter* is basically a tunable filter with some means of detecting the signal at the filter output. It allows crude spectrum analysis of a signal by manually tuning through the frequencies of interest. Commercial units designed for microwave frequencies often include a carefully-calibrated dial for reading the frequency with some precision. Typically a diode detector is used to indicate the output signal level. A wavemeter suitable for HF or VHF frequencies can be constructed with one or more coils and a variable capacitor.

DIP METERS

Old timers know this instrument as a grid-dip oscillator (GDO), so-called because the indicating "dip" was in the grid current of the vacuum-tube oscillator. Most dip meters these days are solid-state but the principle is the same. The oscillator coil is external, extending from the end of the instrument. A set of plug-in coils is provided to cover the unit's frequency range.

Along with resonant frequency measurements, the dip meter can also serve as a crude signal generator, capacitor and inductor meter, and antenna and transmission line tester, among other uses.[5] If you are purchasing a dip meter, look for one that is mechanically and electrically stable. On used units, the socket where the coils plug in is a common cause of intermittent operation. The coils should be in good condition. A headphone connection is helpful. Battery-operated models are convenient for antenna measurements.

If you hold the coil near a tuned circuit and adjust the dip meter tuning dial to the frequency of the tuned circuit, there is a dip in the meter reading as the resonant circuits interact with each other. To avoid detuning the circuit being tested, always use the minimum coupling that yields a noticeable indication.

Most dip meters can also serve as absorption wavemeters by turning off the oscillator and looking for a peak instead of a dip in the meter reading. Sometimes frequencies can be detected in this way that would be difficult to read on a frequency counter because of the presence of harmonics. Further, some dip meters have a connection for headphones. The operator can usually hear signals that do not register on the meter.

A dip meter may be coupled to a circuit either inductively or capacitively. Inductive coupling results from the magnetic field generated by current flow. Therefore, inductive coupling should be used when a coil or a conductor with relatively high current is convenient. Maximum inductive coupling results when the axis of the pick-up coil is placed perpendicular to the current path and the coil is adjacent to the wire.

High-impedance circuits have high voltage and low current. Use capacitive coupling when a point of relatively high voltage is convenient. An example might be the output of a 12-V powered RF amplifier. (For safety's sake, *do not* attempt dip-meter measurements on true high-voltage equipment such as vacuum-tube amplifiers or switching power supplies while they are energized.) Capacitive coupling is strongest when the end of the pick-up coil is near a point of high impedance. In either case, the circuit under test is affected by the presence of the dip meter.

To measure resonance, use the following procedure. First, bring the dip meter gradually closer to the circuit while slowly vary-

Table 25.1
Standard Frequency Stations
(Note: In recent years, frequent changes in these schedules have been common.)

Call Sign	Location	Frequency (MHz)
BPM	China	2.5, 5, 10, 15
BSF	Taiwan	5, 15
CHU	Ottawa, Canada	3.330, 7.850, 14.670
dcF	Germany	0.0775
HLA	South Korea	5.000
JJY	Japan	0.04, 0.06
MSF	Great Britain	0.06
RID	Irkutsk	5.004, 10.004, 15.004
RWM	Moscow	4.996, 9.996, 14.996
TDF	France	0.162
WWV	USA	2.5, 5, 10, 15, 20
WWVB	USA	0.06
WWVH	USA (Hawaii)	2.5, 5, 10, 15
ZSC	South Africa	4.291, 8.461, 12.724 (part time)

ing the dip-meter frequency. When a current dip occurs, hold the meter steady and tune for minimum current. Once the dip is found, move the meter away from the circuit and confirm that the dip comes from the circuit under test (the depth of the dip should decrease with distance from the circuit until the dip is no longer noticeable). Finally, move the meter back toward the circuit until the dip just reappears. Retune the meter for minimum current and read the dip-meter frequency from the dial or with a calibrated receiver or frequency counter.

The current dip of a good measurement is smooth and symmetrical. An asymmetrical dip indicates that the dip-meter oscillator frequency is being significantly influenced by the test circuit, degrading the accuracy of the measurement. Increase the distance between the dip meter and the circuit until a shallow symmetrical dip is obtained.

FREQUENCY CALIBRATION

The best test equipment is of limited use if it is not well-calibrated. The traditional frequency calibration method is to zero-beat a crystal oscillator (or its harmonic) with a radio station of known frequency, preferably a standard frequency station such as WWV or WWVH. **Table 25.1** contains the locations and frequencies of some of those stations. A receiver is tuned to one of those frequencies and the oscillator is loosely coupled to the antenna. It may be necessary to use frequency multiplication or division to obtain a common frequency. The frequency difference between the two causes a *beat note*, a rapid variation in the strength of the tone received in the speaker that slows down as the frequencies are brought close together. Maximum beat-note modulation occurs when the off-the-air and oscillator signals are approximately equal in amplitude

While the transmitted frequencies from WWV and WWVH are highly accurate, better than 1 part in 10^{11}, after propagation via the ionosphere the received accuracy is significantly degraded by Doppler shift, typically to a few parts in 10^7. Also, due to fading of the received signal, it can be difficult to zero-beat the oscillator to better than about 1 Hz accuracy. Best results generally occur on the highest frequency that provides good reception.

VLF time standards and surplus rubidium standards can be used for frequency references.[6,7] The Global Positioning System (GPS) satellites offer further possibilities for very precise frequency calibration. Various companies sell *disciplined oscillator* units that correct the frequency using the cesium-clock-based signals from the GPS satellites. These can sometimes be found on the surplus market.[8] Amateur-level kits are also available or you can build one from scratch.[9]

25.3.4 Oscilloscopes

An *oscilloscope* ("scope" for short) is an instrument that displays voltage versus time on a screen, similar to the waveforms seen in electronics textbooks. Scopes are broken down into two major classifications: analog and digital. This does not refer to the signals they measure, but rather to the methods used inside the instrument to process signals for display.

ANALOG OSCILLOSCOPES

Figure 25.12 shows a simplified diagram of a triggered-sweep oscilloscope. At the heart of all analog scopes is a cathode-ray tube (CRT) display. An electron beam inside the CRT strikes the phosphorescent screen causing a glowing spot. Unlike a television CRT, an oscilloscope uses electrostatic deflection rather than magnetic deflection. The exact location of the spot is a result of the voltage applied to the vertical and horizontal deflection plates. To trace how a signal travels through the oscilloscope circuitry, start by assuming that the trigger select switch is in the INTERNAL position.

The input signal is connected to the input COUPLING switch. The switch allows selection of either the ac part of an ac/dc signal or the total signal. If you wanted to measure, for example, the RF swing at the collector of an output stage including the dc level, you would use the *dc-coupling* mode. In the *ac-coupled* mode, dc is blocked from reaching the vertical amplifier chain so that you can measure a small ac signal superimposed on a much larger dc level. For example, you might want to measure a 25 mV 120-Hz ripple on a 13-V dc power supply. Note that you should not use ac coupling at frequencies below the low-frequency cutoff of the instrument in that mode, typically around 30 Hz, because the value of the blocking capacitor represents a high series impedance to very low-frequency signals.

After the coupling switch, the signal is connected to a calibrated attenuator. This is used to reduce the signal to a level within

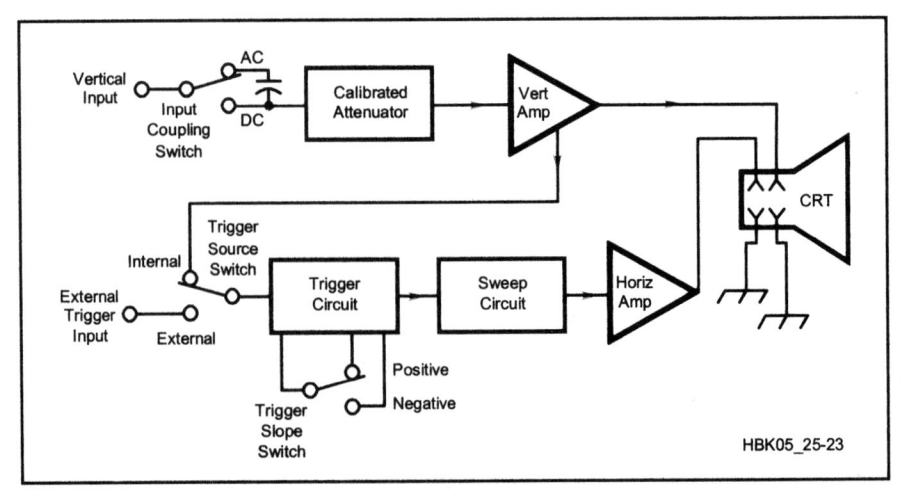

Figure 25.12 — Typical block diagram of a simple triggered-sweep oscilloscope.

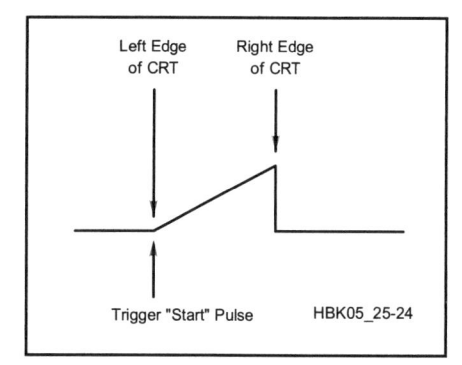

Figure 25.13 — The sweep trigger starts the ramp waveform that sweeps the CRT electron beam from side to side.

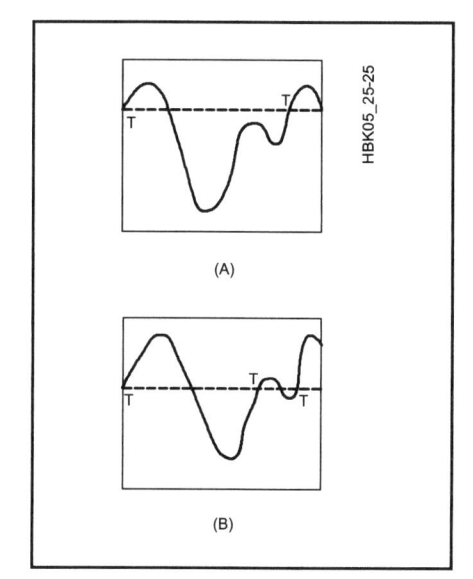

Figure 25.14 — In order to produce a stable display the selection of the trigger point is very important. Selecting the trigger point in A produces a stable display, but the trigger shown at B will produce a display that "jitters" from side

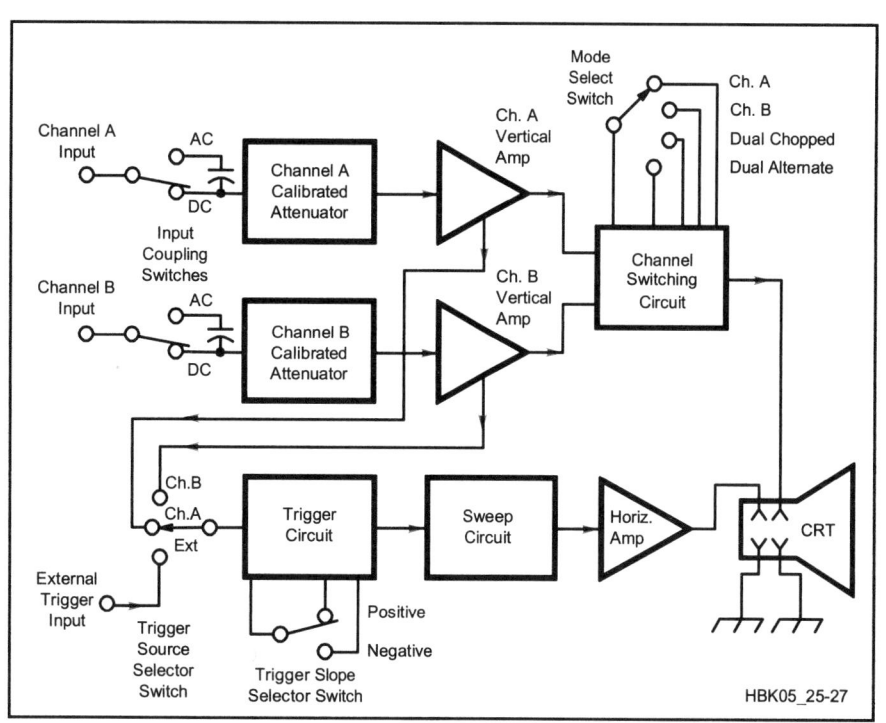

Figure 25.15 — Simplified dual-trace oscilloscope block diagram. Note the two identical input channels and amplifiers.

the range of the scope's vertical amplifier. The vertical amplifier boosts the signal to a level that can drive the CRT and also adds a bias component to position the waveform on the screen. The result is that the vertical position of the beam on the CRT represents input voltage.

A small sample of the signal from the vertical amplifier is sent to the trigger circuitry. The trigger circuit feeds a start pulse to the sweep generator when the input signal reaches a certain level (*level triggering*) or exhibits a positive- or negative-going edge (*edge triggering*). The sweep generator gives a precisely timed voltage ramp (see **Figure 25.13**). The rising edge of the ramp signal feeds the horizontal amplifier that, in turn, drives the CRT. This causes the scope trace to sweep from left to right, with the zero-voltage point representing the left side of the screen and the maximum voltage representing the right side of the screen. The result is that the horizontal position of the beam on the CRT represents time. At the end of the ramp, the sharp edge of the ramp quickly moves the beam back to the left side of the screen.

The trigger circuit controls the horizontal sweep. It looks at the trigger source (internal or external) to find out if it is positive- or negative-going and to see if the signal has passed a particular level. **Figure 25.14A** shows a typical signal and the dotted line on the figure represents the trigger level. It is important to note that once a trigger circuit is "fired" it cannot fire again until the sweep has moved all the way across the screen from left to right. There normally is a TRIGGER LEVEL control to move the trigger level up and down until a stable display is seen. Some scopes have an AUTOMATIC position that chooses a level to lock the display in place without manual adjustment.

Figure 25.14B shows what happens when the level has not been properly selected. Because there are two points during a single cycle of the waveform that meet the triggering requirements, the trigger circuit will have a tendency to jump from one trigger point to another. This will make the waveform jitter from left to right. Adjustment of the TRIGGER LEVEL control will fix that problem.

It is also possible to trigger the sweep system from an external source (such as the system clock in a digital system). This is done by using the external input jack with the trigger select switch in the EXTERNAL position.

DUAL-TRACE OSCILLOSCOPES

Dual-trace oscilloscopes have two vertical input channels that can be displayed together on the screen. Although the best dual-trace scopes use a CRT with two electron beams, it is possible to trick the eye into seeing two traces simultaneously using a single-beam CRT. **Figure 25.15** shows a simplified block diagram of a dual-trace oscilloscope using this method. The only differences between this scope and the previous example are the additional vertical amplifier and the "channel switching circuit." This block determines whether we display channel A, channel B or both (simultaneously).

The dual display is not a true dual-beam display but the appearance of dual traces is created by the scope using one of two methods, referred to as *chopped mode* and *alternate mode*. In the chopped mode a small portion of the channel A waveform is written to the CRT, then a corresponding portion of the channel B waveform is written to the CRT. This procedure is continued until both waveforms are completely written on the CRT. The switching from one channel to the other is so fast that each trace looks as though it were continuous. The chopped mode is essential for *single-shot* signals (signals that do

Test Equipment and Measurements 25.13

not repeat periodically). It is most useful at slow sweep speeds. At fast sweep speeds, the switching from channel to channel becomes visible, making each trace into a dotted line.

In the alternate mode, the complete channel A waveform is written to the CRT followed immediately by the complete channel B waveform. This happens so quickly that it appears that the waveforms are displayed at the same time. This mode of operation is not very useful at very slow sweep speeds since the two traces no longer appear simultaneous. It also does not work for single-shot events.

Most dual-trace oscilloscopes also have a feature called "X-Y" mode. This feature allows one channel to drive the horizontal amplifier of the scope (called the X channel) while the other channel (called Y in this mode of operation) drives the vertical amplifier. Some single-trace oscilloscopes support this mode as well. X-Y operation allows the scope to display *Lissajous patterns* for frequency and phase comparison and to use specialized test adapters such as curve tracers or spectrum analyzer front ends. Because of frequency limitations of most scope horizontal amplifiers the X channel is usually limited to a 5 or 10-MHz bandwidth.

DIGITAL OSCILLOSCOPES

In recent years, semiconductor and display technology have advanced to the point that much of the analog signal processing in an oscilloscope can be replaced with low-cost microprocessor-based digital circuitry. This results in dramatically improved accuracy for both amplitude and time measurements as well as enabling sophisticated features that would be difficult or impossible in an analog scope. For example, a trace can be displayed with infinite persistence and stored as a computer file if desired.

In a digital oscilloscope the vertical amplifiers are replaced with an analog-to-digital converter (ADC), which samples the signal at regular time intervals and stores the samples in digital memory. The samples are stored with an assigned time, determined by the trigger circuits and the microprocessor clock. The samples are then retrieved and displayed on the screen with the correct vertical and horizontal position.

Early digital oscilloscopes used a CRT with electrostatic deflection, similar to an analog scope, with the horizontal and vertical deflection signals generated by digital-to-analog converters (DACs). Modern instruments usually use either a raster-scan CRT similar to a television picture tube or a solid state (LCD) display. The microprocessor determines which pixels to light up to draw the traces on the screen. Even though a digital scope does not have the same internal circuitry as an analog scope, many of the same terms are used to control operation. For example,

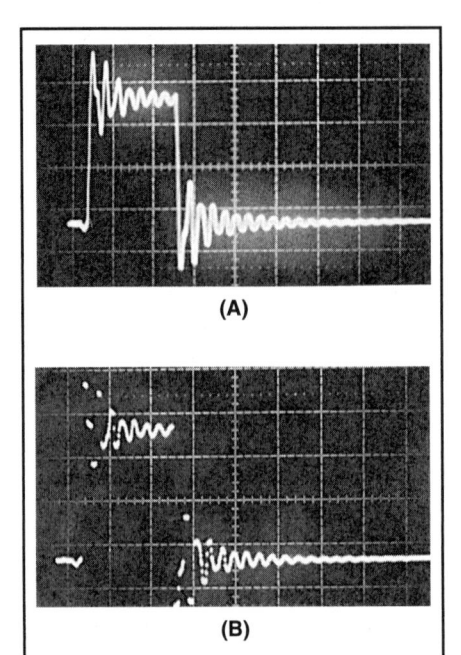

Figure 25.16 — Comparison of an analog scope waveform (A) and that produced by a digital oscilloscope (B). Notice that the digital samples in B are not continuous, which may leave the actual shape of the waveform in doubt for the fastest rise time displays the scope is capable of producing.

"Sweep speed" still describes the amount of time per horizontal division, even though there is no electron beam to be swept across the display in the original sense.

For the vertical signals you will see manufacturers refer to "8-bit digitizing," or perhaps "10-bit resolution." This is a measure of the number of digital levels that are shown along the vertical (voltage) axis. More bits give you better resolution and accuracy of measurement. An 8-bit vertical resolution means each vertical screen has 2^8 (or 256) discrete values; similarly, 10-bit resolution yields 2^{10} (or 1024) discrete values.

It is important to understand some of the limitations resulting from sampling the signal rather than taking a continuous, analog measurement. When you try to reconstruct a signal from individual discrete samples, you must take samples at least twice as fast as the highest frequency signal being measured. If you digitize a 100-MHz sine wave, you should take samples at a rate of 200 million samples a second (referred to as 200 Megasamples/second). Actually, you really would like to take samples even more often, usually at a rate at least five times higher than the input signal. (See the **DSP and Software Radio Design** chapter for more information on sampled signals.)

If the sample rate is not high enough, very fast signal changes between sampling points will not appear on the display. For example, **Figure 25.16** shows one signal measured using both analog and digital scopes. The large spikes seen in the analog-scope display are not visible on the digital scope. The sampling frequency of the digital scope is not fast enough to store the higher frequency components of the waveform. If you take samples at a rate less than twice the input frequency, the reconstructed signal has a wrong apparent frequency; this is referred to as *aliasing*. In Figure 25.16 you can see that there is about one sample taken per cycle of the input waveform. This does not meet the 2:1 criteria established above. The result is that the scope reconstructs a waveform with a different apparent frequency.

Many older digital scopes had potential problems with *aliasing*. A simple manual check for aliasing is to use the highest practical sweep speed (shortest time per division) and then to change to other sweep speeds to verify that the apparent frequency doesn't change. Some modern oscilloscopes use a special technique to increase the effective sample rate for repetitive signals. The phase of the sample clock is adjusted slightly on each successive sweep, so that the new samples occur in between the previous ones. After several sweeps the missing data in the spaces between the original samples are filled in, producing a continuous trace. This only works with periodic signals that trigger at exactly the same point on each sweep.

OSCILLOSCOPE LIMITATIONS

Oscilloscopes have fundamental limits, primarily in frequency of operation and range of input voltages. For most purposes the voltage range can be expanded by the use of appropriate probes. The frequency response (also called the bandwidth) of a scope is usually the most important limiting factor. For example, a 100-MHz 1-V sine wave fed into an oscilloscope with a 100-MHz 3-dB bandwidth will read approximately 0.7 V on the display. The same instrument at frequencies below 30 MHz should be accurate to about 5%.

A parameter called *rise time* is related to bandwidth. This term describes a scope's ability to accurately display voltages that rise very quickly. For example, a very sharp and square waveform may appear to take some time in order to reach a specified fraction of the input voltage level. The rise time is usually defined as the time required for the display to show a change from the 10% to 90% points of the input waveform, as shown in **Figure 25.17**. Assuming the frequency response is primarily limited by a single-pole roll off in the amplifier circuitry, the mathematical definition of rise time is given by:

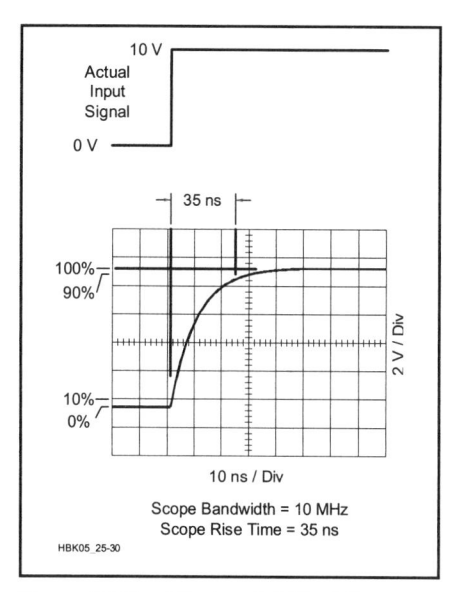

Figure 25.17 — The bandwidth of the oscillo-scope vertical channel limits the rise time of the signals displayed on the scope.

$$t_r = \frac{0.35}{BW}$$

where t_r = rise time in µs and BW = bandwidth in MHz of the amplifier.

It is also important to note that inexpensive analog oscilloscopes may not have better than 5% accuracy in these applications. Even moderately-priced oscilloscopes are still useful, however. The most important value of an oscilloscope is that it presents an image of what is going on in a circuit, which is very useful for troubleshooting waveforms and other time-varying phenomena. It can show modulation levels, relative gain between stages, clipping distortion, intermittent oscillations and other useful information.

USING AN OSCILLOSCOPE

An oscilloscope can measure a signal's shape, amplitude, frequency and whether it is dc, ac or a mixture of both. For example, in **Figure 25.18** it is clear from the shape that the signal is a sine wave. Assuming that the center horizontal line or axis represents zero volts, the signal has no dc component since there is as much above the axis as below it. If the vertical gain has been set to 1 V per division, then the peak value is 2 V and the peak-to-peak value is 4 V.

The horizontal travel of the trace is calibrated in units of time. If the sweep speed is known and we count the number of divisions (vertical bars) between peaks of the waveform (or any similar well-defined points that occur once per cycle) we can find the period of one cycle. The frequency is the reciprocal of the period. In Figure 25.18, for example,

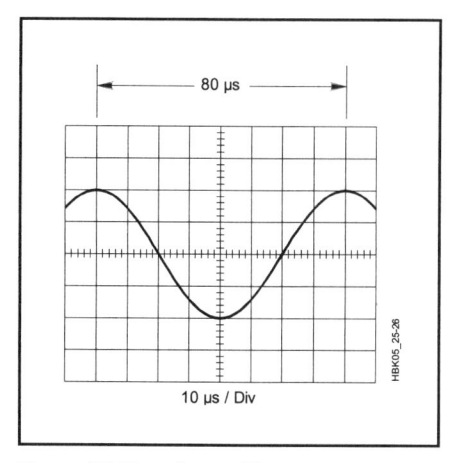

Figure 25.18 — An oscilloscope can measure frequency as well as amplitude. Here the waveform shown has a frequency of 80 microseconds (8 divisions × 10 µs per division) and therefore a frequency

the distance between the peaks is 8 divisions. If the sweep speed is 10 µs/division then the period is 80 µs. That means that the frequency of the waveform is 1/80 µs, or 12,500 Hz. The accuracy of the measured frequency depends on the accuracy of the scope's ramp generator, typically a few percent for an analog instrument. This accuracy cannot compete with even the least-expensive frequency counter, but the scope can still be used to determine whether a circuit is functioning properly.

Oscilloscopes are usually connected to a circuit under test with a short length of shielded cable and a probe. At low frequencies, a piece of small-diameter coax cable and some sort of insulated test probe might do. However, at higher frequencies the capacitive reactance of the cable would be much less than the one-megohm input impedance of the oscilloscope. In addition each scope has a certain built-in capacitance at its input terminals (usually between 5 and 35 pF). The total capacitance causes problems when probing an RF circuit with relatively high impedance.

Most new oscilloscopes come with specially-designed *scope probes*, one for each vertical channel. They can also be purchased separately. The most common type is a *×10 probe* (called a "times ten" probe), which forms a 10:1 voltage divider using the built-in resistance of the probe and the input resistance of the scope. When using a ×10 probe, all voltage readings must be multiplied by 10. For example, if the scope is on the 1 V/division range and a ×10 probe were in use, the signals would be displayed on the scope face at 10 V/division. Some scopes can sense whether a ×10 probe is in use, and automatically change the scale of the scope's display.

Unfortunately a resistor alone in series with the scope input seriously degrades the scope's rise-time performance and bandwidth because of the low-pass filter formed by the series resistance along with the parallel capacitance

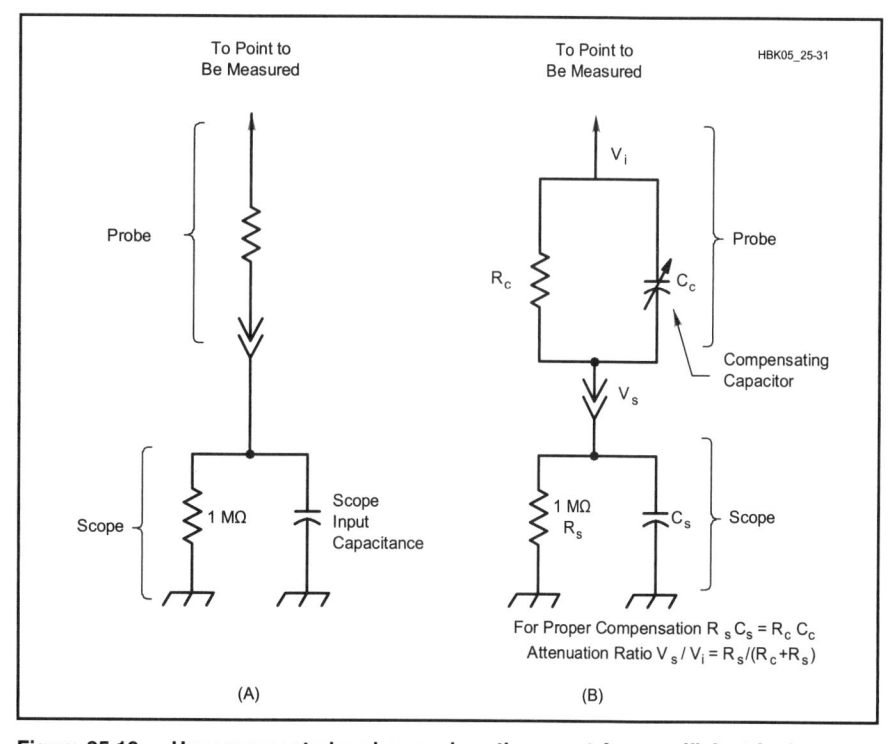

Figure 25.19 — Uncompensated probes such as the one at A are sufficient for low-frequency and slow-rise-time measurements. However, for accurate display of fast rise times with high-frequency components the compensated probe at B must be used. The variable capacitor is adjusted for proper compensation (see text for details).

For Proper Compensation $R_s C_s = R_c C_c$
Attenuation Ratio $V_s / V_i = R_s/(R_c + R_s)$

Test Equipment and Measurements 25.15

of the cable and scope input. This may be corrected by using a compensating capacitor in parallel with the series resistor. If the capacitor value is chosen so that the R-C time constant is the same as the R-C network formed by the input resistance and capacitance of the scope, as shown in **Figure 25.19**, then the probe and scope should have a flat response curve throughout the whole bandwidth of the scope. A ×10 probe not only reduces the voltage by a factor of 10 but it increases the input resistance and reduces the capacitance as well, which reduces loading on the circuit under test.

To account for manufacturing tolerances in the scope and probe the compensating capacitor is made variable. Most scopes include a "calibrator" output that produces a fast-rise-time square wave for the purpose of adjusting the compensating capacitor in a probe. **Figure 25.20** shows possible responses when the probe is connected to the oscilloscope's calibrator jack. A misadjusted compensating capacitor can greatly affect the frequency response of the scope and create artifacts in signals that are not actually present.

If a probe cable is too short, do not attempt to extend the length of the cable by adding a piece of common coaxial cable. The compensating capacitor in the probe is chosen to compensate for the provided length of cable. It usually does not have enough range to compensate for extra lengths.

The shortest ground lead possible should be used from the probe to the circuit ground. Long ground leads act as inductors at high frequencies where they create ringing and other undesirable artifacts in the displayed signal.

For the best high-frequency performance, the scope probe can be eliminated entirely and the oscilloscope input converted to a 50-Ω impedance. Some scopes have a switch to choose between a high-impedance or 50-Ω input. For others, you can purchase a 50-Ω *through-line* termination, which is just a connector with a male BNC on one end, a female BNC on the other, and an internal 50-Ω termination resistor in parallel. Plug the male connector to the scope's high-impedance vertical input and connect the 50-Ω cable from the device under test to the female connector.

Some situations may require the use of a scope to measure a *current* waveform, rather than a voltage. Specialized current probes are available that make this task possible, with some capable of measuring both dc and ac.

Be wary of using a scope to judge harmonic content or distortion of a sine wave. A waveform that "looks good" to the eye may have significant distortion or high-frequency components unsuitable for on-the-air signals. A spectrum analyzer (described below) should be used for determining the spectral content of signals.

CHOOSING AN OSCILLOSCOPE

For many years a scope (even a so-called portable) was big and heavy. In recent years, microprocessors and other ICs have reduced the size and weight. Modern scopes can take other forms than the traditional large cabinet with built-in CRT. Nearly all digital oscilloscopes use an LCD display for true portability. (See **Figure 25.21**) You can use your personal computer as an oscilloscope with an external signal digitizer that connects to the PC via a high-speed USB or Firewire interface. This saves money by using the cabinet, power supply, processor and display of the PC. Even stand-alone scopes can attach to a PC and download their data for storage and analysis or transfer it to memory storage devices. Many high-end scopes now incorporate non-traditional functions, such as the Fast Fourier Transforms (FFT). This allows spectrum analysis or other advanced mathematical techniques to be applied to the displayed waveform.

Features

When choosing an oscilloscope, the first decision is analog versus digital. Used and surplus instruments are usually analog but more modern units are shifting to digital as the prices of solid-state displays and other components come down. Digital models are generally more accurate and tend to have lots of features not found on analog oscilloscopes.

The next big decision is how many input channels you need. There are many situations in which having a second channel is extremely helpful and even more than two channels is often useful, especially when troubleshooting digital circuits. With two or more channels you typically also get X-Y mode.

Trace storage is essential for viewing very slow signals or single-shot transients. In the old days, high-end analog scopes used special CRTs that could store a trace in an analog fashion. They tended to be rather difficult to adjust properly and the CRTs are expensive and/or impossible to replace if they should ever fail. Trace storage is very easy to implement in a digital scope and nearly all of them have the feature. Ideally, one or more stored traces can be displayed simultaneously with the current trace for easy comparison.

Most scopes come with the ability to select internal, external or power-line synchronous triggering as well as an adjustable trigger level. Digital scopes may draw a horizontal line on the screen so you can see exactly where the trigger level is with respect to the signal, which is very handy. Automatic adjustment of trigger level is a common feature as well. Some scopes offer a noise-rejection feature that adds hysteresis to reduce false triggering. *Single sweep* is useful for looking at a non-repetitive signal. The single sweep can be *armed*, that is, reset and ready to start the next sweep, by pushing a button or sometimes with an external signal. *Trigger delay* allows horizontal centering of

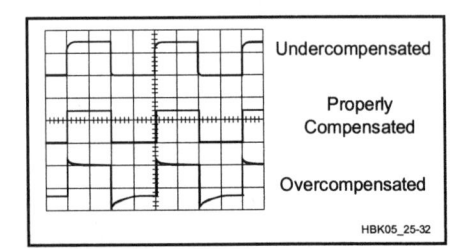

Figure 25.20 — Displays of a square-wave input illustrating undercompensated, properly compensated and overcompensated probes.

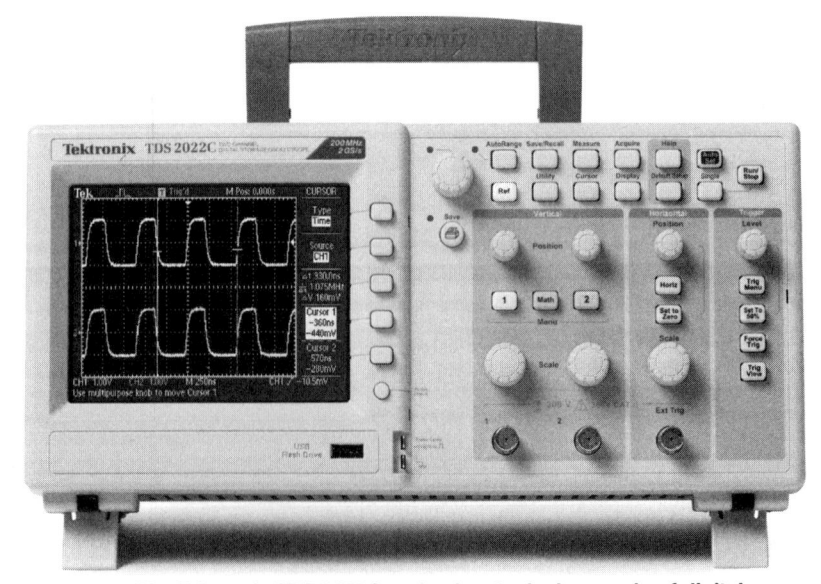

Figure 25.21 — The Tektronix TDS 2000C series is a typical example of digital oscilloscopes using an LCD display.

the display at a different place from the trigger point. *Trigger hold-off* inhibits the trigger for a selectable time after the sweep to prevent unwanted multiple triggers.

Some older tube-type scopes offered only ac input coupling, but most nowadays have a switch to select between ac, dc and ground. As mentioned before, some include a switch to select 50-Ω or high input impedance. Some high-speed scopes include a switchable input low-pass filter to reduce wideband noise when measuring lower-frequency signals. A feature sometimes found on multiple-channel scopes is the ability to add or subtract two or more channels.

Digital oscilloscopes often include various data-analysis features. Averaging reduces noise and peak mode makes transient peaks visible. A common feature is the ability to calculate and display the peak, peak-to-peak and RMS values of a signal. For repetitive signals, the period and frequency can be calculated as well. Some scopes include amplitude and/or time markers that allow accurate measurements of specific points on a waveform. Sometimes the instrument state can be stored to one of several internal memories, which can be very handy on complicated instruments that take a long time to set up.

Computer connectivity used to be available only on high-end instruments but is now becoming more and more common. It allows storing traces for later reference and you can produce nice graphical screen shots for that magazine article or notebook entry about your latest creation. With the proper software it allows automated testing as well. Older instruments usually have a GPIB (general purpose interface bus) interface, also known as IEEE-488 or as HPIB on Hewlett-Packard equipment. GPIB-to-USB adapters are available from Prologix and a number of other companies. More modern scopes usually come with an RS-232 or USB interface.

Specifications

Bandwidth is the main "money spec" for an oscilloscope. The higher the frequency range, the more expensive it tends to be. Rise time is also sometimes specified. For digital scopes, the sample rate is just as important. Theoretically it must be at least twice the bandwidth but practically should be much higher than that to avoid aliasing. For repetitive waveforms, some scopes can do tricks with the sample phase to eliminate aliasing with a lower sample rate, as explained previously

The range of input signals is normally specified as the maximum and minimum volts per division. Amplitude accuracy is usually specified as a percent of the reading, typically 5-10% for inexpensive analog scopes and perhaps 1-2% for high-quality digital ones. Another important specification is the maximum input signal that can be accepted without damage. It is typically presented as a maximum dc plus peak ac voltage, that is, the maximum peak voltage of the complete signal. This is increased when using a ×10 probe, subject to the probe specifications.

For digital scopes, the resolution of the input analog-to-digital converter (ADC) is typically specified as a number of bits. Sometimes the lowest-voltage input ranges are obtained simply by using only the low end of the ADC range, which results in the displayed signal having a stepped response rather than a smooth curve.

The sweep speed is generally specified in seconds (milliseconds, microseconds) per division. The accuracy is typically a few percent for analog scopes and much better than that for digital scopes, often limited just by the screen resolution. The triggering system is a major factor that determines how useful a scope is in actual operation, but it can be hard to tell how well it works by studying the specifications. The trigger sensitivity is the main parameter to look for. It is specified in fractions of a division for internal trigger and in mV for external trigger.

BUYING A USED SCOPE

Many hams end up buying a used scope due to price. If you buy a scope and intend to service it yourself, be aware all scopes that use tubes or a CRT contain lethal voltages. Treat an oscilloscope with the same care you would use with a tube-type high-power amplifier. The CRT should be handled carefully because if dropped it will crack and implode, resulting in pieces of glass and other materials being sprayed everywhere in the immediate vicinity. You should wear a full-face safety shield and other appropriate safety equipment to protect yourself.

Another concern when servicing an older scope is the availability of parts. The CRTs in older units may no longer be available. Many scopes made since about 1985 used special ICs, LCDs and microprocessors. Some of these may not be available or may be prohibitive in cost. You should buy a used scope from a reputable vendor— even better yet, try it out before you buy it. Make sure you get the operator's manual also.

Older tube-type models are generally quite serviceable, often needing nothing more than a new tube or two. The massive lab-grade instruments from days of yore made by Tektronix and Hewlett-Packard can still give good service with a little care. They are so large and heavy that a special scope cart was often used to house them and allow easy movement from lab bench to lab bench.

Early generation digital scopes are now showing up on the surplus market at reasonable prices. Unfortunately, the user interface leaves much to be desired on some models, sometimes requiring the operator to use several layers of menus to access common functions. Look for one with an analog-like feel with separate buttons or knobs for most of the important functions.

25.3.5 Audio-Frequency Oscillators and Function Generators

There are a number of ways to generate an audio-frequency tone. If a square-wave output is acceptable, then a simple oscillator can be built with a 555 timer IC, two resistors and two capacitors. It is an inexpensive, time-tested design with good frequency stability.

If a sine-wave signal is needed, a *twin-T* oscillator made with a single bipolar transistor is about the simplest solution. The oscillator in **Figure 25.22** can be operated at any frequency in the audio range by varying the component values. R1, R2 and C1 form a low-pass network, while C2, C3 and R3 form a high-pass network. As the phase shifts are opposite, there is only one frequency at which the total phase shift from collector to base is 180°: Oscillation will occur at that frequency. C1 should be about twice the capacitance of C2 or C3. R3 should have a resistance about 0.1 that of R1 or R2 (C2 = C3 and R1 = R2). Output is taken across C1, where the harmonic distortion is least. Use a relatively high impedance load — 100 kΩ or more. Most small-signal AF transistors can be used for Q1. Either NPN

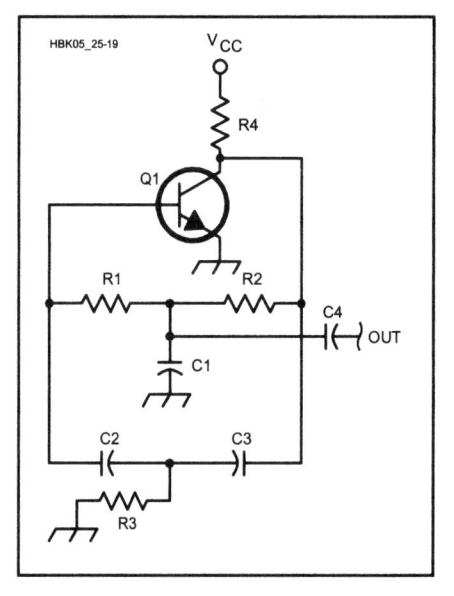

Figure 25.22 — Values for the twin-T audio oscillator circuit range from 18 kΩ for R1-R2 and 0.05 µF for C1 (750 Hz) to 15 kΩ and 0.02 µF for 1800 Hz. For the same frequency range, R3 and C2-C3 vary from 1800 Ω and 0.02 µF to 1500 Ω and 0.01 µF. R4 is 3300 Ω and C4, the output coupling capacitor, can be 0.05 µF for high-impedance loads.

or PNP types are satisfactory if the supply polarity is set correctly. R4, the collector load resistor may be changed a little to adjust the oscillator for best output waveform.

While the twin-T oscillator does give a roughly sinusoidal output, the distortion is rather high and the frequency is not easily tunable. Both of those problems are addressed in the *Wien bridge* oscillator illustrated in **Figure 25.23** The key to low distortion is to prevent the amplifier from going into saturation. If equal values of R and C are used in both sections of the positive feedback network, then the gain through that network is ⅓. If the negative feedback network also has a 3:1 ratio, then the total loop gain is exactly 1, the condition for oscillation. The light bulb in the bottom leg has a positive temperature coefficient. (Note that a true incandescent bulb must be used — an LED may not be substituted.) As the signal level increases, its resistance goes up, lowering the gain. In this way the amplitude is held steady so that the amplifier does not saturate. The frequency may be tuned with a single control by using a two-section potentiometer for the two resistors labeled R. Typically small fixed-value resistors are placed in series with each potentiometer section to give about a 10:1 tuning range. Additional ranges can be had by switching the capacitors, selected using the equation

$$C = \frac{1}{2\pi fR}$$

A suitable bulb is a number 327 or 1819. Under normal operation, it should be lit to a bit less than full brightness, which is determined by the value of the negative feedback resistor R_F, typically around 400 Ω.

The idea of using the positive temperature coefficient of resistance of a light bulb to stabilize the output of a tunable oscillator was used in the very first instrument produced by the Hewlett-Packard company. (The Model 200A audio oscillator circuit was first described in company founder Hewlett's 1939 college thesis.)

FUNCTION GENERATORS

A *function generator*, also known as a *waveform generator*, is a type of audio oscillator that can generate several waveforms. In addition to sine waves, most can also generate square waves, triangle waves and sawtooth ramp waveforms. A pulse output with variable duty factor is another common feature. Many models can also linearly sweep the frequency. Frequency coverage is typically from below audio frequencies up to a few MHz.

The heart of most analog function generators is a triangle wave oscillator. To create the sine wave, a diode shaping circuit rounds off the top and bottom of the triangles, resulting in a reasonably-accurate sine wave with distortion on the order of a percent or two. Circuitry that determines when the triangle wave is rising or falling is used to generate the square wave as well. The rise/fall duty factor of the triangle wave can be varied, which also varies the duty factor of the square wave. If the triangle wave duty factor is set near 100% or 0%, it becomes either a rising or falling sawtooth wave.

The easiest way to build your own analog function generator is to use a waveform generator IC that includes most of what you need in one package. The two most common such ICs available today are the MAX038 and XR2206. The ICL8038 is seen in many older circuits but is obsolete and no longer in production. The AD9833 direct digital synthesis (DDS) IC (see **Figure 25.24**) is also designed to be used as a low frequency function generator.[10] (DDS is discussed in the **Oscillators and Synthesizers** and **DSP and Software Radio Design** chapters.)

An *arbitrary waveform generator* (AWG or ARB) has capabilities that are a superset of a waveform generator. The sinusoidal waveform ROM look-up table in Figure 25.24 is replaced by RAM so that data which creates waveforms other than a sine wave can be used. Usually a large amount of memory is included so that long non-repetitive waveforms can be generated in addition to periodic signals. ARBs generally include a microprocessor and provide means to generate complicated sequences that may combine repeating and nonrepeating segments.

CHOOSING A FUNCTION GENERATOR

For many applications, the basic analog sine/square wave generator based on a Wien bridge oscillator works fine. The sine wave is adequate for testing the gain, frequency response, and maximum signal level of an audio-frequency circuit. The square wave is useful for checking the transient response of circuits.

The additional wave shapes offered by a function generator are useful for more esoteric applications. Sawtooth and triangle waves can be used to sweep a voltage through a range to test the response of a circuit to various voltages. The pulse output is useful for testing digital circuitry, especially if the instrument has provision for adjusting the on and off voltage levels. Frequency sweep capability is very handy for testing the frequency response of an audio circuit, especially if a sweep ramp or sweep trigger output is provided for synchronizing an oscilloscope. Some instruments provide an input to control the frequency by means of an external voltage.

When selecting a function generator, the first specification to look at is the frequency range. Many units cover low radio frequencies as well as audio. The frequency accuracy may be important for many applications. Digitally-synthesized models use a quartz crystal clock oscillator so are much more accurate than analog models. Some analog models do have a built-in frequency counter, but the accuracy may still be limited by frequency drift.

The amplitude range and accuracy should also be considered. An amplitude of several volts is useful for testing power devices and the ability to accurately set the amplitude to a

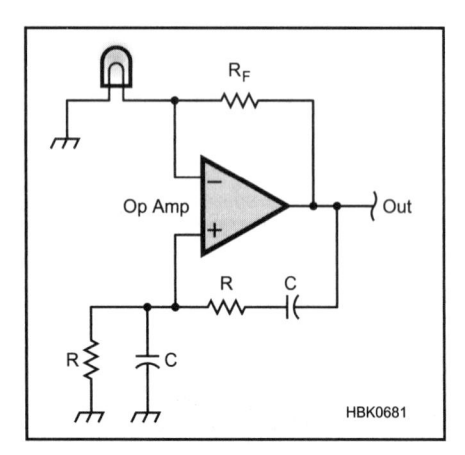

Figure 25.23 — A Wien bridge oscillator has lower distortion than a twin-T oscillator. The light bulb acts to stabilize the feedback to prevent distortion due to amplifier clipping.

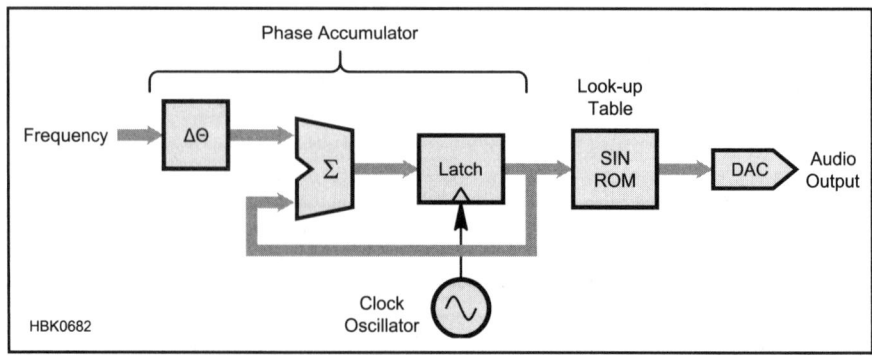

Figure 25.24 — A direct digital synthesizer (DDS) sine-wave generator. Not shown is a low-pass filter at the output that attenuates unwanted spurious frequencies above one-half the clock frequency.

few millivolts may be needed for driving the microphone input of a transmitter. The output impedance is usually either 600 Ω or 50 Ω.

Function generators are available for a wide range of prices, from inexpensive hand-held units to sophisticated bench instruments costing thousands of dollars. Surplus tube-type models can be good values, starting with the venerable Hewlett-Packard 200A, manufactured until the early 1970s. More-recent models can also be found on the used-equipment market made by HP, its successor company Agilent Technologies, Tektronix, B&K, Keithley, Wavetek, Leader, Fluke and others.

An even less-expensive solution is to use a computer sound card as a function generator. A variety of free function generator software can be found on the Internet. Since the sound card output is ac-coupled it is not possible to adjust the dc offset voltage as it is with most function generators. Also, the frequency range, the level range and accuracy, and the output drive capability are not as good as you would expect from a special-purpose instrument. However, quite sophisticated waveforms may be generated with the right software and the price is right.

25.3.6 Measuring Inductance and Capacitance

The traditional way to measure inductance (L), capacitance (C), or resistance (R) is with an *LCR bridge* consisting of a Wheatstone bridge driven by a sine-wave voltage and with an ac voltmeter for the null detector. In **Figure 25.25**, the box labeled Z is the reference component. It must be the same type as the device under test, an inductor, capacitor or resistor. The bridge is nulled when the ratio of the variable resistor R_V to R is the same as the ratio of the impedance of the device under test to that of Z. The value of R_V is proportional to the resistance or inductance and inversely proportional to the capacitance. To make it proportional to C, simply swap the positions of R_V and R in the circuit. In all cases, when R_V = R, the null is achieved when the value of the device under test equals the value of Z.

Most commercial LCR bridges include a switch to select various values of Z. Typically they are in decade steps so that the dial calibration works on all scales. The frequency of the sine-wave source should be such that the reactance of the capacitor or inductor under test is not so low as to present too small a load impedance to the sine-wave source and not so high that the load presented by the ac voltmeter reduces the depth of the null. Often several frequencies may be selected, the lower frequencies being used for large-value L and C and higher frequencies used for the smaller values.

A dip meter may be used for measuring either L or C as long as a component of the opposite type is available whose value is accurately known. The technique is to make a tuned circuit by connecting the inductor and capacitor in parallel and then measure the resonant frequency with a grid dip meter. The inductance or capacitance can be determined from the dip frequency, f, using the formula

$$L = \frac{1}{(2\pi f)^2 C} \text{ or}$$

$$C = \frac{1}{(2\pi f)^2 L}$$

Some multimeters have built-in capability to measure inductors and capacitors. It is also possible to build an adapter to allow measuring L and C with any multimeter. Circuit examples are given in the Construction Projects section at the end of this chapter.

The use of capacitors in high-frequency switchmode supplies (see the **Power Sources** chapter) makes it important to measure their *equivalent series resistance (ESR)* and *equivalent series inductance (ESL)*. ESR and ESL cause loss and affect the switching circuit's ability to regulate properly. An ESR meter measures a capacitor's ESR by using short pulses or ac signals. Some ESR meters can be used with the capacitor in-circuit although they should not be used with the capacitor charged or energized. ESL is typically measured with an inductance meter as descibed above.

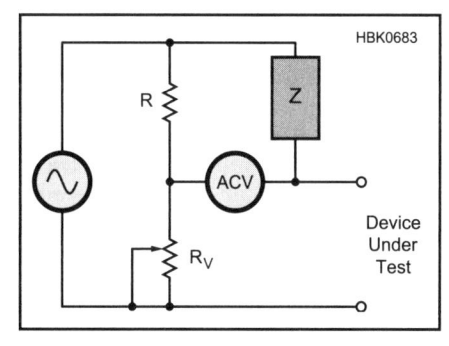

Figure 25.25 — An LCR bridge, which is a type of Wheatstone bridge used to measure inductors (L), capacitors (C) and resistors (R). The box labeled "Z" is the reference component to which the device under test is compared.

25.4 RF Measurements

RF measurements are a special case of ac measurements. While everything in the previous section about measuring low-frequency ac applies, there are additional factors to take into consideration for high frequency measurements, such as parasitic values and operational bandwidth. This section concentrates on equipment and techniques especially suited to measuring at radio frequencies. The **RF Techniques** chapter has additional information on circuits at high frequencies.

25.4.1 Measuring RF Voltage and Current

An *RF probe* rectifies a radio-frequency signal so that its amplitude can be measured with a dc instrument such as a multimeter. The circuit is typically quite simple, consisting of a diode, a resistor and a couple capacitors, as in the example of **Figure 25.26**. The resistor value is chosen so that the rectified output voltage is approximately equal to the RMS value of a sine wave input signal. The 390 kΩ value shown assumes the meter has a 1 MΩ input resistance. The diode can be a high-speed switching diode such as a 1N914 or 1N4148, or it can be a Schottky diode for greater sensitivity.

The detector is located as close to the measuring point as possible to minimize stray inductance and capacitance. The leads to the

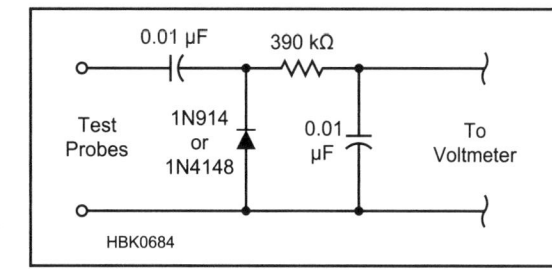

Figure 25.26 — A basic RF probe, used to convert an RF signal into a dc voltage that can be measured by a voltmeter.

Test Equipment and Measurements   25.19

dc voltmeter can be longer. The RF probe can be housed in any convenient enclosure that fits easily in the hand and the circuitry can be constructed on a scrap of perforated phenolic board, as long as the leads are kept short. A much more elaborate version with a coaxial input and an integrated compensated voltmeter is described with the downloadable supplemental content.

Measuring RF current is a little more difficult. When measuring the current on an antenna or feed line, it may not be practical to break the connection to insert an ammeter. Even when that can be done, the meter itself often upsets the measurement, either because it must be plugged into ac power or simply because of the instrument's size.

A time-honored technique is to wire a small incandescent lamp in series with the antenna or feed line to be measured. Although you can get a rough idea of the amount of RF current by comparing the brightness to the brightness with a known dc current, this method is only useful for relative measurements where the absolute value does not need to be known.

Another alternative is to construct an RF ammeter using a current transformer that clamps over the wire.[11] That method has the advantage that the wire does not need to be disconnected. It is important that the leads to the meter not couple to the wire or cable being measured.

Highly-accurate commercial RF ammeters made to measure the base current of AM broadcast station antennas can sometimes be found on the surplus market. If you can find one it would give much better accuracy than a homebrew device.

25.4.2 Measuring RF Power

Transmitter power is normally given in units of watts. Lower-power RF signals found in receiver and transmitter circuits may be specified in units of milliwatts (mW) or microwatts (µW) but it is perhaps more common to see units of *dBm*, decibels with respect to one milliwatt. For example, it is much easier to express the power of an S1 signal as −121 dBm than 0.00000000076 µW. The formula is dBm = 10 log (1000 P), where P is the power in watts. One milliwatt (P = 0.001) is 0 dBm, 10 mW is +10 dBm, 0.01 mW is −20 dBm and so on. **Table 25.2** lists common dBm and power equivalent.

Measuring RF power can be a little confusing because there are several ways to do it. We have already covered the difference between peak and RMS voltage and current. RF power is always based on RMS values. For example, if the RF voltage into a 50-Ω dummy load is 70.7 V RMS (100 V at the peak of the RF sine waves), then the power is P = E^2/R = $70.7^2/50$ = 100 W. (See **www.eznec.com/Amateur/RMS_Power.pdf** for a more extensive explanation of power and RMS.)

Peak envelope power (PEP) has nothing to do with the difference between the peak and average voltage of a sine wave. It is a measure of the power of an RF signal at the modulation peak, averaged over one RF cycle. For a CW signal, the PEP is simply the power when the key is closed, as read on any wattmeter. However, for an SSB signal, the power is constantly changing as you speak. An average-reading wattmeter will read a value much lower than the PEP.

Measuring the peak envelope power is more difficult than measuring the average power. An oscilloscope can be a highly-accurate method within its bandwidth limitations if the load impedance is known accurately. Don't forget that the oscilloscope shows peak-to-peak rather than RMS voltage, so you must divide the maximum reading by $2 \times \sqrt{2}$ or 2.828. Some wattmeters do have PEP-reading capability. Their circuitry must have very fast response to the detected RF signal to give an accurate reading of the peaks.

A *directional wattmeter* is a device that measures power flowing in each direction on a transmission line. The manner in which RF signals propagate on transmission lines is covered in the **Transmission Lines** chapter. Many amateurs keep a wattmeter permanently connected at their station to monitor the condition of their transmitter and antennas. See the **Station Accessories** chapter for a further discussion of directional wattmeters.

A *bolometer* is a device for measuring transmitter power by measuring the heat dissipated in a resistive load. A thermistor or other device measures the temperature. The device is calibrated with a dc voltage, since dc voltage and current can be measured very precisely. With careful construction and calibration, very high accuracy can be obtained. However, the response time of the measurement is very slow, so a bolometer is normally used to calibrate another wattmeter rather than being used directly for measurements. Bolometers are made commercially, however it is possible to homebrew one using a plastic picnic cooler.[12]

Commercial laboratory power meters are generally intended for measuring power levels in the milliwatt or microwatt range. There are two basic types, based on either diode or thermocouple detectors. Below a certain power level, the dc output from a diode detector is directly proportional to power, that is, the square of the RF voltage. With a suitable dc amplifier, the detector output can drive a meter with a linear scale to read power directly.

Thermocouple-type power meters feed the RF signal into a resistor that heats up in proportion to the power level. The temperature is measured with a *thermocouple*, which consists of a pair of junctions of dissimilar metals. A voltage is generated based on the temperature difference of the two junctions, which is proportional to the RF power. The thermocouple method gives high accuracy and wide bandwidth, but the measurement time can be up to several seconds at low power levels, rather than being nearly instantaneous as with a diode detector. Older-model surplus diode and thermocouple-type meters can often be found for reasonable prices, but the proper sensors for the desired frequency range and power level often cost more than the power meter itself.

Analog Devices makes a series of integrated circuits that can detect RF signals and output a dc voltage proportional to the logarithm of the power level. That makes it easy to construct an RF power meter that reads directly in dBm. For example, the AD8307 covers dc to 500 MHz with 1-dB accuracy over an 88-dB (nearly 1 billion-to-one) power range.

Table 25.2
Power and dBm Equivalents

dBm	Power	dBm	Power
−60 dBm	1 nW	3 dBm	2 mW
−30 dBm	1 µW	6 dBm	4 mW
−20 dBm	10 µW	10 dBm	10 mW
−10 dBm	100 µW	20 dBm	100 mW
−6 dBm	¼ mW	30 dBm	1 W
−3 dBm	½ mW	60 dBm	1 kW
0 dBm	1 mW	61.7 dBm	1.5 kW

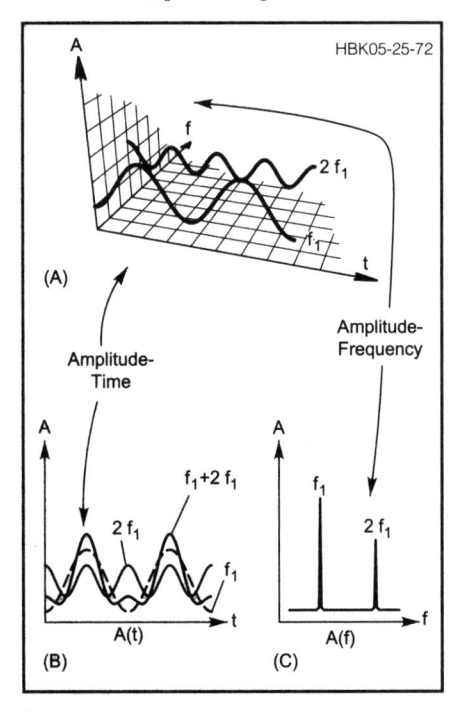

Figure 25.27 — A complex signal in the time and frequency domains. A is a three-dimensional display of amplitude, time and frequency. B is an oscilloscope display of time vs amplitude. C is spectrum analyzer display of the frequency domain and shows frequency vs amplitude.

25.4.3 Spectrum Analyzers

A spectrum analyzer is similar to an oscilloscope. Both present a graphical view of an electrical signal. The oscilloscope is used to observe electrical signals in the *time domain* (amplitude versus time). The time domain, however, gives little information about the frequencies that make up complex signals, which are best characterized in terms of their frequency response. This information is obtained by viewing electrical signals in the *frequency domain* (amplitude versus frequency). One instrument that can display the frequency domain is the spectrum analyzer.

TIME AND FREQUENCY DOMAIN

To better understand the concepts of time and frequency domain, see **Figure 25.27**. The three-dimensional coordinates in Figure 25.27A show time as the line sloping toward the bottom right, frequency as the line rising toward the top right and amplitude as the vertical axis. The two discrete frequencies shown are harmonically related, so we'll refer to them as f1 and 2f1.

In the representation of time domain in Figure 25.27B, all frequency components of a signal are summed together. In fact, if the two discrete frequencies shown were applied to the input of an oscilloscope, we would see the solid line (which corresponds to the sum of f1 and 2f1) on the display.

In the frequency domain, complex signals (signals composed of more than one frequency) are separated into their individual frequency components. A spectrum analyzer measures and displays the power level at each discrete frequency; this display is shown at C.

The frequency domain contains information not apparent in the time domain and therefore the spectrum analyzer offers advantages over the oscilloscope for certain measurements, such as harmonic content or distortion as mentioned previously. For measurements that are best made in the time domain, the oscilloscope is the tool of choice.

SPECTRUM ANALYZER BASICS

There are several different types of spectrum analyzer, but the most common is nothing more than an electronically tuned superheterodyne receiver. The receiver is tuned by means of a ramp voltage. This ramp voltage performs two functions: First, it sweeps the frequency of the analyzer local oscillator; second, it deflects a beam across the horizontal axis of a CRT display, as shown in **Figure 25.28**. The vertical axis deflection of the CRT beam is determined by the strength of the received signal. In this way, the CRT displays frequency on the horizontal axis and signal strength on the vertical axis.

Most spectrum analyzers use an up-converting technique in which a wide-band input

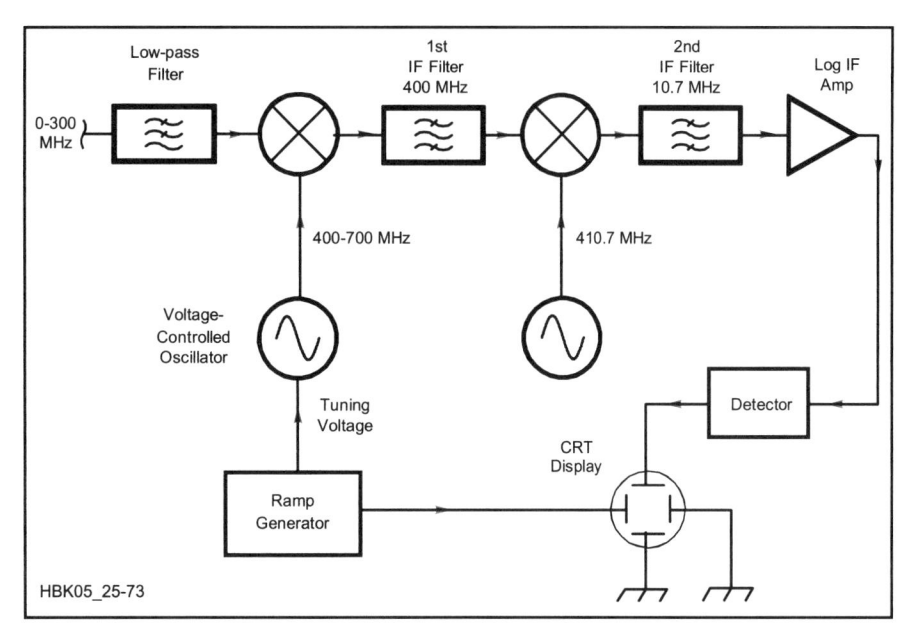

Figure 25.28 — A block diagram of a typical superheterodyne spectrum analyzer. Input frequencies of up to 300 MHz are up-converted by the local oscillator and mixer to a fixed frequency of 400 MHz.

is converted to an IF higher than the highest input frequency. Up-conversion is used so that a fixed-tuned input filter can remove any image signals and only the first local oscillator needs to be tuned to tune the receiver. As with most up-converting communications receivers, it is not easy to achieve the desired ultimate selectivity at the first IF, because of the high frequency. For this reason, multiple conversions are used to generate an IF low enough so that the desired selectivity is practical. In the example shown, dual conversion is used: The first IF is at 400 MHz; the second at 10.7 MHz.

In the example spectrum analyzer, the first local oscillator is swept from 400 MHz to 700 MHz; this converts the input (from nearly 0 MHz to 300 MHz) to the first IF of 400 MHz. The usual rule of thumb for varactor-tuned oscillators is that the maximum practical tuning ratio (the ratio of the highest frequency to the lowest frequency) is an octave, a 2:1 ratio. In our example spectrum analyzer, the tuning ratio of the first local oscillator is 1.75:1, which meets this specification.

The range of image frequency extends from 800 MHz to 1100 MHz and is easily eliminated using a low-pass filter with a cut-off frequency around 300 MHz. The 400-MHz first IF is converted to 10.7 MHz where the ultimate selectivity of the analyzer is obtained. The image of the second conversion, (421.4 MHz), is eliminated by the first IF filter. The attenuation of the image should be large, on the order of 60 to 80 dB. This requires a first IF filter with a high Q, which is achieved by using helical resonators, SAW resonators or cavity filters. Another method of eliminating the image problem is to use triple conversion; converting first to an intermediate IF such as 50 MHz and then to 10.7 MHz. As with any receiver, an additional frequency conversion requires added circuitry and adds potential spurious responses.

Most of the signal amplification takes place at the lowest IF, 10.7 MHz in this example. Here the communications receiver and the spectrum analyzer differ. A communications receiver demodulates the incoming signal so that the modulation can be heard or further demodulated for RTTY or packet or other mode of operation. In the spectrum analyzer, only the signal strength is needed.

In order for the spectrum analyzer to be most useful, it should display signals of widely different levels. As an example, consider two signals that differ by 60 dB, which is a thousand to one difference in voltage or a million to one in power. That means that if power were displayed, one signal would be one million times larger than the other. In the case of voltage one signal would be a thousand times larger. In either case it would be difficult to display both signals on a CRT. The solution to this problem is to use a logarithmic display that shows the relative signal levels in decibels. Using this technique, a 1000:1 ratio of voltage reduces to a 60-dB difference.

The conversion of the signal to a logarithm is usually performed in the IF amplifier or detector, resulting in an output voltage proportional to the logarithm of the input RF level. This output voltage is then used to drive the CRT display.

SPECTRUM ANALYZER PERFORMANCE

The performance parameters of a spectrum analyzer are specified in terms similar to those used for radio receivers, in spite of the fact that there are many differences between a receiver and a spectrum analyzer.

The sensitivity of a receiver is often specified as the *minimum discernible signal* (MDS), which means the smallest signal that can be heard. In the case of the spectrum analyzer, it is not the smallest signal that can be heard, but the smallest signal that can be seen. The *dynamic range* of the spectrum analyzer determines the largest and smallest signals that can be simultaneously viewed on the analyzer. As with a receiver, one factor that affects dynamic range is *second- and third-order intermodulation distortion* (IMD). IMD dynamic range is the maximum difference in signal level between the minimum detectable signal and the level of two signals of equal strength that generate an IMD product equal to the minimum detectable signal. (See the **Receivers** chapter for more information on IMD.)

Although the communications receiver is an excellent example to introduce the spectrum analyzer, there are several differences such as the previously explained lack of a demodulator. Unlike the communications receiver, the spectrum analyzer is not a sensitive radio receiver. To preserve a wide dynamic range, the spectrum analyzer often uses passive mixers for the first and second mixers. Therefore, referring to Figure 25.28, the noise figure of the analyzer is no better than the losses of the input low-pass filter plus the first mixer, the first IF filter, the second mixer and the loss of the second IF filter. This often results in a combined noise figure of more than 20 dB. With that kind of noise figure the spectrum analyzer is obviously not a communications receiver for extracting very weak signals from the noise but a measuring instrument for the analysis of frequency spectrum. For some applications, it may be useful to add an external wide-band, low-noise preamplifier to improve the noise figure.

The selectivity of the analyzer is called the *resolution bandwidth* (RBW). This term refers to the minimum frequency separation of two signals of equal level so that the signals are separated by a drop in amplitude of 3 dB between them. The IF filters used in a spectrum analyzer differ from a communications receiver in that they have very gentle skirts and rounded passbands, rather than the flat passband and very steep skirts of an IF filter in a high-quality communications receiver. The rounded passband is necessary because the signals pass through the filter passband as the spectrum analyzer sweeps the desired frequency range. If the signals suddenly pop into the passband (as they do if the filter has steep skirts), the filter tends to ring. A filter with gentle skirts has less ringing. Another effect, which occurs even with rounded-passband filters, is that the signal amplitudes are reduced at fast sweep rates, which distorts the display and requires that the analyzer not sweep frequency too quickly. When adjusting the resolution bandwidth or the width of the *frequency span* (the range of frequencies being measured), the scan rate may need to be reduced so that the signal amplitude is not affected by fast sweeping.

The signal produced by the detector is known as the *video* signal. Most spectrum analyzers include a low-pass video filter to reduce the displayed noise level. The *video bandwidth* (VBW) is the bandwidth of this filter. Like the RBW, the VBW must also be taken into consideration when setting the sweep speed.

USING A SPECTRUM ANALYZER

Spectrum analyzers are used in situations where the signals to be analyzed are complex, for very low-level signals, or when the frequency of the signals to be analyzed is very high. Although high-performance oscilloscopes are capable of operation into the UHF region, moderately priced spectrum analyzers can be used well into the gigahertz region.

Unlike the oscilloscope which is a wide-bandwidth instrument, the spectrum analyzer measures the waveform using a narrow bandwidth; thus it is capable of reducing the noise power displayed.

Probably the most common Amateur Radio application of a spectrum analyzer is the measurement of the harmonic content and other spurious signals in the output of a radio transmitter. **Figure 25.29** shows two ways to connect the transmitter and spectrum analyzer. The method shown at A should not be used for wide-band measurements since most line-sampling devices do not exhibit a constant-amplitude output over a broad frequency range. Using a line sampler is fine for narrow-band measurements, however.

The method shown at B is used in the ARRL Lab. The attenuator must be capable of dissipating the transmitter power. It must also have sufficient attenuation to protect the spectrum analyzer input. Many spectrum analyzer input mixers can be damaged by only a few milliwatts, so most analyzers have an adjustable input attenuator to provide a reasonable amount of attenuation for protection. The power limitation of the attenuator itself is usually on the order of a watt or so, however. This means that the power attenuator must have 20 dB of attenuation for a 100 W transmitter, 30 dB for a 1000 W transmitter and so on, to limit the input to the spectrum analyzer to 1 W. There are specialized attenuators that are made for transmitter testing; these attenuators provide the necessary power dissipation and attenuation in the 20 to 30-dB range.

When using a spectrum analyzer it is very important that the proper amount of attenuation be applied before a measurement is made. In addition, it is a good practice to start with maximum attenuation and view the entire spectrum of a signal before the attenuator is adjusted. The signal being viewed could appear to be at a safe level, but another spectral component, which is not visible, could be above the damage limit. It is also very important to limit the input power to the analyzer when pulse power is being measured. The average power may be small enough so the input attenuator is not damaged, but the peak pulse power, which may not be readily visible on the analyzer display, can destroy a mixer, literally in microseconds.

Spurious Responses in Spectrum Analyzers

When using a spectrum analyzer it is neces-

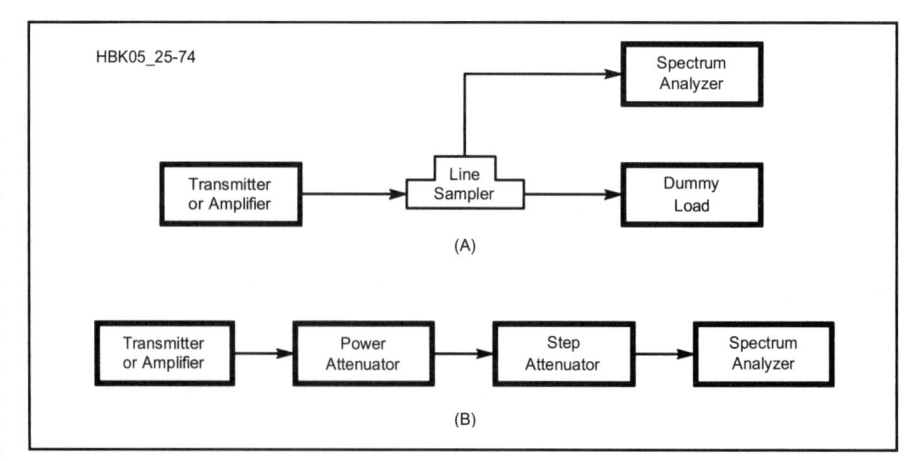

Figure 25.29 — Alternate bench setups for viewing the output of a high power transmitter or oscillator on a spectrum analyzer. A uses a line sampler to pick off a small amount of the transmitter or amplifier power. In B, most of the transmitter power is dissipated in the power attenuator.

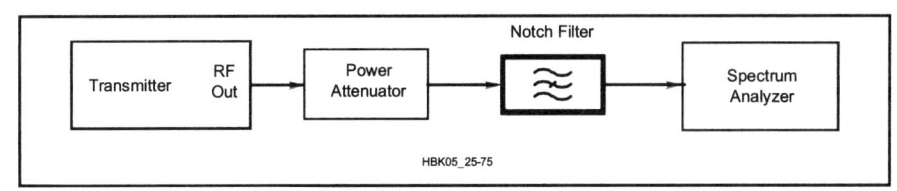

Figure 25.30 — A notch filter is another way to reduce the level of a transmitter's fundamental signal so that the fundamental does not generate harmonics within the analyzer. However, in order to know the amplitude relationship between the fundamental and the transmitter's actual harmonics and spurs, the attenuation of the fundamental in the notch filter must be known.

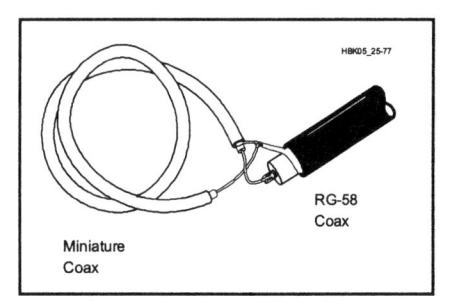

Figure 25.32 — A "sniffer" probe consisting of an inductive pick-up. It has the advan-tage of not directly contacting the circuit under test.

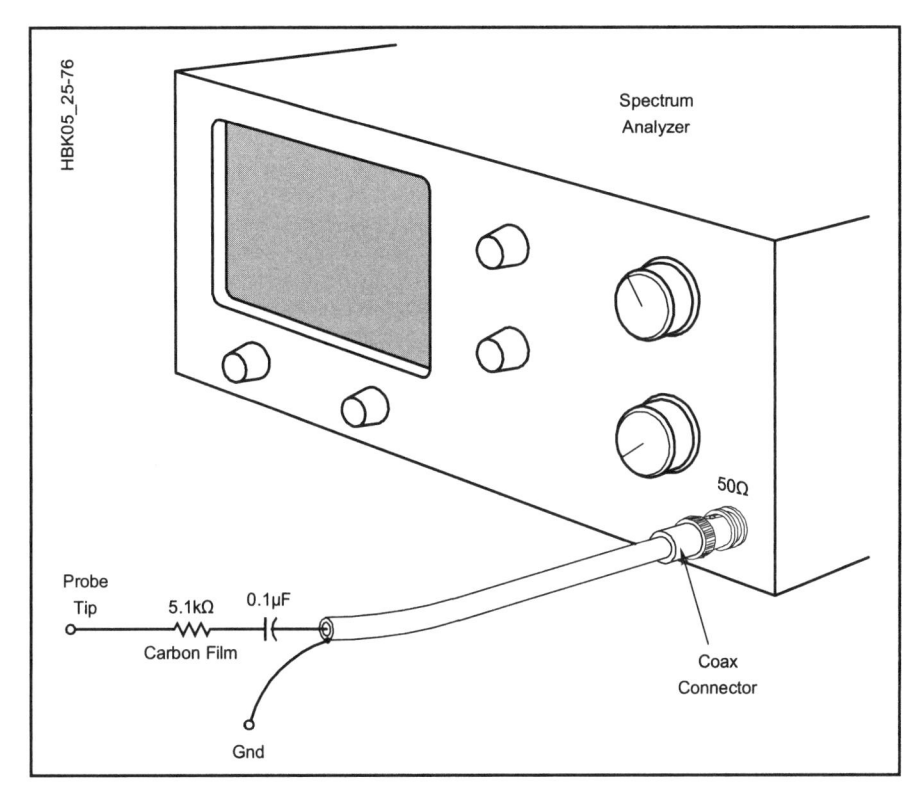

Figure 25.31 — A schematic representation of a voltage probe designed for use with a spectrum analyzer. Keep the probe tip (resistor and capacitor) and ground leads as short as possible.

sary to ensure that the analyzer does not generate additional spurious signals that are then attributed to the system under test. Some of the spurious signals that can be generated by a spectrum analyzer are harmonics and IMD. It is good practice to check for the generation of spurious signals within the spectrum analyzer. When an input signal causes the spectrum analyzer to generate a spurious signal, adding attenuation at the analyzer input will cause the internally generated spurious signals to decrease by an amount greater than the added attenuation. If attenuation added ahead of the analyzer causes all of the visible signals to decrease by the same amount, this indicates a spurious-free display.

If it is desired to measure the harmonic levels of a transmitter at a level below the spurious level of the analyzer itself, a notch filter can be inserted between the attenuator and the spectrum analyzer as shown in **Figure 25.30**. This reduces the level of the fundamental signal and prevents that signal from generating harmonics within the analyzer, while still allowing the harmonics from the transmitter to pass through to the analyzer without attenuation. Use caution with this technique; detuning the notch filter or inadvertently changing the transmitter frequency will allow potentially high levels of power to enter the analyzer. In addition, use care when choosing filters; some filters (such as cavity filters) respond not only to the fundamental but notch out odd harmonics as well.

The input impedance for most RF spectrum analyzers is 50 Ω, however not all circuits have convenient 50-Ω connections that can be accessed for testing purposes. Using a probe such as the one shown in **Figure 25.31** allows the analyzer to be used as a troubleshooting tool. The probe can be used to track down signals within a transmitter or receiver, much like an oscilloscope is used. The probe shown offers a 100:1 voltage reduction and loads the circuit with about 5000 Ω. A different type of probe is shown in **Figure 25.32**. This inductive pickup coil (sometimes called a "sniffer") is very handy for troubleshooting. The coil is used to couple signals from the radiated magnetic field of a circuit into the analyzer. A short length of miniature coax is wound into a pickup loop and soldered to a larger piece of coax that connects to the spectrum analyzer. The dimensions of the loop are not critical, but smaller loop dimensions enable the loop to more precisely locate the source of radiated RF. Coax is used for the loop to provide shielding from the electric field component (capacitive coupling). Connecting the coax shield on only one end provides a complete electrostatic shield without introducing a shorted turn.

The sniffer allows the spectrum analyzer to sense RF energy without contacting the circuit being analyzed. If the loop is brought near an oscillator coil, the oscillator can be tuned without directly contacting (and thus disturbing) the circuit. The oscillator can then be checked for reliable startup and the generation of spurious sidebands. With the coil brought near the tuned circuits of amplifiers or frequency multipliers, those stages can be tuned using a similar technique.

Even though the sniffer does not contact the circuit being evaluated, it does extract some energy from the circuit. For this reason, the loop should be placed as far from the tuned circuit as is practical. If the loop is placed too far from the circuit, the signal will be too weak or the pickup loop will pick up energy from other parts of the circuit and not give an accurate indication of the circuit under test.

The sniffer is very handy to locate sources of RF leakage. By probing the shields and cabinets of RF generating equipment (such as transmitters) egress and ingress points of RF energy can be identified by increased indications on the analyzer display.

Measuring Very Low-Level Signals

One very powerful characteristic of the spectrum analyzer is the instrument's capa-

Test Equipment and Measurements 25.23

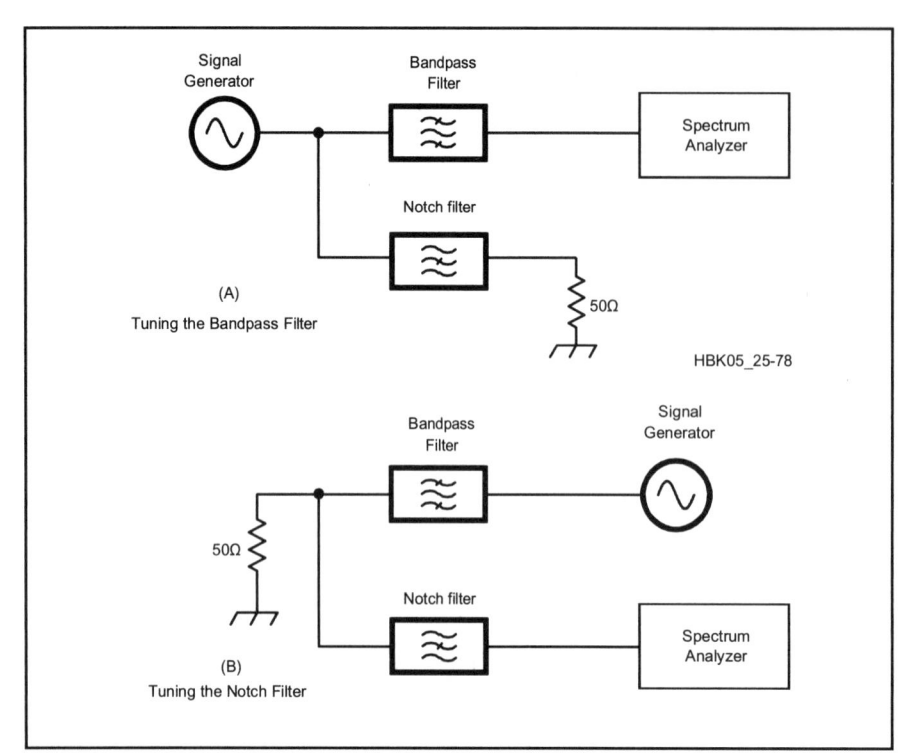

Figure 25.33 — Block diagram of a spectrum analyzer and signal generator being used to tune the band-pass and notch filters of a duplexer. All ports of the duplexer must be properly terminated and good quality coax with intact shielding used to reduce leakage.

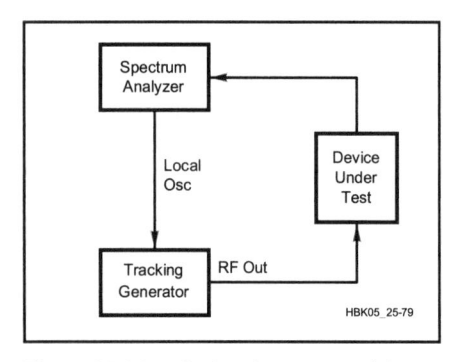

Figure 25.34 — A signal generator (shown in the figure as the "Tracking Generator") locked to the local oscillator of a spectrum analyzer can be used to determine filter response over a range of frequencies.

bility to measure very low-level signals. This characteristic is very advantageous when very high levels of attenuation are measured. **Figure 25.33** shows the setup for tuning the notch and passband of a VHF duplexer. The spectrum analyzer, being capable of viewing signals well into the low microvolt region, is capable of measuring the insertion loss of the notch cavity more than 100 dB below the signal generator output. Making a measurement of this sort requires care in the interconnection of the equipment and a well-designed spectrum analyzer and signal generator. RF energy leaking from the signal generator cabinet, line cord or even the coax itself, can get into the spectrum analyzer through similar paths and corrupt the measurement. This leakage can make the measurement look either better or worse than the actual attenuation, depending on the phase relationship of the leaked signal.

EXTENSIONS OF SPECTRAL ANALYSIS

Many measurements involve a signal generator tuned to the same frequency as the spectrum analyzer. It would be a real convenience not to have to continually reset the signal generator to the desired frequency. It is, however, more than a convenience. A signal generator connected in this way is called a *tracking generator* because the output frequency tracks the spectrum analyzer input frequency. The tracking generator makes it possible to make swept frequency measurements of the attenuation characteristics of circuits, even when the attenuation involved is large.

Figure 25.34 shows the connection of a tracking generator to a circuit under test. In order for the tracking generator to create an output frequency exactly equal to the input frequency of the spectrum analyzer, the internal local oscillator frequencies of the spectrum analyzer must be known. This is the reason for the interconnections between the tracking generator and the spectrum analyzer. The test setup shown will measure the gain or loss of the circuit under test.

Only the magnitude of the gain or loss is available; in some cases, the phase angle between the input and output would also be an important and necessary parameter. That is the function of a *vector network analyzer*, covered in a following section.

CHOOSING A SPECTRUM ANALYZER

The frequency range is perhaps the most important specification when choosing a spectrum analyzer. Of course it must cover the amateur bands you wish to test, but it must also cover harmonics of those frequencies if you wish to test transmitter harmonics. Many higher-frequency spectrum analyzers only cover down to 10 kHz, so they are not useful for audio spectrum analysis (spectrum analyzers for audio use are also available). Some instruments use a harmonic sampler on the higher microwave bands. You may need to use an external filter to remove any unwanted signals at harmonics or sub-harmonics of the signal you wish to examine.

Frequency stability is vital for narrowband measurements such as looking at modulation spectra. Some older instruments include a frequency lock scheme that stabilizes the display after the analyzer is tuned to the desired signal.

The range of resolution bandwidths (RBW) available determines what kinds of measurements are possible. To measure two-tone intermodulation distortion of an SSB signal, the minimum RBW must be narrow enough to resolve the two tones, that is, no more than about 100 Hz. If you wish to view the demodulated time-domain video from a fast-scan television signal, the RBW must be wide enough to include the entire signal, perhaps 5 or 6 MHz.

Input sensitivity is normally not very important. An external preamplifier can always be added if needed for a particular measurement. However, dynamic range is a key specification, as previously discussed. Also, the screen display range is important. For example, if there are 8 divisions on the display and the maximum dB-per-division setting is 10 dB/div, then the maximum display range is 80 dB. Many spectrum analyzers can display signals in linear as well as logarithmic (dB) mode, which can be useful to look at modulation.

For accurate power measurements, the amplitude accuracy is important. For doing relative measurements, which are important for measuring spurious signals relative to the carrier, logarithmic linearity is the key specification.

There are several features that expand the spectrum analyzer's utility. *Markers* are pips that can be moved with a knob back and forth across the signals on the display. By placing a marker at the top of a signal you can read the frequency and amplitude directly. *Peak search* is a feature that automatically places a marker at the peak of the strongest signal. *Marker delta* measures the difference in frequency and amplitude of two markers.

Zero span means setting the sweep width to zero hertz to view the change in signal versus time. This is useful for looking at modulation. Many spectrum analyzers include a sweep triggering feature for this purpose, similar to the triggering circuit in an oscilloscope. Some include a speaker so you can hear what the modulating signal sounds like.

Modern spectrum analyzers have many of the features found in digital oscilloscopes, such as trace storage and retrieval. Most include computer connectivity, both to store measured data and to control the instrument with the proper software.

In addition to traditional swept-frequency spectrum analyzers, some modern units use the *Fast Fourier Transform* (FFT) either in place of, or in addition to, the swept-frequency architecture. The FFT allows for much faster screen updates when using narrow spans. Some RF and microwave instruments have a *digital IF* based on the FFT. For narrow spans, the local oscillator is held at a constant frequency and the "sweep" is performed mathematically by the FFT.

There are many used spectrum analyzers on the surplus market, at all different vintages and price points. As usual, try before you buy if at all possible and obtain the operator's and service manuals, if available. Another alternative is a spectrum analyzer built on a card that plugs into a personal computer or that consists of an external digitizing pod connected to the PC via a serial data link. As with PC-based oscilloscopes, they can represent excellent value because they save the cost of the display, cabinet, power supply, and microprocessor provided by the computer.

The least-expensive alternative is an audio spectrum analyzer based on a PC's sound card. Free spectrum analysis software is available on the Internet. The main limitation is the frequency coverage, which is typically about 40-45% of the sample rate of the sound card. The sound card that comes standard in a PC typically has a 48 kHz sample rate, so that the frequency response is limited to about 20 kHz. That is plenty for checking out the audio circuits in a communications receiver or transmitter.

25.4.4 Measuring RF Impedance

Most RF impedance-measuring devices are based on the Wheatstone bridge, as previously described in the section on LCR bridges. The difference is that an impedance bridge does not require that the device under test be a pure inductance, capacitance or resistance but may be a complex impedance that includes both resistance and reactance. That means that two adjustments are required to balance the bridge, rather than just one as with an LCR bridge. Both the resistance and reactance must match.

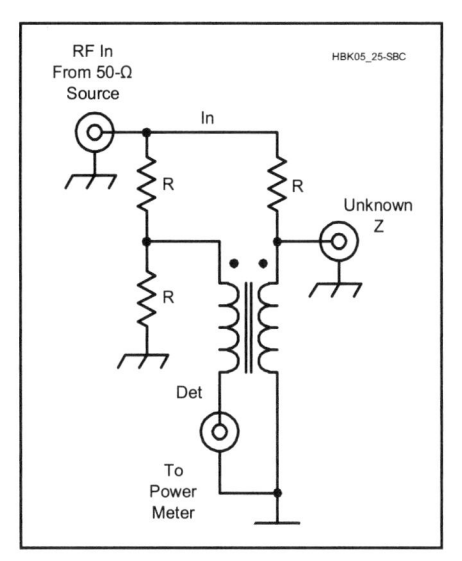

Figure 25.35 — A return-loss bridge for RF. See text for details.

In addition, since an impedance bridge is typically designed to operate at higher frequencies, circuit layout and the connection to the device under test are more important. Usually a coaxial connector is used to connect to the device and the impedance measurements are referenced to 50 Ω.

A *return-loss bridge* (RLB) is an RF bridge with fixed, usually 50-Ω, resistors in each leg except the one connected to the device under test. *Return loss* is the ratio of the reflected signal to the signal incident on a component, usually expressed in dB, which is always a positive number for a passive device.[13] (See the **RF Techniques** chapter for a discussion of return loss.)

The schematic of a simple return-loss bridge is shown in **Figure 25.35**. The circuit can also be used as a *hybrid combiner* (see the RF and Microwave Test Accessories section of this chapter), where the port labeled UNKNOWN is the common port and the other two are isolated from each other. For good results at high frequencies, it should be built in a small box with short leads to the coax connectors.

Apply the output of a signal generator or other signal source to the RF IN port of the RLB. The power level should be appropriate for driving the device connected to the UNKNOWN port, after accounting for the 6-dB loss of the bridge. Connect the bridge POWER METER port to a power meter or other power-measuring device through a step attenuator and leave the UNKNOWN port of the bridge open circuited. Set the step attenuator for a relatively high level of attenuation and note the power meter indication.

Now connect the unknown impedance to the bridge. The power meter reading will decrease. Adjust the step attenuator to produce the same reading obtained when the UNKNOWN port was open circuited. The difference between the two settings of the attenuator is the return loss, measured in dB.

25.4.5 Network Analyzers

An electronic *port* is a pair of terminals with equal and opposite current flows. An antenna analyzer can measure the impedance of a single-port network such as an antenna, the input port of an antenna tuner, or a two-terminal component like a resistor or capacitor. An example of a two-port network is an amplifier. The input is one port, the output the other. A low-pass filter is another example. An example of a three-port network is a diplexer, used to connect one transceiver to two antennas. The theory behind two-port networks is covered in the **RF Techniques** chapter.

A *scalar network analyzer* (SNA) is an instrument that can measure, as a function of frequency, the magnitude of the gain or loss between the two ports of a two-port device as well as the magnitude of the return loss (equivalent to the SWR) of each port. The term "scalar" means that only magnitudes of those quantities are measured and not phase angles. In **Figure 25.36**, the signal labeled "REF" is proportional to the sweep oscillator output and the one labeled "A" is proportional to the signal that is reflected back from the device under test due to an imperfect 50-Ω match. The ratio of A to REF can be used to calculate the return loss and SWR of the device. Signal "B" is proportional to the signal that travels between the two ports of the device. The ratio of B to REF gives the device gain. To find the gain in the opposite direction and the return loss of the other port, simply turn the device around and swap the two ports. Some network analyzers come with a *test set* that includes RF switches to do that automatically.[14]

The box labeled "Signal processing and display" includes circuitry to take the logarithm of the signals so they can be displayed in dB. In modern instruments it normally includes a microprocessor, which does much of the signal processing as well as controlling the sweep oscillator and other circuitry.

A *vector network analyzer* (VNA) is an instrument that can measure both the magnitude and phase of the gain and return loss of a two-port network. The block diagram is identical to Figure 25.36 except that the detectors can measure not only the magnitude, but also the phase of each signal with respect to the reference, REF. The measured data are usually presented in terms of *scattering parameters*, or *S parameters*. S_{11} is the ratio of the incident to the reflected signal at port 1, S_{22} is the equivalent on port 2, S_{21} is the gain from port 1 to 2, and S_{12} is the gain from port 2 to 1. Each S parameter is a complex number, representing both magnitude and phase. Further discussions of S parameters can be found in the **Computer-Aided Circuit Design** and the **RF Techniques** chapters. Usually the VNA provides the capability to plot the S parameters on a Smith chart overlaid on the display for easy evaluation. The Smith chart is discussed in the **Transmission Lines** chapter.

The accuracy of a VNA depends on the performance of the directional couplers, detectors, and other circuitry. The coupler directivity is a key contributor to measurement errors. For example, if the directivity is 20 dB, then even a perfect 50-Ω load will show 20 dB of return loss, equivalent to a 1.22:1 SWR. Fortunately it is possible to eliminate most errors by measuring several terminations of known impedance and calculating a series of correction factors. The mathematics involved is quite complex, but it is all handled by the instrument software and is invisible to the user. The most popular technique is called a Short-Open-Load-Through (SOLT) calibration because it uses four calibration standards, a short-circuit, an open-circuit, a 50-Ω load and a through connection between the two ports. One of the sources of error removed by the calibration is any error due to the length of the coaxial cables that connect to the device under test. For that reason, the calibration standards should always be connected at the end of the cables that are to be used for the test. A thorough discussion of VNA error-correction techniques can be found in an Agilent Technologies application note.[15]

CHOOSING A NETWORK ANALYZER

A spectrum analyzer with tracking generator can be the basis of a high-performance scalar network analyzer. Referring to Figure 25.36, the only pieces that need to be added are the directional coupler and a pair of 50-Ω loads. The tracking generator takes the place of the sweep oscillator. Connect the spectrum analyzer input to A, B or REF and terminate the other two with 50-Ω loads. Unlike a conventional scalar network analyzer, a spectrum analyzer has a tuned receiver so it does not respond to spurious frequencies generated by the sweep oscillator or the device under test.

At the other end of the performance "spectrum" a simple SNA for measuring gain or attenuation can be made with any sweep os-

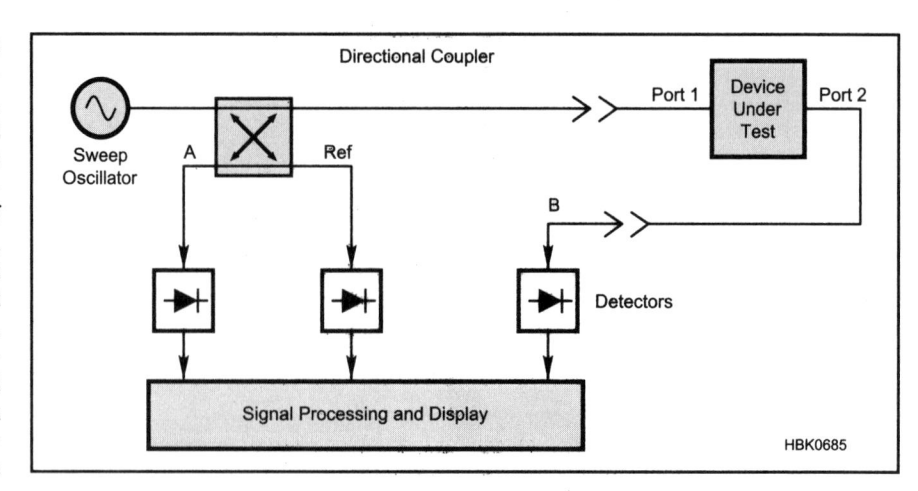

Figure 25.36 — Block diagram of a scalar network analyzer (SNA). A vector network analyzer has the same block diagram except that the detectors can measure phase as well as amplitude.

cillator, perhaps a function generator with sweep capability, plus a detector of some kind and an oscilloscope to display the detected voltage. If the oscilloscope bandwidth is great enough to cover the desired frequency range, no detector is needed and the RF signal can be displayed directly. Dynamic range is limited with this technique since the displayed signal is linear and not logarithmic. However it is sufficient for many purposes, such as measuring the passband ripple of a filter or the gain versus frequency of an amplifier.

Used scalar network analyzers are readily available on the surplus market. The sweep oscillator is normally a separate unit. Vector network analyzers also may be purchased surplus. Some require an external sweep oscillator while others include an internal signal source. The tests sets may be internal or external as well.

In recent years, several amateur VNA designs have appeared. These tend to be much smaller, lighter and lower-cost than commercial units. One by DG8SAQ down-converts the signals to be detected to frequencies in the audio range so they can be fed to the sound card on a personal computer.[16] It uses a pair of Analog Devices DDS chips for the sweep oscillator and the down-converter's local oscillator. All signal processing and control is done in the microprocessor in the PC. Paul Kiciak, N2PK, also developed a VNA using DDS chips for the source and a direct-conversion architecture which performs the detection function at dc. Like the DG8SAQ design, it relies on a PC for the processing, control, and display. His design has become available in kit form from several suppliers, and numerous third-parties have written software to support it. A number of VNA kits and products are available, most using a PC as a basis.[16,17,18]

Many VNAs have a low-frequency limit in the range of 100 kHz to 1 MHz. This limit is imposed by the variable frequency oscillator of the analyzer. The range of the VNA can be extended lower to the audio frequency range by using an external adapter that shifts the output RF signal from the VNA, applies it to the circuit under test, and then re-shifts the circuit's output signal into the VNA's RF range. A low frequency adapter project is described later in the projects section at the end of this chapter.

25.4.6 RF Signal Generators

An *RF signal generator* is a test oscillator that generates a sine-wave signal that has an accurately-calibrated frequency and amplitude over a wide radio-frequency range. Usually AM and FM modulation capability is provided and sometimes other modulation types as well.

Some instruments also have built-in sweep capability. If not, narrow-band sweep can be obtained by feeding a sawtooth waveform into the FM input. Another feature that is very useful for transceiver testing is *reverse power protection*. It protects the sensitive output circuits in the event that the transceiver accidentally goes into transmit mode while connected to the signal generator.

Before the days of modern digital electronics, all signal generators used free-running oscillators. There is a wide variation in frequency stability and accuracy between the best and the worst. Nearly any modern synthesized signal generator has good enough accuracy for most amateur purposes. However that accuracy sometimes comes at the price of phase noise, a type of wideband noise caused by short-term fluctuations in phase that usually drops off gradually from the carrier frequency. The old tube-type Hewlett-Packard 608-series signal generators have better performance in this respect than some modern synthesized instruments. See **Figure 25.37**. Phase noise is discussed in the **Oscillators and Synthesizers** chapter.

Some signal generators, even professional laboratory-grade types, may not have enough output attenuation to accurately measure the minimum discernible signal (MDS) on a sensitive communications receiver. A 10-dB noise figure in a 500 Hz bandwidth implies an MDS of –137 dBm, which is well below the minimum amplitude level on many signal generators. The problem is easily resolved by adding an external fixed 20-dB attenuator. Just remember to subtract 20 dB from all amplitude readings.

Many signal generators include some way to connect them to a computer so they can be controlled for automated testing. That is useful for testing a receiver at many frequencies across a band to be able to plot sensitivity or dynamic range as a function of frequency, for example. Older instruments usually have a GPIB interface while modern ones are more likely to have RS-232, USB or Ethernet.

Probably the most common use for signal generators is for receiver testing. That is covered in detail in a later section. They are also useful for general-purpose test signals. For example, when developing a new receiver design, you could test the RF, IF and audio stages before the VFO is completed by using a signal generator as the local oscillator.

Critical specifications include the frequency range, frequency accuracy and stability, amplitude range, amplitude accuracy, and the spectral purity, including phase noise, harmonics and non-harmonic spurious emissions. Modulation accuracy and the capabilities of the internal modulation generator, if present, may be important as well, depending on the application.

Many inexpensive signal generators made for the hobbyist and consumer electronics service industry are not suitable for measuring receiver sensitivity because when the output attenuator is at maximum, there is more signal leaking out the cabinet and radiating from the power cord than is coming out the coax connector. Such instruments also tend to have poor frequency stability and the tuning dial tunes so fast that they are difficult to set to a precise frequency. They are useful for simple troubleshooting but are not capable of making accurate measurements.

Better-quality signal generators intended for servicing land-mobile and other communications equipment sometimes become available on the surplus market. They don't have the precision specifications of lab instruments but are generally rugged, reliable and easy to use.

Laboratory-grade signal generators are generally too expensive for the home hobbyist if purchased new but older models such as the HP8640B or its military version (AN/USM323) are widely available and have excellent specifications. Of course they may be less reliable than new instruments but in many cases the older technology is repairable without special equipment. Service manuals are sometimes available from the manufacturer on their website.

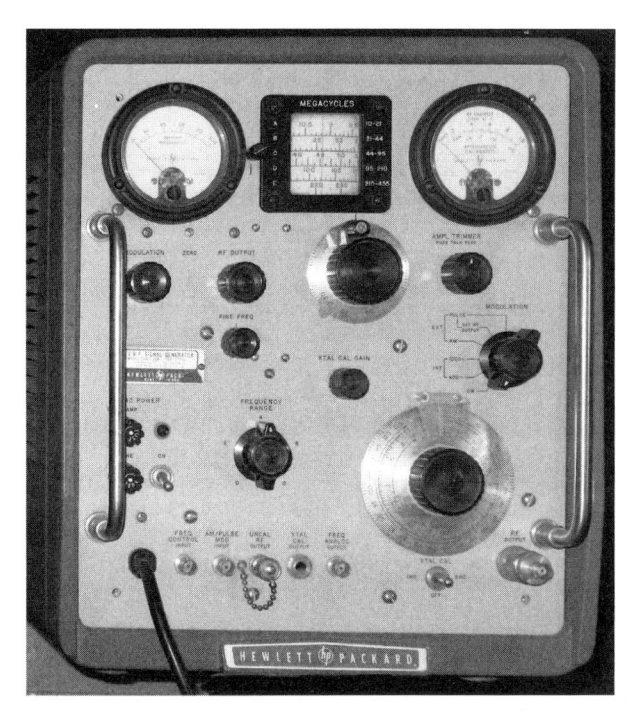

Figure 25.37 — A classic Hewlett-Packard 608F tube-type signal generator. While not as stable as modern synthesized signal generators, in other respects the performance is quite up to date.

25.4.7 Using Noise Sources

Most of the time, noise is something to be avoided in electronic circuits. It can be quite useful for testing, however, precisely because the calibrated noise that you create on purpose has the same properties as the unwanted circuit noise that you are trying to minimize. Thus, calibrated sources of noise are used as test instruments for various measurements. (See the **RF Techniques** chapter for a discussion of noise and its associated terminology.)

MEASURING RECEIVER NOISE FIGURE

A noise source can be used to measure the noise figure of an SSB or CW receiver. The *excess noise ratio (ENR)* is the ratio of the noise added by the noise source to the thermal noise level, normally expressed in dB. An explanation of noise figure is given in the **RF Techniques** chapter. The basic idea is to connect the noise source to the receiver antenna input and then measure the difference in the noise level at the receiver speaker terminals when the noise source is turned on or off. When it is off, the measured noise contains only thermal noise and the noise contributed by the receiver. When it is on, the noise includes the excess noise from the noise source. The noise figure can then be calculated from the ratio of those two values,

$$NF_M = ENR - 10\log\left(\frac{E_{ON}^2}{E_{OFF}^2} - 1\right)$$

where NF_M is the measured noise figure in dB, ENR is the excess noise ratio in dB, E_{ON} is the RMS output noise voltage with the noise source on, and E_{OFF} is the RMS output noise voltage with the noise source off.

Rather than using the equation, another technique is to include a step attenuator with 1-dB steps at the noise source output. See **Figure 25.38**. Adjust the attenuator so that the noise increases by 3 dB (1.414 times the voltage) when the noise source is turned on. The noise figure is then simply the ENR of the noise source minus the attenuation.

The nice thing about measuring noise with noise is that the accuracy of the voltage reading is not important so long as the ratio of the two readings is accurate. A non-RMS ac voltmeter is not accurate when measuring noise, but so

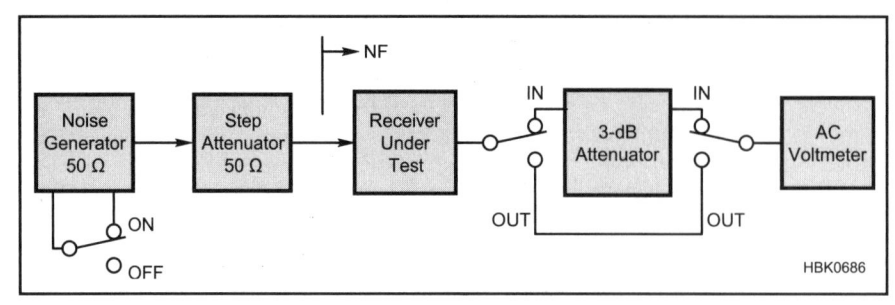

Figure 25.38 — Setup for measuring receiver noise figure.

long as the inaccuracy is the same for both voltage levels the ratio is correct. When using a non-RMS instrument, follow the step attenuator technique described in the previous paragraph along with a 3-dB attenuator (1/1.414 voltage divider) in front of the ac voltmeter. First take a voltmeter reading with the noise source off and the 3-dB attenuator bypassed. Then turn on the 3-dB attenuator and the noise source and adjust the step attenuator for the same reading. The noise figure is the ENR of the noise source minus the attenuation.

There are some potential errors to watch out for. The receiver AGC must be turned off for this test so that the gain does not change when the noise source is turned on or off. In addition, the audio gain and perhaps the IF gain must be adjusted so that there is no clipping of the noise peaks under any condition. With the noise source turned on, the RMS value of the noise at the speaker output should be adjusted to no more than 1/3 the maximum output level to prevent the peaks from clipping.

OTHER USES FOR A NOISE SOURCE

You can take advantage of the flat spectrum of a noise source to measure the frequency response of RF devices. It requires either a spectrum analyzer or a receiver that can be tuned manually across the frequency range of interest. With sufficient averaging, the output noise level at each frequency accurately reflects the response of the device at that frequency. For example it is quite easy to measure the total response of a receiver from antenna to speaker output using an RF noise source and free software running on a PC that turns the computer sound card into an audio spectrum analyzer. With the noise source connected to the receiver antenna and the audio output connected to the sound card input, the total response, including the IF crystal filter and all the audio stages, is shown by the average noise level in the spectrum analyzer window.

In addition to receivers, noise sources can also be used to measure the noise figure of other devices such as amplifiers. The technique is basically the same, except that the output signal to be measured is at a radio frequency instead of audio. Another difference is that the noise figure of the measuring instrument can affect the results. That is almost never a concern when measuring receivers since the gain from the antenna to the speaker output is normally so high as to swamp out the effect. The corrected noise figure is

$$NF = 10\log\left[10^{NF_M/10} - 10^{(NF_{NMI}-G)/10}\right]$$

where NF_M is the measured noise figure in dB, NF_{NMI} is the noise figure of the noise-measuring instrument in dB, and G is the gain of the device under test in dB. For that equation to be valid, the bandwidth of the measuring instrument must be no greater than the bandwidth of the device under test.

Commercial noise figure meters combine everything you need to perform noise figure measurements of amplifiers and other devices into one box. While the noise source itself is usually a separate module, the switched power is provided by the noise figure meter. Calculations are performed internally and the noise figure reads out directly on a meter or display. The noise source is repeatedly switched on and off to produce a continuously-updated noise figure reading, which is handy for adjusting or tuning the device under test. Older units typically operate at a small number of fixed intermediate frequencies and it is up to the user to heterodyne the signal to the IF. Many modern units operate over a wide range of frequencies and some can sweep to provide a plot of noise figure versus frequency. Agilent Technologies has a good application note on noise figure measurement that is available for free download.[19]

25.4.8 RF and Microwave Test Accessories

The following section assumes that all coaxial devices are designed for 50-Ω characteristic impedance. While that is by far the most common value for Amateur Radio systems, most of the information applies as well for other impedances, such as 75 Ω which is common in the video and television industry.

ATTENUATORS AND TERMINATIONS

Most amateurs are familiar with the concept of a *dummy load*, which is nothing more than a high-power 50-Ω resistor with a coaxial connector. The term comes from the fact that it is often used as a dummy antenna to provide a low-SWR load for transmitter testing. The resistor must have low stray reactance throughout the desired frequency range. Common wire-wound power resistors are not suitable for a dummy load because they have too much inductance. Commercial loads, such as the power attenuator in **Figure 25.39**, use special resistors encased in a finned enclosure for dissipating the heat generated by the power absorbed from the transmitter. One technique used in some amateur dummy loads is to enhance the power dissipation capability of less-expensive, lower-power resistors by submerging them in a bath of oil.

Low-power dummy loads, normally called *terminations*, are used whenever a device being tested needs to have one of its coaxial connectors terminated in a load that has good return loss over a wide band of frequencies. A *feed-through termination*, such as the one in **Figure 25.40**, is one that has two coaxial connectors with a straight-through connection between them as well as a 50-Ω load resistor connected between the center conductors and the shield. It is used to provide a 50-Ω load

Figure 25.39 — A 100-watt power attenuator rated for dc-3000 MHz. The transmitter is connected to the male type-N connector. The female connector is for the low-power connection.

25.28 Chapter 25

when using a measuring device with a high-impedance input, such as an oscilloscope. To avoid standing waves on the coaxial transmission line connected to the device under test, it is important to place the feed-through termination directly at the oscilloscope's input connector so that the transmission line is properly terminated.

Another technique to maintain a low SWR is to use a *T connector* at the oscilloscope input. The device under test is connected to one side of the T and some other device that provides a good 50-Ω load is connected to the other side. The high-impedance oscilloscope input does not excessively disturb the 50-Ω system. This is a good way to "tap into" a signal traveling between two devices on a coaxial line while maintaining the connection between the devices.

A *fixed attenuator* is useful both for reducing a signal level as well as for improving the 50-Ω match. For example, a 10-dB attenuator guarantees a minimum of 20 dB of return loss (1.22:1 SWR) even if the load SWR is infinite. A 20-dB attenuator makes a high-quality 50-Ω termination, even with nothing connected to its output.

A *step attenuator* is used when you need to adjust the signal level in fixed steps. The term "10-dB step attenuator" means that the step size is 10 dB. The maximum attenuation would typically be perhaps 70 to 120 dB. An attenuator with 1 dB steps and 10 dB of maximum attenuation would be called a "1 dB step attenuator" or a "0 to 10 dB step attenuator." Two attenuators, one with 10 dB steps and one with 1 dB steps, can be connected in series to obtain 1 dB resolution over a very wide range of attenuation. At microwave frequencies, continuously-variable attenuators are available for waveguide transmission lines. They can sometimes be obtained used at reasonable prices.

RF Measurement Test Set

Many low-level RF measurements require similar test setups so why not combine them into one package? This also makes it easier to perform the tests and get consistent results. NØADL and KE4PT show an example in the *QEX* article "Apparatus for RF Measurements" that you can download with the supplemental online information.

OTHER TEST ACCESSORIES

Other accessories available for waveguide include coax-to-waveguide adapters, detectors, directional couplers, isolators, absorption wavemeters, mixers and terminations of various kinds. Each size of waveguide covers about a 1.5:1 frequency range. Be aware that over the years there have been several systems for assigning letters to the various microwave frequency bands. For example, "X" band in the Agilent Technologies (formerly part of Hewlett-Packard) catalog is 8.2 to 12.4 GHz, but the old US Navy definition was 6.2 to 10.9 GHz, and the ITU assignment for X-band radar is 8.5 to 10.68 GHz. The IEEE standard definition is 8.0 to 12.0 GHz. When buying surplus waveguide accessories be sure they cover the frequency range you need.

A *coaxial detector* is just what the name implies, a diode detector in a coaxial package, usually with a 50-Ω RF load impedance. Silicon Schottky diodes are usually used to obtain good sensitivity although gallium arsenide devices are sometimes employed for the high microwave and millimeter-wave frequencies. Below a certain signal level, typically about –15 dBm, the detected output voltage is proportional to the square of the input voltage, that is, it is proportional to the input power. Sensitivity is typically specified in mV/mW, assuming a high-impedance load for the detected signal.

Wideband amplifiers can often be useful in test systems. They are available with various connector types in packages sized appropriately for the power level. A low-noise amplifier is useful as a preamplifier for a spectrum analyzer, for example. A higher-power amplifier can be used at the output of a signal generator either for receiver dynamic range testing or as an input signal for testing an RF power amplifier.

Directional couplers and bridges are useful network analyzer accessories as previously described but can also be used to acquire a small amount of signal for other test purposes. For example, a 30-dB coupler at the output of a 100-W transmitter produces a 100-mW signal that can be fed to a coaxial detector or a spectrum analyzer, while passing the rest of the 100-W signal through to the antenna or dummy load.

A *power divider*, also known as a *splitter*, is a device that divides an input signal equally among its output ports. A *combiner* is basically a power divider hooked up backward; the signals from the input ports are combined at the output port. Some power

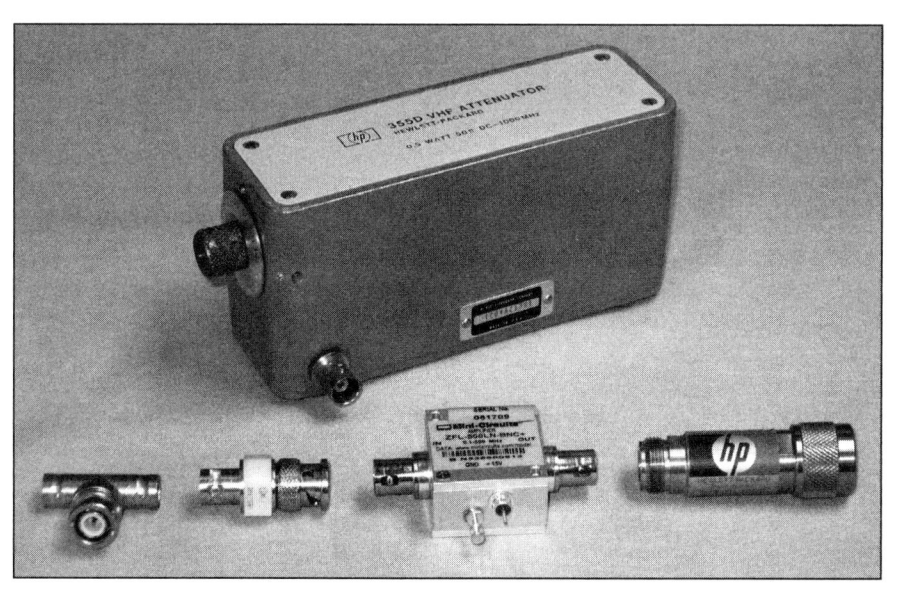

Figure 25.40 — Various RF test accessories. At the rear is a 10 dB step attenuator with a 0-120 dB range. In the foreground from left to right are a BNC "T" connector, a 50-Ω feed-through termination, a 0.1-500 MHz low-noise amplifier, and a 10-dB fixed attenuator.

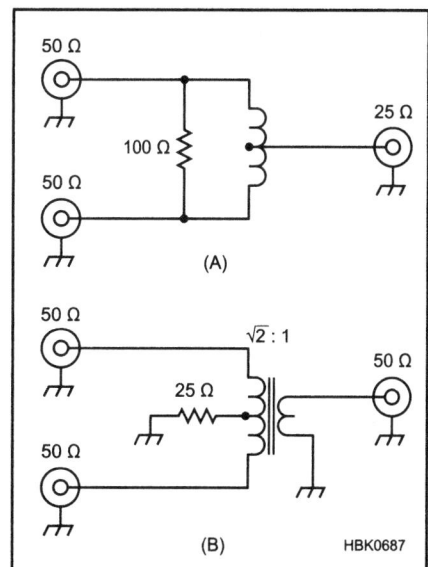

Figure 25.41 — Two forms of a lumped-element Wilkinson hybrid combiner. The one at B is 50 Ω on all three ports. In both circuits, the two input ports on the left are isolated from each other so long as the output port sees a low-SWR termination.

dividers consist only of a network of resistors. The insertion loss is typically at least 6 dB for 2-port splitters, meaning that a quarter of the power comes out each port and half the power is absorbed in the resistors.

A *hybrid combiner*, such as the *Wilkinson combiner* shown in **Figure 25.41**, includes a transformer as part of the network. It has the advantage that, so long as there is a good, low-SWR match on the output port, there is excellent isolation between the two input ports. That is very useful when combining the signals from two signal generators for high-level dynamic range testing of a receiver. The port-to-port isolation prevents the two signals from combining in the output amplifiers of the signal generators, where they could generate distortion products greater than the ones generated by the receiver that you are trying to measure. The insertion loss is nominally 3 dB.

The traditional Wilkinson combiner has a 2:1 ratio of input to output impedance. The variation in Figure 25.41B uses a transformer with a $\sqrt{2}$: 1 turns ratio (2:1 impedance ratio) to obtain 50 Ω on all ports.

Adapters such as those shown in **Figure 25.42** are useful for making connections among various pieces of test equipment.

Figure 25.42 — Coaxial connector adapters. From the left are: BNC male to type-N male, BNC female to UHF male, BNC female to SMA male, type-N male to SMA female, and type-N female to SMC male.

25.5 Receiver Measurements

Receivers present a special measurement challenge because of the wide range of signal levels they must be able to handle. In a state-of-the-art receiver, the difference between the minimum discernible signal and the blocking level can be as high as 130 or 140 dB. It requires special care and high-quality test equipment to measure that level of performance.

25.5.1 Standard ARRL Lab Tests

The ARRL laboratory staff has standardized on a suite of tests for receivers, transmitters and several other types of RF equipment. The exact procedures for each test are meticulously specified in a 163-page document to ensure that tests performed at different times by different people are done in the same way. We won't attempt to repeat that level of detail here but rather describe the tests in general terms suitable for use by the home experimenter. (The full set of procedures is available online in the Product Review Testing area of the ARRL website at **www.arrl.org/product-review**.) Additional information on receiver design and performance is available in the **Receiving** and **RF Techniques** chapters.

RECEIVER SENSITIVITY

Several methods are used to determine receiver sensitivity. The modulation mode often determines the best choice. One of the most common sensitivity measurements is *minimum discernible signal* (MDS) or *noise floor*, which is suitable for CW and SSB receivers. The minimum discernible signal is defined as that which will produce the same audio-output power as the internally generated receiver noise. Hence, the term "noise floor."

To measure MDS, use a signal generator tuned to the same frequency as the receiver. Be certain that the receiver is peaked on the generator signal. In **Figure 25.43** a step attenuator is included at the receiver input since most signal generators cannot accurately generate the low signal levels required for MDS measurements. An audio-frequency ac voltmeter is connected to the receiver's speaker terminals. If no speaker is connected, then a resistor of the same resistance as the speaker impedance should be substituted. Set the receiver to CW mode with a bandwidth of 500 Hz, or the nearest to that bandwidth that is available. Since the noise power is directly proportional to the bandwidth, always use identical filter bandwidths when comparing readings. Turn off the AGC, if possible. With the generator output turned off, you should hear nothing but noise in the speaker. Note the voltmeter reading at the receiver audio output. Next, turn on the generator and increase the output level until the voltmeter shows a 3-dB increase (1.414 times the voltage). The signal input at this point is the minimum discernible signal, which can be expressed in μV or dBm.

In the hypothetical example of Figure 25.43, the signal generator was adjusted to −133 dBm to cause the 3-dB increase in audio output power and the step attenuator is set to 4 dB. MDS is calculated with this equation:

$$MDS = -133 \text{ dBm} - 4 \text{ dB} = -137 \text{ dBm}$$

where the MDS is the minimum discernible signal and 4 dB is the loss through the attenuator.

Note that the voltmeter really should be a true-RMS type to accurately measure the RMS voltage of the noise. A typical average-reading multimeter is calibrated to indicate the RMS voltage of a sine wave but reads low on Gaussian noise. The error is small for the MDS test, however. To correct for the error, adjust the signal generator for a 3.2-dB increase (1.445 times the voltage) instead of 3.0 dB.

Another issue to watch out for is that the peak noise voltage is much greater than the RMS, typically by a factor of 4 or 5. The receiver volume should be adjusted so that the RMS output voltage is no more than about one-fifth the clipping level of the audio amplifier.

Sherwood Labs Receiver Testing

Rob Sherwood, NCØB, is a long-time contributor to amateur testing of receiver performance. He has contributed four papers to the downloadable supplemental information for this book. The subjects include his procedures and lab setup, along with a discussion of receiver noise and band noise.

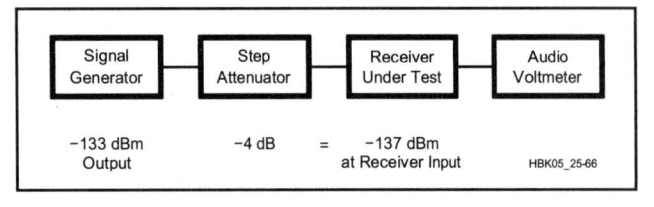

Figure 25.43 — A general test setup for measuring receiver MDS, or noise floor. Signal levels shown are for an example discussed in the text.

For AM modulation, receiver sensitivity is expressed as the RF signal level that results in a 10 dB signal plus noise to noise ratio at the audio output. The AM signal is 30% modulated with a 1000 Hz tone. Otherwise, the test setup is the same as for the MDS test. The signal generator output level is adjusted until there is a 10 dB (3.16 voltage ratio) increase in audio output voltage when the modulation is switched from off to on. Again, there is an error if a typical average-reading multimeter is used instead of a true-RMS voltmeter. For the AM sensitivity measurement, the error is 0.8 dB. Adjust the signal generator output to give a 10.8 dB (3.47 voltage ratio) increase in signal when the modulation is turned on. If an audio distortion meter is used in place of the RMS voltmeter, you can leave the modulation turned on and adjust the signal generator output level for 31.6% distortion.

For FM modulation, receiver sensitivity is expressed as the RF signal level that results in 12 dB SINAD. SINAD stands for "signal plus noise and distortion" and is calculated from

$$\text{SINAD} = 10 \log \left[\frac{\text{signal} + \text{noise} + \text{distortion}}{\text{noise} + \text{distortion}} \right] \text{dB}$$

where signal, noise and distortion are all entered in units of power (watts or milliwatts). It is very similar to the signal plus noise to noise ratio used for AM testing except that any distortion in the audio signal is added to the noise measurement. It means, however, that the signal, the noise and the distortion must all be measured at the same time, without turning off the modulation. For that, a distortion analyzer is needed as shown in **Figure 25.44**. A distortion analyzer includes a switchable band-reject filter to null out the 1 kHz tone for the noise-and-distortion measurement. The filter is bypassed for the signal-plus-noise-and-distortion measurement. For the test, the signal generator is set for FM modulation with a 1 kHz tone and the desired FM deviation, normally 3 kHz for VHF repeater operation. Adjust the signal generator output level until the distortion analyzer indicates 25% distortion, which is equivalent to 12 dB SINAD. Don't forget to subtract the attenuation of the step attenuator from the signal generator output level, as was done for the MDS test.

Noise figure is a measure of receiver sensitivity that, unlike the other methods presented so far, is independent of the receiver bandwidth and operating mode. It can be calculated from the MDS so long as the noise bandwidth of the receiver filtering is known. *Noise bandwidth* is the bandwidth of a hypothetical perfect filter with a rectangular spectrum shape that would produce the same total noise power as the receiver filter. Accurate measurement of a filter's noise bandwidth requires integrating the spectral response using a swept signal source, but the filter's 3 dB bandwidth can be used as a reasonable approximation. The formula is

$$\text{NF} = \text{MDS} - \left(10 \log(\text{BW}) - 174\right) \text{ dB}$$

where MDS is the minimum discernible signal in dBm and BW is the noise bandwidth in Hz. Assuming the noise bandwidth is 500 Hz, we get NF = MDS + 147 dB. For example, if the MDS is –137 dBm then NF = –137 + 147 = 10 dB.

RECEIVER DYNAMIC RANGE

Dynamic range is a measure of a receiver's ability to receive weak signals without being overloaded by strong signals. It is easy to design a receiver with good sensitivity to weak signals. It is also easy to design a receiver that is not overloaded by strong signals. It is much more difficult to design a receiver that can do both at the same time.

Blocking dynamic range (BDR) is the difference between the noise floor and the signal level at which *blocking* occurs, that is, the level that causes a 1 dB reduction in gain for nearby weaker signals. The noise floor is just the MDS and can be measured using the technique described in the previous section.

The blocking level is measured using a test setup similar to the one used for measuring MDS except that two signal generators are connected to the input through a hybrid combiner, as shown in **Figure 25.45**. The receiver AGC should be turned off for this test. The mode is set to CW and the bandwidth to 500 Hz or the closest available. Two signal generators are used. One generates the weak signal that the receiver is tuned to. The ARRL standard specifies –110 dBm at the receiver input, which requires –97 dBm at the input to the hybrid combiner, assuming it has 3 dB loss. The other signal generator generates the strong interfering signal on a nearby frequency. Standard frequency separations are plus and minus 20, 5 and 2 kHz. The level of the strong signal is increased until the level of the weaker signal measured at the receiver audio output decreases by 1 dB.

Referring to Figure 25.45, the blocking level is the level from the signal generator minus the loss of the hybrid combiner and attenuator,

$$\text{BL} = -7 - 3 - 10 = -20 \text{ dBm}$$

The blocking dynamic range is given by

$$\text{BDR} = \text{BL} - \text{MDS} = -20 - (-137) = 117 \text{ dB}$$

assuming an MDS of –137 dBm as in the previous examples.

One complication is that it may be difficult to measure the amplitude of the audio tone because of the presence of noise caused by the phase noise of the signal generator and the receiver's local oscillator, especially at the 2 and 5 kHz frequency spacings. The solution is to use an audio-frequency spectrum analyzer to measure the change in tone amplitude. The absolute accuracy of the spectrum analyzer is not important so long as it can accurately show a 1-dB change in signal level. An instrument based on a computer sound card and free spectrum analysis software should be adequate.

Reciprocal mixing is the name for the mix-

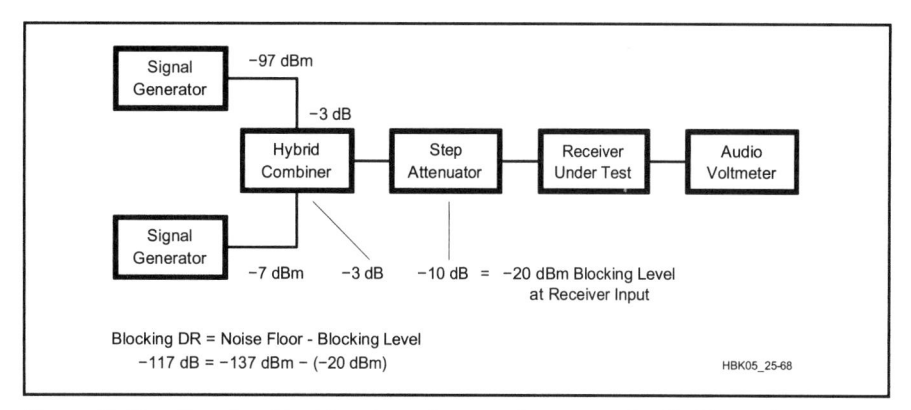

Figure 25.45 — Receiver blocking dynamic range is measured with this equipment and arrangement. Signal levels shown are for the example discussed in the text.

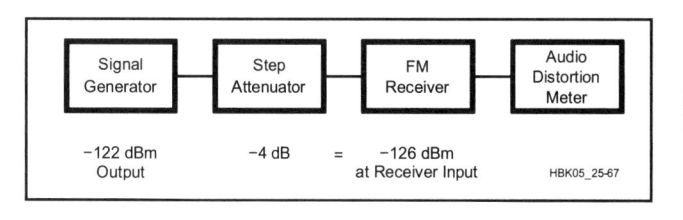

Figure 25.44 — FM SINAD test setup.

ing of a nearby interfering signal with the phase noise of the receiver's local oscillator, which causes noise in the audio output. Although the ARRL BDR test eliminates this effect from the measurement, in actual on-the-air operation the phase noise is often the factor that limits the effective dynamic range. To address this issue, the ARRL test suite includes a separate measurement for reciprocal mixing. The test setup is the same as for MDS except that the signal generator in Figure 25.43 is replaced with a low-phase-noise crystal oscillator with an output power level of +15 dBm. The step attenuator block should include both a unit with 10-dB steps to be able to adjust the signal level over a wide range as well as a 1-dB step attenuator for fine adjustment. The receiver is tuned to 20, 5 or 2 kHz above or below the oscillator frequency. The output noise level is first measured with the oscillator turned off, then the oscillator is turned on and the step attenuator gradually reduced until the noise increases by 3 dB. Reciprocal mixing is expressed as a negative number:

$$\text{reciprocal mixing} = \text{MDS} - (+15 - A) \text{ dB}$$

where MDS is the noise floor, +15 is the signal level of the crystal oscillator in dBm, and A is the total attenuation in dB.

Intermodulation distortion (IMD) means the creation of unwanted signals at new frequencies because of two or more strong interfering signals modulating each other. If there are two interfering signals at frequencies f1 and f2, then *second-order IMD* products occur at f1 + f2. If f1 and f2 are close together, then the second-order products occur near the second harmonics. *Third-order IMD* products occur at 2f1 − f2 and 2f2 − f1. If f1 and f2 are close together, then the third-order products occur close by. For example, if f1 and f2 differ by 10 kHz, then the third-order IMD products are 10 kHz above the higher frequency and 10 kHz below the lower.

The two-tone IMD test setup shown in **Figure 25.46** is the same for second and third-order IMD. To obtain sufficient output power and isolation of the two signal generators, it may be necessary to follow each one with a wide-band power amplifier, not shown. The receiver under test is set to receive CW with the same bandwidth as for the MDS test and is tuned to the frequency of the distortion product to be measured. The two signal generators are always set to the same output amplitude level, which is increased until IMD products equal in amplitude to the noise floor appear, resulting in a 3-dB increase in the audio voltmeter reading. The *IMD dynamic range* is then the difference in dB between the level of the interfering signals and the MDS.

For the second-order IMD measurement, the standard ARRL test sets the two signal generators to 6.000 MHz and 8.020 MHz and the receiver is tuned to 14.020 MHz. For the third-order IMD measurements, the two signal generators are set to frequencies 20, 5 and 2 kHz apart, separated from the receiver frequency by plus and minus 20, 5 and 2 kHz so that the lower or upper IMD product falls within the receiver passband.

For example, tune the receiver to 14.020 MHz and the two signal generators to 13.980 MHz and 14.000 MHz. With the signal generators turned off, measure the noise level with the audio voltmeter. Turn on the signal generators and increase their amplitudes until the voltmeter shows a 3-dB increase. If the signal generator amplitudes are −10 dBm, the loss in the hybrid combiner is 3 dB, and the step attenuator is set to 30 dB attenuation, then the third-order IMD level is

$$\text{IMD} = -10 - 3 - 30 = -43 \text{ dBm}$$

If the MDS is −137 dBm, then the third-order IMD dynamic range is

$$\text{IMD\_DR} = \text{IMD} - \text{MDS} = -43 - (-137) = 94 \text{ dB}$$

As with the blocking dynamic range test, the phase noise of the signal generators and the receiver LO may obscure the IMD product being measured. Again, the solution is to use an audio spectrum analyzer to measure the tone amplitude. Calibrate the amplitude by temporarily tuning one of the signal generators to the receiver frequency and setting the amplitude level so that the signal level at the receiver is the MDS. Note the level on the spectrum analyzer. Then return the signal generator to the interfering frequency and adjust the signal generators' amplitudes until the IMD product is at the same level as the MDS signal. The ARRL test bench actually uses a third signal generator and a second hybrid combiner at the receiver input to generate the calibration signal so that it and the IMD product can be seen on the spectrum analyzer at the same time for a more-accurate

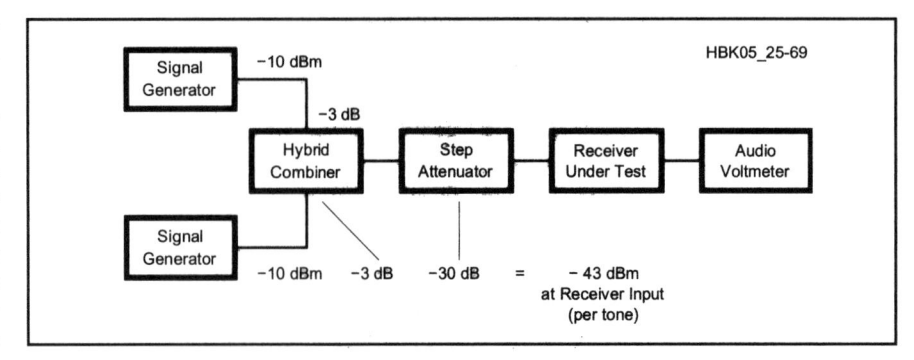

Figure 25.46 — The test setup for receiver intermodulation distortion dynamic range. Signal levels shown are for the example discussed in the text.

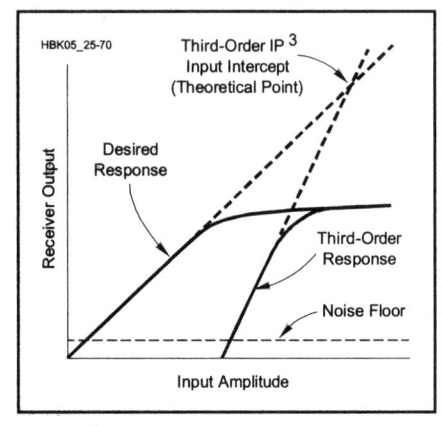

Figure 25.47 — The third-order intercept point can be determined by extending the lines representing the interfering signal level and the third-order intermodulation products on a plot of the signal levels in dB.

comparison.

In most analog components such as mixers and amplifiers, the second-order products increase in amplitude by 2 dB for each 1 dB increase in the interfering signals and third-order products increase 3 dB per dB. If the output signal levels are plotted versus the input levels on a log-log chart (that is, in units of dB), the desired signal and the undesired IMD products theoretically trace out straight lines as shown for third-order products in **Figure 25.47**. Although the IMD products increase more rapidly than the desired signal, the lines never actually cross because blocking occurs before that level, however, the point where the extensions of those two lines cross is called the *third-order intercept point* (IP3).

Although the third-order intercept is an artificial point, it is a useful measure of the strong-signal-handling capability of a receiver. It can be calculated from the equation

$$\text{IP3} = \text{MDS} + 1.5 \times \text{IMD\_DR dBm}$$

where IP3 is the third-order intercept point,

MDS is the minimum discernible signal in dBm and IMD_DR is the third-order IMD dynamic range in dB. Using the numbers from the previous example, IP3 = –137 + 1.5 × 94 = +4 dBm.

The second-order intercept may be calculated in an analogous way.

$$IP2 = MDS + 2 \times IMD\_DR$$

where IP2 is the second-order intercept and IMD_DR is the second-order IMD dynamic range in this case.

An alternate method of measuring third-order IMD is to use S5 (–97 dBm) instead of the MDS as the reference level to which the IMD products are adjusted. That results in a higher IMD level but a smaller value of IMD dynamic range (the difference between the IMD level and the reference). It may be a more accurate method of determining the third-order intercept because the signal levels do not have to be measured in the presence of noise that is at the same level as the signal.

The third-order intercept is generally not a valid concept for software-defined receivers (SDRs) that do not use an analog front end. Some SDRs do not use a mixer but feed the signal from the antenna directly to an analog-to-digital converter (ADC). ADCs usually do not exhibit the 3 dB per dB relationship between signal level and third-order products, at least over major portions of their operating range. Comparing third-order dynamic range measurements of an SDR and a conventional analog radio may give misleading results.

Figure 25.48 shows the relationship between the various dynamic range values. The base line represents different power levels, with very small signals at the left and large signals at the right. The numbers listed are from the previous examples for a typical receiver. The thermal noise and the noise floor are referenced to a 500 Hz bandwidth. The third-order IMD dynamic range is less than the blocking dynamic range, which means that signals as low as –43 dBm may cause IMD interference while signals must exceed –20 dBm to cause blocking. However, the intermodulation distortion may actually cause fewer problems since the IMD products only appear at certain discrete frequencies. A signal that exceeds the blocking level can cause interference across the entire band.

Third-order IMD dynamic range may also be measured on an FM receiver. The test setup is the same as Figure 25.46 except that the audio voltmeter is replaced with an audio distortion meter, as in Figure 25.44. The frequencies involved are the same as in that example. For this test, one of the signal generators (the one tuned to the frequency farthest from the receiver under test) is FM-modulated with a 1000 Hz tone at 3 kHz deviation. That causes the IMD products also to be FM-modulated,

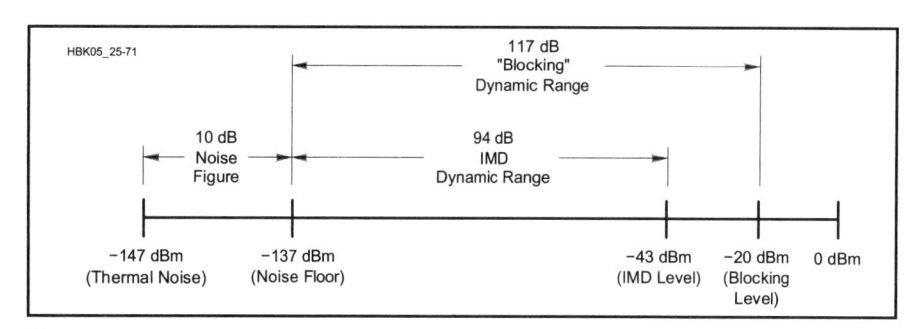

Figure 25.48 — Performance plot of the example receiver discussed in the text.

Dynamic Range Metrics: Superheterodyne vs. SDR Receivers
By Bob Allison, WB1GCM, ARRL Laboratory Assistant Manager

Reciprocal Mixing (RM) is the noise generated in a superheterodyne receiver when noise from the local oscillator (LO) mixes with strong, adjacent signals. All oscillators have noise sidebands, and some types and designs have more than others. The noise sidebands mix with the strong adjacent off-channel signal, creating noise products in the mixer's output. This noise can degrade the sensitivity of the receiver and is most notable when a strong signal is just outside the IF passband. Reciprocal mixing is worse with a single strong signal 2 kHz away from the tuned frequency than it is 5 or 20 kHz away.

It's interesting to compare to the two-tone third-order IMD dynamic range (3IMD DR) to the reciprocal mixing dynamic range (RMDR). In the case of 3IMD, two strong adjacent signals add up to cause an unwanted effect, but in the case of RM, a *single* strong adjacent station 5 or 2 kHz away from the desired signal has more of an impact on the ability to hear a desired weak signal. For most superheterodyne receivers, RMDR is the worst dynamic range figure at 2 kHz spacing.

It has been observed in the ARRL Laboratory that many direct-sampling SDR receivers exhibit little, if any reciprocal mixing up to the point of analog-to-digital converter (ADC) overload. These receivers have no front-end mixer and local oscillator, thus, no sideband noise of an oscillator to mix with adjacent signals.

We perform the reciprocal mixing test at 14.025 MHz, using a very low-noise Wenzel test oscillator with a measured output of +14 dBm to generate the off-channel, strong signal. A test oscillator must have the lowest sideband noise as possible — considerably lower than the reciprocal mixing being measured. An excellent receiver will exhibit 100 dB of RMDR at 2 kHz spacing.

Blocking — an apparent reduction in receiver gain due to the presence of a strong signal — was problematic in years past. With the AGC off, the desired signal, especially if weak, would disappear from the receiver audio if a strong, off-channel signal was present. The ability to reject adjacent signals has improved greatly in recent years, so much so that blocking dynamic range (BDR) greatly exceeds the other dynamic ranges. During Lab tests, reciprocal mixing in a receiver can raise the audio output noise enough to drown out the desired signal! Some of our laboratory consultants have expressed that the BDR figure is a bit useless because of this behavior. Agreed! Still, some still wish for us to report blocking, since we have the use of signal analyzers set to narrow audio bandwidths (2 or 5 Hz).

Many SDR receivers measured for *QST* Product Review exhibit little or no blocking effects up to the point of analog-to-digital converter (ADC) overload. This behavior, along with an SDR's reciprocal mixing behavior is most desirable. Typical BDR of modern receivers at 2 kHz spacing is 110 dB or greater.

Two-tone Third-Order Intermodulation Distortion (3IMD) happens when two strong signals (2 and 4 kHz away from the tuned frequency, for example) appear at the antenna jack, with a resulting unwanted "phantom" signal heard at the tuned frequency. With a superheterodyne receiver, IMD is generated at the input stages to the first IF, with the undesired mixing products passing through the rest of the receiver stages. In an SDR receiver, the ADC clock quality and the cumulative signal level input to the ADC determines the level of IMD at the speaker (see other sidebar). Due to design improvements of both superheterodyne and SDR receivers, typical 3IMD DR at 2 kHz spacing is 90 dB or greater.

Due to changes in technology, most modern receivers do not exhibit a 3:1 relationship between the IMD signal level and the IMD input level. The ratio can be significantly greater or less than 3:1. Since the third order intercept point (IP3) figure is calculated based on the assumption of a 3:1 ratio, this figure is meaningless with today's receivers. Emphasis must be placed on all three dynamic ranges. The lowest dynamic range at 2 kHz of the three dynamic ranges we publish is the dynamic range of the receiver. The benchmark for excellent performance is 100 dB.

SDR Behavior with Two-tone Third Order Intermodulation Dynamic Range: the Third Signal
By Bob Allison, WB1GCM, ARRL Laboratory Assistant Manager

The ARRL Laboratory determined that our normal two-tone third order IMD dynamic range (3IMD DR) tests did not always apply to the way software defined radio (SDR) receivers work in the real world.* With an SDR receiver, all of the demodulation is done by software. An SDR converts a block of analog RF spectrum to a digital stream of data, then uses software to select and demodulate a desired signal from that data. The digitization of an analog signal results in a sequence of small steps in signal level. These small steps are a type of nonlinearity that forms intermodulation (IMD) products, similar to those observed in analog receivers.

For analog receivers, once intermodulation occurs, it gets strong quickly as the off-channel signals used for testing are increased. With an SDR, however, because the small steps are the same for all levels of the signal being digitized, intermodulation at low levels does not vary significantly with the level of test signals. For the steady-state sine waves seen from signal generators in a laboratory environment, the steps are the same for each cycle of RF. Any intermodulation that is created adds coherently in the receiver output.

In some SDR designs, random noise is added to the RF input to randomize the digitization process, preventing intermodulation products from adding coherently. This technique is called dithering. When a receiver is connected to the antenna, band noise present at the input to the analog to digital converter (ADC) can, in most cases, serve to randomize the digitization. The net effect is the same — low-level intermodulation seen in a laboratory test environment will not be present when that receiver is connected to an antenna and used to receive on-the-air signals. This effect was verified by measurements in the Lab by adding a receive antenna (acting as our dithering source) to our two-tone IMD test fixture; the level of band noise varied with local conditions and propagation, thus, the amount of dithering present also varied, causing IMD products to vary as well.

With such observations, we had to find out if the IMD products varied as a function of noise or as a function of level. We substituted a random noise generator as our dithering source. The result: low-level IMD products were masked by the raised noise level with little change in the level of the IMD products. Varying the level of the noise had no effect, except the unwanted effect of a raised noise floor. Since noise or its level had no effect on the level of the IMD products, the only other dithering source received on an antenna must be discrete signals!

We soon discovered that by using a strong, off frequency, single signal as our dithering source (the third signal), the IMD product level could be reduced. By varying the level of the third signal (generator), the IMD product level also varied. Thus, when connected to an antenna, the levels of all the signals at the input to the ADC vary considerably with propagation and mode, and thus the dynamic range varies with propagation and mode. This significant discovery determined that adding noise (dithering) does not necessarily improve an SDR's 3IMD DR, but that a single, strong, constant, off-frequency signal does. By experimenting, we found that by varying both the third signal's level and frequency, a "sweet spot" could easily be found that maximizes the 3IMD DR. A third signal at a level of –43 dBm, 200 kHz away from the tuned frequency is a good example of a "sweet spot."

This single additional signal, at a specific level and frequency, hardly represents actual on-air conditions. In reality, the 3IMD DR can be a moving target, varying by 30 dB or more depending on conditions! With SDRs that exhibit improved 3IMD DR, QST Product Reviews report "up to XX dB", which represents the absolute best-case dynamic range. A user of such devices can expect much lower dynamic range under average band conditions, with an effort made to mention the expected dynamic range during "quiet" conditions.

It is interesting to note that by design, some manufacturers of SDRs now employ a "third signal" to improve 3IMD DR; the third signal is internally generated and tracks with the tuned signal, at a specific level, which minimizes IMD products and maximizes 3IMD DR.

Please keep in mind that when an antenna is attached to a receiver, atmospheric, solar and man-made noise will mask much of the low-level IMD products that are measured in a laboratory environment. That is, the dynamic range can be higher under laboratory "quiet" conditions, where a receiver's noise floor is measurable.

*Allison, Bob, WB1GCM, "Testing the SDR-IQ in the ARRL Lab," February, 2010 QST, p 52.

which can be measured with the distortion meter. The signal generator amplitudes are increased until the distortion product produces 12 dB SINAD (25% distortion) on the meter. The FM third-order IMD dynamic range is calculated using the same equation as for SSB and CW except that the SINAD sensitivity is substituted for the MDS. For example, if the 12 dB SINAD sensitivity is –120 dBm, the signal generator outputs are –10 dBm, the combiner loss is 3 dB, and the step attenuator is set to 30 dB, then

$$FM\_IMD\_DR = -10 - 3 - 30 - (-120) = 77 \text{ dB}$$

where FM_IMD_DR is the third-order FM IMD dynamic range.

OTHER ARRL RECEIVER TESTS

Most modern communications receivers are superheterodyne types. The first *IF rejection* and *image rejection* test measures the signal levels at the intermediate frequency and the image frequency that produces an audio output signal equivalent to the MDS, or noise floor. The test setup is the same as for the MDS test, as shown in Figure 25.43. The receiver is set to CW mode and 500 Hz bandwidth. The signal generator is tuned to the receiver first intermediate frequency or to the image frequency, which is the receiver frequency plus or minus two times the IF. The signal generator output level is gradually increased until there is a 3-dB increase in the audio voltmeter reading. As with the MDS test, if a multimeter is used instead of a true-RMS voltmeter, the signal generator should be adjusted for a 3.2-dB increase. The IF or image rejection is just the signal generator level at the receiver input less the MDS. For example, if the MDS is –137 dBm, the signal generator level is –40 dBm, and the attenuator is set for 10 dB, then the IF or image rejection is IR = –40 – 10 – (–137) = 87 dB.

FM adjacent-channel rejection is a measure of an FM receiver's ability to detect a weak signal in the presence of a strong interfering FM-modulated signal on an adjacent frequency channel. The test setup is the same as for the two-tone IMD dynamic range test shown in Figure 25.46 except that a distortion meter is substituted for the audio voltmeter, as was done for the FM SINAD test illustrated in Figure 25.44. The standard channel spacing is 20 kHz. The weak signal is modulated with a 1000 Hz tone and the interfering signal with a 400 Hz tone, both with 3 kHz deviation. The receiver under test is set for FM modulation and is tuned to the frequency of the weak signal. The weak signal is adjusted for 12 dB SINAD (25% distortion) on the distortion meter and then the interfering signal level is increased until the SINAD drops to 6 dB (50% distortion). The adjacent channel rejection is the difference between the power of the interfering signal and the 12 dB SINAD sensitivity, which is just the difference in level between the two signal generators.

Another test that applies especially to FM receivers is the *squelch sensitivity test*. As usual, the signal generator is set for FM modulation with a 1 kHz tone and 3 kHz deviation. If squelch is available for SSB, it can be tested in that mode as well. With the signal generator off, the squelch control on the receiver is adjusted just to the point where the noise is squelched. Then the signal generator is turned on and the level increased until the signal is heard.

Audio power output is tested with the same setup as the FM SINAD test illustrated in Figure 25.44. The receiver under test is set for SSB mode with the widest bandwidth available. A load resistor of the specified resistance, usually 8 Ω, is connected to the speaker output in place of the speaker. The signal generator level is set for an S9 level and the receiver is tuned for a 1 kHz output tone frequency. The receiver volume control is increased until the specified distortion level, usually 10%, is indicated on the distortion meter. The output power is given by the equation

$$P = V_{RMS}^2 / R$$

where P is the power in watts, V_{RMS} is the RMS output voltage, and R is the load resistance.

The audio and IF frequency response measures the audio frequencies at which receiver audio output drops by 6 dB from the peak. It includes the total response of the entire receiver, from the antenna connector to the speaker output. The test setup is the same as for the audio power output test except that some method must be included to measure the output audio frequency, such as a digital oscilloscope or frequency counter. The receiver is set for SSB mode at the bandwidth to be tested and the AGC is turned off. First tune the signal generator for a peak audio output signal and record the level of the audio signal. Then tune the signal generator downward until the signal drops 6 dB (½ the voltage) and record the audio frequency. Then tune the signal generator upward and record the high-end frequency at which the signal drops by 6 dB. The 6-dB bandwidth is the difference between the two frequencies.

There are several other miscellaneous ARRL receiver tests that are commonly reported in product reviews. The S meter test measures the signal level required to produce an S9 indication on the meter. The notch filter test uses a setup similar to the IMD dynamic range test in Figure 25.46 with an audio spectrum analyzer at the output. One signal is notched and the other is used as a level reference; the notch depth is the amplitude difference between the two tones. The DSP noise reduction test uses a similar setup except that one signal generator is replaced with a wideband noise generator. The signal generator is adjusted for S9 and the noise source for a 3-dB increase in the audio voltmeter so that the noise and signal are at the same level. The DSP noise reduction is then turned on and the reduction in noise level recorded.

25.5.2 Other Common Receiver Measurements

There are a few other useful receiver tests that are not covered in the standard ARRL test suite. For example, in addition to the IF and image response, it is possible for a receiver to have spurious responses at other frequencies as well. Testing for that can be a time-consuming process since it involves tuning the signal generator through a wide frequency range with the receiver tuned to each of a number of representative frequencies, typically at least one on each band. Start with the signal generator at maximum output power. When you find a response, reduce the level until the received signal level is at the noise floor (MDS). The spurious response amplitude is the difference between the signal generator level and the MDS.

Another time-consuming test is for internally-generated spurious signals, sometimes called *birdies* because they sometimes sound like a bird chirping as you tune through the signal. Birdies are typically caused by harmonics of the local oscillator(s) and BFO and their IMD products. For this test, connect a 50-Ω termination to the antenna connector and tune the receiver through its entire frequency range, writing down the frequency and S meter reading for each spurious signal found. You must tune very slowly because many birdies pass through the IF passband much faster than regular signals, sometimes in the opposite direction.

The ARRL S meter test only measures the response at the S9 level. If the S meter is accurate throughout its range it can be used to measure signal levels off the air. The standard definition is that, on the HF bands, S9 should correspond to –73 dBm (50 μV into 50 Ω) and each S unit corresponds to 6 dB, or a doubling of RF voltage. So S8 is –79 dBm or 25 μV, S7 is –85 dBm or 12.5 μV, and so on. The S unit calibration of most commercial equipment varies considerably from 6 dB per S unit, but the S meters accuracy can easily be measured with a calibrated signal generator.

The automatic gain control circuitry has a major effect on the operation of a receiver. The static AGC performance can be measured on a CW or SSB receiver with a signal generator and an audio voltmeter connected to the speaker output. You can plot a graph of audio output in dBV (decibels with respect to one volt) versus RF input level in dBm to see how good a job the receiver does in keeping the output level constant. Some receivers have menu settings to set the slope of the curve and the threshold, which is the small signal level at which the AGC circuitry starts to reduce the gain. The dynamic response is also important, although it is difficult to measure. A short attack time is important to reduce transients on sudden strong signals, but if it is too short then in-channel intermodulation distortion between strong signals can make signals sound "mushy."

The ARRL test suite includes a measurement of the 6 dB bandwidth at the audio output, but the sound is also affected by slope and ripple in the passband response. Using the same test setup as for the 6 dB measurement, you can measure the output voltage at a number of equally-spaced frequencies and plot the results on a graph. Output power is measured at the 10% distortion level, but it also is useful to measure the distortion at a volume level closer to what is used in actual practice. An output level of 1 V_{RMS} is commonly used for that test.

Frequency accuracy and stability are important performance criteria for a receiver. If a signal generator of sufficient frequency accuracy is not available, a standard time signal such as from radio station WWV can be used. The traditional method is to put the receiver in SSB mode and *zero-beat* the carrier, which means to tune the receiver until the audio tone (the beat note) is at zero Hz. Since most receivers' audio frequency response only extends down to a couple hundred Hertz, it is difficult to get good accuracy using that method. If a frequency counter or other means of measuring the audio output frequency is available, you can tune the receiver to obtain a 1000 Hz tone and add (for LSB) or subtract (for USB) 1000 Hz from the receiver's indicated frequency. The frequency drift from cold turn-on can be measured by plotting the audio output frequency versus time.

25.6 Transmitter Measurements

The signal levels found in a transmitter do not vary nearly as much as in a receiver. All the signals are generated internally, rather than being received off the air, so are much better controlled. Partly for that reason transmitter measurements tend to be simpler than receiver measurements and there are fewer of them.

Figure 25.49 — The transmitter spectral purity test uses a spectrum analyzer to display the spurious frequencies.

25.6.1 Standard ARRL Lab Tests

For a transmitter, the RF power output is probably the first measurement that comes to mind. The test setup is straightforward: connect the transmitter output to the input of an RF wattmeter and connect the wattmeter output to a suitable dummy load. For CW, AM and FM modes, simply key the transmitter and measure the power on the wattmeter. For AM and FM the modulation should be turned off. For SSB, a two-tone audio oscillator should be connected to the microphone input to take the place of the voice signal. For the SSB test the wattmeter must be a peak-reading type to measure the PEP power

TRANSMITTER SPECTRAL PURITY

Ideally a transmitter confines its emissions to a narrow frequency range around the desired signal. Unwanted emissions can be divided into two categories, those that fall close to the desired signal and those that extend far away.

In the latter category are included harmonics and other discrete spurious frequencies. The measurement is done with the transmitter in CW mode using the test setup shown in **Figure 25.49**. Tune up the transmitter as specified in the manual, set it for the desired power level, and adjust the frequency from one end of the band to the other while observing the spectrum analyzer. This should be done on each band. It may be necessary to retune the transmitter occasionally as the frequency is adjusted. The spurious-signal and harmonic suppression is the difference in dB between the carrier and the maximum spurious signal. It is important that the power level into the spectrum analyzer be maintained at a low enough level that spurious signals are not generated in the spectrum analyzer itself. To test for that, try changing the step attenuator setting; the desired carrier and all spurious signals should change by the same amount. If not, increase the attenuation until they do.

Representative spectrum analyzer plots are shown in **Figure 25.50**. The horizontal (frequency) scale is 5 MHz per division. The desired carrier frequency at 7 MHz appears 1.4 divisions from the left of the plot. Although not shown, a large apparent signal is often seen at the extreme left edge. This signal at zero Hz is caused by leakage of the spectrum analyzer local oscillator frequency and should be ignored.

In addition to the discrete spurious signals measured by the previous test, a transmitter may also generate broadband noise. It can be due both to the phase noise of the local oscillator as well as AM noise from all the devices in the amplifier chain. Generally the phase noise predominates, at least for frequencies close to the carrier. The composite noise test measures the total noise from both sources as well as any close-in spurious frequencies that don't show up in the wideband spurious signal and harmonic suppression test. Measuring phase noise requires high-performance test equipment and special measuring techniques.[20] The ARRL lab uses a special low-noise oscillator and a Hewlett-Packard (now Agilent Technologies) phase noise test set under computer control to perform this sophisticated measurement, which takes about 15 minutes to perform once it is set up. The result is a plot of the noise spectrum such as the one in **Figure 25.51**.

The most important unwanted emissions close to the carrier frequency are caused by distortion in the transmitter amplifier stages. In an SSB transmitter, this distortion creates a signal that is wider than the bandwidth of the original modulation and causes interference to other stations. For this test, the same test setup is used as for the harmonics and spurious frequencies test shown in Figure 25.49 except that a two-tone audio generator is connected to the transmitter microphone input to simulate a voice signal, which contains many frequency components. The two tone frequencies must be non-harmonically related to prevent tone harmonics from being confused with IMD products. The ARRL Lab uses 700 Hz and 1900 Hz for these tests. Because many transmitters' modulation frequency response is not flat, the relative amplitudes of the two audio-frequency tones

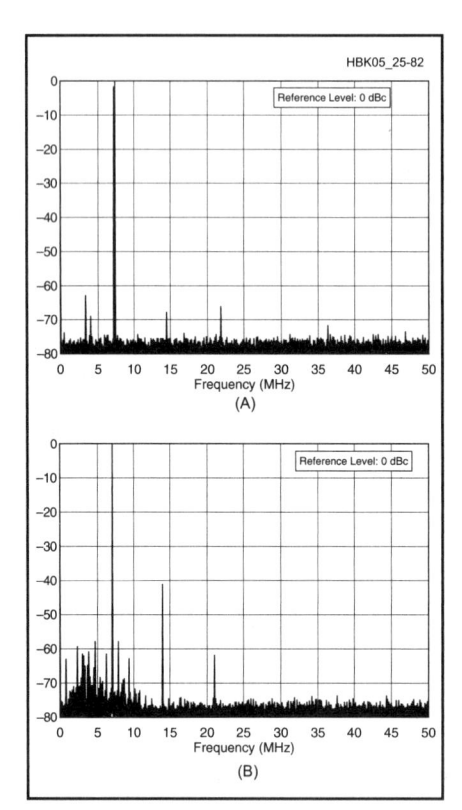

Figure 25.50 — Comparison of the spurious signal levels of two 100-watt transmitters, as shown on the spectrum analyzer display. The display on the top shows about 63 dB worst-case spurious signal suppression while the one on the bottom has a second harmonic suppressed approximately 42 dB. For transmitters below 30 MHz installed after January 1, 2003, the worst-case spurious emission must be at least 43 dB below the carrier power.

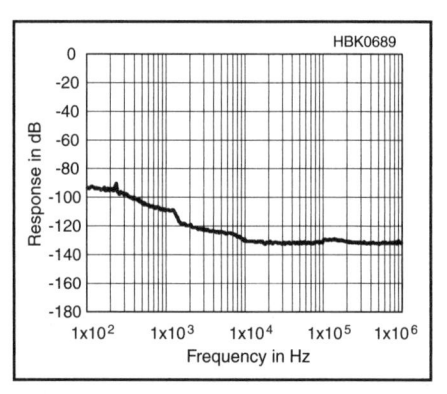

Figure 25.51 — Spectral display of an amateur transmitter output during composite-noise testing in the ARRL Lab. Power output was 200 W on the 14 MHz band. The carrier, off the left edge of the plot, is not shown. This plot shows composite transmitted noise 100 Hz to 1 MHz from the carrier on a logarithmic scale. The vertical scale is in dB with respect to the carrier.

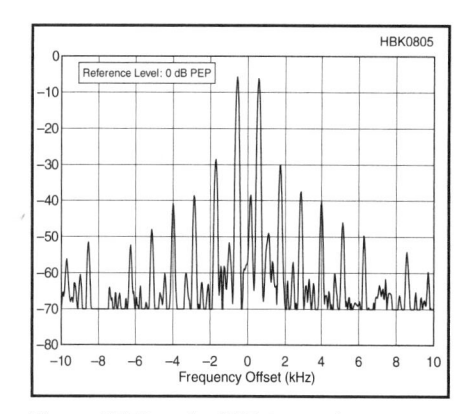

Figure 25.52 — An SSB transmitter two-tone test as seen on a spectrum analyzer. Each horizontal division represents 2 kHz and each vertical division is 10 dB. The third-order products are 30 dB below the PEP (top line), the fifth-order products are down 38 dB and seventh-order products are down 40 dB.

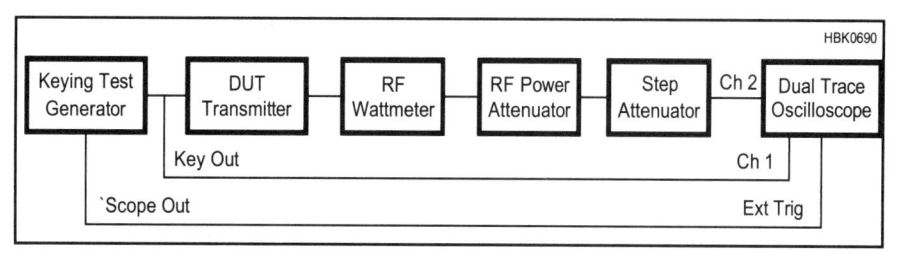

Figure 25.53 — CW keying waveform test setup.

must be adjusted to obtain equal-amplitude RF tones on the spectrum analyzer. The test should be done for both lower and upper-sideband modes.

Two-tone IMD products are measured with respect to the transmitter peak-envelope power (PEP) which is 6 dB greater than the amplitude of either of the two tones. By adjusting the spectrum analyzer reference level to place the two tones 6 dB below the zero-dB reference line, as shown in **Figure 25.52**, the IMD distortion may be read out directly. For the signal shown, the third-order products are at –30 dB from PEP.

Carrier and unwanted sideband suppression may be measured with the same setup. In this case the 700 Hz tone of the two-tone generator is turned off and only the 1900 Hz tone is used. The single tone is set to the 0-dB reference line of the spectrum analyzer. For USB, the suppressed carrier shows as a small pip 1900 Hz below the desired signal and the unwanted sideband is 3800 Hz below. For LSB the unwanted signal frequencies are above the desired signal.

TESTS IN THE TIME DOMAIN

Oscilloscopes are used for transmitter testing in the time domain. Dual-trace instruments are best in most cases, providing easy to read time-delay measurements between keying input and RF- or audio-output signals. Common transmitter measurements performed with 'scopes include CW keying waveform and SSB/FM transmit-to-receive turnaround tests (important for many digital modes).

A typical setup for measuring CW keying waveform and time delay is shown in **Figure 25.53**. A keying test generator is used to key the transmitter at a controlled rate. The generator can be set to any reasonable speed, but ARRL tests are usually conducted at 20 ms on and 20 ms off (25 Hz, 50% duty cycle), which corresponds to a series of dits at 60 WPM. **Figure 25.54** shows a typical display. The first two dits at the beginning of the transmission are displayed in order to show any transients or truncations that occur when the transceiver transitions from receive

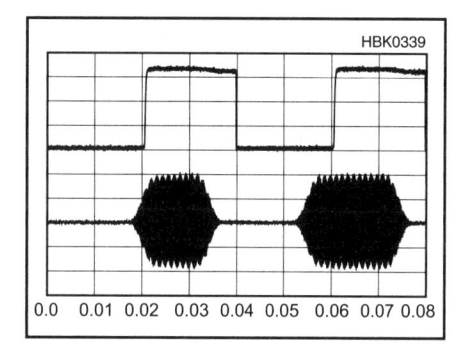

Figure 25.54 — Typical CW keying waveform for a modern Amateur Radio transceiver during testing in the ARRL Lab. This plot shows the first two dits in full break-in (QSK) mode using external keying. Equivalent keying speed is 60 WPM. The upper trace is the actual key closure; the lower trace is the RF envelope. (Note that the first key closure starts at the left edge of the figure.) Horizontal divisions are 10 ms. The transceiver was being operated at 100 W output on the 14 MHz band.

to the transmit state. The rise and fall times of the RF output pulse are measured between the 10% and 90% points on the leading and trailing edges, respectively. The delay times are measured between the 50% points of the keying and RF output waveforms. Look at the **Transmitting** and **Transceiver Design Topics** chapters for further discussion of CW keying issues.

For voice modes, a PTT-to-RF output test is similar to CW keying tests. It measures rise and fall times, as well as the on- and off-delay times just as in the CW test. See **Figure 25.55** for the test setup. For SSB the transmitter is modulated with a single 700-Hz tone. For FM the transmitter is unmodulated. The keying generator is set to a speed that allows plenty of time for the transceiver to recover between dits. The ON or OFF delay times are measured from the 50% point of the falling or rising edge of the key out line to the 50% point of the RF waveform.

The transmit-receive turnaround time is the time it takes for a transceiver to switch from the 50% rise time of the key line to 50% rise of audio output. Turnaround time is an important consideration in some digital modes with required turnaround times of less than 50 ms in some cases. The test setup is shown in **Figure 25.56**. This test requires

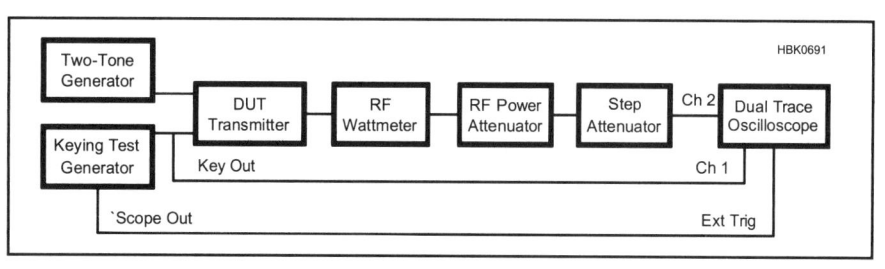

Figure 25.55 — PTT-to-RF-output test setup for voice-mode transmitters.

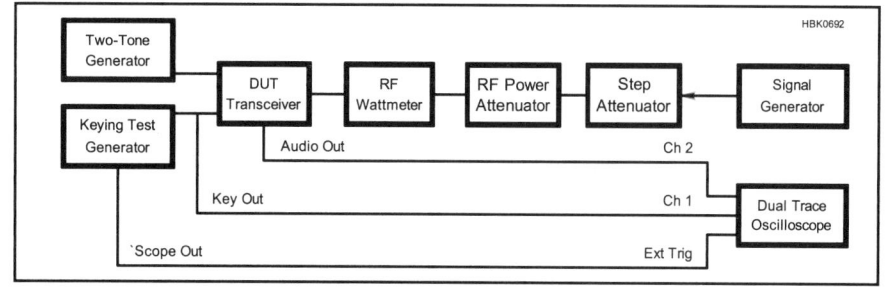

Figure 25.56 — Transmit-receive turnaround time test setup.

extreme care to prevent excessive transmitter power from reaching the signal generator and exceeding its specifications. The step attenuator is preset to maximum and gradually decreased until the receiver's S meter reads S9. Receiver AGC is usually on and set for the fastest response for this test but experimentation with AGC and signal input level can reveal surprising variations. As for the PTT-to-RF output test, the transmitter is tuned to full power output with a single 700 Hz tone. The keying rate must be considerably slower than the turnaround time; rates of 200 ms on/200 ms off or faster, have been used with success in Product Review tests at the ARRL Lab.

25.6.2 Other Common Transmitter Measurements

The peak envelope power (PEP) of a 100%-modulated AM signal is four times the average power. For that reason, the specified AM power level of most SSB transmitters is generally about 25% of the PEP SSB power rating.

The modulation percentage can most easily be measured with a wide-band oscilloscope connected to the 50-Ω dummy load. It is OK to exceed the specified bandwidth somewhat as long as a clean signal is displayed since this is a relative measurement only. With 100% modulation, the negative modulation peaks just reach zero signal level and the positive peaks are twice the amplitude of the unmodulated carrier. The exact value can be calculated with the equation,

$$M = 100 \frac{\max - \min}{\max + \min}$$

where M is the modulation percentage, max is the signal amplitude at the peaks and min is the amplitude at the troughs. An alternative is to use an RF spectrum analyzer. With 100% sine-wave modulation, the two sidebands are each –6 dB with respect to the carrier. In this case, $M = 100 \times 10^{(S+6)/20}$, where S is the sideband level with respect to the carrier (a negative number) and M is the modulation percentage.

The equivalent measurement for an FM transmitter is the *deviation*, which is the amount the RF frequency deviates from the center carrier frequency. It is possible to purchase an instrument that measures FM deviation directly; the function is generally included in two-way radio test sets. Another way is to use slope detection with a standard analog spectrum analyzer. Start by choosing a resolution bandwidth (RBW) on the spectrum analyzer such that as you tune away from the unmodulated carrier the signal level changes approximately linearly (the same number of kHz per dB) over at least a 10 kHz range. An RBW of 10 kHz is usually about right. Record the kHz per dB sensitivity value. Then adjust the frequency for the middle of the linear range and set the spectrum analyzer for zero span. With modulation applied to the transmitter, the deviation is equal to one-half the peak-to-peak dB variation of the signal on the screen, times the kHz per dB value determined previously.

Yet another way to measure FM deviation with a spectrum analyzer is to use the fact that the carrier disappears for a modulation index of 2.405, as explained in the **Modulation** chapter. To set the deviation to 3 kHz, for example, apply sine wave modulation at a frequency of 3.0/2.405 = 1.25 kHz and adjust the modulation level to null the carrier.

25.7 Antenna System Measurements

This section discusses measurements of antenna systems. The antenna system typically includes the antenna along with the transmission line and any other accessories such as switches, filters, matching networks, antenna tuners, and so forth. The instruments and measurements in this section assist with construction and installation, performance assessment, and troubleshooting of the entire antenna system. Related information is available in the **Transmission Lines**, **Antennas**, and **Station Construction** chapters.

25.7.1 Field Strength Measurements

To determine how well an antenna is actually radiating, a way to detect the signal level at some distance from the antenna is needed. For measurements in the vicinity of the antenna, a *field-strength meter*, generally with a built-in antenna, picks up the radiated signal off the air and indicates the level on a meter or display. Professional field-strength meters use a carefully-calibrated antenna and circuitry that can read out the actual radiated signal strength in volts per meter or watts per square meter. Most amateur field-strength meters such as the one shown in **Figure 25.57** are not calibrated but give a relative indication only. They are useful for tuning an antenna, antenna tuner, or transmitter for maximum signal as well as for comparing different antennas. A field strength meter is a simple one-evening construction project. **Figure 25.58** shows the schematic of a simple field strength meter. [21] (This article is also included in the book's downloadable supplemental material.)

If you have a *reference antenna* (such as a half-wave dipole) that has a known gain, then the gain of a second antenna can be calculated by alternately transmitting with each antenna and measuring the difference in signal level at a receiver whose antenna is located far enough away to be outside the *near field*, typically up to several wavelengths from the antenna under test. At first glance, it seems like this should be an easy measurement to make but in practice there are a number of devilish details that can ruin the measurement accuracy.

The biggest issue is reflections. If there is any significant reflector of RF signals between the transmitting and receiving an-

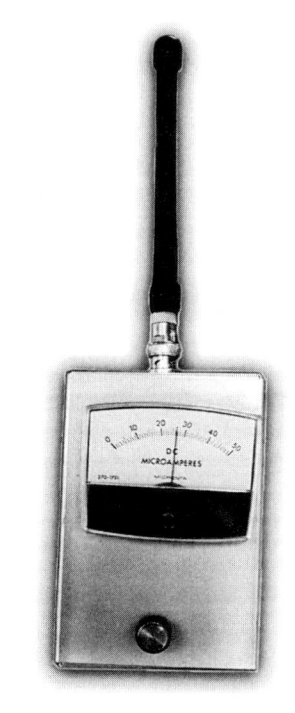

Figure 25.57 — The VE7NI field-strength meter.

tennas, the signal comparison may not be accurate if the test and reference antenna patterns are significantly different. Even if there are no wires, bodies of water, fences or other conducting objects in the vicinity, the ground reflection can result in an apparent additional gain of 6 dB or conversely a loss of many dB if the receive antenna happens to be in a null. At microwave frequencies it is sometimes possible to use a high-gain, narrow-beamwidth receive antenna and mount the antenna under test high enough so that the ground reflection is outside the receive antenna's beamwidth.[22] At HF frequencies that is rarely possible.

Commercial antenna companies use elaborate *antenna test ranges* that employ various techniques to assure measurement accuracy. Absent a proper test range, the best solution is probably to measure the reference antenna and antenna under test at various heights above ground to get an idea of how much ground reflections are affecting the measurement. [The subject of antenna measurements is addressed by Paul Wade, W1GHZ in his "Microwavelengths" *QST* columns for October 2012 (covering the antenna range) and January 2013 (discussing measurements and equipment).]

The most common way to compare antennas is to ask for signal reports on the air. Unfortunately, propagation is so variable on most amateur bands (fading of more than 20 dB in a few seconds is common) that a signal report gives only a very rough idea of how well your antenna is working, unless it can be compared with another antenna (perhaps at another local amateur's station) at the same time.

An improved method of assessing antenna performance from distant stations is to use one of the automated receiving systems; the *Reverse Beacon Network* or RBN (**reversebeacon.net** for CW signals), *PSKReporter* (**pskreporter.info** for PSK signals) and *WSPRNet* (**wsprnet.org** for WSPR signals). These systems consist of a worldwide network of independent receivers that decode signals and report the call sign and signal strength to a central server. To use the systems for antenna system testing, the server can be queried for comparative signal strengths after switching between antennas or making adjustments.

25.7.2 SWR Meters

The modern SWR meter is a descendent of the 1959 "Monimatch," introduced to amateurs by Lew McCoy, W1ICP, and explained by Walter Bruene, W5OLY.[26,27] Additional information about standing wave ratio is provided in the in the **Transmission Lines** chapter. Directional RF wattmeters are covered in this chapter's section on Measuring RF Power.

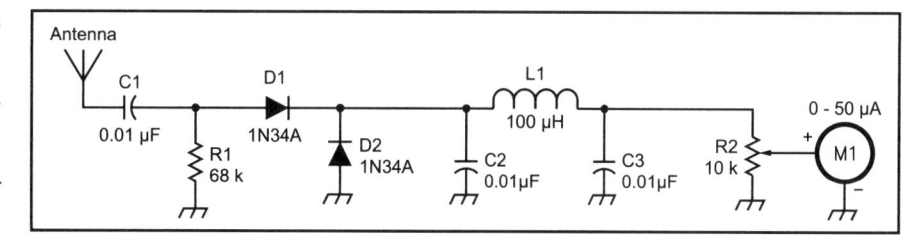

Figure 25.58 — Schematic diagram of the VE7NI field-strength meter.

C1-C3 — 0.01 μF capacitors.
D1, D2 — 1N34A diodes.
L1 — 100 μH inductor.
M1 — Analog meter, 50 μA.
R2 — Sensitivity control potentiometer, 10 kΩ.

Antenna—BNC female chassis mount socket. Antenna selection should match the frequency band for VHF and UHF. A random length of wire might work best for close field measurements on HF to 40 meters. Metal box enclosure is mandatory.

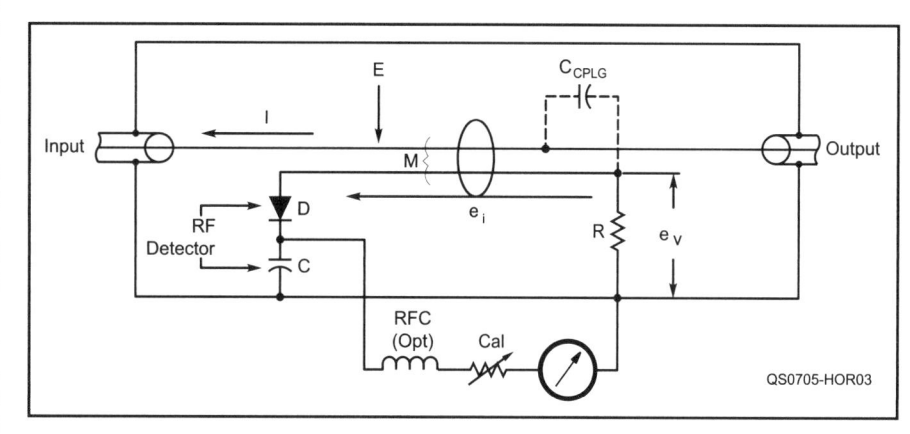

Figure 25.59 — One-half of a Monimatch directional coupler circuit that senses the reflected voltage and current components. The samples of induced voltage e_i and line voltage e_v sum in the RF detector formed by D and C, producing a voltage that drives the meter. The Cal control is adjusted so that a full-scale reading is obtained. The meter is then switched to display the output of an identical circuit oriented in the opposite direction to picks up the forward components. The meter is then calibrated according to the SWR equation in the text.

Figure 25.59 shows the schematic of a typical unit. SWR can be computed from forward and reflected power, as shown by the following equation:

$$SWR = \frac{1+\sqrt{P_R/P_F}}{1-\sqrt{P_R/P_F}}$$

If voltages representing the two powers are provided, it's straightforward to create a circuit that computes SWR. This is the reason for the CAL (calibration) control on the meter. The meter is set to FWD (indicating the voltage representing forward power), power is applied, and the CAL control adjusted so that the forward power indication is the full-scale value of 1. By assuming $P_F = 1$ and P_R is a value between 0 and 1, the equation for SWR simplifies to:

$$SWR = \frac{1+\sqrt{P_R}}{1-\sqrt{P_R}}$$

The voltage representing reflected power will always be some fraction of the full-scale voltage, so the meter scale can then be calibrated to read SWR directly, instead of voltage. (An alternative SWR meter design is provided in the **Station Accessories** chapter.)

THE DIRECTIONAL COUPLER

Inductive and capacitive coupling are used to create a *directional coupler* that can provide the independent measurement voltages. The coupling provides samples of forward and reflected voltage and current from the undisturbed center conductor of the coaxial feed line. Figure 25.59 shows how voltages representing reflected power are obtained. As described by W5OLY, "A pickup wire placed parallel to the inner conductor samples the line current by inductive coupling. The voltage e_i induced in the pickup is determined by spacing, length, line current, and frequency. The mechanical dimensions determine the mutual inductance, M. The induced voltage due to line current is:

$$e_i = -j\omega IM = -j2\pi fM$$

where f is frequency in Hz and j represents a phase shift of 90°. This shows that the higher the frequency, the larger the induced voltage.

"The sample of voltage is picked up by capacitive coupling (C_{CPLG}) from the inner conductor to the pickup wire. A current due to this capacitance flows through R and develops a voltage across it; this voltage also increases with frequency because the reactance of the coupling capacitance goes *down* with frequency. That is:

$$e_v = E R / X_C R = ER / -j(1/2\pi fC) = j2\pi fERC$$

when X_C is much larger than R." D and C form an RF detector that sums e_i and e_v, creating a single voltage proportional to the power in the line.

Since the line current and voltage contain components of both forward and reflected power, the single resulting output voltage also contains components of both. The current and voltage components of reflected power are 180° out-of-phase, compared to those of forward power. So e_i is added to e_v, producing a voltage proportional only to reflected power in the figure.

The different polarities of e_i are obtained by reversing the current sensing pickup. This is accomplished by two identical pickup circuits in the meter; e_v is the same in both circuits, but the e_i pickup direction is reversed from one to the other. One circuit produces a voltage proportional only to forward power and the other proportional only to reflected power. Display or forward or reflected power is controlled by the switch that selects which voltage is applied to the meter.

Continuing with a note from W5OLY, "Since the current and voltage pickups both increase with frequency, their ratio will stay the same. The variation in pickup just means that the sensitivity goes down at lower frequencies." That's why the CAL adjustment is necessary not only at different power levels, but at different frequencies. The meter scale is calibrated according to the equation for SWR when the calibration adjustment places the voltage representing P_F at full-scale.

For best performance from a Monimatch type of directional coupler, the value of R in one of the detector circuits should be adjusted so that the two circuits produce the same value of e_i for any given current. In addition, balanced detector diodes would also provide better performance at low power levels where the detected voltage level is small enough for variations in the diode forward voltage to introduce significant errors. However, for low-cost equipment, using fixed components is generally "good enough."

For meters that have been damaged, repair is very simple. The manufacturer calibrated the meter assuming very similar component values. Replace both detector diodes with the same type of diode, preferably from the same batch of components. The diodes can be matched by using a multimeter with a diode test function that displays the diode's forward voltage. If one of the original diodes is undamaged, choose a pair of diodes with a similar forward drop.

25.7.3 Noise Bridges

The noise bridge includes an adjustable bridge circuit similar to that in Figure 25.35. A wide-band noise generator is connected as the source and a conventional receiver is attached to the Power Meter port as a detector. Tune the receiver to the desired frequency and adjust the resistance and reactance controls for minimum noise in the receiver. If the receiver has a panadapter display, the null frequency can be seen on the screen, speeding the adjustment. Noise bridges are rarely used today in favor of the more convenient antenna analyzers as described in the following section. See the References entry for "The Noise Bridge" by Althouse for a more complete description of how a noise bridge works and how it is used.

25.7.4 Antenna Analyzers

Traditionally, amateurs have measured coax-fed antennas using a standing wave ratio (SWR) meter as described above. While often used to determine an antenna's resonant frequency, the meter can only measure SWR at the point in the feed line where the meter is placed, relative to the SWR meter's calibrated impedance. The actual SWR on the feed line is determined solely by how well-matched the load or the antenna's feed point impedance is to the characteristic impedance of the feed line.

Most SWR meters are calibrated for 50 Ω. Because most transmitters are designed to drive a 50 Ω load, the measured SWR indicates how closely the feed line impedance matches that of the transmitter output. When the antenna feed point impedance at resonance is not 50 Ω (for example, a dipole might present 70-85 Ω at the feed point), the frequency of minimum indicated SWR will differ by 1-2% from the actual antenna resonant frequency. i.e. Where the feed point resistance is purely resistive.

More information about the impedance can be very helpful in determining antenna resonant frequency and feed point impedance. An RF impedance analyzer capable of measuring both the magnitude and the phase of impedance is often called an *antenna analyzer*, since the most common use by amateurs is for measuring antennas. Such an instrument can obtain more detailed information about the complex impedance versus frequency anywhere in the antenna system.

To keep size and cost to a minimum, portable antenna analyzers usually use a narrow-band source (an internal oscillator) and wide-band detector (a diode). Some units include a microprocessor and can display SWR, return loss, resistance, reactance, and the magnitude and phase of the impedance. Antenna analyzers suitable for amateur use are available from a number of manufacturers — search for "antenna analyzers" on the Internet to find them.

When shopping for an antenna analyzer, pay careful attention to the capabilities and limitations. Several basic designs are available with tradeoffs between performance and cost. Be aware that some units measure only the SWR or impedance magnitude while others measure both the resistive and reactive parts of the impedance. Some units give the magnitude of the reactance but not the sign, requiring the operator to change frequency

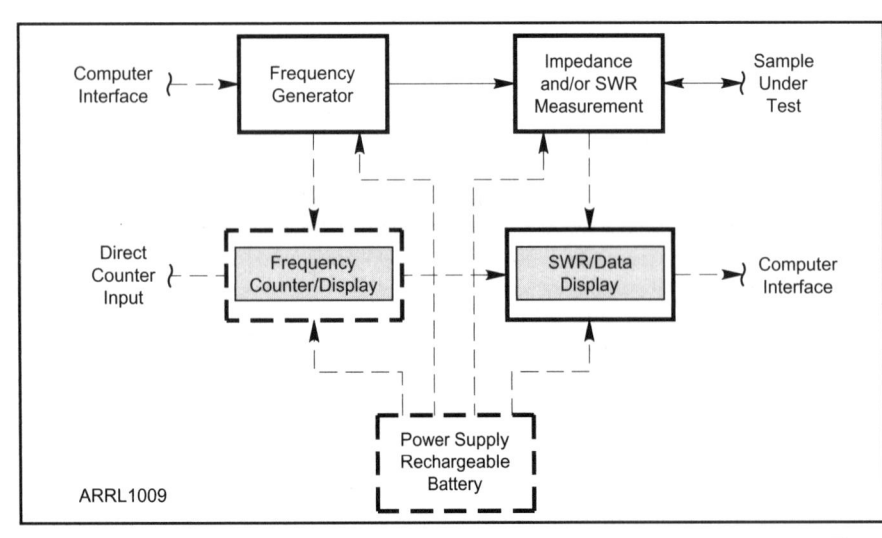

Figure 25.60 — Block diagram showing the elements of typical antenna analyzers. The items shown with dashed lines may not be part of every model.

a small amount and watch the change in impedance magnitude to determine the sign and thus the type of the impedance, inductive or capacitive.

These analyzers have many more uses than impedance and SWR measurements. Paul Wade, W1GHZ, has contributed the paper "Antenna Analyzer Pet Tricks" in this book's downloadable supplemental information. It includes how-to guides for a number of useful antenna system measurements.

Some users have reported difficulties in obtaining accurate impedance measurements on low-band antennas when there is a nearby AM broadcast station. This is due to the wideband detector responding to the incoming signal from the AM station. Some manufacturers offer external high-pass broadcast-reject filters to allow the analyzers to be used in the presence of these strong signals. The filter can affect measurements near the broadcast band, particularly in the 3.5 MHz and lower-frequency bands. Check with the filter manufacturer about the limitations of using filters with the analyzer.

BASIC OPERATION

Figure 25.60 shows the block diagram of a typical antenna analyzer. The functions in solid lines are required and those in dashed lines are included depending on feature set and price.

Figure 25.61 shows a relatively simple circuit that uses diodes for detecting voltages corresponding to voltage and current at the external load. This inexpensive circuit is useful but at low signal levels the diodes introduce some non-linearity and temperature drift which may be an issue. This type of diode detector responds to signals over a wide frequency range and there may be stray pickup from nearby broadcasting stations that makes the measurement results inaccurate.

The rectified voltages can be digitized by a microprocessor and the results displayed numerically. The signal source is typically a varactor-tuned LC oscillator in the "analog" units or a direct digital synthesizer (DDS) in more sophisticated models. The DDS signal source is very stable since it is controlled by a crystal oscillator and it can be set to the desired frequency quickly with a keyboard entry. The DDS version costs somewhat more but compared to the varactor-tuned oscillator, it has significant performance and operating conveniences. (See the **Oscillators and Synthesizers** chapter for information on DDS signal sources.)

For a more detailed analysis of the antenna system, an instrument with a narrowband detector such as for a radio receiver gives much better performance than the broadband diode detector. **Figure 25.62** shows how two DDSs can be used with one applied to the antenna system and the other used as a reference. Typically, the clock oscillator is crystal-controlled for high accuracy. One DDS is programmed to output a signal at the actual test frequency and the other DDS is programmed to a slightly higher frequency in the 1 to 10 kHz range, shown in the figure as 2 kHz. See the reference entry for an article by Michael Knitter, DG5MK, that gives a detailed design description of this type of analyzer.

The signals are then mixed to produce a low frequency output that can easily digitized by an inexpensive analog to digital converter (ADC). The measurements are then processed mathematically in a microprocessor or PC to yield full information about the complex impedance being measured. This type of analyzer is actually a one-port, swept-frequency impedance meter that measures both the magnitude and phase of a test impedance over a wide range of frequencies. A two-port vector network analyzer (VNA)

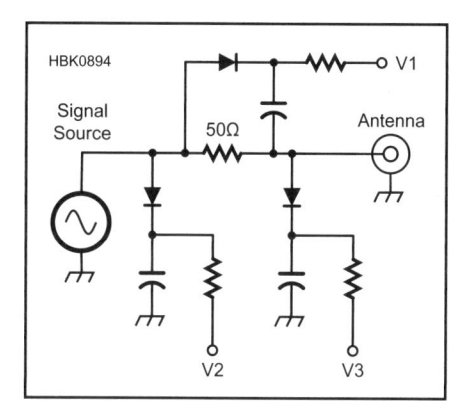

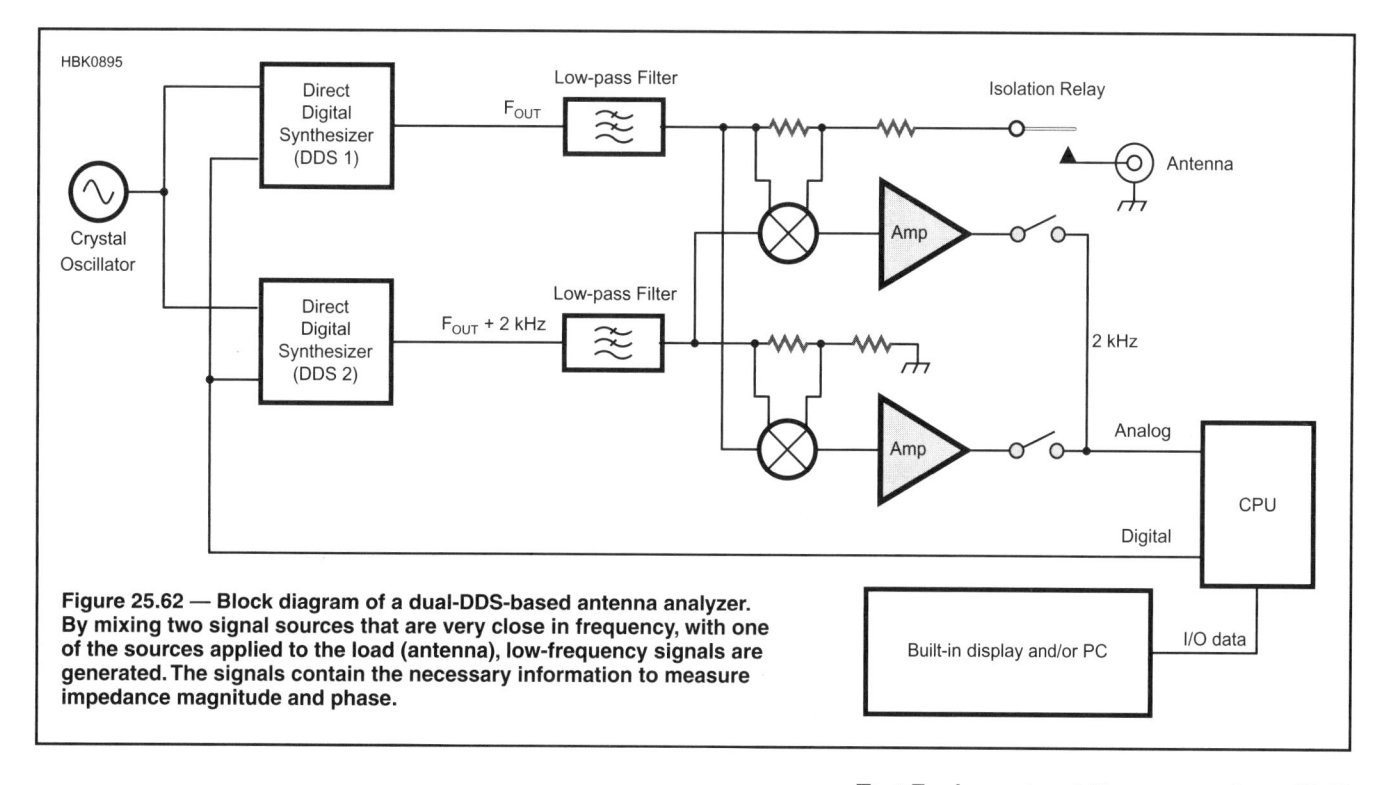

Figure 25.61 — A relatively diode detector circuit for measuring impedance that gives adequate results for many applications.

Figure 25.62 — Block diagram of a dual-DDS-based antenna analyzer. By mixing two signal sources that are very close in frequency, with one of the sources applied to the load (antenna), low-frequency signals are generated. The signals contain the necessary information to measure impedance magnitude and phase.

can also be configured to do one-port swept frequency measurements.

One signal corresponds to the voltage applied to the antenna system and the other signal corresponds to the current flowing in the antenna system. The ratio of these signals is the impedance of the circuit and the difference of their phases is the phase angle of the circuit:

Magnitude(Z) = Magnitude(V1)/ Magnitude(V2)

Phase(Z) = Phase(V1) – Phase(V2)

The PC shown in the figure can be a desktop computer or a small tablet computer. The tablet provides good portability, but if the size of the screen is too small it may be hard to read. The analyzer is able to generate a lot of data and it's helpful to be able to see as much as possible at one time on one screen, especially when making tuning adjustments. Another tradeoff is the size of the menu buttons on a tablet. If they are too small it may be hard to make menu selections.

Some analyzers can store sets of measurements in a file for review later and transfer to a PC for further processing and display. The standard format for swept impedance data (frequency and impedance) is called *Touchstone* (**en.wikipedia.org/wiki/Touchstone_file**). Files in the Touchstone format can be read and processed by a wide variety of software, including as the input to design software.

The most useful analyzers can create a calibration table to automatically correct for imperfections in the analyzer. The calibration process takes data at selected frequencies over the measurement range. This is usually done by sequentially attaching three known loads to the input of the analyzer and running a special calibration routine that saves the data for each load in memory. (See this chapter's section on vector network analyzers.) This process is very quick and easy and the final results of any measurement are much more accurate than from a simple analyzer that does not have a calibration procedure. The calibration is performed with three known loads: a short circuit, an open circuit, and a resistor of known value. The mathematics to apply this correction data is very complex but the microprocessor does it easily and the user does not have to worry about the details.

The impedance data can be used to calculate several parameters for the antenna system. Using the specified value for the system reference impedance, which can be any value (it doesn't have to be 50 Ω), For example, the reflection coefficient (ρ or rho) can be calculated as:

$$\rho = (Z_L - Z_0) / (Z_L + Z_0)$$

where Z_L is the measured impedance of the load and Z_0 is the specified impedance of the transmission line, which can be any value. Z_L is a complex number; therefore, ρ is, in general, a complex number with a magnitude between zero and one. Rho is approximately equal to zero when the line is matched to the antenna because there is no reflection, all the transmitter power is absorbed by the antenna. When the antenna is poorly matched to the line, ρ is larger and it approaches 1 when the mismatch is large.

$$SWR = (1 + |\rho|) / (1 - |\rho|)$$

Note that SWR only depends on the *magnitude* of ρ denoted by the vertical bars as |ρ| so it is not a complex number.

CALIBRATION

Different test situations may require adapters, interconnecting cables, common-mode chokes, isolation transformers, or filters. The calibration process is able to compensate for the externally connected accessories, so their exact properties are not critical. By placing the calibration loads *after* the external hardware, characteristics of the whole measurement system can be accounted for in the calibration table. The point at which the calibration loads are attached is called the analyzer's *reference plane.* (See the Agilent application note on vector network analyzers — reference 15.) For example, a filter with a response that is less than perfect can be used as long as it is included in the measurement system during calibration. The effects of the filter on measurements can then be cancelled mathematically.

Most antenna analyzers have a single-ended (unbalanced) output with a coax connector. For making measurements on a two-wire transmission line, such as window line or ladder line, a common-mode choke can be added between the analyzer's RF connector and the input to the transmission line as in **Figure 25.63.** The calibration loads are attached to the output side of this balun so that its imperfections are automatically canceled during the measurement. The measurement results displayed by the analyzer program then correspond to the input to the transmission line itself.

This calibration procedure can be extended to allow measuring the actual driving point impedance of the antenna. The transmission line is disconnected at the antenna, and the calibration loads are attached at the far end instead of the antenna. This shifts the measurement point (the reference plane) to the antenna itself which is handy when designing matching networks. The final result is much more accurate than using a transmission line that is one-half of a wavelength long because the calibration of the analyzer compensates for the transmission line parameters: length, velocity factor and loss.

A word of caution when using an antenna analyzer is in order. These are sensitive instruments with low-power components at their input. They can be damaged by static electricity if care is not exercised. Antennas can collect a significant static charge from rain or wind. Be sure to momentarily ground the transmission line before connecting it to an analyzer to reduce the risk of damage to the sensitive components on the input.

Static buildup can be minimized by providing a dc path between center conductor and the grounded shield for the antenna being measured, offering some protection both for the analyzer and for station equipment. The dc path can be a shunt indicator in the tuning circuit or it can be a large value resistor with a power rating suitable for the transmitter power. (Antennas with elements mounted directly on a grounded

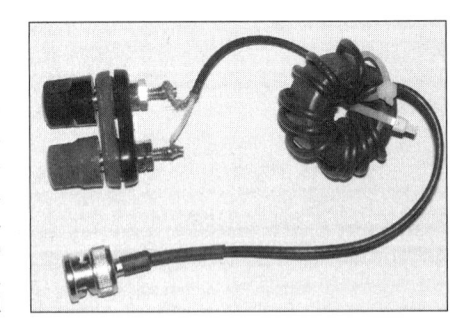

Figure 25.63 — A simple choke balun made by winding multiple turns of coax through a ferrite toroid, creating a high-impedance on the shield's outer surface. The choke is made of 12 turns of RG-193 miniature coax through a 2.4-inch OD, Type 31 core (Fair-Rite 2631803802 or Amidon FT-240-31) and is effective from 1.8 through 30 MHz. The best choke should present at least 5,000 Ω of resistive impedance at the measurement frequency.

Determining Reactance Type

Some antenna analyzers can show the positive or negative sign of the reactance. Less expensive units may only show a reactance magnitude. To determine whether reactance is inductive or capacitive on a unit that doesn't indicate the sign, make a slight increase in frequency. If the reactance increases, it is inductive, and if reactance decreases, it is capacitive. This is a helpful trick when adjusting antennas with a portable analyzer that doesn't indicate reactance sign.

boom or support are also dc-grounded.)

Using the analyzer when another transmitter is active can also cause damage if enough signal is picked up by the antenna under test. The analyzer illustrated in Figure 25.62 includes an isolation relay that protects the input when a measurement is not in progress.

MEASURING COMPONENT VALUES

The antenna analyzer can be used to measure components other than antennas. For example, an inductor can be measured over a wide frequency range to see if it is resonant within the frequency range where it will be used.

Figure 25.64 shows a graph generated from swept-frequency impedance data collected by an antenna analyzer of the type in Figure 25.62. The figure shows the impedance of an air-core inductor with a nominal inductance of 7.4 µH at low frequencies. (The traces are labeled with the measurement they represent.) The self-resonant frequency is 45.4 MHz. This resonance occurs because of the coil's inter-turn capacitance. (See the **RF Techniques** chapter for a discussion of stray and parasitic capacitance.)

Far below the resonant frequency the inductance has a positive reactance and the coil presents its expected value, 7.4 µH. As the test frequency approaches the self-resonant frequency, the parasitic (stray) capacitance that causes self resonance causes the total reactance to increase, so the inductance appears to be larger. At resonance, the impedance is a resistance of high value. Above the self-resonant frequency, the component increasingly looks like a capacitor, as indicated by the negative phase angle.

The analyzer is also very handy for determining the material of a toroid core. Cores of different ferrite or powdered iron mixes cannot be told apart by their physical appearance, but you can sometimes separate them by comparison with a core of known material. Small inductances of one or two turns can be tested side by side to differentiate the cores of different mixes. A single turn through the center of a core or bead will create enough inductance for an accurate measurement on a good analyzer. Be wary of confusing mixes that are designed for EMI suppression with mixes intended for inductive applications. The permeability of the different mixes has resistive and reactive components that dominate over different frequency ranges. See the discussion of ferrites in the **RF Techniques** chapter for an explanation. Comparison to cores of known material is much more reliable than a simple calculation of µ (mu — permeability) or A_L, the inductance index.

Capacitors are usually closer to the ideal component than inductors, but they do have some inductance in their leads and eventually at some high frequency they too become self-resonant. This self-resonance should be checked for capacitors that will be used in the VHF/UHF range, and ESR can be critical in power handling circuits. Above the self-resonant frequency, a capacitor looks like an inductor. Depending on their construction, capacitors also have some loss. While the loss may be due to leakage in the dielectric, it is mostly commonly described as an "equivalent series resistance" (ESR), which appears in series with its capacitive reactance. The ESR in most capacitors increases with frequency. (See the **Circuits and Components** chapter.)

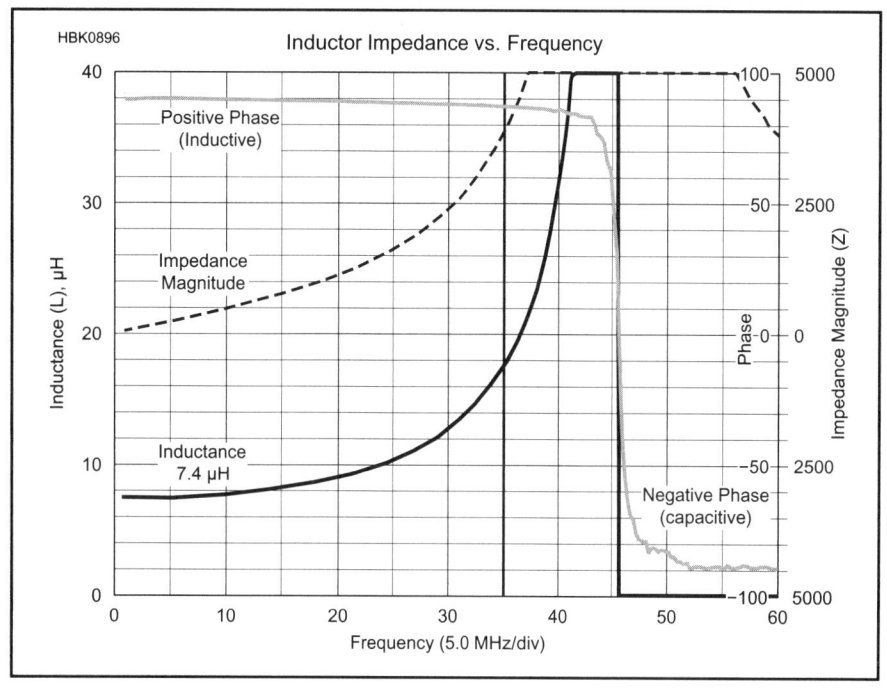

Figure 25.64 — Example of an antenna analyzer (AIM-4170 and companion software) being used to measure an air-core inductor's behavior. The inductor has a nominal value of 7.4 µH and a self-resonant frequency of 45.4 MHz.

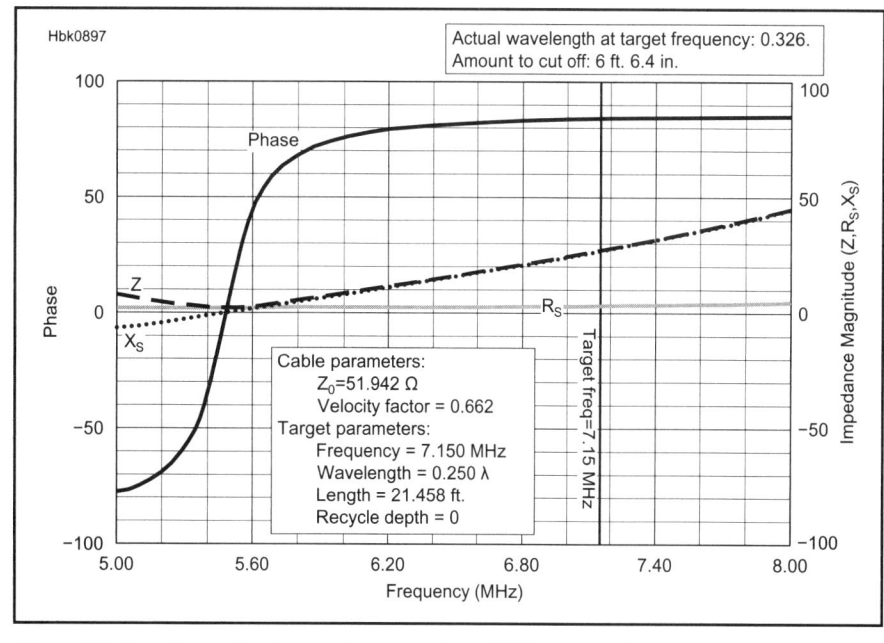

Figure 25.65 — Example of an antenna analyzer (AIM-4170 and companion software) being used to trim a transmission line stub. The cable is being trimmed to get a phase shift of 90° (0.25 wavelengths) at 7.15 MHz. From the current length (where the three curves intersect at the left), cut off 6 feet 6.4 inches (199.1 cm). As the cable is trimmed, the phase plot will move toward the target line at the right.

Test Equipment and Measurements 25.43

Resistors have an effective capacitance in parallel with them as well as inductance in their leads so they are not ideal over a wide frequency range. Physically large power resistors used for dummy loads have larger parasitic components. (Thin-film power resistors in TO-220 packages are available with significantly lower reactance.) Tubular metal and carbon film resistors are often trimmed with a laser to create a spiral track in the deposited film, creating inductance. If the resistor is to be used in an RF circuit, it is prudent to verify its effective frequency range.

TRANSMISSION LINE MEASUREMENTS

Sections of transmission line can be used to make tuning stubs for antennas as discussed in the **Transmission Lines** chapter. These stubs can be measured with the antenna analyzer as shown in **Figure 25.65** and cut to the proper length for the required phase shift. Some analyzer software can measure phase shift and indicate how much needs to be trimmed to achieve the desired amount. Be cautious when using this information to make large changes in line length. Because VF varies with frequency (see the section Effect of Velocity Factor), stubs should be measured as close as practical to the frequency at which they are intended to operate. (The highest accuracy is achieved by computing the frequency nearest the operating frequency at which the stub should look like a short circuit, then trimming it to present the short circuit at that frequency.)

As discussed in the next section on time domain reflectometry (TDR), some analyzers have a software feature called *Distance to Fault*. This measures the length of a transmission line to any point(s) along the line where the impedance differs from its characteristic impedance (Z_0). The "different impedance" can be an open or short circuit, the point at which an antenna is connected, or it can be some small change in the impedance such as that which occurs at a connector, or is the result of damage to the cable. With the best TDR systems, the line can be accurately measured with or without an antenna connected.

If the line is disconnected from the antenna, the distance to fault is the total length of the line. If the line has been damaged somewhere this measurement gives you an idea where the damage is, which is very handy when the line is buried or otherwise requires special access. TDR can also locate impedance discontinuities or other changes in the line's characteristic impedance.

To measure transmission line loss with an antenna analyzer, a calibrated mismatch is often used. This method is described in the **Transmission Lines** chapter section on Transmission Line Loss.

25.7.5 Time-Domain Reflectometry

Time domain reflectometry (TDR) shows what happens to a short, abrupt pulse as it travels through a transmission line. The pulse is reflected by any changes in impedance, such as an open or short (complete reflection) or a change in the line's characteristic impedance (partial reflection). The resulting series of pulses and reflections is displayed as a sequence in time, thus the name of the technique.

In an ideal transmission line terminated by its characteristic impedance, Z_0, the pulse will travel to the far end and be dissipated in the termination, so the trace will be a perfectly flat line. But at any point along the line where the impedance changes (called a *discontinuity*) some of the pulse's energy will be reflected back toward the line's input. The reflected component of the pulse creates an artifact (visually, a "bump") on the otherwise straight line.

The sequence of pulses and their reflections is the *impulse response* of the line. An *impulse* is basically a very short pulse that begins and ends before the system can respond and stabilize. A mathematical impulse is an infinitely-narrow made up of all frequencies from zero to infinity.

While it is not possible to create an ideal (perfect) impulse, a very fast rising edge of a longer pulse is a good enough approximation to measure the line's impulse response and the same information can be measured. The longer pulse is called a *step function*. The ideal step function is an infinitely fast change from one level to another, after which it remains at that level. The response of the line to the longer pulse is called the *step response*. Like the impulse, the infinitely fast change in level also contains all frequencies.

A *time domain reflectometer* is the instrument that generates the pulse and displays the results. A TDR displays amplitude (voltage) on the vertical axis and time on the horizontal axis. The position of each artifact along the TDR trace corresponds to the distance from the transmission line input to the discontinuity that produced it. Large discontinuities occur when a line is open-circuited or short-circuited, or when it is connected to an antenna. (Most antennas are matched to the line at their operating frequency, but at other frequencies they are not. Since the pulse contains all frequencies, an antenna is a large discontinuity.) Small discontinuities occur at splices or when a line is damaged.

The delay between the input pulse's rising edge and the artifact is the round-trip time in the line from the TDR to the discontinuity. If the line's velocity of propagation (VF) is known, the physical distance from the input to the discontinuity can be calculated. The shape of each reflection can sometimes provide a clue as to the nature of the discontinuity.

In this sense, the TDR is very much like a radar display in which a pulse is transmitted (shown at the center on a radar display) and any echoes from discontinuities in the air (i.e. targets) reflect some of the pulse back toward the transmitter. The farther away the target, the longer it takes for the pulse to travel to the target and back to the receiver. A radar screen shows echoes from all directions. The TDR only shows echoes from one direction, along the line. The larger the echo, the larger the target or discontinuity.

The usefulness of TDR is not limited to RF systems. Some of the first uses of TDR

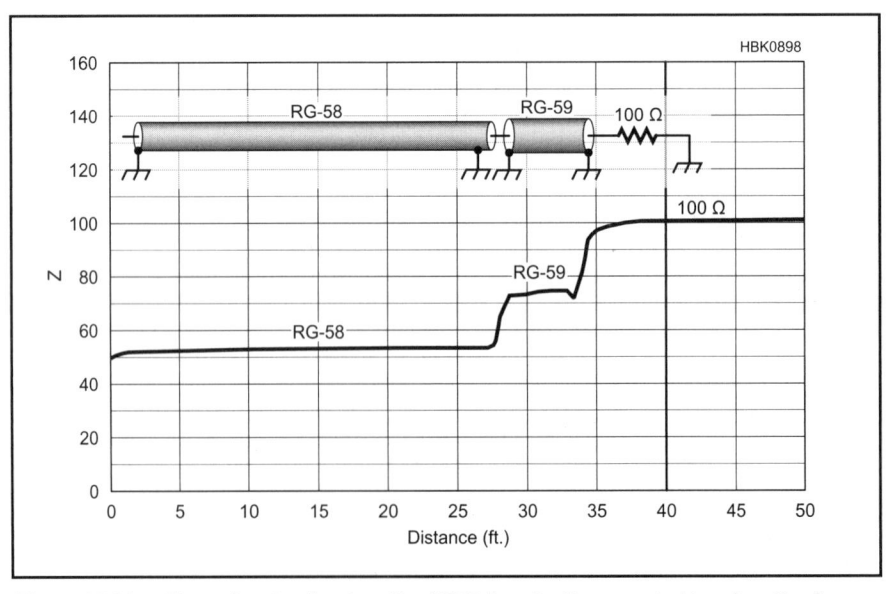

Figure 25.66 — Example of a direct method TDR (see text) connected to a length of RG-58 coaxial cable (50 Ω impedance) followed by a short length of 75 Ω RG-59 and a 100 Ω load. The discontinuities are clearly shown as the reflections add to the input pulse.

were for finding faults in cabling systems carrying all sorts of signals, including ordinary telephone lines, and it is still widely used for that purpose.

DIRECT METHOD TDR

There are two common TDR implementations, with variations of both. In the "direct method," which is the oldest and simplest, the line is driven by a pulse. This can be a single pulse, or it may be a train of pulses like a square wave.

The pulse and all of the reflections are displayed on an oscilloscope trace that is triggered by the pulse's rising edge. The rise time of the pulse must be much shorter than the round-trip time for the impulse to travel to and from the discontinuity. **Figure 25.66** shows an example of a direct method TDR with the pulse generator and cable attached to the oscilloscope which is displaying the pulse.

Although a digital scope can capture a single pulse and its reflections, making the pulse repetitive means that multiple responses can be averaged to improve the signal-to-noise ratio. The signal-to-noise ratio of a system excited by a single pulse can be rather limited. Repeated pulses also sustain the trace so the operator to see it if the scope is an analog model. The repetition rate of the pulse must be much slower than it takes for the impulse to make a complete round trip time through the line, however. This insures the line's response dies out completely before the next pulse excites the line again. See the reference article by King about this type of TDR and the *ARRL Antenna Book* also includes material on TDR.

Modern antenna analyzers can use the direct method, as well. For example, the AIM family of analyzers, designed by W5BIG and sold by Array Solutions (**www.arraysolutions.com**), excite the line with a step function waveform having a very fast rise time. This implementation provides a display of the impedance at every point on the line — it can, for example, show the relative impedance of cables having different Z_0, as well as the position of discontinuities. **Figure 25.66** shows a TDR display from an AIM analyzer connected to a length of RG-58 (50 Ω cable), a short length of RG-59 (75 Ω), and a 100 Ω load. The discontinuities at the cable and load transitions are clearly shown. Software converts the raw data from the pulse amplitudes into impedance and the time is converted into distance along the line.

The TDR function can be used to determine if the line has been degraded, for example, by water leaking into the coax or if the line has been shorted or cut somewhere between the transmitter and the antenna. Damage or defects can be located within a few inches and this reduces the effort required to repair the line. Defective connectors can also be indicated by short glitches in the trace corresponding to the location of the connectors.

TRANSFORM METHOD TDR

The other common implementation could be described as the "transform method." Instead of determining the impulse response of the cable with a pulse, the excitation is a sine wave swept over a range of frequencies and the analyzer captures the *frequency response*. An inverse Fourier Transform (see the chapter on **Digital Signal Processing**) is performed on that frequency response, producing the time-domain response. (Frequency and time are the inverse of each other; the complete frequency response of a system contains its time response and the response to an ideal impulse contains the frequency response. A Fourier Transform (FFT) of the time response provides the frequency response, an Inverse FFT of the frequency response provides the time response.)

Some antenna analyzers and vector network analyzers use this method. (Several well-suited for amateur use can be found by an Internet search for "vector antenna analyzer" or "vector network analyzer.") One example is the handheld SARK-110 vector impedance antenna analyzer (**www.steppir.com**) The sine wave exciting the cable need not be a continuous sweep — rather, it can be stepped over a wide range of frequencies and the frequency response is computed from that data. Sweep range, spacing between data points, and the settling time at each data point are set by the user.

An inverse Fourier Transform produces spurious artifacts which must be removed by applying a mathematical windowing function to the transformed data. Several mathematically different windowing functions are commonly used, and which of the windows provides the most useful display depends on the shape of the impulse response.

The frequency content of the excitation strongly influences the degree of detail that the measurement can reveal. When the excitation is an impulse, a very fast rise time reveals greater detail. When the excitation is a swept sine wave, a wider frequency range reveals the greatest detail. Currently available analyzers can sweep from 1 kHz to more than 1 GHz.

For TDR studies using the sweep method, a sweep from 5 to 500 MHz (or from 500 MHz to 1 GHz) will clearly show detail that would be missed with a sweep to only 100 MHz, while a 5 MHz to 1GHz sweep may provide too much detail (or show discontinuities that don't matter below 50 MHz). Beginning the sweep in the HF range avoids smearing of the data due to the variation of VF with frequency (see section Effect of Velocity Factor).

EXAMPLES OF USING THE TRANSFORM METHOD

Figure 25.67 is the impulse response of the feed line for a 30 meter half-wave dipole at a height of 100 feet, computed from a sweep over the range of 50 to 500 MHz. Marker 1 shows the effect of lightning protectors at the station entry bulkhead. Marker 2 is a coax splice (two PL-259s and a PL-258 double-receptacle). Markers 3, 4, and 5 are coax defects. Marker 6 is the antenna feed point. Marker 7 is the end of the antenna (displayed distances are for the feed line, so for the antenna are divided by 0.795) the peak at Marker 8 is unexplained, but most TDR sweeps show multiple reflections after the antenna.

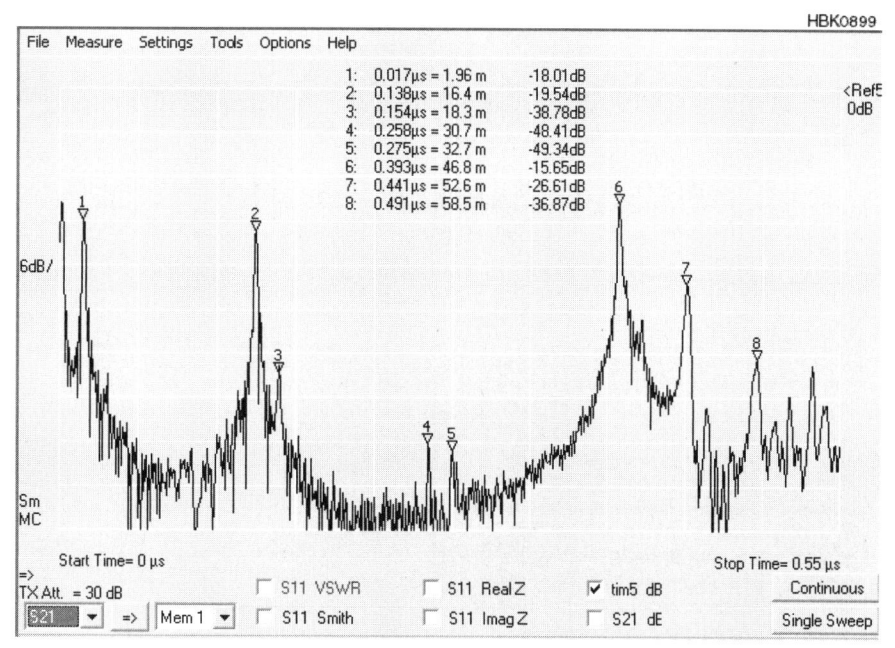

Figure 25.67 — The impulse response of a feed line attached to a 30 meter dipole. The system is swept from 50 to 500 MHz. See text for an explanation of the markers.

Figure 25.68 is the step response (similar to that from the direct method shown in Figure 25.66) computed from the same sweep as that used for Figure 25.67. The data revealed (and a visual inspection confirmed) that the cable inside the shack and from the bulkhead to the coax splice is 50 Ω, but that the cable from there to the antenna is 75 Ω.

TDR measures time; to convert that measurement to physical distance, we must provide the velocity factor. The 75 Ω cable is Belden 8213, this sample of which has a measured VF of 0.795 at VHF. The 50 Ω cable has a measured VF of 0.8425 at VHF. In the setup screen for this TDR measurement, VF was set at 0.795, so distance measurements will be correct for the 75 Ω cable, but wrong for the 50 Ω cable. Computed results could be made correct for the 50 Ω cable by changing VF in that setup screen, or by leaving VF at 0.795 and applying a correction factor of (0.8425/0.795) to the dimensions of the 50 Ω cable.

THE EFFECT OF VELOCITY FACTOR

The velocity of propagation in any transmission line is not constant — it varies with frequency. At the lowest audio frequencies, the velocity factor (VF) is quite a bit lower than the published specification, rising rapidly throughout the audio spectrum, continuing to increase through the radio spectrum until it reaches a nearly constant value in the VHF range. It is this constant value that is computed by simple equations for VF that don't take frequency into account.

For most cables, VF at 2 MHz is typically 1-2% slower than this constant value. In other words, an actual transmission line is 1-2% longer electrically than using the "nominal" (VHF) value that the simplified equation for VF predicts. Because of this change, the physical length of a stub for the lower frequency bands is 1-2% shorter than predicted from the specified value.

When using software to transform antenna measurements made in the station to the actual impedance at the feed point, the variability of VF must be applied to data for antennas for the lower bands (14 MHz and below). AC6LA's free *Zplots* shareware (based on *Excel* spreadsheets, see **ac6la.com/zplots.html**) computes and plots VF, Z_0, and attenuation versus frequency from measure-

---

Transforming Analyzer Data

Like the trace on a simple oscilloscope, the TDR plot of the impulse response contains all frequencies (or the range of frequencies if it is transformed from a sweep). The scope and the TDR plot are "frequency blind" — that is, they display information only about the time response, and no information about the frequency response.

An impulse or sweep measurement can, theoretically, be manipulated mathematically to compute the impedance at every point in the line over the same range of frequencies. The precision of that computation and whether it is practical, depends on how the data is gathered (sweep rate, sweep range, spacing of data points) and the software tools available. Frequency sweep ranges chosen for TDR may be inappropriate for examination of other line properties.

Free software such as *SimSmith* (**www.ae6ty.com/smith_charts.html**) and *ZPlots* (**ac6la.com/zplots.html**) can accept swept measurements made at discrete frequencies to compute and plot the impedance at any point on a line if the characteristics of the line are known. Data is interchanged between a measurement device and software programs (and between one software program and another) by means of a plain text file. These files, defined by the Touchstone format (see text) can take several forms that are defined by the first line(s), called a "header." The filename extension indicates the type of measurements: .s1p files describe single port measurements, like impedance or a time response and .s2p files describe two-port measurements such as the S21 (gain) transfer function produced by a vector network analyzer.

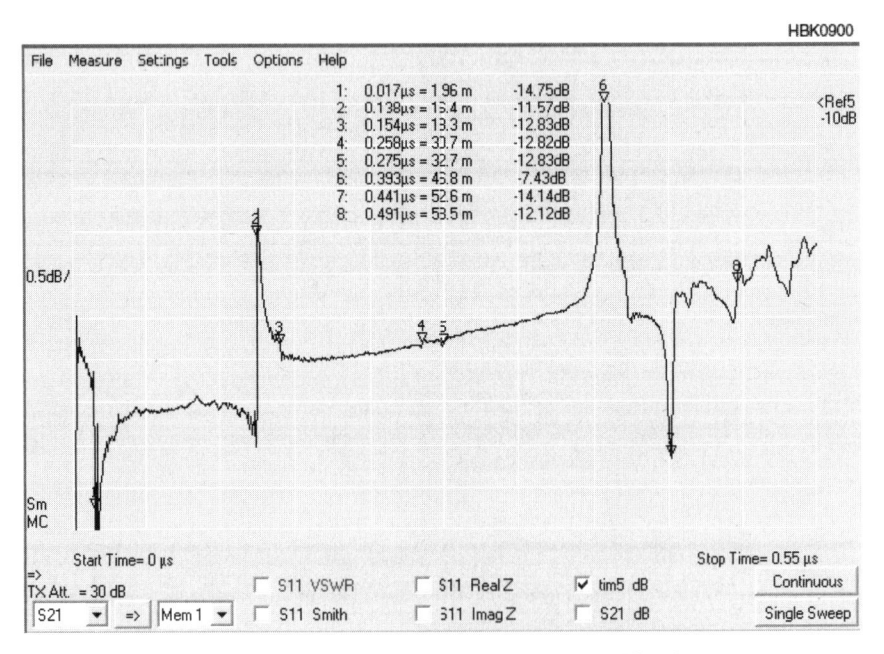

Figure 25.68 — The step response similar to the direct method for the same antenna system in Figure 25.10. See text for an explanation of the graph.

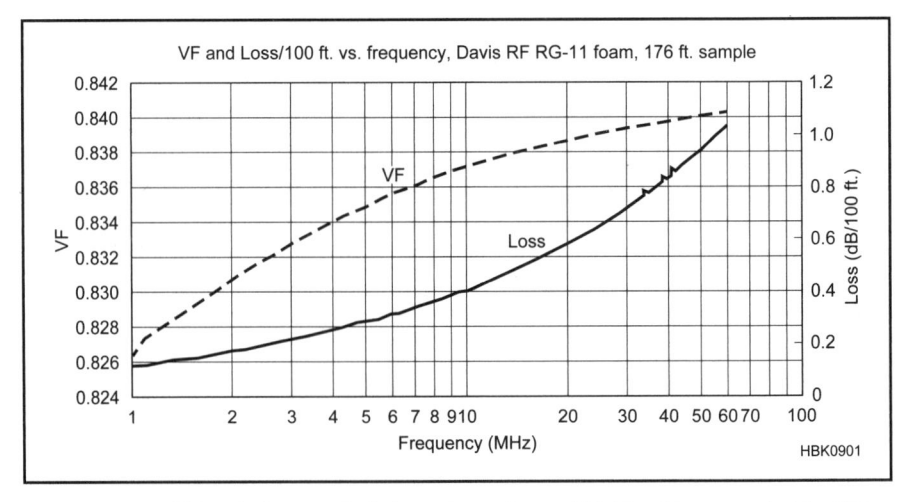

Figure 25.69 — VF and characteristic impedance for an RG-11 cable computed by *ZPlots* software from a swept-frequency measurement. See text.

ments of a known length of a transmission made with the far end open and with the far end shorted. *ZPlots* can accept data in the Touchstone format discussed earlier.

Figure 25.69 is a plot of VF and attenuation computed by *ZPlots* from such measurements on a 176 foot length of RG-11 cable with a #14 AWG solid copper center conductor, a foam dielectric, and a copper braid shield. This behavior and general curve shape are typical of all transmission lines as predicted by fundamental transmission line equations. Exact values for each line will differ based on their physical dimensions and their dielectric.

It should also be noted that Z_0 also varies with frequency and below VHF is complex — that is, not a pure resistance, and is slightly capacitive. The *TLW* program (*Transmission Lines for Windows* by N6BV), included with the *ARRL Antenna Book*, provides Z_0 data for most commonly used cables, and can plot voltage and current along the line. These plots clearly show standing waves on a line at 2 MHz when the termination is only resistive. The mismatch is small and the effect on attenuation is insignificant, but it clearly shows up in carefully made measurements of long cable lengths over a range of frequencies as a small ripple in attenuation values.

25.8 Miscellaneous Measurements

While receiver and transmitter measurements are perhaps the type of testing most associated with Amateur Radio, the home experimenter will have occasion to do other measurements as well.

25.8.1 Testing Digital Circuitry

Virtually every electronic device these days includes digital circuitry. Even a simple QRP transceiver usually either includes or is used with a digital keyer and it may include other digital circuitry, such as a display, as well. A multimeter is generally of little use for testing digital circuits because it cannot respond fast enough to indicate the high and low transitions.

An oscilloscope is a very useful tool because it gives a visual display of the digital signal versus time. It can show impairments such as transient glitches, overshoot, slow rise times, and high or low logic levels that are out of spec. A scope with at least two channels is greatly desired because you often to need to see the time relationships between different signals. A separate external trigger input is also very useful for the same reason. The oscilloscope's bandwidth must be high enough to accurately display the signals to be tested. Bandwidths in the GHz range are needed for state-of-the-art digital circuitry, but 100 MHz should be adequate for most needs.

A hand-held *logic probe* is a device that indicates whether a circuit node is high, low or toggling in between the two states (even with very narrow pulses). While it does not give as much information as an oscilloscope, it is much smaller, cheaper and easier to use. In many cases it is all that is needed to troubleshoot a circuit of moderate complexity. For example, many circuit faults result in a "stuck bit" that remains high or low all the time, which is easy to detect with a logic probe. Typically the logic probe has two wires with clip leads on the ends that connect to the ground and power supply of the circuit under test. The operator then touches the probe tip to the point to be tested and LEDs light up to indicate the logic state.

At the other end of the complexity spectrum is the *logic analyzer*. This is typically the size of an oscilloscope with one or more external pods that can connect to dozens or hundreds of circuit nodes at the same time. Models that use an external digitizing pod and connect to a PC via USB are also available.

A graphics screen shows individual signals with an oscilloscope-like display or multiple signals can be treated as a bus, with the display reading out the values as a series of hexadecimal numbers versus time. Unlike an oscilloscope, a logic analyzer does not indicate actual voltage levels, but only whether a signal is high or low and the timing of the transitions. Sophisticated triggering modes allow synchronization to various clocks or data patterns. Usually a large on-board memory allows capturing long data traces for display or later analysis. Some models include a pattern generator to generate a long series of multi-bit test vectors. Logic analyzers are quite expensive to buy new but are commonly available on the surplus market.

25.8.2 Service Monitors

A *service monitor* is a "one-box tester" for transceivers. It includes a signal generator for testing the receiver and a spectrum analyzer for testing the transmitter, using the same RF connector so that only one connection to the transceiver's antenna jack is required. Other common features are an RF wattmeter and dummy load, a frequency counter, an FM deviation meter, audio tone generators to connect to the microphone, and an audio voltmeter and distortion analyzer/SINAD meter to connect to the speaker output. Some units contain additional features such as DTMF (touch-tone) and CTCSS (sub-audible tone) generators, an audio frequency counter and adjacent-channel power (ACP) measurement capability.

Older service monitors found on the surplus market were designed for testing analog two-way radios and repeaters. Many are portable for easy transportation to a mountaintop repeater site. Later units may be more oriented to testing cellular telephone base stations. Modern instruments cover the latest digital modes, with bit error rate (BER) testers for the receiver and various modulation quality tests for the transmitter.

While all the functions of a service monitor are available in separate instruments, having everything integrated in one box is more convenient and allows faster testing, which is something a commercial enterprise is willing to pay extra for. A brand-new service monitor is not inexpensive, but older used units made by such companies as Singer-Gertsch, Cushman and IFR that are suitable for testing analog radios can sometimes be found for reasonable prices.

25.8.3 Testing Digital Modulation

As digital modulation modes become more and more important in Amateur Radio, it is increasingly important to have ways of testing the performance. There are dozens of different digital formats in use, from traditional radio teleprinting (RTTY) using frequency-shift keying (FSK) to the latest systems that employ sophisticated error detection and correction along with various modulation types that pack multiple bits into each symbol. Despite the wide differences in modulation and coding, nearly all have in common a relatively-narrow bandwidth suitable for use with a voice transceiver using SSB or FM modulation.

If you're having trouble with reception or transmission of digital signals using a PC sound card, one straightforward troubleshooting technique is to install the software on two computers and see if you can transmit data from one computer to the other by connecting the sound card output of one to the input of the other and vice versa. If you don't get perfect reception, that indicates a problem with the computer software or hardware.

The next step is to transmit into a dummy load and receive the signal with a separate receiver located close by so it picks up the stray radiation from the dummy load. A piece of wire plugged into the receiver antenna connector can be moved around to adjust the signal level. Many software programs for receiving digital signals include a spectrum display, which can indicate faults in the transmitted signal such as distortion and *skew*, the amplitude imbalance among the tones of a multi-tone modulation signal. To see what the signal is supposed to look like, connect the two computers directly, as previously described. Then when you examine the RF signal transmitted into the dummy load, any additional bandwidth due to distortion or skew in the spectrum shape should be apparent.

If the demodulation software does not include a spectrum display, there are separate programs available that can display the spectrum of the signal at the sound-card input, as discussed in the Spectrum Analyzer section of this chapter. An RF spectrum analyzer measuring the RF output signal directly would give an even better idea of modulation quality because it is not affected by the filters and other circuitry of the receiver. A receiver panadapter as described earlier is a less-expensive substitute.

Comprehensive testing of a digital communications system is quite complicated because of all the variables involved. The *bit error ratio* (BER) is the number of single-bit errors divided by the number of bits sent in a certain time interval. It requires special test equipment to measure because the individual bits are typically decoded deep inside the demodulation software where they are difficult to access. The *packet error ratio* (PER) is easier to measure. In a packetized data system it is the number of incorrect packets divided by the number of packets sent. It can be measured either before or after error correction. In a non-packetized system like PSK31 the character error ratio is a useful figure of merit. BER is affected by the signal-to-noise ratio (SNR), interference, distortion, synchronization errors and multipath fading. PER is further affected by the effectiveness of the coding and error correction of the particular digital mode used.

It is interesting to measure BER or PER as a function of the SNR. For some digital systems with lots of error correction the errors are nearly zero down to a certain signal level and then degrade very sharply below that. However, in real-world operation the SNR is almost never constant. The signal is constantly changing, both in amplitude and phase, as propagation changes due to movement of the ionosphere (on HF) or of the vehicle (VHF and above), as explained in the **Propagation of Radio Signals** chapter. Measuring actual on-the-air performance is not a good way to compare systems because propagation varies so much at different times. For a repeatable test, you need a *channel simulator,* which is a device that intentionally degrades a test signal in a precise way as to simulate an over-the-air radio channel. Moe Wheatley, AE4JY offers a free software HF channel simulator which can be downloaded from the Internet.[23] A hardware HF channel simulator has been described by Johann B Forrer, KC7WW.[24]

25.8.4 Software-Based Test Equipment

Most amateurs these days own a personal computer with a powerful microprocessor, tons of memory and mass data storage, a large color display and a sound card that provides stereo high-fidelity audio input/output. It doesn't take a great deal of imagination to realize that these resources can be harnessed to make low-cost measuring instruments of various types.

Audio-frequency instruments can be implemented directly using the computer sound card, which typically has a frequency response from perhaps 50 Hz up to about 20 kHz. While computer sound cards can be quite useful for measurement, the low-cost sound cards built into computers may not have good noise performance. They may also distort at levels near their rated output. It is good practice to keep their output level at least 6 dB below rated output to minimize distortion on signal peaks. Signal levels should also be set so that the lowest amplitude components are at least 10 dB above the noise floor.

Inexpensive (less than $100) USB sound cards made for use in semi-pro recording studios have better quality than most, and work well in ham applications such as computer-to-radio interfaces for digital modes. Because these products are made for a mass market, models tend to be updated every year or two, but the quality brands tend to offer stable designs. Careful testing has found older models made by Tascam and Numark to work well for digital modes.

Free software is available on the Internet for instruments such as audio function generators, DTMF and CTCSS tone generators, DTMF and CTCSS decoders, two-tone generators for SSB transmitter testing, distortion/SINAD analyzers, oscilloscopes and audio spectrum analyzers. In addition to the frequency-response limitations of a typical sound card, another issue is that the device can be damaged by applying excessive voltage to the inputs or outputs. It is wise to add external buffer amplifiers that include over-voltage protection.

Radio-frequency test equipment can also use the sound card inputs by means of some type of frequency converter, consisting of a local oscillator and mixer. If the mixer is a quadrature type, the two outputs may be fed to the stereo sound card inputs so that software can treat the left and right channels as the in-phase and quadrature signals. A common application is a narrow-band RF spectrum analyzer. The RF bandwidth is typically limited to twice the sound card's audio bandwidth. Low-cost hardware is available in kit form that can be used with free software downloaded from the Internet.[25]

One problem with using a sound card is that the signals may be susceptible to ground loops and radio-frequency interference (RFI). Since the computer and the device under test are grounded separately to the ac power system, hum and noise can be generated from currents flowing in the ground connection between the two. It is helpful to use a short, low-resistance ground connection between the sound card and the device under test. It is also possible to use isolation transformers or differential amplifiers to isolate the grounds and thus break the ground loop. Good quality cables and attention to proper shielding and grounding help prevent hum and noise pickup.

It is always good practice to bond together the chassis or shielding enclosure of every piece of equipment in a system with short, heavy copper wires (#14 AWG or larger). Failure to do so often results in hum, buzz, and RFI being introduced into the signals and data. For the same reasons, all interconnected equipment should be powered from the same ac outlet or from outlets that share the same 'green wire' (that is, they plug into the same multiple wall outlet box). If the equipment is powered from different outlets, the green wires of those outlet boxes should be bonded together. Good quality cables and attention to proper shielding help prevent hum, buzz, noise, and RFI. (See the discussions of bonding in the **Safety** and **RF Interference** chapters.)

25.9 Construction Projects

25.9.1 Bipolar Transistor Tester

Here is a basic "good/bad" tester for bipolar transistors, designed by Alan Bloom, N1AL. This tester is small enough to carry in your pocket to a flea market (**Figure 25.70**). A printed-circuit board is available from FAR Circuits (www.farcircuits.net) but the simple circuit can easily be hand-wired on perfboard. (Printed-circuit board layout graphics are also available with the downloadable supplemental content.)

To test an unknown NPN or PNP transistor, just remove the tester's working NPN or PNP transistor from its socket and replace it with the device to be tested. If you hear a tone in the headphones the transistor is good, otherwise it is bad. More elaborate instruments can measure various transistor parameters such as current gain, breakdown voltage and high-frequency performance, however this simple tester suffices in most situations. It is rare for a transistor to be damaged in such a way that it still works but no longer meets its specifications.

When testing a batch of transistors of unknown condition you can use this tester to quickly sort them into a "good" and a "bad" pile and be fairly confident that the ones in the "good" pile are working correctly.

Metal-can TO-5 transistors are shown here, but small plastic transistors work just as well if you bend the leads a little. The TO-5 parts can be pressed down flat against the socket and so are less likely to fall out in a pocket.

The circuit in **Figure 25.71** is simply two transistors connected with positive feedback through a frequency-selective network, forming an oscillator at a frequency of approximately 500 Hz. Each transistor is configured for a voltage gain of about 2.0 and the feedback network has a gain of about ⅓, so that the total loop gain is a little greater than unity, the condition required for oscillation.

It should be nearly impossible to damage an unknown transistor by plugging it in wrong or into the wrong socket because the supply voltage is less than the base-emitter breakdown voltage of a bipolar transistor and the current is limited to a few milliamps. No on/off switch is included; simply unplug the headphones when you're done testing.

The prototype was built in an Altoids tin, as shown in **Figure 25.72**, but any handy enclosure would do. You'll need four mounting holes for the circuit board and two clearance holes for the transistor sockets. The headphone jack is best mounted on the side of the enclosure. If such a shallow enclosure is used, line the inside bottom with some insulating material such as electrical tape.

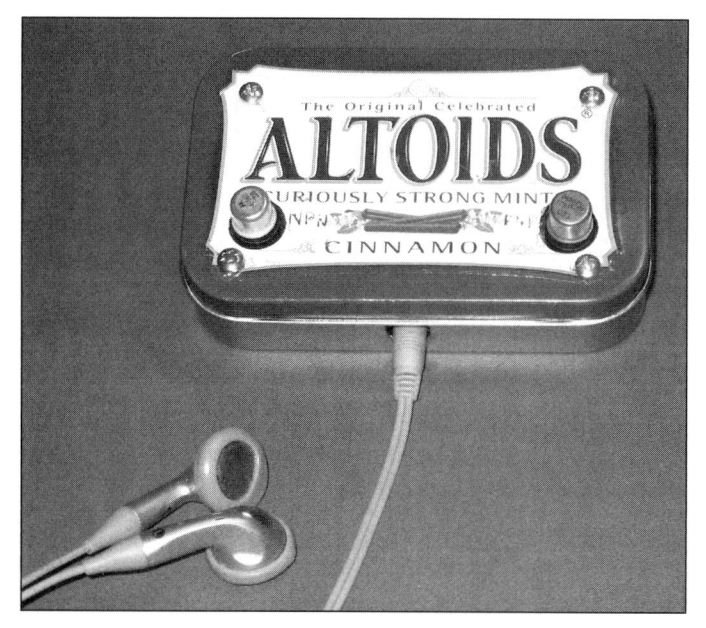

Figure 25.70 — A transistor tester built into an Altoids tin.

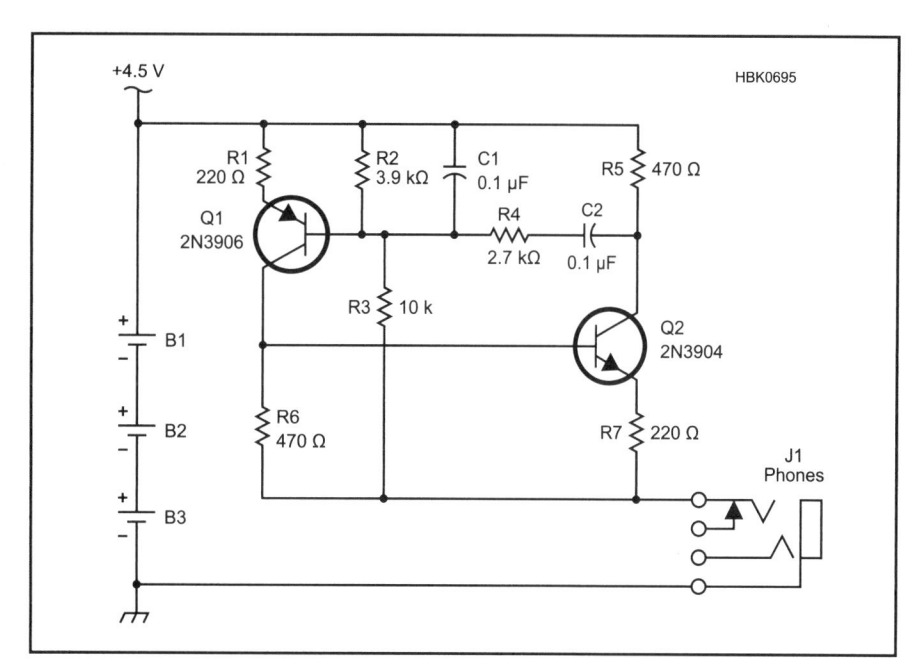

Figure 25.71 — Schematic diagram and parts list of the transistor tester. All parts can be obtained from Digi-Key at www.digikey.com except for the printed circuit board, available from FAR Circuits at www.farcircuits.net.

C1, C2 — 0.1 µF ceramic capacitor (Digi-Key 490-3873-ND)
J1 — Stereo 3.5 mm phone jack (Digi-Key CP1-3554NG-ND)
Q1 — 2N3906 PNP transistor (Digi-Key 2N3906FS-ND)
Q2 — 2N3904 NPN transistor (Digi-Key 2N3904FS-ND)
R1, R7 — 220 Ω, ¼ W, 5% resistor (Digi-Key 220QBK-ND)
R2 — 3.9 kΩ, ¼ W, 5% resistor (Digi-Key 3.9KQBK-ND)
R3 — 10 kΩ, ¼ W, 5% resistor (Digi-Key 10KQBK-ND)
R4 — 2.7 kΩ, ¼ W, 5% resistor (Digi-Key 2.7KQBK-ND)
R5, R6 — 470 Ω, ¼ W, 5% resistor (Digi-Key 470QBK-ND)
Quantity 2 — 3-pin, TO-5 transistor socket (Digi-Key ED2150-ND)
Quantity 6 — AAA-size battery clips (Digi-Key 82K-ND)
PCB — Printed circuit board (FAR Circuits)

Test Equipment and Measurements 25.49

Figure 25.72— Mounting of the circuit board inside the case.

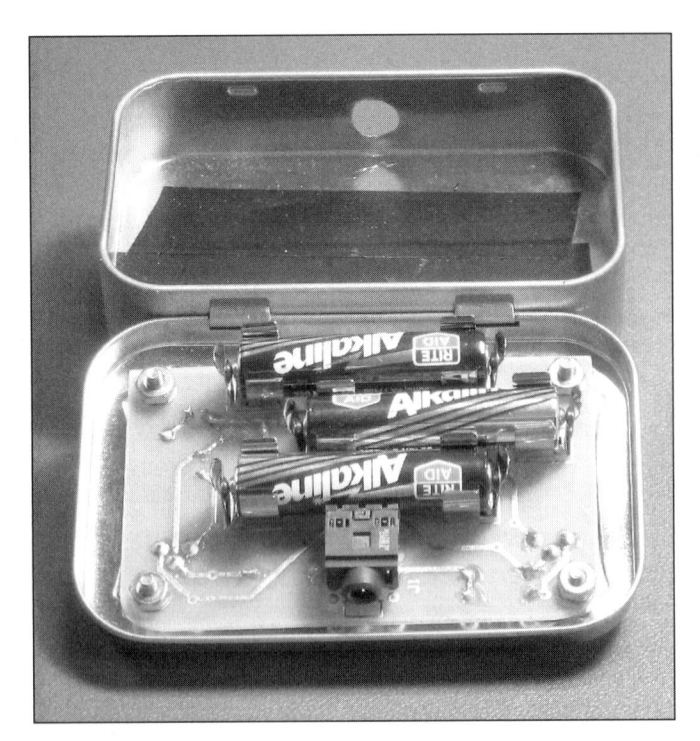

Figure 25.73 — A logic probe is small and easy to use.

All components are mounted on the top side of the printed circuit board except the battery clips and the headphone jack, which go on the bottom. Leave a little extra lead length on the two 0.1 µF capacitors if they need to be bent over to clear the enclosure cover. The PC board from FAR Circuits does not have plated-through holes, so the leads of R5 and R6 must be soldered on both sides.

The transistor sockets are designed for TO-5 metal-can transistors but the smaller TO-18 or TO-92 plastic-cased devices can also be tested by bending the leads to fit. Nearly all TO-92 bipolar transistors have the base lead in the middle. Bend the center (base) lead toward the flat side of the transistor body, spread the three leads a little, and it should plug right in. Additional solder pads are provided for the base, emitter and collector of each transistor in case you wish to wire up additional sockets for other case types such as TO-220 or TO-3 power transistors. A transistor cross-reference guide is also handy to have to determine lead assignments.

25.9.2 Logic Probe

This simple logic probe (**Figure 25.73**) was designed by Alan Bloom, N1AL. It works with several different logic types, including TTL, 5 V CMOS and 3.3 V CMOS. A printed circuit board is available from FAR Circuits at **www.farcircuits.net** or the simple circuit may be hand-wired on perfboard. (Printed-circuit board layout graphics are also available with the downloadable supplemental content.)

The purpose of a logic probe is to indicate whether signals are present at various circuit nodes. That's most of what troubleshooting a simple digital circuit requires. The probe has indicators to show whether the signal is high, low or toggling between the two states. It doesn't give as much information as an oscilloscope or logic analyzer but it is much smaller, cheaper and easier to use.

CIRCUIT OPERATION

This logic probe features a seven-segment LED display that forms letters to indicate the state of the signal at the probe's tip. A capital "L" is displayed if the signal is low and "H" if the signal is high. If it is toggling between low and high with roughly a 50% duty factor, the letter "B" is displayed to indicate that "Both" high and low are present. If the signal is mostly low with short-duration positive pulses, then a "C" is displayed. If the signal is mostly high with low-going pulses, the LED indicates an "A". "C" and "A" can be remembered as Cathode (mostly low) and Anode (mostly high), respectively.

The circuit is shown in **Figure 25.74**. Each of the common-anode seven-segment LED display segments is lit when its pin is low. The 74ACT04 inverters are arranged so that a continuous low input signal lights up the proper segments to form an "L" and a continuous high forms an "H". The 74LS122 retriggerable multivibrator outputs a 33-ms pulse whenever there is a positive-going transition on its B2 input. Repetitive transitions with a period less than about 33 ms (30 Hz or greater) assert the 74LS122 output continuously, which causes the top segment to light. If the signal is mostly low, the "L" turns into a "C" and if the signal is mostly high, the "H" turns into an "A".

CONSTRUCTION

The logic probe can be built in a plastic spice jar as in **Figure 25.75** but any clear plastic container big enough to accommodate the 1.2 × 3.5-inch printed-circuit board would also work. Batteries B1 and B2 and the test lead jack, J1, are mounted on the bottom side; all other components are on the top. Place a piece of tape under the top terminal of B3 to keep it from shorting to the ground plane. The PC board from FAR circuits does not have plated-through holes so at least the following must be soldered on both sides: R5, R6, R8, B1 and B3 (inner contacts), U2 pins 1 and 14, and U3 pins 1, 2, 3, 7 and 11. Also solder a wire to both sides of the via hole to the left of pin 1 of the display (U1). If you wish, you can use a socket for the LED display to raise it up higher, but don't use sockets for U2 and U3 since some of their leads must be soldered on both sides. Note that the L-brackets that attach the board to the bottle cap have a long and a short side. The long side is placed against the board.

The socket for the probe is a standard 0.08 inch diameter tip jack. The probe is just a nail soldered into the end of a mating tip plug. You can also use a standard test lead plugged into the jack. The component labeled "J2" on the

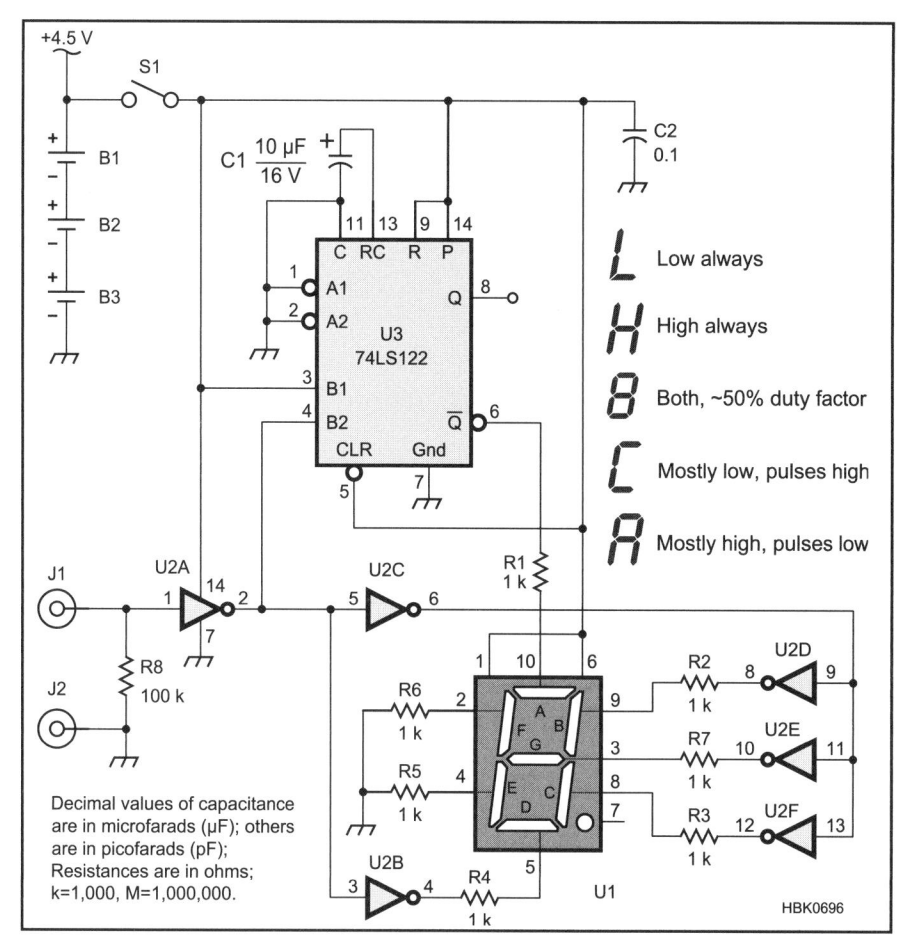

Figure 25.74 — Schematic diagram and parts list of the logic probe. All parts can be obtained from Digi-Key at www.digikey.com except for the printed circuit board, available from FAR Circuits at www.farcircuits.net.

C1 — 10 µF electrolytic capacitor (Digi-Key P807-ND)
C2 — 0.1 µF ceramic capacitor (Digi-Key 490-3873-ND)
J1 — Horizontal tip jack (Digi-Key J110-ND)
R1-R7 — 1 kΩ, ¼ W, 5% resistor (Digi-Key 1.0KQBK-ND)
R8 — 100 kΩ, ¼ W, 5% resistor (Digi-Key CF1/4100KJRCT-ND)
S1 — SPDT, right-angle slide switch (Digi-Key CKN9559-ND)
U1 — 7-segment common-anode LED (Digi-Key 160-1525-5-ND)
U2 — 74ACT04 hex inverter (Digi-Key 296-4351-5-ND)
U3 — 74LS122 monostable multivibrator (Digi-Key 296-3639-5-ND)
Qty 6 — Battery clips (Digi-Key 82K-ND)
Qty 2 — L-bracket (Digi-Key 621K-ND)
Printed circuit board (FAR Circuits)

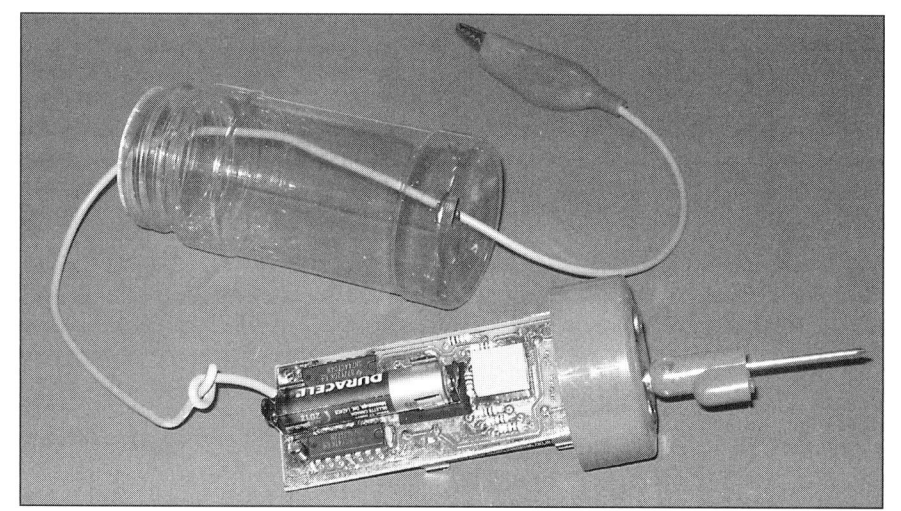

Figure 25.75 — The logic probe was built into a spice bottle.

schematic is just a solder pad for the ground lead. Tie a knot in the ground lead where it exits the bottle for strain relief.

USING THE LOGIC PROBE

The probe includes a self-contained, battery-operated power supply so only the ground lead needs to be connected to circuit ground.

It's amazing how much useful information you can get from such a simple device. One of the most common faults in a digital circuit is a node that is "stuck" low or high due to a short circuit or a faulty component. The logic probe is perfect for detecting that condition.

You can also get a rough idea of what percentage of time the signal is low or high by looking at the relative brightness of the segments. If the signal is low 100% of the time, an "L" is displayed. If there are narrow positive pulses, a "C" is shown. As the pulse width increases, the center and the two right segments start to glow dimly, finally forming a "B" when the duty factor is near 50%. As the duty factor increases further, the bottom segment dims, eventually turning the "B" into an "A". And finally, if the signal is high 100% of the time, the top segment goes out, leaving an "H".

25.9.3 Inductance Tester

Many inexpensive DVMs offer a capacitance measurement feature but measuring inductance is much less common. This project describes a simple test fixture for using a signal generator to measure inductance. It was originally published as "Mystery Inductor Box," by Robert J. Rogers, WA1PIO, in the January 2011 issue of *QST*.

MEASURING INDUCTANCE

One way to measure the value of an inductor is to connect it in parallel with a known capacitance and measure the resulting resonant frequency. In the past, grid-dip oscillators (GDO) have been used to determine the resonant frequency of such parallel tuned circuits. (See the project "Gate-Dip Oscillator" elsewhere in this section.) Using a dip oscillator, a dip, or drop in meter current was noted at the point of resonance.

This test fixture provides a convenient substitute for the dip meter method. A separate signal generator is used to provide the needed signal source and switched internal capacitors are used to resonate the inductors. An internal meter is provided as is a port for an external detector to indicate resonance. The schematic with parts list is shown in **Figure 25.76**.

BUILDING THE BOX

Figure 25.77 shows the layout of the internal components. Construction is straightforward with no critical dimensions or layout requirements. The 470-Ω resistor is used to

Test Equipment and Measurements 25.51

provide a better peak in the voltage seen at resonance by the oscilloscope or meter movement. Most of the generator voltage will appear across this resistor until the point of resonance when the highest fraction of the applied signal voltage will then appear across the parallel circuit.

An oscilloscope is connected to the right BNC connector and its high input impedance, typically 1 MΩ, will not load the parallel tuned circuit at the relatively low frequencies used with this test fixture. Instead of the oscilloscope, the internal meter movement may be used to give a peak indication at resonance. Large capacitance values were used to minimize the effects of lead length, a concern while operating test equipment at higher frequencies.

USING THE TEST FIXTURE

The test fixture can be used to accurately determine the value of inductors in the mH and µH range. Selecting the 0.01 µF capacitor allows measurement of inductors in the µH range using a signal generator with a 159 kHz to 5 MHz output. Selecting the 0.22 µF capacitor measures larger mH-range inductors using signal generator frequencies in the 1 to 34 kHz region.

Figure 25.78 shows a typical test setup using the built-in meter as the peak indicator. A signal generator's sine wave output is connected to J1, the input BNC connector, and the unknown inductor to the terminal posts. Select one of the capacitors with the switch. Connect an oscilloscope to J2, the output BNC connector, or use the built-in meter. Adjust the signal generator output to give some indication on the meter. Adjust the frequency of the signal generator until a peak is obtained on the oscilloscope or meter.

If the switch is in the wrong position, there will not be a sharp peak in the voltage seen by the oscilloscope or built-in meter. Avoid the band edges of the generator frequency range where output voltages tend to fall off from the mid-range values. Use the capacitor value selected, C, and the frequency of the signal generator at resonance, f, in the following formula:

$$L = \frac{1}{4\pi^2 f^2 C} = \frac{1}{39.5 f^2 C}$$

where f is in hertz, C is in farads and the resulting L is in henrys. A chart of frequency versus inductance for each of the two internal capacitors used to measure small and large inductors is shown in **Table 25.3**.

The SPDT switch also has a center-off position which disconnects the internal

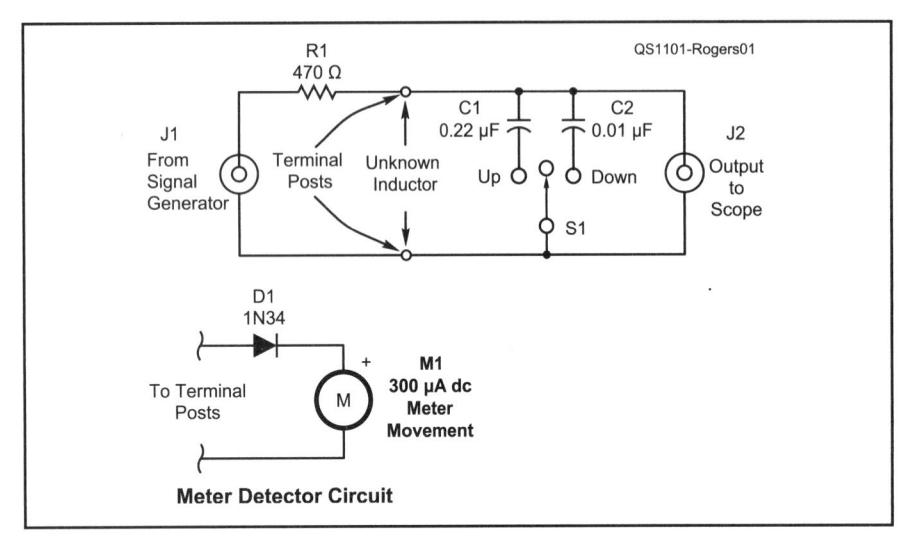

Figure 25.76 — Schematic diagram and parts list of the inductor test fixture. The switch's center-off position is used to disconnect the internal capacitors so that a desired value of capacitance can be placed in parallel with the inductor under test at the terminal posts. Measurement accuracy will depend on the actual value of C1 and C2 — determining the capacitor values with a capacitance meter will result in more accurate inductance values.

C1 — 0.22 µF ceramic capacitor.
C2 — 0.01 µF ceramic capacitor.
D1 — Germanium diode, 1N34 or 1N34A.
J1, J2 — BNC chassis-mount connectors.
M1 — 300 µA meter movement in a plastic case
R1 — 470 Ω, ¼ W resistor.
S1 — SPDT, center-off, toggle switch.

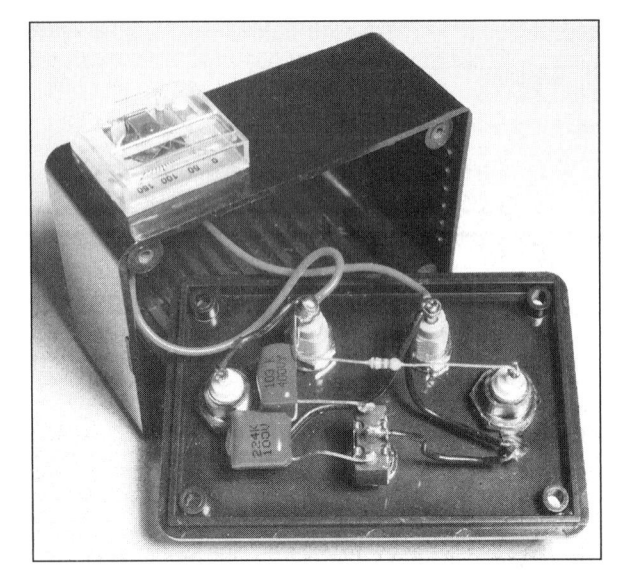

Figure 25.77 — Layout of the internal components.

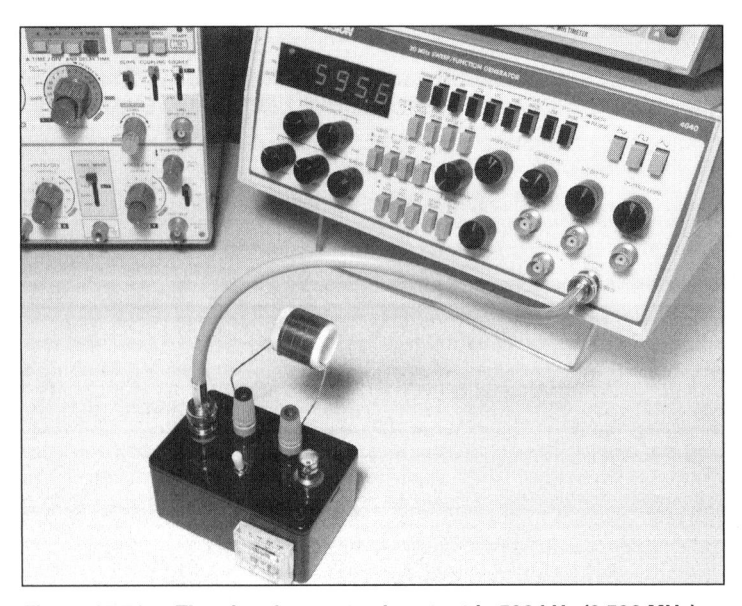

Figure 25.78 — The signal generator's output is 596 kHz (0.596 MHz) with the switch in the position selecting the 0.01 µF capacitor. Using the formula given results in an calculated inductance of 7.1 µH.

capacitors. This allows testing a particular capacitor-inductor combination connected to the terminal posts. The internal meter movement is always connected across the banana terminal posts.

25.9.4 Fixed-Frequency Audio Oscillator

An audio signal generator should provide a reasonably pure sine wave. The best oscillator circuits for this use are RC-coupled, the amplifiers operating as close to class A as possible. Variable frequencies covering the entire audio range are needed for determining frequency response of audio amplifiers.

A circuit of a simple RC oscillator that is useful for general testing is given in **Figure 25.79**. This Twin-T arrangement gives a waveform that is satisfactory for most purposes.

The oscillator can be operated at any frequency in the audio range by varying the component values. R1, R2 and C1 form a low-pass network, while C2, C3 and R3 form a high-pass network. As the phase shifts are opposite, there is only one frequency at which the total phase shift from collector to base is 180°: Oscillation will occur at this frequency. When C1 is about twice the capacitance of C2 or C3 the best operation results.

R3 should have a resistance about 0.1 that of R1 or R2 (C2 = C3 and R1 = R2). Output is taken across C1, where the harmonic distortion is least. Use a relatively high impedance load — 100 kΩ or more. Most small-signal AF transistors can be used for Q1. Either NPN or PNP types are satisfactory if the supply polarity is set correctly. R4, the collector load resistor may be changed a little to adjust the oscillator for best output waveform.

25.9.5 Wide-Range Audio Oscillator

A wide-range audio oscillator that will provide a moderate output level can be built from a single 741 operational amplifier (see **Figure 25.80**). Power is supplied by two 9-V batteries from which the circuit draws 4 mA. The frequency range is selectable from about 7 Hz to around 70 kHz. Distortion is approximately 1%. The output level under a light load (10 kΩ) is 4 to 5 V. This can be increased by using higher battery voltages, up to a maximum of plus and minus 18 V, with a corresponding adjustment of R_F.

Pin connections shown are for the eight-pin DIP package. Variable resistor R_F is trimmed for an output level of about 5% below clipping as seen on an oscilloscope. This should be done for the temperature at which the oscillator will normally operate, as the lamp is sensitive to ambient temperature. This unit was originally described by Shultz in November 1974 *QST*; it was later modified by Neben as reported in June 1983 *QST*.

25.9.6 Two-Tone Audio Generator

This generator is used in the ARRL Laboratory to test SSB transmitters for ARRL Product Reviews and makes a very convenient signal source for testing the linearity of a single-sideband transmitter. To be suitable for transmitter evaluation, a generator of this type must produce two non-harmonically related tones of equal amplitude. The level of harmonic and intermodulation distortion must be sufficiently low so as not to confuse the measurement. The frequencies used in this generator are 700 and 1900 Hz, both well inside the normal audio passband of an SSB transmitter. Spectral analysis and practical application with many different transmitters has shown this generator to meet all of the requirements mentioned above. While designed specifically for transmitter testing it is also useful any time a fixed-frequency, low-level audio tone is needed.

CIRCUIT DETAILS

Each of the two tones is generated by a separate Wien bridge oscillator, U1B and U2B. (see **Figure 25.81**) The oscillators are followed by RC active low-pass filters, U1A and U2A. Because the filters require nonstandard capacitor values, provisions have been made on the circuit board for placing two capacitors in parallel in those cases where standard values cannot be used. (The circuit board artwork for layout and part placement is available as graphics with the downloadable supplemental content.) The oscillator and filter capacitors should be polystyrene or Mylar film types if available.

The two tones are combined by op amp U3A, a summing amplifier. This amplifier has a variable resistor, R4, in its feedback loop which serves as the output LEVEL control. While R4 varies the amplitude of both tones together, R3, the BALANCE control, allows the level of tone A to be changed without affecting the level of tone B. This is necessary because some transmitters do not have

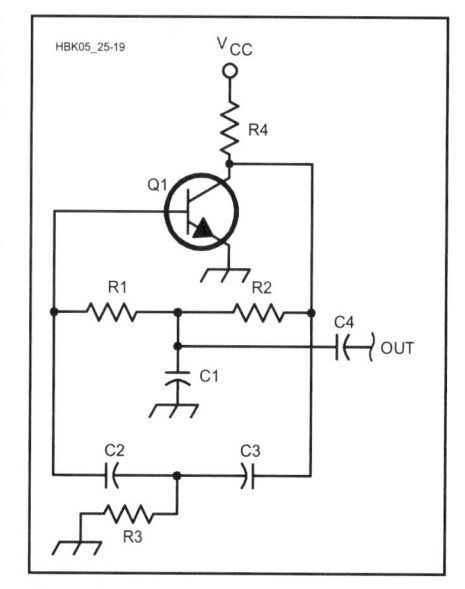

Figure 25.79— Values for the twin-T audio oscillator circuit range from 18 kΩ for R1-R2 and 0.05 µF for C1 (750 Hz) to 15 kΩ and 0.02 µF for 1800 Hz. For the same frequency range, R3 and C2-C3 vary from 1800 Ω and 0.02 µF to 1500 Ω and 0.01 µF. R4 is 3300 Ω and C4, the output coupling capacitor, can be 0.05 µF for high-impedance loads.

Table 25.3
Inductance Value at Resonant Frequency

0.22 µF Selected

Inductance (mH)	Frequency (kHz)
0.10	33.931
0.25	21.460
0.50	15.174
0.75	12.390
1.00	10.730
5.00	4.796
10.00	3.393
20.00	2.399
30.00	1.959
40.00	1.696
50.00	1.517
60.00	1.385
70.00	1.282
80.00	1.199
90.00	1.131
100.00	1.073

0.01 µF Selected

Inductance (µH)	Frequency (MHz)
0.118	4.633
0.25	3.183
0.50	2.251
0.75	1.838
1.00	1.592
2.00	1.125
5.00	0.712
10.00	0.503
20.00	0.356
30.00	0.291
40.00	0.252
50.00	0.225
60.00	0.205
70.00	0.190
80.00	0.178
90.00	0.168
100.00	0.159

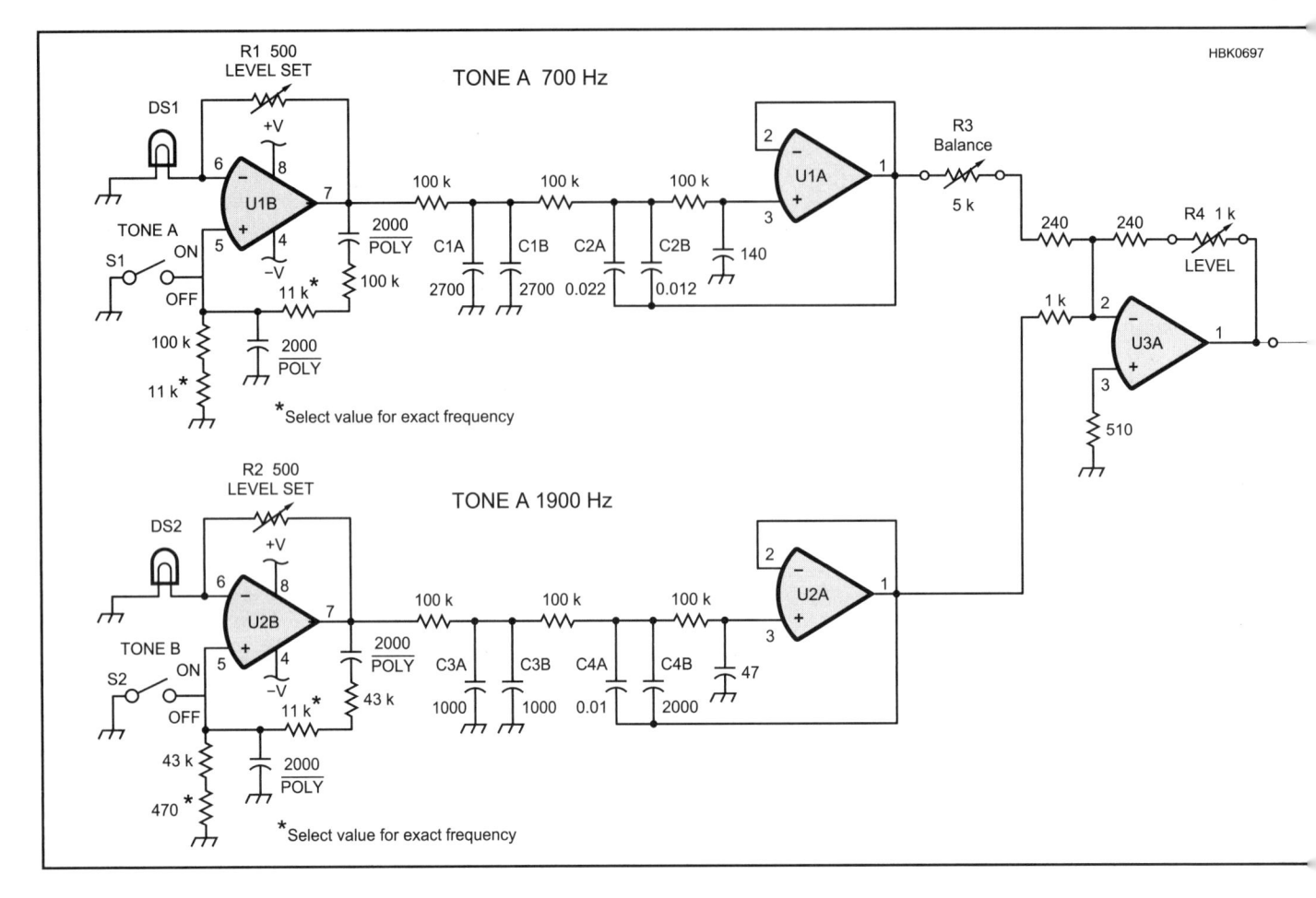

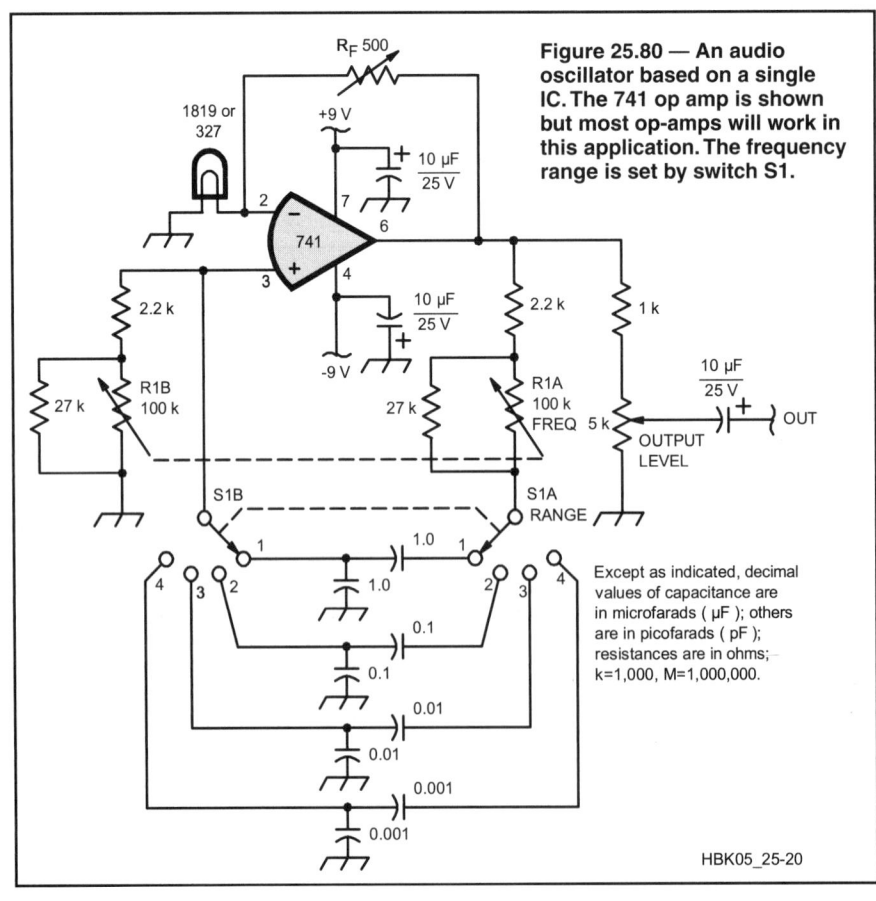

Figure 25.80 — An audio oscillator based on a single IC. The 741 op amp is shown but most op-amps will work in this application. The frequency range is set by switch S1.

Except as indicated, decimal values of capacitance are in microfarads (µF); others are in picofarads (pF); resistances are in ohms; k=1,000, M=1,000,000.

25.54   Chapter 25

Decimal values of capacitance are in microfarads (µF); others are in picofarads (pF); Resistances are in ohms; k=1,000, M=1,000,000.

HBK0697

Figure 25.81— Two-tone audio generator schematic.
BT1, BT2 — 9 V alkaline.
C1A,B — Total capacitance of 0.0054 µF, ±5%.
C2A,B — Total capacitance of 0.034 µF, ±5%.
C3A,B — Total capacitance of 0.002 µF, ±5%.
C4A,B — Total capacitance of 0.012 µF, ±5%.
DS1, DS2 — 12 V, 25 mA lamp.
R1, R2 — 500 Ω, 10-turn trim potentiometer.
R3 — 500 Ω, panel mount potentiometer.
R4 — 1 kΩ, panel mount potentiometer.
S1, S2 — SPST toggle switch.
S3 — Single pole, 6-position rotary switch.
S4 — SPDT toggle switch.
S5 — DPDT toggle switch.
U1, U2, U3 — Dual JFET op amp, type LF353N or TL082.

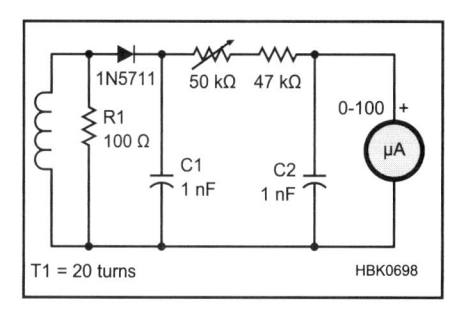

Figure 25.82 — The schematic of the RF current probe. See text for component information.

equal audio response at both frequencies. Multi-turn pots are recommended for both R3 and R4 so that fine adjustments can be made. Following the summing amplifier is a step attenuator; S3 controls the output level in 10-dB steps. The use of two output level controls, R4 and S3, allows the output to cover a wide range and still be easy to set to a specific level.

The remaining op amp, U3B is connected as a voltage follower and serves to buffer the output while providing a high-impedance load for the step attenuator. Either high or low output impedance can be selected by S4. The values shown are suitable for most transmitters using either high- or low- impedance microphones.

CONSTRUCTION AND ADJUSTMENT

Component layout and wiring are not critical, and any type of construction can be used with good results. Because the generator will normally be used near a transmitter, it should be enclosed in some type of metal case for shielding. Battery power was chosen to reduce the possibility of RF entering the unit through the ac line. With careful shielding and filtering, the builder should be able to use an ac power supply in place of the batteries.

The only adjustment required before use is the setting of the oscillator feedback trimmers, R1 and R2. These should be set so that the output of each oscillator, measured at pin 7 of U1 and U2, is about 0.5 volts RMS. A DVM or oscilloscope can be used for this measurement. If neither of these is available, the feedback should be adjusted to the minimum level that allows the oscillators to start reliably and stabilize quickly. When the oscillators are first turned on, they take a few seconds before they will have stable output amplitude. This is caused by the lamps, DS1 and DS2, used in the oscillator feedback circuit. This is normal and should cause no difficulty. The connection to the transmitter should be through a shielded cable.

25.9.7 RF Current Meter

The following project was designed by Tom Rauch, W8JI (**http://w8ji.com/building_a_current_meter.htm**). The circuit of **Figure 25.82** is based on a current transformer (T1) consisting of a T157-2 powdered-iron toroid core with a 20-turn winding. The meter is used with the current-carrying wire or antenna inserted through the middle of the core as a one-turn primary

When 1 A is flowing in the single-turn primary, the secondary current will be 50 mA = primary current divided by the turns ratio of 20:1. R1 across the transformer flattens the frequency response and limits the output voltage. The RF voltage is then detected and filtered by the D1 (a low-threshold Schottky diode for minimum voltage drop) and C1. The adjustable sum of R2 and R3 allow for full-scale (FS) calibration of the 100 µA meter. C2 provides additional filtering. The toroid core and all circuitry are glued to the back of the meter case with only R2 exposed — a screwdriver-adjustable calibration pot.

It is important to minimize stray capacitance by using a meter with all-plastic construction except for the electrical parts. The meter in **Figure 25.83** has an all-plastic case including the meter scale. The meter movement and all metallic areas are small. The lack of large metallic components minimizes stray capacitance from the proximity of the meter. Low stray capacitance ensures the instrument has the least possible affect on the circuit being tested.

A value of 100 Ω for R1 gave the flattest response from 1.8 to 30 MHz. With 50 mA of secondary current, the voltage across R1

Test Equipment and Measurements 25.55

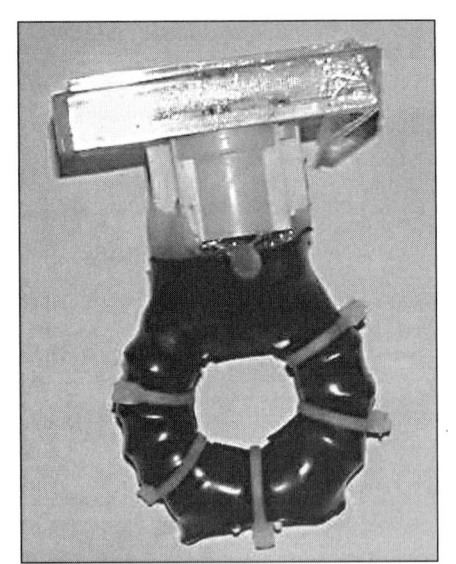

Figure 25.83 — Assembly of the RF current probe. Use an all-plastic meter and mount the circuits and toroid directly on the back of the meter case.

Table 25.4
Step Attenuator Performance at 148, 225 and 450 MHz
Measurements made in the ARRL Laboratory

Attenuator set for Maximum attenuation (71 dB)		Attenuator set for minimum attenuation (0 dB)	
Frequency (MHz)	Attenuation (dB)	Frequency (MHz)	Attenuation (dB)
148	72.33	148	0.4
225	73.17	225	0.4
450	75.83	450	0.84

Note: Laboratory-specified measurement tolerance of ±1 dB

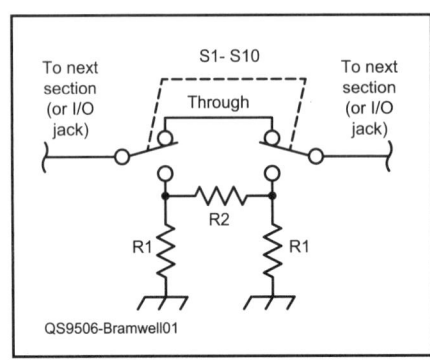

Figure 25.84 — Schematic of one section of the attenuator. All resistors are ¼-W, 1%-tolerance metal-film units. See Table 25.5 for the resistor values required for each attenuator section. There are six 10 dB sections and one each of 1, 2, 3 and 5 dB.

Table 25.5
Closest 1%-Tolerance Resistor Values

Attenuation (dB)	R1 (Ω)	R2 (Ω)
1.00	866.00	5.60
2.00	436.00	11.50
3.00	294.00	17.40
5.00	178.00	30.10
10.00	94.30	71.50

is $0.05 \times 100 = 5$ V$_{RMS}$. The peak voltage is then $1.414 \times 5 = 7.1$ V. At full current, power dissipation in R1 = 50 mA × 5 V$_{RMS}$ = 0.25 W so a ½-W or larger resistor should be used.

The meter used here was a 10,000 Ω/V model so for full-scale deflection from a primary current of 1 A producing a secondary voltage of ~7 V, the sum of R2 and R3 must be set to $7 \times 10,000 = 70$ kΩ. The low-current meter combined with high detected voltage improves detector linearity.

Calibration of the meter can be performed by using a calibrated power meter and a test fixture consisting of two RF connectors with a short piece of wire between them and through the transformer core. With 50 W applied to a 50-Ω load, the wire will be carrying 1 A of current. Full-scale accuracy is not required in comparison measurements, since the meter references against itself, but linearity within a few percent is important.

This transformer-based meter is much more reliable and linear than thermocouple RF ammeters and perturbs systems much less. Stray capacitance added to the system being tested is very small because of the proximity of the meter and the compact wiring area. Compared to actually connecting a meter with its associated lead lengths and capacitance in line with the load, the advantages of a transformer-coupled meter become apparent.

25.9.8 RF Ammeters

When it comes to getting your own RF ammeter, there's good news and bad news as related by John Stanley, K4ERO. First, the bad news. New RF ammeters are expensive, and even surplus pricing can vary widely between $10 and $100 in today's market. AM radio stations are the main users of new units. The FCC defines the output power of AM stations based on the RF current in the antenna, so new RF ammeters are made mainly for that market. They are quite accurate, and their prices reflect that!

The good news is that used RF ammeters are often available. For example, Fair Radio Sales in Lima, Ohio has been a consistent source of RF ammeters. Ham flea markets are also worth trying. Some grubbing around in your nearest surplus store or some older ham's junk box may provide just the RF ammeter you need. Be sure you are really buying an RF ammeter as meters labeled "RF Amps" may just be regular current meters intended for use with an external RF current sensing unit.

RF AMMETER SUBSTITUTES

Don't despair if you can't find a used RF ammeter. It's possible to construct your own. Both hot-wire and thermocouple units can be homemade. Pilot lamps in series with antenna wires, or coupled to them in various ways, can indicate antenna current (F. Sutter, "What, No Meters?," *QST*, Oct 1938, p 49) or even forward and reflected power (C. Wright, "The Twin-Lamp," *QST*, Oct 1947, pp 22-23, 110 and 112).

Another approach is to use a small low-voltage lamp as the heat/light element and use a photo detector driving a meter as an indicator. (Your eyes and judgment can serve as the indicating part of the instrument.) A feed line balance checker could be as simple as a couple of lamps with the right current rating and the lowest voltage rating available. You should be able to tell fairly well by eye which bulb is brighter or if they are about equal. You can calibrate a lamp-based RF ammeter with 60-Hz or dc power.

As another alternative, you can build an RF ammeter that uses a dc meter to indicate rectified RF from a current transformer that you clamp over a transmission line wire (Z. Lau, "A Relative RF Ammeter for Open-Wire Lines," *QST*, Oct 1988, pp 15-17).

25.9.9 RF Step Attenuator

A good RF step attenuator is one of the key pieces of equipment that belongs on your workbench. The attenuator in this project offers good performance yet can be built with a few basic tools. The attenuator is designed for use in 50-Ω systems, provides a total attenuation of 71 dB in 1-dB steps, offers respectable accuracy and insertion loss through 225 MHz and can be used at 450 MHz as shown in **Table 25.4**. This material was originally published as "An RF Step Attenuator" by Denton Bramwell, K7OWJ, in the June 1995 *QST*.

The attenuator consists of 10 resistive π-attenuator sections such as the one in **Figure 25.84**. Each section consists of a DPDT slide switch and three ¼-W, 1%-tolerance metal-film resistors. The complete unit contains single 1, 2, 3 and 5-dB sections, and six 10-dB sections. **Table 25.5** lists the resistor values required for each section.

The enclosure is made of brass sheet stock, readily available at hardware and hobby stores. By selecting the right stock, you can avoid having to bend the metal and need only perform a minimum of cutting.

CONSTRUCTION

The enclosure can be built using only a nibbling tool, drill press, metal shears, and a soldering gun or heavy soldering iron. (Use a regular soldering iron on the switches and resistors.) One method of cutting the small pieces of rectangular tubing to length is to use a drill press equipped with a small abrasive cutoff wheel.

Brass is easy to work and solder. For the enclosure, you'll need two precut 2 × 12 × 0.025-inch sheets and two 1 × 12 × 0.025-inch sheets. The 2-inch-wide stock is used for the front and back panels; the 1-inch-wide stock is used for the ends and sides. For the internal wiring, you need a piece of 5/32 × 5/16-inch rectangular tubing, a 1/4 × 0.032-inch strip, and a few small pieces of 0.005-inch-thick stock to provide inter-stage shields and form the 50-Ω transmission lines that run from the BNC connectors to the switches at the ends of the step attenuator.

For the front panel, nibble or shear a piece of 2-inch-wide brass to a length of about 9½ inches. Space the switches from each other so that a piece of the rectangular brass tubing lies flat and snugly between them (see **Figure 25.85**). Drill holes for the #4-40 mounting screws and nibble or punch rectangular holes for the bodies of the slide switches.

Before mounting any parts, solder in place one of the 1-inch-wide chassis side pieces to make the assembly more rigid. Solder the side piece to the edge of the top plate that faces the "through" side of the switches; this makes later assembly easier (see **Figure 25.86**). Although the BNC input and output connectors are shown mounted on the top (front) panel, better lead dress and high-frequency performance may result from mounting the connectors at the ends of the enclosure.

DPDT slide switches designed for sub-panel mounting often have mounting holes tapped for #4-40 screws. Enlarge the holes to allow a #4-40 screw to slide through. Before mounting the switches, make the "through" switch connection (see Figure 25.84) by bending the two lugs at one end of each switch toward each other and soldering the lugs together or solder a small strip of brass between the lugs and clip off the lug ends. Mount the switches above the front panel, using 5/32-inch-high by 7/32-inch-OD spacers. Use the same size spacer on the inside. On the inside, the spacer creates a small post that helps reduce capacitive coupling from one side of the attenuator to the other. The spacers position the switch so that the 50-Ω

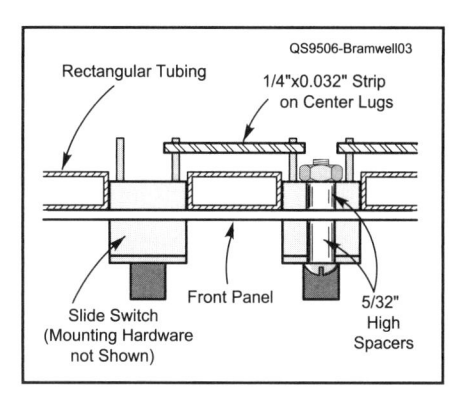

Figure 25.85 — Key to obtaining acceptable insertion loss in the "through" position is to make the whole device look as much as possible like 50-Ω coax. The rectangular tubing and the ¼ × 0.032-inch brass strip between the switch sections form a 50-Ω stripline.

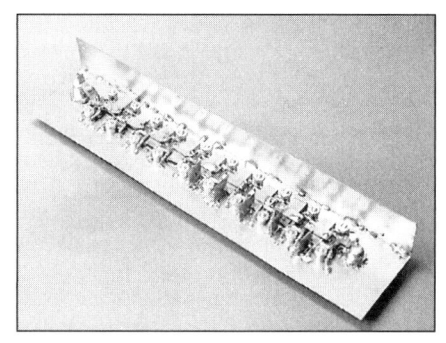

Figure 25.86 — Solder one of the 1-inch-wide chassis side pieces in place to make the assembly more rigid during construction. Solder the side piece to the edge of the top plate that faces the "through" side of the switches; this makes the rest of the assembly easier.

Figure 25.87 — The attenuator before final mechanical assembly. The ¼-inch strips are spaced 0.033 inch apart to form a 50-Ω connection from the BNC connector to the stripline. There are ½-inch square shields between 10-dB sections. The square shields have a notch in one corner to accommodate the end of the rectangular tubing.

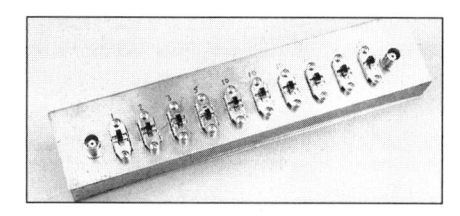

Figure 25.88 — The completed step attenuator in the enclosure of brass sheet. The BNC connectors may be mounted on the front panel at the end of the switches or on the end panels.

stripline can be formed later.

The trick to getting acceptable insertion loss in the "through" position is to make the attenuator look as much as possible like 50-Ω coax. That's where the rectangular tubing and the ¼ × 0.032-inch brass strip come into the picture (see Figure 25.85); they form a 50-Ω stripline. (See the **Transmission Lines** chapter for information on stripline.)

Cut pieces of the rectangular tubing about ¾-inch long, and sweat solder them to the front panel between each of the slide switches. Next, cut lengths of the ¼-inch strip long enough to conveniently reach from switch to switch, then cut one more piece. Drill 1/16-inch holes near both ends of all but one of the ¼-inch strips. The undrilled piece is used as a temporary spacer, so make sure it is flat and deburred.

Lay the temporary spacer on top of the rectangular tubing between the first two switches, then drop one of the drilled ¼-inch pieces over it, with the center switch lugs through the 1/16-inch holes. Before soldering, check the strip to make sure there's sufficient clearance between the ¼-inch strip and the switch lugs; trim the corners if necessary. Use a screwdriver blade to hold the strip flat and solder the lugs to the strip. Remove the temporary spacer. Repeat this procedure for all switch sections. This creates a 50-Ω stripline running the length of the attenuator.

Next, solder in place the three 1%-tolerance resistors of each section, keeping the leads as short as possible. Use a generous blob of solder on ground leads to make the lead less inductive. Install a ½-inch-square brass shield between each 10-dB section to ensure that signals don't couple around the sections at higher frequencies.

Use parallel ¼-inch strips of 0.005-inch-thick brass spaced 0.033 inch apart to form 50-Ω feed lines from the BNC connectors to the switch contacts at each end of the stripline as shown in Figure 25.86. (Use the undrilled piece of 0.032-inch-thick brass to insure the proper line spacing.) The attenuator with all switches and shields in place is shown ready for final mechanical assembly in **Figure 25.87**.

Finally, solder in place the remaining enclosure side, cut and solder the end pieces,

Test Equipment and Measurements 25.57

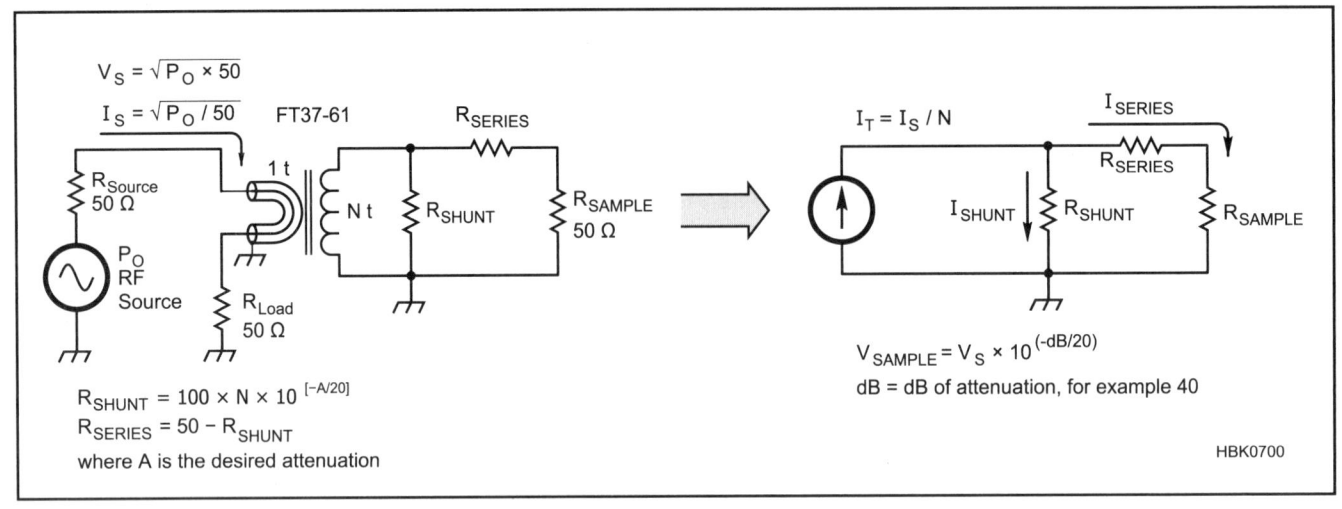

Figure 25.89 — RF sampler circuit diagram and equivalent circuit showing calculations.

and solder brass #4-40 nuts to the inside walls of the case to hold the rear (or bottom) panel. Drill and attach the rear panel and round off the sharp corners to prevent scratching or cutting anyone or anything. Add stick-on feet and labels and your step attenuator of **Figure 25.88** is ready for use.

Remember that the unit is built with ¼-W resistors, so it can't dissipate a lot of power. Remember, too, that for the attenuation to be accurate, the input to the attenuator must be a 50-Ω source and the output must be terminated in a 50-Ω load.

25.9.10 High-Power RF Samplers

If one wants to measure characteristics of a transmitter or high-powered amplifier, some means of reducing the power of the device to 10 or 20 dBm must be used. The most straightforward way to do this is to use a 30 or 40 dB attenuator capable of handling the high power. A 30 dB attenuator will reduce a 100 W transmitter to 20 dBm. A 40 dB attenuator will reduce a 1 kW amplifier to 20 dBm. If further attenuation is needed, a simple precision attenuator may be used after the signal has been reduced to the 20 dBm level.

The problem with high-powered attenuators is that they are expensive to buy or build since the front end of the attenuator must handle the output power of the transmitter or amplifier. If one already has a dummy load, an RF sampler may be used to produce a replica of the signal at a reduced power level. The sampler described here was originally presented in *QST* Technical Correspondence for May 2011 by Tom Thompson, WØIVJ.

A transformer sampler passes a single conductor (usually the insulated center conductor from a piece of coaxial cable) from the transmitter or amplifier to the dummy load through a toroidal inductor forming a transformer with a single turn primary. The secondary of the transformer is connected to a resistor network and then to the test equipment as shown in **Figure 25.89**. Assume that the source, whether a transmitter or amplifier, is a pure voltage source in series with a 50-Ω resistor. This most likely is not exactly the case but is sufficient for analysis.

If a current, I, flows into the dummy load, then a current, I / N flows in the secondary of the transformer, where N is the number of turns on the secondary. Figure 25.89 also shows the equivalent circuit, substituting a current source for the transformer. The attenuation is 40 dB and 15 turns for the secondary of the transformer. If $R_{SHUNT} = 15\ \Omega$, and $R_{SERIES} = 35\ \Omega$, then the voltage across a 50-Ω load resistor, R_{SAMPLE}, is 1/100 of the voltage across the dummy load, which is 40 dB of attenuation.

Reflecting this resistor combination back through the transformer yields 0.06 Ω in series with the 50-Ω dummy load impedance. This is an insignificant change. Furthermore, reflecting 100 Ω from the primary to the secondary places 22.5 kΩ in parallel with R_{SHUNT}, which does not significantly affect its value. The test equipment sees a 50-Ω load looking back into the sampler. Even at low frequencies, where the reactance of the secondary winding is lower than 15 Ω, the impedance looking back into the sample port remains close to 50 Ω.

The samplers described here use an FT37-61 ferrite core followed by two resistors as described above. The through-line SWR is good up to 200 MHz, the SWR is fair looking into the sampled port, and the useful bandwidth extends from 0.5 MHz to about 100 MHz. If you are interested in an accurate representation of the third harmonic of your HF transmitter or amplifier, it is important

Figure 25.90 — RF sampler using box construction.

for the sampler to give accurate attenuation into the VHF range.

Figure 25.90 shows a photo of a sampler built into a 1.3 × 1.3 × 1 inch (inside dimensions) box constructed from single-sided circuit board material. The through-line connection is made with a short piece of UT-141 semi-rigid coax with the shield grounded only on one side to provide electrostatic shielding between the toroid and the center conductor of the coax. (Do not ground both ends of the shield or a shorted turn is created.) R_{SHUNT} is hidden under the toroid, and R_{SERIES} is shown connected to the sample port. This construction technique looks like a short piece of 200-Ω transmission line in the through-line which affects the SWR at higher frequencies. This can be corrected by compensating with two 3 pF capacitors connected to the through-line input and output connectors as shown in the photo. The through-line SWR was reduced from 1.43:1 to 1.09:1 at 180 MHz by adding the capacitors. This compensation, however, causes the attenuation to differ at high frequencies depending on the direction of the through-line connection. A sampler constructed using the box technique is useable from below 1 MHz through 30 MHz.

Figure 25.91 shows a different approach using 9/16 inch diameter, 0.014 inch wall thickness, hobby brass tubing. This lowers the impedance of the through-line so that no compensation is needed. The through-line SWR for the tube sampler is 1.08:1 at 180 MHz which is as good as the box sampler and the sensitivity to through-line direction is reduced. Although the high frequency attenuation is not as good as the box sampler, the construction technique provides a more consistent result. A sampler constructed using the tube technique should be useable through 200 MHz.

CONSTRUCTION OF THE TUBE SAMPLER

Both samplers use 15 turns of #28 AWG wire on an FT37-61 core, which just fits over the UT-141 semi-rigid coax. R_{SHUNT} is a 15 Ω, 2 W, non-inductive metal oxide resistor and R_{SERIES} is a 34.8 Ω, ¼ W, 1% non-inductive metal film resistor. The power dissipation of the resistors and the flux handling capability of the ferrite core are adequate for sampling a 1500-W source. For those uncomfortable using BNC connectors at high power, an SO-239 version may be constructed using an FT50A-61 core and larger diameter tubing. Construction details are included with the downloadable supplemental content.

25.9.11 RF Oscillators for Circuit Alignment

Receiver testing and alignment can make use of inexpensive RF signal generators which are available as complete units and in kit form. Any source of signal that is weak enough to avoid overloading the receiver usually will serve for alignment work and troubleshooting.

A crystal oscillator is often a satisfactory signal source for amplifier testing and receiver repair or alignment. Several example circuits can be found in the **Oscillators and Synthesizers** chapter. The output frequencies of crystal oscillators, while not adjustable, are quite precise and very stable. The Elecraft XG2 (**www.elecraft.com**) and NorCal S9 (**www.norcalqrp.org**) are good examples of a simple fixed-frequency signal source kits. The harmonics of the output signals are on known frequencies and can also be used as low-level signal sources. The fundamental signals have known output amplitudes for calibrating S meters and other gain stages.

Variable frequency oscillators can be used as signal generators and there are several kits or assembled units available based on a direct digital synthesis (DDS) integrated circuit. (See the **DSP and Software Radio Design** chapter.) The Elecraft XG3 is a programmable signal source that operates from 1.5 to 200 MHz with four programmable output levels between –107 and 0 dBm.

For receiver performance testing, precise frequency control, signal purity, noise, and low-level signal leakage become very important. A lab-quality instrument is required to make these measurements. Commercial and military-surplus units such as the HP608-series are big and stable, and they may be inexpensive. Recently, the HP8640-series of signal generators have become widely available at very attractive prices. When buying a used or inexpensive signal generator, look for these attributes: output level is calibrated, the output doesn't "ring" too badly when tapped, and doesn't drift too badly when warmed up.

25.9.12 Hybrid Combiners for Signal Generators

Many receiver performance measurements require two signal generators to be attached to a receiver simultaneously. This, in turn, requires a combiner that isolates the two signal generators (to keep one generator from being frequency or phase modulated by the other). Commercially made hybrid combiners are available from Mini-Circuits Labs (**www.minicircuits.com**).

Alternatively, a hybrid combiner is not difficult to construct. The combiners described here (see **Figure 25.92**) provide 40 to 50 dB of isolation between ports, assuming the

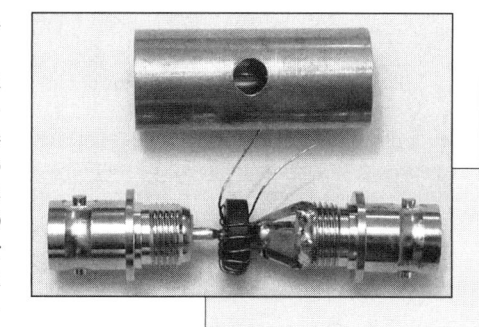

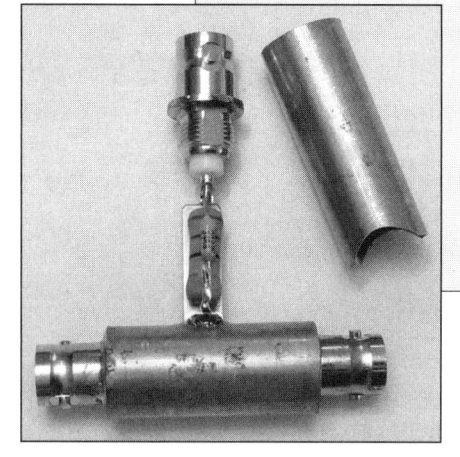

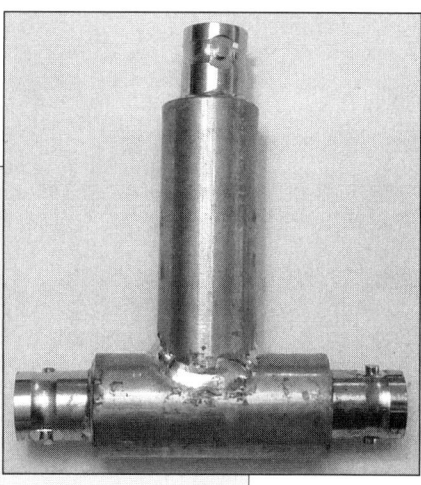

Figure 25.91— RF sampler using tube construction.

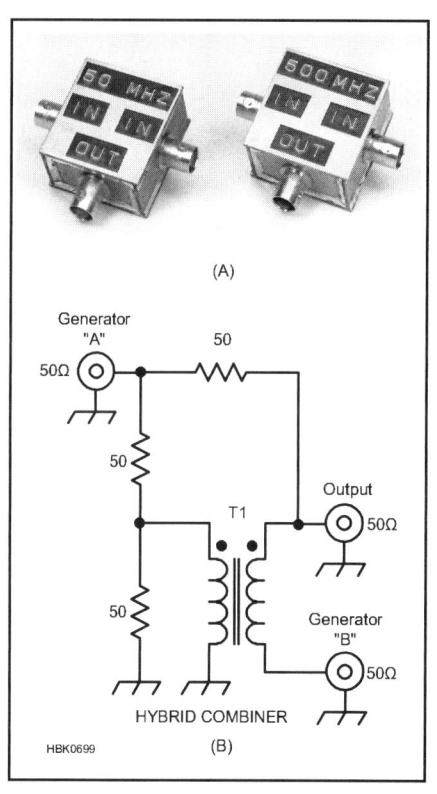

Figure 25.92 —The hybrid combiner on the left of A is designed to cover the 1 to 50-MHz range; the one on the right 50 to 500 MHz. B shows the circuit diagram of the hybrid combiner. Transformer T1 is wound with 10 bifilar turns of #30 AWG enameled wire. For the 1 to 50-MHz model, T1 is an FT-23-77 ferrite core. For the 50 to 500-MHz model, use an FT-23-67 ferrite core. Keep all leads as short as possible when constructing these units.

common port is terminated in a 50-ohm load. Attenuation in the desired signal paths (each input to output) is 6 dB. Loads with low return loss typical of receiver inputs will reduce isolation.

The combiners are constructed in small boxes made from double-sided circuit-board material as shown in Figure 25.92A. Each piece is soldered to the next one along the entire length of the seam. This makes a good RF-tight enclosure. BNC coaxial fittings are used on the units shown. However, any type of coaxial connector can be used. Leads must be kept as short as possible and precision non-inductive resistors (or matched units from the junk box) should be used. The circuit diagram for the combiners is shown in Figure 25.92B

The combiner may also be constructed and used as a *return loss bridge* as described in the *QST* article by Jim Ford, N6JF, "Build a Return Loss Bridge," from September 1997 and included with the downloadable supplemental content. Return loss is discussed in the **RF Techniques** chapter.

25.9.13 Gate-Dip Oscillator (GDO)

The project is adapted from the May 2003 *QST* article, "A Modern GDO — the "Gate" Dip Oscillator" by Alan Bloom, N1AL. A GDO is a tunable oscillator with the coil mounted outside of the chassis. The external coil allows you to measure the resonant frequency of a tuned circuit without any electrical connection to it. Just place the GDO coil near the tuned circuit and tune the GDO while watching for a dip in its meter reading.

This "no connection" measurement capability is handy in other applications. For example, you can measure the resonant frequency of a Yagi's parasitic elements that don't have a feed line connection or measure the resonant frequency of antenna traps. The GDO can "sniff out" spurious resonances

Figure 25.93 — The "gate dipper" fits comfortably in the hand.

in a linear amplifier's tank circuit with the amplifier powered down. (Be sure no high voltage is present!)

The GDO has other uses on the workbench. To measure inductance, temporarily connect a known-value capacitor in parallel with the unknown inductor and find the circuit's resonant frequency. Use the formula $L = 1/(2\pi f)^2 C$ or the reactance vs frequency chart in the **Electrical Fundamentals** chapter to find the value of the inductor. (If C is measured in µF and f in MHz, the resulting value of L is in µH.) The same process works to find the value of a capacitor, such as that of an unmarked air-variable capacitor at a hamfest, by using the formula $C = 1/(2\pi f)^2 L$.

A GDO can be used as a simple signal generator to test amplifiers, mixers, and filters. To troubleshoot a receiver, tune the GDO to each of the IF frequencies, starting with the last IF stage and hold the coil close to that part of the circuitry. If you can hear a signal at the receiver's output, then that IF stage and all circuitry after it are working. This is especially handy on densely packed, surface-mount boards that are difficult to probe.

With the oscillator turned off, the GDO functions as a tuned RF detector known as an *absorption frequency meter* or *wavemeter*. An obvious use is to determine if RF energy in a tuned circuit has the right frequency. Using the capacity probe as an antenna, it can be used as a frequency-selective field-strength meter. By holding the coil near a cable, you can detect RF current flowing on the outside of a shield and the GDO makes an excellent

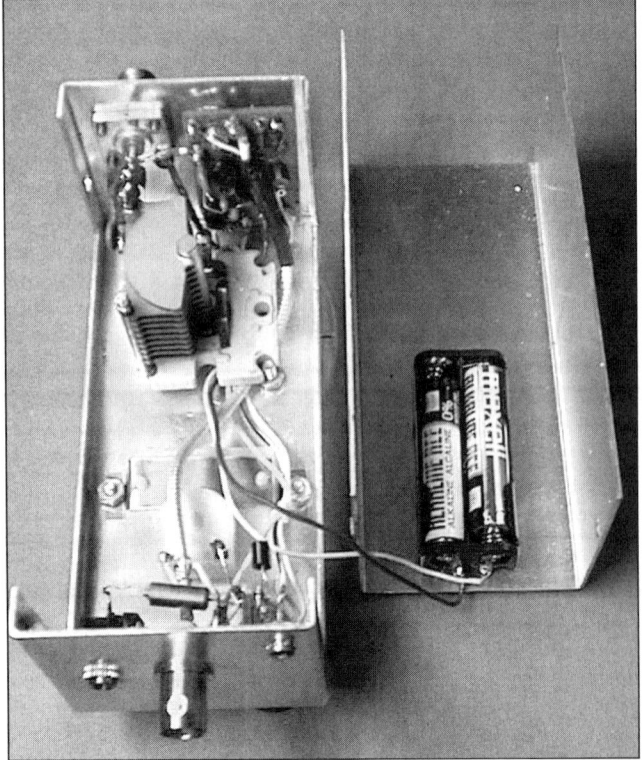

Figure 25.94 — Photograph of the GDO with the cover off. The tuning capacitor was oriented for the shortest possible connection to the coil connector. The prototype was constructed with two batteries but three result in better operation.

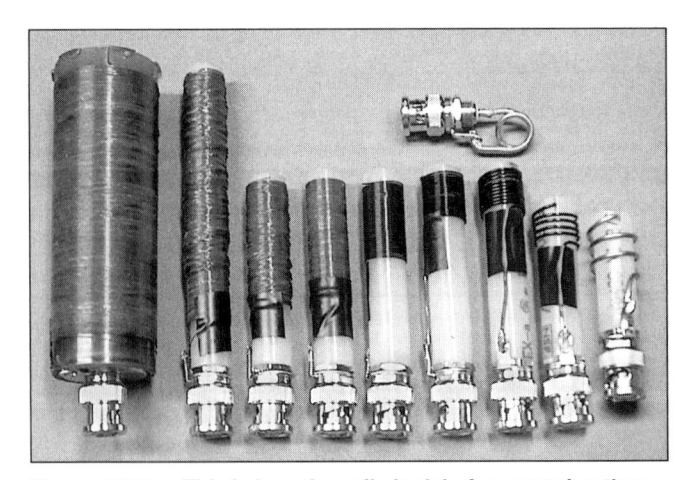

Figure 25.95 — This is how the coils look before covering them with heat-shrink tubing or tape. Small pieces of electrical tape are used to hold the turns in place during construction.

"sniffer" to detect RF leakage from a shielded transmitter at the fundamental and harmonic frequencies.

A headphone output is provided to listen for key clicks, hum or buzz, and low-frequency parasitic oscillations in a transmitted signal. By coupling the coil to an antenna, you can even use the GDO as a tunable "crystal radio"!

CIRCUIT DESIGN

Figure 25.93 shows the completed GDO. **Figure 25.94** is a view inside the case and **Figure 25.95** pictures the entire set of coils. The schematic and parts list are shown in **Figure 25.96**. A pair of source-coupled N-channel JFETs (Q1 and Q2) form the oscillator portion of the circuit. No RF chokes are required. This eliminates false resonances resulting from self-resonance of the chokes.

Q4, a bipolar 2N3904 transistor, serves a dual purpose. Its base-emitter junction acts as the RF detector. Further, it amplifies the rectified current flowing in the base and sends it to the emitter-follower Q5, a 2N2907. Transistor Q3 is a JFET source-follower amplifier for the output RF connector. The RF output may be used as a signal source or to drive a frequency counter for more accurate frequency display.

Determine the value of R5 using the formula $R5 = (1.5/I_m) - R_m$, where I_m is the full-scale meter current and R_m is the meter resistance. To measure your meter's resistance, be sure to use an ohmmeter that does not use more than the GDO meter's full-scale current. Most modern DVMs use test currents in the range off 50-200 µA for measuring resistance. The value of R5 in the parts list is for a 200 µA full-scale meter used by the author. Meters from 50 to 500 µA full-scale are suitable.

In detector mode, the power to the oscillator and RF buffer is turned off. Q4 detects and amplifies any signals picked up by the coil. The meter sensitivity control works in both oscillator and wavemeter mode and also controls the volume to the headphones. Battery current is 3-5 mA with the oscillator on and zero in wavemeter mode when no signal is being received.

CONSTRUCTION

Feel free to substitute parts on hand for those in the parts list. The exceptions are

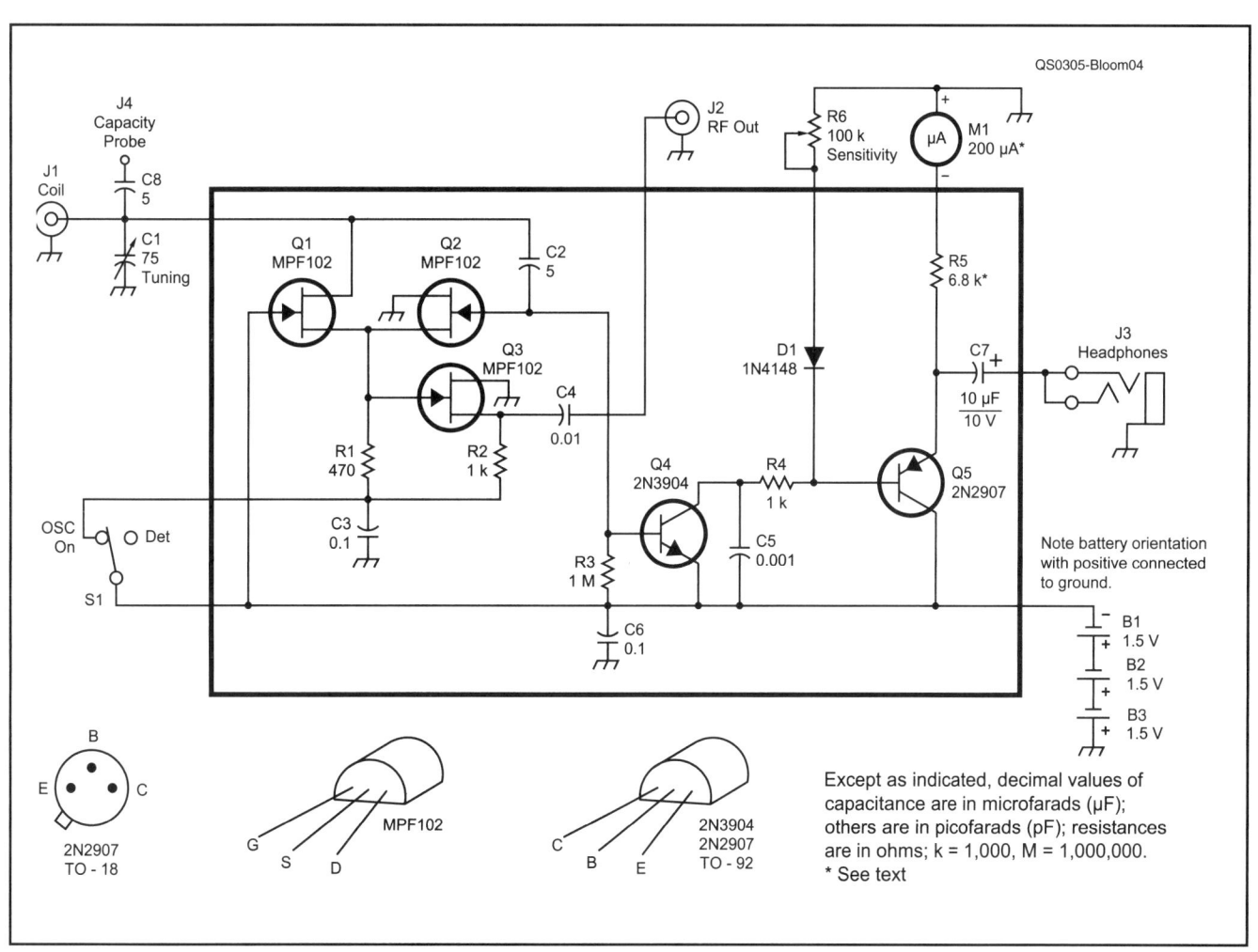

Figure 25.96 — Schematic diagram of the GDO.

B1, B2, B3 — 1.5 V AA or AAA cell.
C1 — 75 pF or 365 pF variable.
C2, C8 — 5 pF disc capacitor.
C3, C6 — 0.1 µF capacitor.
C4 — 0.01 µF capacitor.
C5 — 0.001 µF capacitor.
C7 — 10 µF, 10 V capacitor.
D1 — 1N4148 diode.
J1, J2 — BNC female chassis-mount connector.
J3 — 3.5 mm stereo phone jack.
J4 — Phone tip jack, phone tip plug.
M1 — 0-200µA, 1⅝ inch square panel meter, (see text).
Q1, Q2, Q3 — MPF102 transistor, JFET.
Q4 — 2N3904 transistor.
Q5 — 2N2907A transistor.
R1 — 470 Ω, ¼ W resistor.
R2, R4 — 1 kΩ, ¼ W resistor.
R3 — 1 MΩ, ¼ W resistor.
R5 — See text.
R6 — 100 kΩ potentiometer, linear taper.
S1 — SPST toggle switch.
Misc: #18, #22 and #26 gauge enameled wire; 10 BNC male chassis-mount connector (for coils); dual AA or AAA battery holder; 2¼ × 2¼ × 5 inch chassis; 3 ft of ⅜ inch PVC water tubing for coils.

transistors Q1, Q2, and Q4, which should be the types specified or their equivalents.

The 2¼ × 2¼ × 5 inch chassis is a compromise; it's large enough to allow all parts to fit easily and small enough to fit comfortably in the hand. The coil is mounted off-center, both to allow the shortest connection to the tuning capacitor and to afford easier coil coupling to an external circuit.

The prototype used a perforated test board for the RF portion of the circuitry and a solder terminal strip for the meter circuitry. If you prefer, a printed circuit board pattern and parts layout are available on this book's CD-ROM and circuit boards are available from FAR Circuits (**www.farcircuits.net**). Note that the battery's *positive* terminal is connected to ground which is backwards from the normal arrangement.

The coil forms are "⅜ inch" flexible plastic water tubing. The inside diameter is actually slightly less than ⅜ inch, which makes a nice force-fit onto the ⅜-inch threads of a chassis-mount BNC plug (not the more common chassis-mount receptacle). The lowest-frequency coil is wound on a pill bottle with two 1-inch diameter aluminum washers at the connector mount for added strength.

To construct the coils, start by running the wire through the center of each form and soldering it to the BNC connector's center pin connection. Then press the form onto the connector threads and cut a small notch in the form's opposite end to hold the wire in place for the winding. After winding the coil, cut and tin the wire end, then solder it to the ground lug mounted on the connector. Cover each coil with a layer of heat-shrink tubing or electrical tape to hold the turns in place and protect the wire. Clear tubing allows you to see the coil and a small label with the coil's frequency range can be placed under the tubing before shrinking. Figure 25.95 shows the coils before the heat shrink tubing is added.

Winding data is listed in **Table 25.6**. Unless you happen to duplicate the prototype exactly, the frequency range of each coil is likely to be different. However, this data can be used as a starting point for your own coil designs.

The heavy wire for the two highest-frequency coils is bare copper scrap from house wiring cable. The other coils are wound with enamel-insulated magnet wire. The exact wire gauge is not critical although it may affect the number of turns required.

The three smallest coils (29.5-150 MHz) were space wound to the lengths listed. The remaining coils were close-wound. On the 0.9-1.5 and 1.5-2.8 MHz coils, there are too many turns to fit in a single layer. Wind these coils by overlapping turns a few at a time. Winding two complete overlapping layers increases the inter-winding capacitance which can cause spurious resonances and reduced tuning range.

The range of the lowest-frequency coil can be extended by connecting it to the GDO through a BNC "T" connector to which one or two 53 pF capacitors are attached using clip leads (see Table 25.6). Adding extra capacitance is a useful way to slow down the tuning rate for measuring narrow-band devices such as crystals.

With the smallest coil, the GDO oscillates over only a small portion of the capacitor tuning range. Fortunately, this range covers the 2 meter amateur band. With the second-smallest coil, the oscillation amplitude drops off at lower frequencies but is useable down to about 62 MHz in the prototype. A lower-inductance tuning capacitor would improve performance at VHF.

The small 75-pF tuning capacitor results in a tuning range of only about 2:1. The advantage of the low ratio is that tuning is not so critical and the frequency dial is easier to read. The disadvantage is that it requires more coils to cover the overall frequency range. Substituting a 365-pF AM broadcast radio tuning capacitor will increase the tuning range to nearly 3:1 with a consequent sharpening of adjustment.

The tuning dial in **Figure 25.97** was made from a circular piece of ¼-inch clear plastic glued to a knob. Making the diameter slightly larger than the chassis width allows one handed operation with a thumb adjusting the tuning as in Figure 25.93. The scale, cemented to the chassis under the dial, was drawn using a computer graphics program although measuring the frequency and creating the scales was very time-consuming. A better solution would be to include a small frequency counter with the GDO using the RF output. 4- or 5-digit accuracy is sufficient.

OPERATION

To measure the resonant frequency of a tuned circuit, switch to oscillator mode and adjust the meter sensitivity to about ¾ scale. Then orient the GDO coil close to and approximately parallel to the coil under test and tune the dial until you get a strong dip on the meter. Tune slowly or you may miss the dip. Overly-close coupling to the circuit under test causes such a strong dip that the oscillator is pulled far off-frequency. Once a dip is found, move the GDO coil farther from the circuit under test until the dip is barely visible — this results in the most accurate measurement.

Coupling to toroids or shielded coils can be difficult. One solution is to connect a wire from the capacitance probe to the "hot" end of the circuit to be tested. For looser coupling, just place the wire close to the circuit under test instead of connecting it to the circuit. When measuring the inductance of a toroid with a test capacitor, the capacitor leads often form enough of a loop to allow coupling to the GDO coil. Some authors recommend coupling the GDO to a one-turn loop through the toroid, but that creates a shorted secondary winding, changing the inductance of the toroid winding.

Antenna measurements are best made at the high-current point of the antenna conductor. For a half-wave dipole, this is near the center. Orient the coil perpendicular to the conductor for maximum coupling. Be sure to short the feed point of the antenna before making the measurement. If you can't find the dip, make the shorting wire into a 1-turn loop for better coupling to the GDO coil You should also see resonance at the odd harmonic frequencies as well as the fundamental.

To measure the electrical length of a trans-

Table 25.6
Coil Winding Data for the GDO

Wire Gauge	Form Diameter (in.)	Form Length (in.)	Coil Length (in.)	Number of Turns	Frequency Range
#12	0.375	—	0.125	2	130-150 MHz
#14	0.5	1.5	.5	3	62-108 MHz
#18	0.5	2.0	0.4	5	29.5-62 MHz
#18	0.5	2.5	0.5	10.5	16.5-35 MHz
#22	0.5	2.5	0.6	21	9.2-19 MHz
#26	0.5	2.5	1.0	46	5.1-10.5 MHz
#30	0.5	2.5	1.5	100	2.8-5.6 MHz
#30	0.5	2.5	1.6	180	1.5-2.8 MHz
#30	0.5	3.9	3.3	390	0.9-1.5 MHz
#30	1.25	3.9	3.4	230	620-980 kHz
				(+53 pF)	505-640 kHz
				(+106 pF)	440-525 kHz

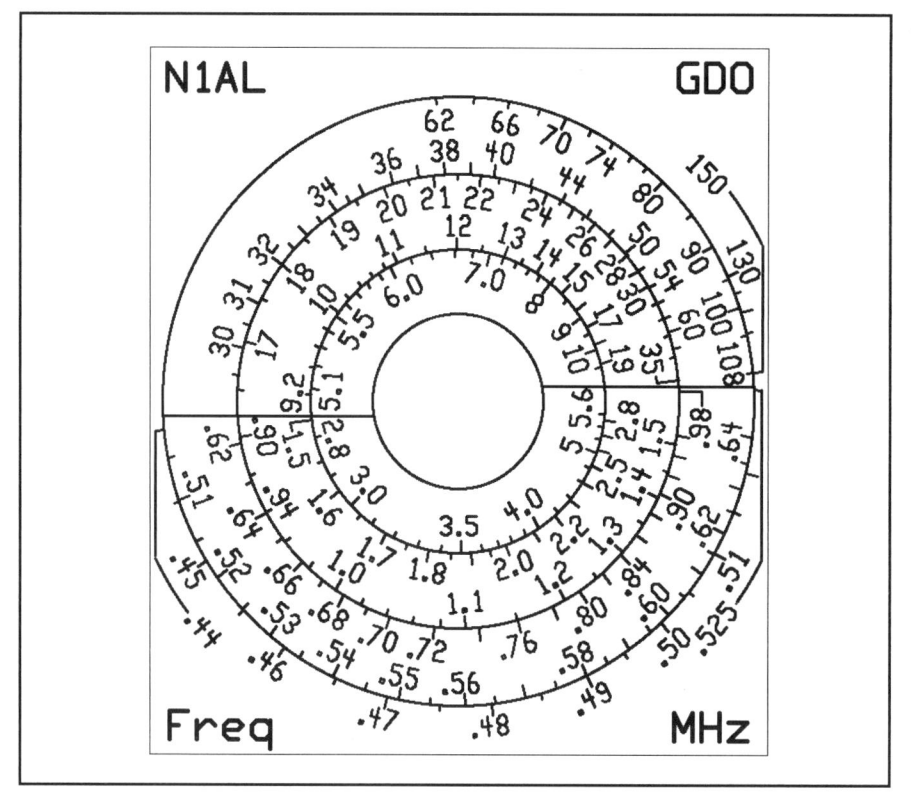

Figure 25.97 — The dial scale for the prototype GDO. Builders of this project should expect to create and calibrate a custom dial for the finished instrument or use a frequency counter as noted in the text.

mission line, couple the GDO to a small wire loop; connect it to one end of the line and leave the other end disconnected. (For best accuracy use the smallest loop that gives sufficient coupling.) The line is ¼ wavelength long at the lowest resonant frequency, so the electrical length in meters is 75/f, where f is the resonant frequency in MHz. Again, you will also see resonance at the odd harmonics.

The voltage level at the RF output connector varies from coil to coil but typically runs about 250 mV$_{RMS}$ into an open circuit and 50 mV$_{RMS}$ into a 50-Ω load. That is sufficient for a typical frequency counter or to serve as a test signal for troubleshooting.

Additional uses of the GDO are presented in the following articles with the downloadable supplemental content: "The Art of Dipping" in Jan 1974 *QST*, "Add-Ons for Greater Dipper Versatility" in Feb 1981 *QST*, and "What Can You Do with a Dip Meter?" in May 2002 *QST*.

25.9.14 RF Power Meter

The following section is an overview of the January 2011 *QST* article by Bill Kaune, W7IEQ, "A Modern Directional Power/SWR Meter". The complete article including firmware and printed circuit board artwork is available with the downloadable supplemental content.

The primary use for this unit is to monitor the output power and tuning of a transceiver. The author's station configuration is shown in **Figure 25.98**. RF power generated by the transmitter is routed via RG-8 coaxial cable through a directional coupler to an antenna tuner, which is connected to the antenna with RG-8. The directional coupler contains circuits that sample the RF power flowing from the transmitter to the tuner (the forward power) and the RF power reflected back from the tuner to the transmitter (the reflected power).

These samples are sent via RG-58 cable to the two input channels of the power meter. This project includes the directional coupler and the power meter. Enough detail is provided in the full article so that an amateur can duplicate the device or modify the design.

DIRECTIONAL COUPLER

The directional coupler is based on the unit described in "The Tandem Match" by John Grebenkemper, KI6WX in the Jan 1987 issue of *QST* and also included with the downloadable supplemental content. A pair of FT-82-67 toroids with 31 turns of #26 AWG magnet wire over lengths of RG-8 form the basis of the directional coupler shown in **Figure 25.99**.

The forward and reflected power samples coupled are reduced by a factor of 1/N^2, where N = 31 is the number of turns of wire on each toroid. Thus the forward and reflected power samples are reduced by about 30 dB. For example, if a transceiver were delivering a power of 100 W to a pure 50 Ω load, the forward power sample from the directional coupler would be about 0.1 W (20 dBm).

The directivity of a directional coupler is defined as the ratio of the forward power sample divided by the reflected power sample when the coupler is terminated in 50 Ω. In this coupler, the directivity measured using an inexpensive network analyzer is at least 35 dB at 3.5 MHz and 28 dB at 30 MHz.

POWER/SWR METER — CIRCUIT DESCRIPTION

Figure 25.100 shows a front panel view of the power meter. An LCD displays the measured peak (PEP) and average (AEP) envelope powers as well as the standing wave ratio (SWR). The power meter calculates either the peak and average envelope power traveling from the transceiver to load (the forward power) or the peak and average enve-

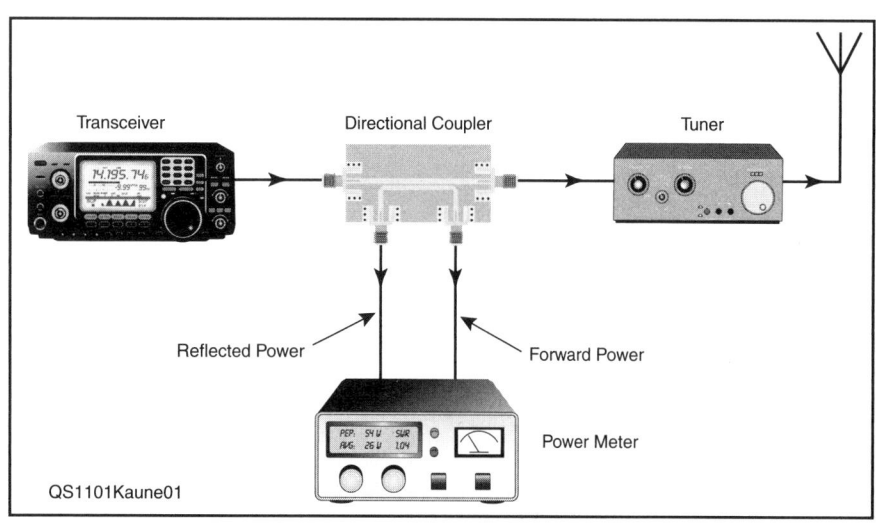

Figure 25.98 — W7IEQ station setup, including the power meter being described here.

Figure 25.99 — Completed directional coupler.

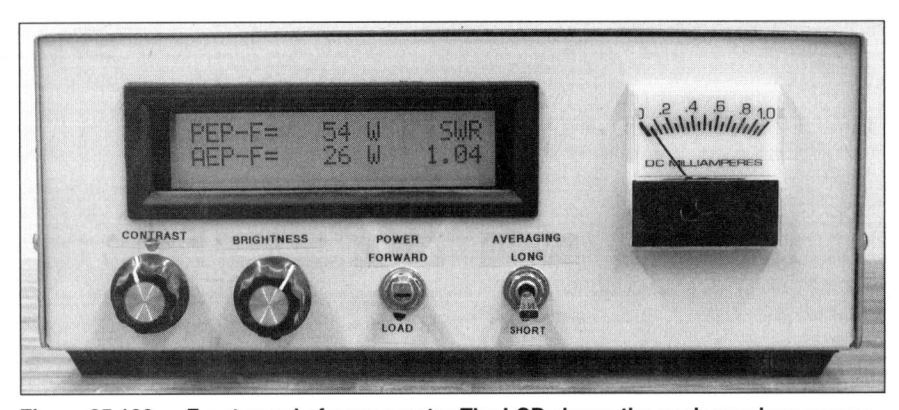

Figure 25.100 — Front panel of power meter. The LCD shows the peak envelope power (PEP), the average envelope power (AEP) and the SWR. The two knobs control the contrast and back lighting of the LCD. One toggle switch determines whether forward or load powers are displayed. A second switch sets the averaging time for the AEP calculation. The meter displays SWR and is used for tuning purposes.

lope powers actually delivered to the load (the forward power minus reflected power). The average envelope power (AEP) represents an average of the forward or load powers over an averaging period of either 1.6 or 4.8 seconds.

A 1 mA-movement analog meter on the front panel facilitates antenna tuning. This meter continuously displays the quantity 1 − 1/SWR, where SWR is the standing wave ratio on the line. Thus, an SWR of 1.0 corresponds to a meter reading of 0 — no deflection of the meter. An SWR of 2 results in a 50% deflection of the meter, while an SWR of 5 produces an 80% deflection of the meter.

The forward and reflected power samples from the directional coupler are applied to a pair of Analog Devices AD8307 logarithmic detectors. External 20 dB attenuators (Mini-Circuits HAT-20) reduce the signals from the directional coupler to levels compatible with the AD8307. As noted earlier, the directional coupler has an internal attenuation of about 30 dB, so the total attenuation in each channel is about 50 dB. Thus, a rig operating at a power level of 1 kW (60 dBm) will result in an input to the forward power channel of about 10 dBm. (The schematic diagram and parts list of the power meter are provided with the downloadable supplemental content.) The detectors are configured such that the time constant of their output follows the modulation envelope of the RF signal.

LF398 sample-and-hold ICs stabilize the voltages from the forward and reflected power logarithmic detectors. In this way both voltages can be sampled at the exact same time and held for subsequent analog-to-digital conversion and calculation of power and SWR by the PIC16F876A microprocessor (**www.microchip.com**). The processor also includes a pulse-width-modulated (PWM)

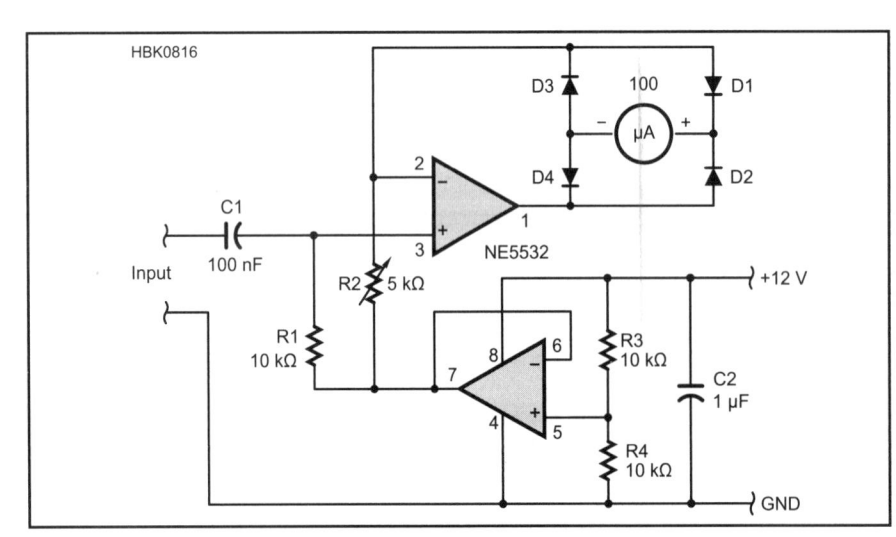

Figure 25.101 — RF voltmeter schematic. See text for op-amp substitution requirements. D1 – D4 are 1N4148.

Figure 25.102 — RF voltmeter construction. Keep leads short. Point-to-point construction can be used and mounted directly on the meter for mechanical simplicity.

25.64 Chapter 25

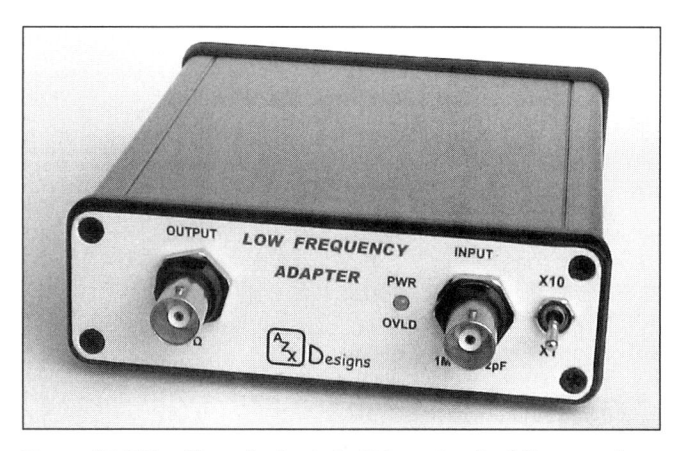

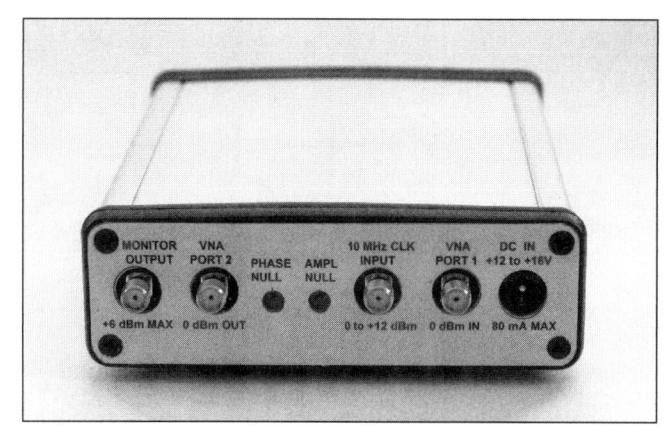

Figure 25.103 — The adapter is built in a standard Hammond extruded aluminum cabinet. Front and rear panels are pictured.

output used to drive the analog SWR meter on the front panel.

25.9.15 RF Voltmeter

Anthony Langton, GM4THU, designed this simple RF voltmeter to measure low RF voltages from oscillators and other low-power RF circuits through several MHz. It has an approximately 10 kΩ input impedance to avoid loading the circuit under test but not so high that it is unduly affected by stray capacitance.

Figure 25.101 shows the meter's circuit. C1 blocks dc voltage and R1 sets the input impedance. The upper section of the NE5532 op-amp is a precision rectifier. D1-D4 should be 1N4148. The lower section of the NE5532 is a supply splitter and can be replaced by a low-bandwidth op-amp, such as a 741 or equivalent. If substituted, the upper op-amp should have a gain-bandwidth product of at least 10 MHz.

R3 adjusts the voltage-to-current conversion ratio. With a 100 µA full-scale meter, maximum voltage range is approximately 1 V. There is enough adjustment range to calibrate the meter for peak, RMS, or peak-to-peak voltage readings.

Figure 25.102 shows the meter circuit construction. Leads should be kept short and the entire circuit can be constructed as point-to-point wiring and mounted directly on the back of the analog meter. The original meter used a BNC connector for input connections.

25.9.16 A Low-Frequency VNA Adapter

(The following project is based on the *QEX* article "A Low Frequency Adapter for you Vector Network Analyzer (VNA)" by Jacques Audet, VE2AZX. An overview is given here while the full description, including links to construction files and other information, is provided in PDF with the downloadable supplemental content.)

The Low Frequency Adapter adds low frequency capability to a vector network analyzer (VNA), as well as adding audio frequency generation, 1 MΩ probe amplified interface, and direct conversion receiver capability. In the VNA application, an IF bandwidth of 10 Hz must be used to extend the lowest frequency down to 20 Hz. The low frequency adapter has allowed the author to measure R, L and C components down to 20 Hz, using a Hewlett Packard 8753D VNA. He has also been able to accurately characterize and document the response of many audio type amplifiers that otherwise would have required tedious measurement methods. More information on this adapter is available at **ve2azx.net/technical/LFA/LowFreqAdapter.htm**.

All S_{21} measurements are performed within the 10 to 15 MHz frequency range of the VNA. The low frequency measurements include:
- S_{21} magnitude and phase
- Group delay
- Compression point at a single frequency
- TRU calibration, with the device under test bypassed with a short circuit, to set a reference amplitude and phase frequency response.

The adapter can also be used as probe buffer/amplifier, a low frequency signal generator, a direct conversion receiver, and a vector voltmeter at low frequencies. S_{11} (reflection coefficient) measurements cannot be made directly with this adapter but the author provides a method and supporting spreadsheet for converting transmission measurements to impedance values. Construction of the adapter is shown in **Figure 25.103** and **Figure 25.104**.

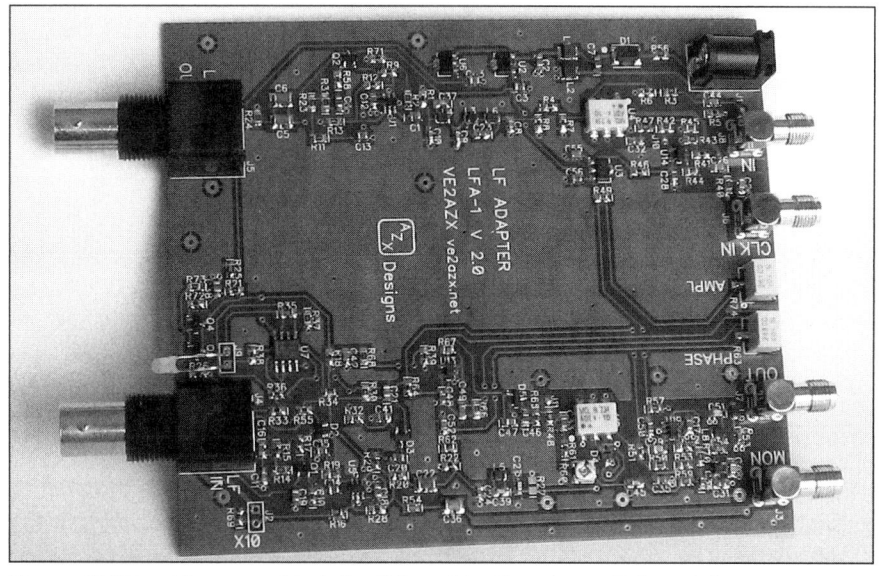

Figure 25.104 — The assembled circuit board for the adapter. R, L, and C components are 0805 SMT packages. Smaller 0603 components may also be used and will fit on the pads. See the CD-ROM version of this article and the author's website for additional information on the PCB.

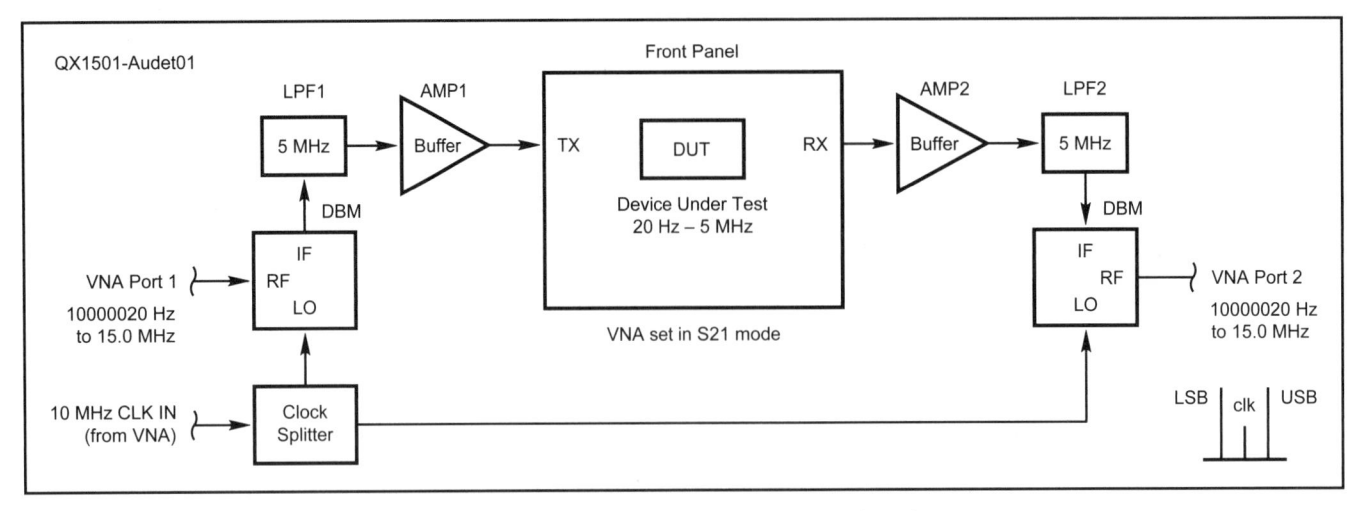

Figure 25.105 — Basic block diagram of the low frequency adapter for vector network analyzers.

The VNA is configured to use frequencies from 10 MHz to 15 MHz on its output (port 1) when measuring S_{21} (attenuation or gain as well as phase shift between ports 1 and 2). **Figure 25.105** shows the adapter's block diagram. The output signal is mixed in a double balanced mixer (DBM) with a local oscillator (LO) of 10 MHz. The difference signals from 20 Hz to 5 MHz are passed through a low-pass filter (LPF) and are available at the transmit (TX) output port for frequency response testing. The output of the device under test (DUT) is fed to a high impedance buffer and to a 5 MHz low pass filter before being re-multiplexed in the 10 to 15 MHz range by a second DBM.

The signal at the RF output of the first mixer generates sidebands (mixing products) above and below the 10 MHz LO frequency. The VNA synchronously demodulates the upper sideband and uses this signal to compute the attenuation or gain of the device under test. Both the first and second 5 MHz filters (LPF1 and LPF2) provide attenuation of the 10 MHz LO signal, so it does not pass thru the device under test. These filters also greatly attenuate the sum frequencies in the 20 to 25 MHz range, which could decrease the accuracy if these were present at the second DBM IF input.

Since the VNA does coherent detection of the signal (in order to measure the phase), it is necessary to synchronize its internal clock with the low frequency adapter LO signal. This is normally done by using a common external 10 MHz clock feeding the VNA and the low frequency adapter. This also enables the low frequency adapter to do S_{21} phase measurements from 20 Hz to 5 MHz.

In order for the low frequency adapter to be as transparent as possible to the VNA, it has unity gain from its input and output. Also the TX output port has a 50 Ω impedance to drive low impedance loads. On the receive side, the input impedance consists of 1 MΩ in parallel with 8 pF so that it is compatible with oscilloscope probes. An additional capacitor may be added to match a specific scope's input capacitance, thus providing a flat frequency response with an external ×10 probe. The high impedance allows the user to terminate the device under test by shunting a parallel termination across the receive (RX) input.

25.10 References and Further Reading

25.10.1 References

1. National Institute of Standards and Technology, **www.nist.gov**
2. Hageman, Steve, "Build a Data Acquisition System for your Computer" (Tech Notes), *QEX*, Jan/Feb 2001, pp 52-57.
3. Prologix is one manufacturer of low-cost GPIB-to-USB converters. **www.prologix.biz**
4. Bryce, Mike, WB8VGE, "A Universal Frequency Calibrator," *QST*, Nov 2009, pp 35-37.
5. Bradley, Mark, K6TAF, "What Can You Do With a Dip Meter?," *QST*, May 2002, pp 65-68.
6. Miller, Bob, KE6F, "Atomic Frequency Reference for Your Shack," *QEX*, Sept/Oct 2009, pp 35-44.
7. Nash, Bob, KF6CDO, "An Event per Unit Time Measurement System for Rubidium Frequency Standards," *QEX*, Nov/Dec 2010, pp 3-17.
8. Jones, Bill, K8CU, "Using the HP Z3801A GPS Frequency Standard," *QEX*, Nov/Dec 2002, pp 49-53.
9. Shera, Brooks, W5OJM, "A GPS-Based Frequency Standard," *QST*, July 1998.
10. Richardson, Gary, AA7VM, "A Low Cost DDS Function Generator," *QST*, Nov 2005, pp 40-42.
11. Z. Lau, "A Relative RF Ammeter for Open-Wire Lines," *QST*, Oct 1988, pp 15-17.
12. Steinbaugh, Gary, AF8L, "An Inexpensive Laboratory-Quality RF Wattmeter," *QEX*, May/Jun 2010, pp 26-32.
13. Bird, Trevor S., "Definition and Misuse of Return Loss," *QEX*, Sep/Oct 2010, pp 38-39.
14. Baier, Thomas C., DG8SAQ, "A Simple S-Parameter Test Set for the VNWA2 Vector Network Analyzer," *QEX*, May/Jun 2009, pp 29-32.
15. AN 1287-3, "Applying Error Correction to Network Analyzer Measurements," Agilent Technologies. (**literature.cdn.keysight.com/litweb/pdf/5965-7709E.pdf?id=1000000361:epsg:apn**)
16. Baier, Thomas C., DG8SAQ, "A Small, Simple USB-Powered Vector Network Analyzer Covering 1 kHz to 1.3 GHz," *QEX*, Jan/Feb 2009, pp 32-36. **www.sdr-kits.net/VNWA/VNWA_Description.html**

17. McDermott, Tom, N5EG, et al, "A Low-Cost 100 MHz Vector Network Analyzer with USB Interface," *QEX*, Jul/Aug 2004. **www.tapr.org/kits_vna.html**
18. Detailed instructions to build N2PK's vector network analyzer are at **http://n2pk.com**.
19. Application Note 57-1, "Fundamentals of RF and Microwave Noise Figure Measurements," (**literature.cdn.keysight.com/litweb/pdf/5952-8255E.pdf?id=1000001634:epsg:apn**). The older Hewlett-Packard application note AN57 may be more useful for legacy noise figure meters such as the HP340 series.
20. Pontius, Bruce E., NØADL, "Measurement of Signal-Source Phase Noise with Low-Cost Equipment," *QEX*, May/Jun 1998.
21. Noakes, John D., VE7NI, "The 'No Fibbin' RF Field Strength Meter, *QST*, Aug 2002, pp 28-29,
22. At microwave frequencies, the antenna and radio are sometimes tested as a system. Wade, Paul, W1GHZ, "Microwave System Test," Microwavelengths, *QST*, Aug 2010, pp 96-97.
23. PathSim, free HF channel simulation software. **www.moetronix.com/ae4jy/pathsim.htm**
24. Forrer, Johann B., KC7WW, "A Low-Cost HF Channel Simulator for Digital Systems," *QEX*, May/Jun 2000, pp 13-22.
25. Information on the Softrock I/Q downconverters is available at **www.softrockradio.org**.
26. Bruene, W., W5OLY (WØTTK), "An Inside Picture of Directional Wattmeters," *QST*, Apr 1959, p 24.
27. McCoy, L., W1ICP, "The Monimatch," *QST*, Oct 1956, p 11.
28. Bold, G., ZL1AN, "The Bruene Directional Coupler and Transmission Lines," Version 1.1, 6 Dec 2006, **www.physics.auckland.ac.nz/staff/geb/SWR.pdf**.

25.10.2 Further Reading

Agilent Technologies, "Resistance; dc Current; ac Current; and Frequency and Period Measurement Errors in Digital Multimeters, Application Note AN 1389-2." (**literature.cdn.keysight.com/litweb/pdf/5988-5512EN.pdf?id=1000002205:epsg:apn**).

Agilent Technologies, "Test-System Development Guide Application Notes 1465-1 through 1465-8." (**literature.cdn.keysight.com/litweb/pdf/5989-2178EN.pdf?id=1309577**). Keysight Technologies, **www.keysight.com**.

Hayward, Wes, W7ZOI et al, *Experimental Methods in RF Design*, Chapter 7, "Measurement Equipment," ARRL, 2003.

Silver, H. Ward, NØAX, "Test Equipment for the Ham Shack." *QST*, May 2005, pp 36-39.

Antenna System Measurements

Althouse, J., K6NY, "The Noise Bridge," *QST*, Sep 1992, pp. 75-78.

Hallas, Joel, W1ZR, Understanding Your Antenna Analyzer, ARRL, 2013.

Knitter, M. DG5MK, "The DG5MK IV Meter — An Accurate Antenna Analyzer," *QEX*, May/June 2017, pp 3-14.

Mack, Ray, W5IFS, "Using Time Domain Reflectometry for Transmission Line Impedance Measurement," *QEX*, July 2013, p 26.

Silver, H. Ward, NØAX, "Experiment #52 — SWR Meters," *QST*, May 2007, pp 57-58.

High-Frequency Measurements

Agilent Technologies, "Fundamentals of RF and Microwave Noise Figure Measurements, Application Note 57-1." (**literature.cdn.keysight.com/litweb/pdf/5952-8255E.pdf?id=1000001634:epsg:apn**).

Carr, Joseph J., *Practical Radio Frequency Test and Measurement: a Technician's Handbook*, Boston, Newness Co., 1999.

Straw, R. Dean, N6BV, *The ARRL Antenna Book*, 21st edition, Chapter 27, "Antenna and Transmission-Line Measurements," ARRL, 2009.

Oscilloscopes

Agilent Technologies, "Agilent Technologies Oscilloscope Fundamentals, Application Note 1606." A similar application note is Keysight Technologies 5989-8064EN, **literature.cdn.keysight.com/litweb/pdf/5989-8064EN.pdf?id=1419669**.

R. vanErk, *Oscilloscopes, Functional Operation and Measuring Examples*, McGraw-Hill Book Co, New York, 1978.

V. Bunze, *Probing in Perspective — Application Note 152*, Hewlett-Packard Co, Colorado Springs, CO, 1972 (Pub No. 5952-1892).

The XYZs of Using a Scope, Tektronix, Inc, Portland, OR, 1981 (Pub No. 41AX-4758).

Basic Techniques of Waveform Measurement (Parts 1 and 2), *Hewlett-Packard Co*, Colorado Springs, CO, 1980 (Pub No. 5953-3873).

J. Millman, and H. Taub, *Pulse Digital and Switching Waveforms*, McGraw-Hill Book Co, New York, 1965, pp 50-54.

V. Martin, *ABCs of DMMs*, Fluke Corp, PO Box 9090, Everett, WA 98206.

Receivers

Rohde, Ulrich L., KA2WEU, "Theory of Intermodulation and Reciprocal Mixing: Practice, Definitions and Measurements in Devices and Systems, Part I," *QEX*, Nov/Dec 2002, pp 3-15.

Rohde, Ulrich L., KA2WEU, "Theory of Intermodulation and Reciprocal Mixing: Practice, Definitions and Measurements in Devices and Systems, Part II," *QEX*, Jan/Feb 2003, pp 21-31.

Wade, Paul, N1BWT, "Noise Measurement and Generation," *QEX*, Nov 1996, pp 3-12.

Spectrum Analysis

Agilent Technologies, "Eight Hints for Making Better Spectrum Analyzer Measurements, Application Note 1286-1." Some Agilent application notes are available from Keysight Technologies, **www.keysight.com**.

Stanley, John O., K4ERO, "The Beauty of Spectrum Analysis — Part 1", *QST*, June 2008, pp 35-38.

Stanley, John O., K4ERO, "The Beauty of Spectrum Analysis — Part 2", *QST*, July 2008, pp 33-35.

Network Analysis

Agilent Technologies, "Understanding the Fundamental Principles of Vector Network Analysis, Application Note AN 1287-1." (**literature.cdn.keysight.com/litweb/pdf/5965-7707E.pdf?id=1000000359:epsg:apn**). Other Agilent application notes with further information on network analyzers are AN 1287-2 through AN 1287-10 and AN 1287-12, available from **www.keysight.com**.

Agilent Technologies, "S-Parameter Techniques for Faster, More Accurate Network Design, Application Note 95-1." (**literature.cdn.keysight.com/litweb/pdf/5952-1130.pdf?id=1112800**).

Hiebel, Michael, *Fundamentals of Vector Network Analysis*, Rohde & Schwarz, 2008.

See also "Test and Measurement Bibliography," an extensive listing of *QEX* and *QST* articles with the downloadable supplemental content.

25.11 Test and Measurement Glossary

Accuracy — The maximum expected error in a measurement.

Ammeter — A device for measuring electrical current.

Antenna analyzer — A device to measure the RF impedance of a one-port network such as an antenna.

Antenna test range — An area designed to minimize the effect of RF reflections to permit accurate antenna gain and pattern testing.

Attenuator — A broadband device that reduces the amplitude of a signal by a specified, well-controlled amount.

Autoranging — The ability of a *multimeter* to set its range automatically based on the signal level.

AWG (arbitrary waveform generator, also ARB) — An instrument that can generate a complex signal based on waveforms stored in memory.

Birdies — Slang term for internally-generated spurious signals in a receiver that may be steady, warble, or pulsate.

Blocking dynamic range — The difference between the *blocking level* and the *MDS*.

Blocking level — The level of an interfering signal that causes weak signals to be reduced in amplitude by 1 dB.

Bolometer — A device for measuring RF power by measuring the heat dissipated in a dummy load.

Bridge — A circuit used to indicate the relative values of passive circuit elements by observing the null on a meter or other indicator. See this chapter's discussion of Wheatstone bridges.

Burden voltage — The full-scale voltage drop of an ammeter.

Coaxial detector — An RF detector with a coaxial connector.

Combiner — A device to combine signals from two sources. A *power splitter* in reverse. See *Hybrid combiner*.

D'Arsonval meter — The most common type of mechanical meter, consisting of a permanent magnet and a moving coil with pointer attached.

Dip meter (dip oscillator) — An instrument with an oscillator whose coil is external to the enclosure so it can be coupled to the circuit under test. The meter value drops (dips) when the oscillator frequency is tuned to the frequency of resonance of the circuit under test.

Directional coupler, directional bridge — A device that senses the RF power flowing in one direction on a transmission line.

DMM (digital multimeter) — A test instrument that measures voltage, current, resistance and possibly other quantities and displays the result on a numeric digit display, rather than on an analog meter.

DVM (digital volt meter) — See *DMM*.

Dynamic error — An error whose value depends on the time of measurement.

Dynamic range — The difference in dB between the strongest and weakest signals that a receiver can handle.

Electronic voltmeter — An amplified analog *multimeter*.

ENR (excess noise ratio) — The ratio of the noise added by a noise source to the thermal noise, normally expressed in dB.

Feed-through termination — See *Through-line termination*.

Field-strength meter — A device to indicate radiated RF field strength.

Four wire — A technique for measuring small resistances or large currents that uses four wires rather than two to reduce errors due to test lead resistance.

Frequency counter — A device that measures the frequency of a periodic signal and displays the result on a digital readout.

Frequency domain — Description of signals as a function of frequency, as opposed to as a function of time.

Function generator — An audio tone generator that generates tones in the shape of various functions, such as sine, square, triangle and ramp waveforms.

Frequency markers — Test signals generated at selected intervals (such as 25 kHz, 50 kHz, 100 kHz) for calibrating the dials of receivers and transmitters.

Gaussian distribution — The distribution of the probability of the instantaneous voltage of a noise signal as a function of the voltage. It forms a bell-shaped curve with a maximum at the dc value of the signal (typically zero volts).

GDO (grid-dip oscillator) — A *dip meter* that uses a vacuum tube.

Harmonic signal — A periodic signal. Its frequency spectrum consists only of the fundamental and harmonics of the repetition rate.

Hybrid combiner — A passive device used to combine two signals in such a way as to reduce the interaction between the signal sources.

IF and image rejection — The difference in level between an interfering signal at a receiver's IF or image frequency and the level of the desired signal that produces the same response.

IMD (intermodulation distortion) — The creation of unwanted frequencies because of two or more strong signals modulating each other.

IMD dynamic range — The difference in signal level between two signals that cause IMD products at the level of the MDS and the MDS.

LCR Bridge — A device for measuring inductors, capacitors or resistors using a Wheatstone bridge.

Lissajous Pattern — As used by amateurs, the combined display of two sine wave signals on an oscilloscope to determine the relationship between their frequencies. (Also called Lissajous figure.)

Logic analyzer — A sophisticated instrument for analyzing digital circuitry.

Logic probe — A simple device for sensing and displaying a digital signal's state.

Marker — An indicator on the screen of a *spectrum analyzer* that allows reading out the frequency and amplitude of a specific signal. See also **Frequency marker.**

Marker delta — A *spectrum analyzer* feature that reads out the difference in frequency and amplitude of two markers.

MDS (minimum discernible signal) — The level of the *noise floor* at the antenna connector of a receiver. Depends on the measurement bandwidth.

Multimeter — A device that measures several electrical quantities, such as voltage, current and resistance, and displays them on an analog meter or digital display.

Multiplier (voltage multiplier) — A resistor placed in series with a meter to increase the full-scale voltage reading.

Near field — The area close to an antenna where the electromagnetic wave is not completely formed. Antenna gain and pattern measurements are not valid in this region.

Network analyzer — An instrument to measure the return loss and transmission gain between the two ports of a two-port network.

NIST (National Institute of Standards and Technology) — A non-regulatory agency of the US federal government that manages measurement standards. It used to be called NBS, the National Bureau of Standards.

NIST traceable — Refers to a device whose accuracy is based on NIST standards using rules and procedures specified by NIST.

Noise bandwidth — The bandwidth of a rectangular-spectrum filter that would produce the same total noise power as the filter under consideration.

Noise density — Noise power per hertz.

Noise figure — A figure of merit for the sensitivity of receivers and other RF devices. It is the ratio of the effective noise level to the thermal noise level, usually expressed in dB.

Noise floor — The noise received by a receiver in a specified bandwidth, referenced to the antenna connector. It is the thermal noise in dBm plus the noise figure in dB.

Noise source — An instrument that generates well-calibrated white noise for test purposes.

OCXO (oven-controlled crystal oscillator) — A crystal oscillator mounted in a temperature-controlled oven to improve the frequency stability.

Ohmmeter — A meter that measures resistance. Usually part of a *multimeter*. See *VOM* and *DMM*.

Ohms per volt — A measure of the sensitivity of a voltmeter that has multiple scales. It is the reciprocal of the current drawn by the meter.

Oscilloscope — An instrument that displays signals in the *time domain*. Has a graphical display that shows amplitude on the vertical axis and time on the horizontal axis.

Peak search — A feature of a *spectrum analyzer* in which a marker is automatically placed on the strongest signal in the display.

Peak to peak value — The difference between the most positive and most negative signal values. For a symmetrical signal it is twice the peak value.

Peak value — The highest value of a signal during the measuring time.

Periodic — Refers to a signal that repeats exactly at a regular time interval, the period.

Phase noise — Wideband noise on an RF signal caused by random fluctuations of the phase.

Port — A pair of connections to a network, typically via a coaxial connector

Power divider (power splitter) — A device to divide an RF signal between two loads. A *combiner* in reverse.

Prescaler — A circuit used ahead of a counter to extend the frequency range. A counter capable of operating up to 50 MHz can count up to 500 MHz when used with a divide-by-10 prescaler.

Random error — A non-repeatable error caused by noise in the measurement system.

Reciprocal mixing — The mixing of a nearby interfering signal with the phase noise of the receiver local oscillator, which causes noise in the audio output.

Resolution — The smallest distinguishable difference in a measured value.

Resolution bandwidth — The smallest frequency separation between two RF signals that a *spectrum analyzer* can resolve. It is determined by the IF filters in the *spectrum analyzer*.

Return loss — The ratio, usually expressed in dB, between the incident and reflected RF signals.

Return-loss bridge (RLB) — A bridge used for measuring the return loss of an RF circuit, transmission line or antenna.

Reverse power protection — A *signal generator* feature to protect the instrument from accidental transmission by a transceiver under test.

RF probe — A hand-held probe with a detector to allow measuring RF signals with a dc voltmeter.

Scalar network analyzer (SNA) — A *network analyzer* that measures only the magnitude of the gain and return loss.

Scattering parameters (S parameters) — A set of four parameters to characterize the complex return loss and transmission gain in both directions of a two-port network.

Scope — Slang for *oscilloscope*.

Second-order IMD — IMD caused by strong signals at frequencies f1 and f2 that occurs at a frequency of f1 + f2.

Service monitor — An integrated package of test equipment packaged as a single instrument for testing receivers and transmitters.

Shunt (meter shunt) — A resistor connected in parallel with a meter to increase the full-scale current reading.

SI (Système International d'Unités) — The modern, revised version of the metric system.

Signal generator — An instrument that generates a calibrated variable-frequency RF signal, usually with adjustable amplitude and modulation capability.

SINAD (signal plus noise and distortion) — A measure of the relative level of signal compared to the noise and distortion at the audio output of an FM receiver.

Single-shot — Refers to a non-periodic signal that can be measured in a single time interval.

Spectrum analyzer — An instrument that displays signals in the *frequency domain*. Has a graphical display that shows amplitude (normally in logarithmic, or dB, form) on the vertical axis and frequency on the horizontal axis.

Spurious emissions, or spurs — Unwanted energy generated by a transmitter or other circuit. These emissions include, but are not limited to, harmonics.

Standard — A rule for the proper method to measure some quantity. A standard may involve a standard artifact that defines the unit.

Step attenuator — An attenuator that can be switched between different attenuation values.

Systematic error — A repeatable error due to some characteristic of the measurement system.

TCXO (temperature-compensated crystal oscillator) — A crystal oscillator that includes circuitry to compensate for frequency drift with temperature.

Termination — A resistor with a coaxial connector used to terminate a transmission line in its characteristic impedance.

Test set — A *network analyzer* accessory that automatically configures the connections to the device under test for various measurements.

Third-order IMD — IMD caused by strong signals at frequencies f1 and f2 that appears at frequencies 2f1 – f2 or 2f2 – f1.

Third-order IMD intercept point (IP3) — The power level representing the intersection of plots on a dBm scale of the power level of the two strong signals and their IMD products.

Through-line termination — A termination with two coaxial connectors that connect straight through and a terminating resistor to ground.

Time base — A highly-accurate reference oscillator used in a frequency counter or other device that needs an accurate time or frequency reference.

Time domain — Refers to the variation in time of electronic signals, as opposed to their frequency spectrum.

Tracking generator — A *spectrum analyzer* accessory that consists of a signal generator whose frequency tracks the frequency of the analyzer.

True RMS — Refers to a meter that measures the actual RMS voltage or current instead of measuring the average or peak value and calculating the RMS value assuming a sinusoidal waveform.

VCXO (voltage-controlled crystal oscillator) — A crystal oscillator whose frequency can be adjusted slightly using an external applied voltage.

Vector network analyzer (VNA) — A *network analyzer* that measures both the magnitude and phase of the gain and return loss of a two-port network.

Video bandwidth — The bandwidth of the post-detection filter in a *spectrum analyzer*. It limits the maximum sweep speed.

VOM (volt-ohm meter) — A *multimeter* that does not include active circuitry such as an amplifier.

VTVM (vacuum-tube voltmeter) — A *multimeter* that uses one or more vacuum tubes.

Wheatstone bridge — See *Bridge circuit*.

Wilkinson combiner — A type of *hybrid combiner*.

Contents

- 26.1 Test Equipment
  - 26.1.1 Senses
  - 26.1.2 Internal Equipment
  - 26.1.3 Bench Equipment
- 26.2 Components
  - 26.2.1 Check the Circuit
  - 26.2.2 Fuses
  - 26.2.3 Wires and Cables
  - 26.2.4 Connectors
  - 26.2.5 Resistors
  - 26.2.6 Capacitors
  - 26.2.7 Inductors and Transformers
  - 26.2.8 Relays
  - 26.2.9 Semiconductors
  - 26.2.10 Tubes
- 26.3 Getting Started
  - 26.3.1 The Systematic Approach
  - 26.3.2 Assessing the Symptoms
  - 26.3.3 External Inspection
- 26.4 Inside the Equipment
  - 26.4.1 Documentation
  - 26.4.2 Disassembly
  - 26.4.3 Internal Inspection
  - 26.4.4 Signal Tracing and Signal Injection
  - 26.4.5 Microprocessor-Controlled Equipment
- 26.5 Testing at the Circuit Level
  - 26.5.1 Voltage Levels
  - 26.5.2 Noise
  - 26.5.3 Oscillations
  - 26.5.4 Amplitude Distortion
  - 26.5.5 Frequency Response
  - 26.5.6 Distortion Measurement
  - 26.5.7 Alignment
  - 26.5.8 Contamination
  - 26.5.9 Solder Bridges
  - 26.5.10 Arcing
  - 26.5.11 Digital Circuitry
  - 26.5.12 Replacing Parts
- 26.6 After the Repairs
  - 26.6.1 All Units
  - 26.6.2 Transmitter Checkout
  - 26.6.3 Other Repaired Circuits
  - 26.6.4 Close It Up
- 26.7 Professional Repairs
  - 26.7.1 Packing Equipment
- 26.8 Typical Symptoms and Faults
  - 26.8.1 Power Supplies
  - 26.8.2 Amplifier Circuits
  - 26.8.3 Oscillators
  - 26.8.4 Transmit Amplifier Modules
- 26.9 Radio Troubleshooting Hints
  - 26.9.1 Receivers
  - 26.9.2 Transmitters
  - 26.9.3 Transceivers
  - 26.9.4 Amplifiers
- 26.10 Antenna Systems
  - 26.10.1 Basic Antenna System Troubleshooting
  - 26.10.2 General Antenna System Troubleshooting
- 26.11 Repair and Restoration of Vintage Equipment
  - 26.11.1 Component Replacement
  - 26.11.2 Powering Up the Equipment
  - 26.11.3 Alignment
  - 26.11.4 Using Vintage Receivers
  - 26.11.5 Plastic Restoration
- 26.12 References and Bibliography

Chapter 26 — Downloadable Supplemental Content

Supplemental Articles
- "Troubleshooting Radios" by Mel Eiselman, NC4L
- "Building a Modern Signal Tracer" by Curt Terwilliger, W6XJ
- "Hands-on Radio — Power Supply Analysis" by Ward Silver, NØAX
- "Amplifier Care and Maintenance" by Ward Silver, NØAX
- "Diode and Transistor Test Circuits" by Ed Hare, W1RFI

PC Board Templates
- Crystal controlled signal source template
- AF/RF signal injector template

Chapter 26

Troubleshooting and Maintenance

The robust and self-reliant ethic of Amateur Radio is nowhere stronger than in the amateur's ability to maintain, troubleshoot and repair electronic equipment. Amateurs work with not just radios, but all sorts of equipment from computers and software to antennas and transmission lines. This flexibility and resilience are keys to fulfilling the Basis and Purpose for Amateur Radio.

The sections on troubleshooting approaches, tools and techniques build on earlier material written by Ed Hare, W1RFI. They will help you approach troubleshooting in an organized and effective manner, appropriate to your level of technical experience and tools at hand. This material shows how to get started and ask the right questions — often the most important part of troubleshooting.

Additional sections on troubleshooting power supplies, amplifiers, radios and antenna systems (contributed or updated by Matt Kastigar, N9ES; Tom Schiller, N6BT; Ted Thrift, VK2ARA; and Ross Pittard, VK3CE) tackle the most common troubleshooting needs. Restoring and maintaining vintage equipment is a popular part of ham radio and so there are some sections by John Fitzsimmons, W3JN, and Pat Bunsold, WA6MHZ, on the special needs of this equipment.

This chapter is organized in three groups of sections to be consulted as required for any particular troubleshooting need. You will not need to read it from end-to-end in order to troubleshoot successfully. The first group of sections covers test equipment details, pertinent information about components, and safety practices. The second group presents general guidelines and techniques for effective troubleshooting. The third group presents specific advice and information on equipment that is commonly repaired by amateurs.

TROUBLESHOOTING — ART OR SCIENCE?

Although some say troubleshooting is as much art as it is science, the repair of electronic gear is not magic. It is more like detective work as you work carefully to uncover each clue. Knowledge of advanced math or electronics theory is not required. However, you must have, or develop, a good grasp of basic electronics and simple measurements, guided by the ability to read a schematic diagram and to visualize signal flow through the circuit. As with most skills, these abilities will develop with practice.

Not everyone is an electronics wizard; your gear may end up at the repair shop in spite of your best efforts. The theory you learned for the FCC examinations and the information in this *Handbook* can help you decide if you can fix it yourself. Even if the problem appears to be complex, most problems have simple causes. Why not give troubleshooting a try to the best of your abilities? Maybe you can avoid the effort and expense of shipping the radio to the manufacturer. It is gratifying to save time and money, but the experience and confidence you gain by fixing it yourself may prove even more valuable.

SAFETY FIRST! — SWITCH TO SAFETY

Always! Death is permanent. A review of safety must be the first thing discussed in a troubleshooting chapter. Some of the voltages found in amateur equipment can be fatal! Only 50 mA flowing through the body is painful; 100 to 500 mA is usually fatal. Under certain conditions, as little as 24 V can kill. RF exposure in a high-power amplifier can create severe burns very quickly. Batteries can deliver huge amounts of power that can melt tools and wires or create an explosion when short-circuited. Charging lead-acid cells can create a buildup of explosive hydrogen gas, as well.

Make sure you are 100% familiar with all safety rules and the dangerous conditions that might exist in the equipment you are servicing. A list of safety rules can be found in **Table 26.1**. You should also read the **Safety** chapter of this *Handbook* — all of it — before you begin to work on equipment.

Remember, if the equipment is not working properly, dangerous conditions may exist where you don't expect them. Treat every component as potentially "live." Some older equipment uses "ac/dc" circuitry. In this circuit, one side of the chassis is connected directly to the ac line, a condition unexpected by today's amateurs who are accustomed to modern safety standards and practices. This is an electric shock waiting to happen.

The maximum voltage rating of voltmeters and oscilloscopes is not often noted by the hobbyist but it is crucial to safety when working on voltages higher than the household ac line voltage. Test equipment designed to measure voltage always has a maximum safe voltage rating

Table 26.1
Safety Rules
1. Keep one hand in your pocket when working on live circuits or checking to see that capacitors are discharged.
2. Include a conveniently located ground-fault current interrupter (GFCI) circuit breaker in the workbench wiring.
3. Use only grounded plugs and receptacles.
4. Use a GFCI protected circuit when working outdoors, on a concrete or dirt floor, in wet areas, or near fixtures or appliances connected to water lines, or within six feet of any exposed grounded building feature.
5. Use a fused, power limiting isolation transformer when working on ac/dc devices.
6. Switch off the power, disconnect equipment from the power source, ground the output of the internal dc power supply, and discharge capacitors when making circuit changes.
7. Do not subject electrolytic capacitors to excessive voltage, ac voltage or reverse voltage.
8. Test leads should be well insulated and without cracks, fraying, or exposed conductors
9. Do not work alone!
10. Wear safety glasses for protection against sparks and metal or solder fragments.
11. Be careful with tools that may cause short circuits.
12. Replace fuses only with those having proper ratings.
13. Never use test equipment to measure voltages above its maximum rating.

between the circuit being measured and the equipment user — you! This is particularly important in handheld equipment in which there is no metal enclosure connected to an ac safety ground. Excessive voltage can result in a flashover to the user from the internal electronics, probes, or test leads, resulting in electric shock. Know and respect this rating.

If you are using an external high voltage probe, make sure it is in good condition with no cracks in the body. The test lead insulation should be in good condition — flexible and with no cracks or wire exposed. If practical, do not make measurements while holding the probe or meter. Attach the probe with the voltage discharged and then turn the power on. Turn power off and discharge the voltage before touching the probe again. Treat high voltage equipment with care and respect!

Soldering Safety

Remember that soldering tools and melted solder can be hot and dangerous! Wear protective goggles and clothing when soldering. A full course in first aid is beyond the scope of this chapter, but if you burn your skin, run the burn immediately under cold water and seek first aid or medical attention. Always seek medical attention if you burn your eyes; even a small burn can develop into serious trouble.

UNDERSTANDING THE BASICS

To fix electronic equipment, you need to understand the system and circuits you are troubleshooting. A working knowledge of electronic theory, circuitry and components is an important part of the process. When you are troubleshooting, you are looking for specific conditions that cause the symptoms you are experiencing. Knowing how circuits are supposed to work will help you to notice things that are out of place or that indicate a problem.

To be an effective troubleshooter, review and understand the following topics discussed elsewhere in this book:
- Ohms law and basic resistor circuits (**Electrical Fundamentals**)
- Basic transistor and diode characteristics (**Circuits and Components**)
- Fundamental digital logic and logic signals (**Digital Basics** supplement)
- Voltage and current measurements (**Test Equipment and Measurements**)
- SWR and RF power measurement (**Transmission Lines**)

You would be surprised at how many problems — even problems that appear complicated — turn out to have a simple root cause found by understanding the fundamentals and methods of one of these categories.

GETTING HELP

Other hams may be able to help you with your troubleshooting and repair problems, either with a manual or technical help. Check with your local club or repeater group. You may get lucky and find a troubleshooting wizard. (On the other hand, you may get some advice that is downright dangerous, so be selective.) Most clubs have one or two troubleshooting gurus who can provide guidance and advice, if not some on-the-workbench help.

There is a wealth of information available online, too. Many of the popular brands of equipment and even specific models have their own online communities or user's groups. The archives of these groups — almost universally free to join — contain much valuable troubleshooting, modification and operating information. If the problem doesn't appear to have been described, you can ask the group.

The Technology area of the ARRL's website also has an extensive section on Servicing Equipment (**www.arrl.org/servicing-equipment**). That page features articles and other resources, including links to schematic databases.

Your fellow hams in the ARRL Field organization may also help. Technical Coordinators (TC) and Technical Specialists (TS) are volunteers who are willing to help hams with technical questions. For the name and address of a local TC or TS, contact your Section Manager (listed in the front of any recent issue of *QST*).

Using Search Engines for Troubleshooting

The power of Internet search engines can save huge amounts of time when troubleshooting equipment. The key is in knowing how to construct the right list of words for them to find. Precision is your friend — be exact and use words others are likely to use if they had the same problem. Use the primary model number without suffixes to avoid being too specific. For example, when troubleshooting the well-known PLL potting compound problem exhibited by Kenwood TS-440 transceivers, entering the search string "TS-440 display dots" immediately finds many web pages dealing with the problem, while simply entering "Kenwood transceiver blank display" returns dozen of unrelated links.

Start with a very specific description of the problem and gradually use less exact terms if you don't find what you want. Learn how to use the "Advanced Search" functions of the search engine, too.

26.1 Test Equipment

Many of the steps involved in efficient troubleshooting require the use of test equipment. We cannot see electricity directly, but we can measure its characteristics and effects. Our test equipment becomes our electrical senses.

The **Test Equipment and Measurements** chapter is where you can find out more about various common types of equipment, how to operate it, and even how to build some of your own. There are many articles in *QST* and in books and websites that explain test equipment and offer build-it-yourself projects, too. Surplus equipment of excellent quality is widely available at a fraction of its new cost.

You need not purchase or build every type of test equipment. Specialty equipment such as spectrum analyzers or UHF frequency counters can often be borrowed from a club member or friend — maybe one of those troubleshooting gurus mentioned earlier. If you own the basic instruments and know how to use them, you'll be able to do quite a bit of troubleshooting before you need the special instruments.

26.1.1 Senses

Although they are not test equipment in the classic sense, your own senses will tell you as much about the equipment you are trying to fix as the most-expensive spectrum analyzer. We each have some of these natural test instruments.

Eyes — Use them constantly. Look for evidence of heat and arcing, burned components, broken connections or wires, poor solder joints or other obvious visual problems.

Ears — Severe audio distortion can be detected by ear. The snaps and pops of arcing or the sizzling of a burning component may help you track down circuit faults. An experienced troubleshooter can diagnose some circuit problems by the sound they make. For example, a bad audio-output IC sounds slightly different from a defective speaker.

Nose — Your nose can tell you a lot. With experience, the smells of ozone, an overheating transformer, and a burned resistor or PC board trace each become unique and distinctive. Many troubleshooting sessions begin with "something smells hot!"

Finger — After using a voltmeter to ensure no hazardous voltages are present, you can use a fingertip to determine low heat levels—never do this in a high-voltage circuit. Use a temperature probe if using a finger is unsafe. Small-signal transistors can be fairly warm, but being very hot indicates a circuit problem. Warm or hot capacitors are always suspect. High-power devices and resistors can be quite hot during normal operation.

Brain — More troubleshooting problems have been solved with a multimeter and a brain than with the most expensive spectrum analyzer. You must use your brain to analyze data collected by other instruments.

26.1.2 Internal Equipment

Some test equipment is included in the equipment you repair. Nearly all receivers include a speaker. An S meter is usually connected ahead of the audio chain. If the S meter shows signals, that indicates that the RF and IF circuitry is probably functioning. Transmitters often have a power supply voltage and current meter, along with power output, SWR, ALC and speech compression readings that give valuable clues about what is happening inside the equipment.

The equipment also has visual indicator lights that provide additional information such as transmit status, high SWR, low voltage, squelch status, and so forth. These readings or indicators are often specifically referenced by the troubleshooting sections of manuals to help sort out problems.

Microprocessor-controlled equipment often provides error indications, either through a display or by indicator lights. In addition, faults detected by the control software are sometimes communicated through patterns of beeps or flashing of LEDs. Each sequence has a specific meaning that is described in the operating or service manual.

26.1.3 Bench Equipment

The following is a list of the most common and useful test instruments for troubleshooting. Some items serve several purposes and may substitute for others on the list. The theory and operation of most of this equipment is discussed in detail in the **Test Equipment and Measurements** chapter. Notes about the equipment's use for troubleshooting are listed here.

Multimeters — The most often used piece of test equipment, the digital multimeter or DMM, can often test capacitors of most values in addition to voltage, current and resistance. Most can test diodes and transistors on a go/no-go basis, while some can measure gain. Some can even measure frequency or use an external probe to measure temperature.

Some DMMs are affected by RF, so most technicians keep an old-style analog moving-needle VOM (volt-ohm-meter) on hand for use in strong RF fields. Some technicians prefer the moving needle for peaking or nulling adjustments.

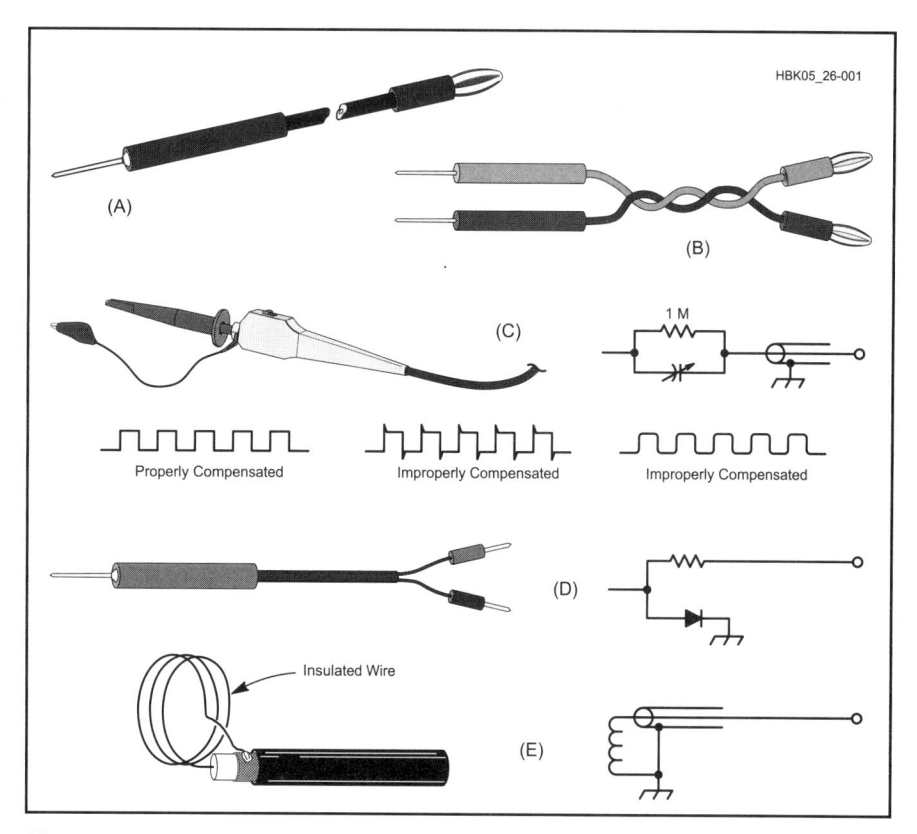

Figure 26.1 — An array of test probes for use with various test instruments.

Test or clip leads — Keep an assortment of these wires with insulated alligator clips. Commercially-made leads have a high failure rate because they use small wire that is not soldered to the clips, just crimped. You can slip off the clip jackets and solder the wire yourself for better reliability. Making a set of heavier-gauge leads is a good idea for currents above several hundred milliamps.

Individual wire leads (**Figure 26.1A**) are good for dc measurements, but they can pick up unwanted RF energy. This problem is reduced somewhat if the leads are twisted together (Figure 26.1B). Coaxial cable test leads can avoid RF pickup but also place a small capacitance across the circuit being measured. The added capacitance may affect performance.

Test probes — The most common probe is the low-capacitance (×10) oscilloscope probe shown in Figure 26.1C. This probe isolates the oscilloscope from the circuit under test, preventing the scope's input and test-probe capacitance from affecting the circuit and changing the reading. A network in the probe serves as a 10:1 divider and compensates for frequency distortion in the cable and test instrument.

Demodulator probes (see the **Test Equipment and Measurements** chapter and the schematic shown in Figure 26.1D) are used to demodulate or detect RF signals, converting modulated RF signals to audio that can be heard in a signal tracer or seen on a low-bandwidth scope.

You can make a probe for inductive coupling as shown in Figure 26.1E. Connect a two or three-turn loop across the center conductor and shield before sealing the end. The inductive pickup is useful for coupling to high-current points and can also be used as a sniffer probe to pick up RF signals without contacting a circuit directly.

Other common types of probes are the non-contact clamp-on probes shown in **Figure 26.2** that use magnetic fields to measure current. A high-voltage probe for use with DMMs or VOMs is shown in **Figure 26.3** and is discussed more in this chapter's section on power supply troubleshooting.

Thermocouple and active temperature sensor probes are also commonly available. These display temperature directly on the meter in °F or °C.

RF power and SWR meters — Simple meters indicate relative power SWR and are fine for adjusting matching networks and monitoring transmission line conditions for problems. However, if you want to make accurate measurements, a calibrated directional RF wattmeter with the proper sensing elements for the frequencies of signals being measured is required.

Dummy load — Do not put a signal on the air while repairing equipment. Defective equipment can generate signals that interfere with other hams or other radio services. A dummy load also provides a known, matched load (usually 50 Ω) for use during adjustments and test measurements. See the **Transmitting** chapter.

Dip meter — As described in the **Test Equipment and Measurements** chapter, dip meters are used to adjust and troubleshoot resonant circuits. Many can perform as an absorption frequency meter, as well. Dip meters can be used as low-power signal sources but are not very stable.

New dip meters are fairly rare. When purchasing a dip meter, look for one that is mechanically and electrically stable. All of the coils should be present and in good condition. A headphone connection is helpful. Battery operated models are easier to use for antenna measurements. Dip meters are not nearly as common as they once were.

Oscilloscope — The oscilloscope, or scope, is the second most often used piece of test equipment, although a lot of repairs can be accomplished without one. The trace of a scope can give us a lot of information about a signal at a glance. For example, when signals from the input and output of a stage are displayed on a dual-trace scope, stage linearity and phase shift can be checked (see **Figure 26.4**).

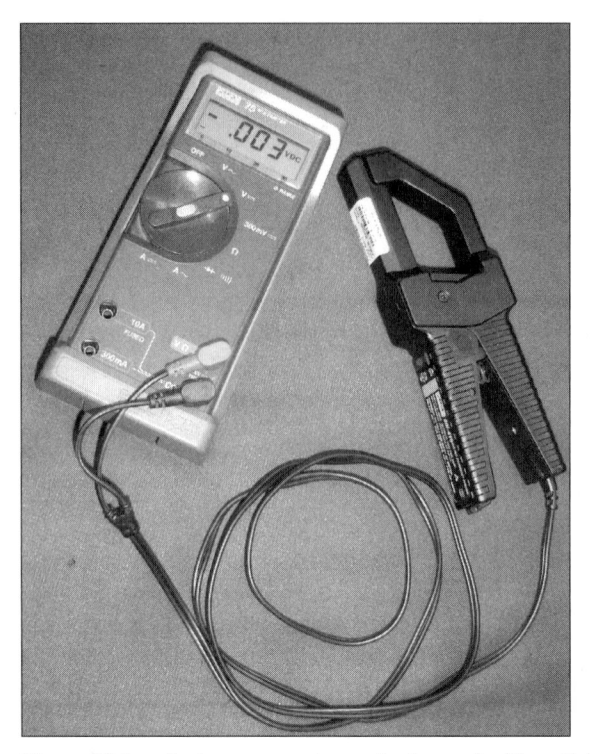

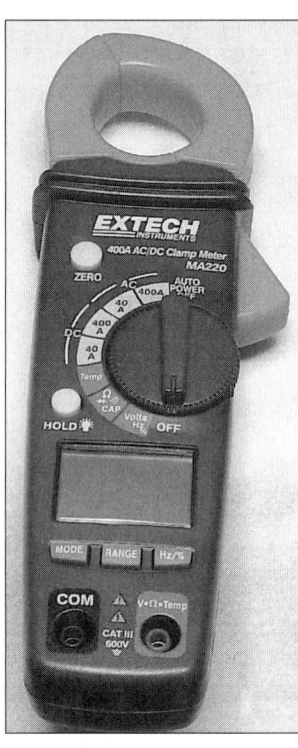

Figure 26.2 — A clamp-on meter probe is used with a digital multimeter for measuring ac current (left). Meters are also available integrated with the clamp-on probe (right).

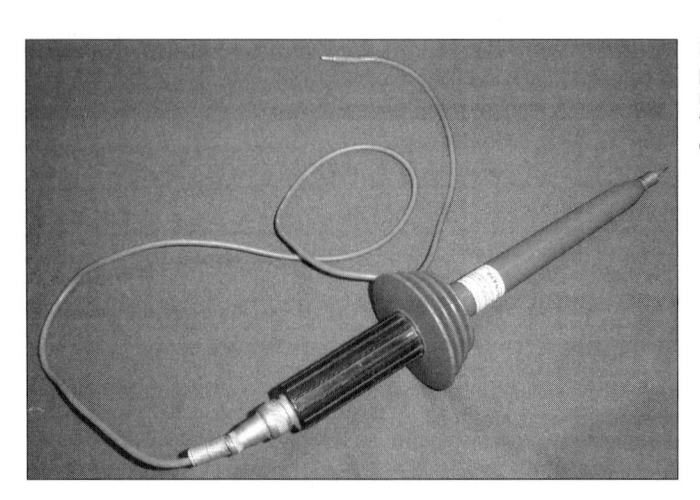

Figure 26.3 — A probe used for measuring high-voltage with a standard multimeter.

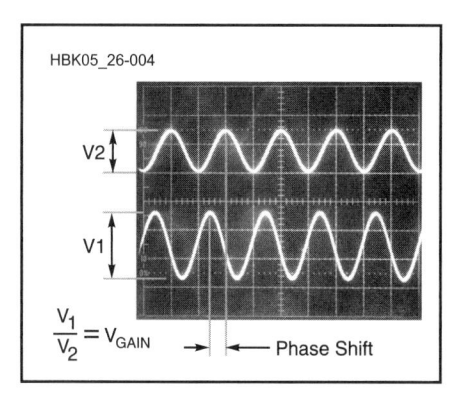

Figure 26.4 — A dual-trace oscilloscope display of amplifier input and output waveforms.

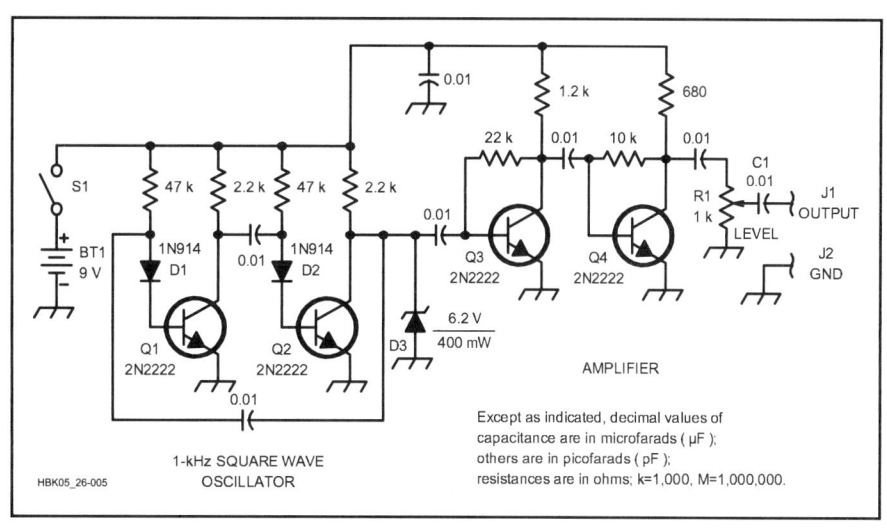

$\frac{V_1}{V_2} = V_{GAIN}$

Figure 26.5 — Schematic of the AF/RF signal injector. All resistors are ¼ W, 5% carbon units, and all capacitors are disc ceramic. A full-size etching pattern and parts-placement diagram can be found in the downloadable supplemental content.

BT1 — 9 V battery.
D1, D2 — Silicon switching diode, 1N914 or equiv.
D3 — 6.2 V, 400 mW Zener diode.
J1, J2 — Banana jack.
Q1-Q4 — General-purpose silicon NPN transistors, 2N2222 or similar.
R1 — 1 kΩ panel-mount control.
S1 — SPST toggle switch.

An oscilloscope will show gross distortions of audio and RF waveforms, but it cannot be used to verify that a transmitter meets FCC regulations for harmonics and spurious emissions. Harmonics that are down only 20 dB from the fundamental would be illegal in most cases, but they would not change the oscilloscope waveform enough to be seen.

When buying a scope, get the highest bandwidth you can afford. Old Hewlett-Packard or Tektronix instruments are usually quite good for amateur use.

Signal generator — Although signal generators have many uses, in troubleshooting they are most often used for signal injection (more about this later) and alignment of vintage equipment.

When buying a generator, look for one that can generate a sine wave signal. A good signal generator is double or triple shielded against leakage. Fixed-frequency audio should be available for modulation of the RF signal and for injection into audio stages. The most versatile generators can generate amplitude and frequency modulated signals. Used Hewlett-Packard (Agilent) and Tektronix units are typically available for reasonable prices but may not be repairable if they fail due to unavailable parts.

Good generators have stable frequency controls with no backlash. They also have multiposition switches to control signal level. A switch marked in dBm is a good indication that you have located a high-quality test instrument. The output jack should be a coaxial connector (usually a BNC or N), not the kind used for microphone connections.

In lieu of a fully tunable generator, you can build some simple equipment that generates a signal. For example, Elecraft makes the XG3 kit — a programmable signal source (**www.elecraft.com**) that generates 160 through 2 meter signals with four calibrated output levels. It's very useful for receiver calibration, sensitivity tests and signal tracing.

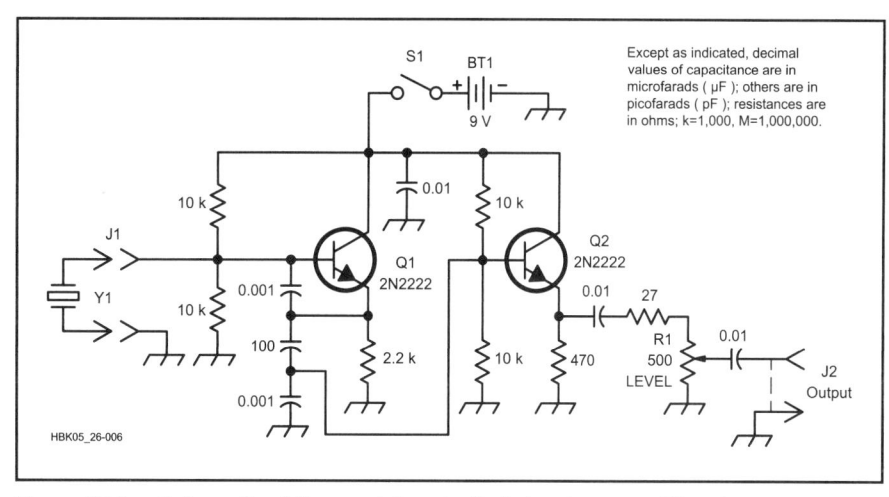

Figure 26.6 — Schematic of the crystal-controlled signal source. All resistors are ¼ W, 5% carbon units, and all capacitors are disc ceramic. A full-size etching pattern and parts-placement diagram can be found in the downloadable supplemental content.

BT1 — 9 V transistor radio battery.
J1 — Crystal socket to match the crystal type used.
J2 — RCA phono jack or equivalent.
Q1, Q2 — General-purpose silicon NPN transistors, 2N2222 or similar.
R1 — 500 Ω panel-mount control.
S1 — SPST toggle switch.
Y1 — 1 to 15-MHz crystal.

Even simpler, you can homebrew the AF/RF signal-injector schematic as shown in **Figure 26.5**. If frequency accuracy is needed, the crystal-controlled signal source of **Figure 26.6** can be used. The AF/RF circuit provides usable harmonics up to 30 MHz, while the crystal controlled oscillator will function with crystals from 1 to 15 MHz. These two projects are not meant to replace standard signal generators for alignment and precision testing, but they are adequate for generating signals that can be used for general troubleshooting. (See the section on Signal Tracing and Signal Injection.)

Troubleshooting and Maintenance 26.5

Signal tracer — Signals can be traced with a voltmeter and an RF probe, a dip meter with headphones or an oscilloscope, but signal tracers combine these functions especially for signal tracing through a receiver or other RF signal processing circuit. Articles describing the use of signal tracers, including a project you can build yourself, are provided with the downloadable supplemental content.

A general-coverage receiver can be also used to trace RF or IF signals, if the receiver covers the necessary frequency range. Most receivers, however, have a low-impedance input that severely loads the test circuit. To minimize loading, use a capacitive probe or loop pickup as in Figure 26.1. When the probe is held near the circuit, signals will be picked up and carried to the receiver. It may also pick up stray RF, so make sure you are listening to the correct signal by switching the circuit under test on and off while listening.

Transistor tester — Most transistor failures appear as either an open or shorted junction. Opens and shorts can be found easily with an ohmmeter or the diode junction checker of a standard DMM; a special tester is not required.

Transistor testers measure device current while the device is conducting or while an ac signal is applied at the control terminal. Transistor gain characteristics vary widely even between units with the same device number. Testers can be used to measure the gain of a transistor. DMM testers measure only transistor dc alpha and beta. Testers that apply an ac signal show the ac alpha or beta. Better testers also test for leakage.

In addition to telling you whether a transistor is good or bad, a transistor tester can help you decide if a particular transistor has sufficient gain for use as a replacement. It may also help when matched transistors are required. The final test is the repaired circuit.

Frequency counter — Most inexpensive frequency counters display frequency with 1 Hz resolution or better up to around low VHF frequencies. Some may include a prescaler that divides higher frequencies by 10 to extend the counter's range. Good quality used counters are widely available.

Power supplies — A well-equipped test bench should include a means of varying the ac-line voltage, a variable-voltage regulated dc supply and an isolation transformer.

AC-line voltage varies slightly with load. An autotransformer with a movable tap (also known by the trade name Variac) lets you boost or reduce the line voltage slightly. This is helpful to test circuit functions with supply-voltage variations.

An isolation transformer is required to work safely on vintage equipment that often ties one side of the ac line to the chassis. An isolation transformer is also required when working on any equipment or circuits that operate directly connected to the line. Note that your test equipment will also have to be powered through the isolation transformer in such cases!

A good multi-voltage supply will help with nearly any analog or digital troubleshooting project. Many electronics distributors stock bench power supplies. A variable-voltage dc supply may be used to power various small items under repair or provide a variable bias supply for testing active devices. Construction details for a laboratory power supply appear in the **Power Sources** chapter.

Heat and cold sources — Many circuit problems are sensitive to temperature. A piece of equipment may work well when first turned on (cold) but fail as it warms up. In this case, a cold source will help you find the intermittent connection. When you cool the bad component, the circuit will suddenly start working again (or stop working). Cooling sprays are available from most parts suppliers.

A heat source helps locate components that fail only when hot. A small incandescent lamp can be mounted in a large piece of sleeve insulation to produce localized heat for test purposes. The tip of a soldering iron set to low heat can also be used.

A heat source is usually used in conjunction with a cold source. If you have a circuit that stops working when it warms up, heat the circuit until it fails, then cool the components one by one. When the circuit starts working again, the last component sprayed was the bad one.

Stethoscope — A stethoscope (with the pickup removed — see **Figure 26.7**) or a long piece of sleeve insulation can be used to listen for arcing or sizzling in a circuit. Remove any metal parts at the end of the pickup tube before use for troubleshooting live equipment.

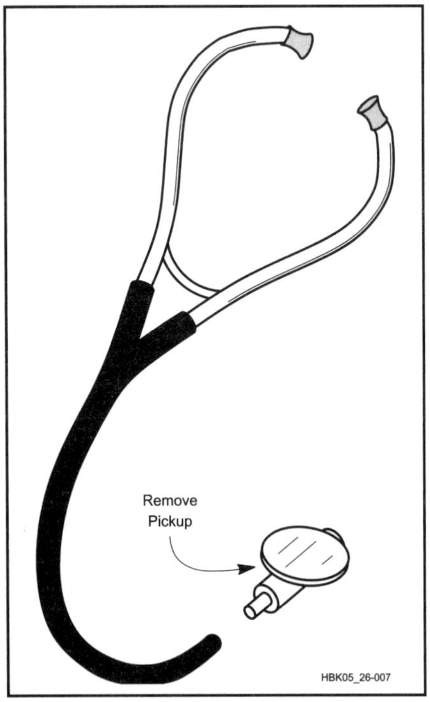

Figure 26.7 — A stethoscope, with the pickup and all metal hardware removed from the listening tube, is used to listen for arcing in crowded circuits.

The Shack Notebook

A shack notebook is an excellent way to keep track of test results, wiring, assembly notes and so forth. If you haven't already started one, now is a good time. All it takes is an inexpensive composition book or spiral-bound notebook. The books filled with graph paper are especially good for drawing and making graphs.

The goal is to have one place where information is collected about how equipment was built, performs, or operates. The notebook is invaluable when trying to determine if performance has changed over time or what color code was used for a control cable, for example.

Before beginning a test session or when adding a new piece of equipment to your shack, get out the shack notebook first and have it available as you work. For new equipment, record serial numbers, when installed, whether it was modified or specially configured to work in your station, etc. For a new antenna or feed line, it's a good idea to make a few SWR measurements so you can refer to them later if something seems wrong in the antenna system. Be sure to include the date of any entries, as well.

You can also make good use of that digital camera, even the one in your mobile phone. Take pictures of equipment, inside and out, to document how it is assembled or configured. This can be very helpful when you have to maintain the equipment later.

26.2 Components

Once you locate a defective part, it is time to select a replacement. This is not always an easy task. Each electronic component has a function. This section acquaints you with the functions, failure modes and test procedures of resistors, capacitors, inductors and other components. Test the components implicated by symptoms and stage-level testing. In most cases, a particular faulty component will be located by these tests. If a faulty component is not indicated, check the circuit adjustments. As a last resort, use a "shotgun" approach — replace all parts in the problem area with components that are known to be good.

26.2.1 Check the Circuit

Before you install a replacement component of any type, you should be sure that another circuit defect didn't cause the failure. Check the circuit voltages carefully before installing any new component, especially on each trace or connection to the bad component. The old part may have died as a result of a lethal voltage. Measure twice — repair once! (With apologies to the old carpenter...) Of course, circuit performance is the final test of any substitution.

26.2.2 Fuses

Most of the time, when a fuse fails, it is for a reason — usually a short circuit in the load. A fuse that has failed because of a short circuit usually shows the evidence of high current: a blackened interior with little blobs of fuse element everywhere. Fuses can also fail by fracturing the element at either end. This kind of failure is not visible by looking at the fuse. Check even fuses thought to be good with an ohmmeter. You may save hours of troubleshooting.

For safety reasons, always use *exact* replacement fuses. Check the current and voltage ratings. The fuse timing (fast, normal or slow blow) must be the same as the original. Never attempt to force a fuse that is not the right size into a fuse holder. The substitution of a bar, wire or penny for a fuse invites a smoke party.

26.2.3 Wires and Cables

Wires seldom fail unless abused. Short circuits can be caused by physical damage to insulation or by conductive contamination. Damaged insulation is usually apparent during a close visual inspection of the conductor or connector. Look carefully where conductors come close to corners or sharp objects. Repair worn insulation by replacing the wire or securing an insulating sleeve (spaghetti) or heat-shrink tubing over the worn area.

When wires fail, the failure is usually caused by stress and flexing. Nearly everyone has broken a wire by bending it back and forth, and broken wires are usually easy to detect. Look for sharp bends or bulges in the insulation.

When replacing conductors, use the same material and size, if possible. Substitute only wire of greater cross-sectional area (smaller gauge number) or material of greater conductivity. Insulated wire should be rated at the same, or higher, temperature and voltage as the wire it replaces.

Cables used for audio, control signals, and feed lines sometimes fail from excessive flexing, being crimped or bent too abruptly, or getting pulled out of connectors. As with replacing wires, use the same cable type or one with higher ratings.

26.2.4 Connectors

Connection faults are one of the most common failures in electronic equipment. This can range from something as simple as the ac-line cord coming out of the wall, to a connector having been inserted into the wrong socket, to a defective IC socket. Connectors that are plugged and unplugged frequently can wear out, becoming intermittent or noisy. Inspect male connectors for bent pins, particular miniature connectors with very small pins. Check connectors carefully when troubleshooting.

Connector failure can be hard to detect. Most connectors maintain contact as a result of spring tension that forces two conductors together. As the parts age, they become brittle and lose tension. Any connection may deteriorate because of nonconductive corrosion at the contacts. Solder helps prevent this problem but even soldered joints suffer from corrosion when exposed to weather.

Signs of excess heat are sometimes seen near poor connections in circuits that carry moderate current. The increase in dissipated power at the poor connection heats the contacts, and this leads to more resistance and soon the connection fails. Check for short and open circuits with an ohmmeter or continuity tester. Clean those connections that fail as a result of contamination.

Occasionally, corroded connectors may be repaired by cleaning, but replacement of the conductor/connector is usually required, especially for battery holders supplying moderate currents. Solder all connections that may be subject to harsh environments and protect them with acrylic enamel, RTV compound or a similar coating. An anti-corrosion compound or grease is a good idea for connections located outside. See the entry on Weatherproofing RF Connectors in the Antenna and Tower Safety section of the **Safety** chapter.

Choose replacement connectors with consideration of voltage and current ratings. Use connectors with symmetrical pin arrangements only where correct insertion will not result in a safety hazard or circuit damage.

26.2.5 Resistors

Resistors usually fail by becoming an open circuit. More rarely they change value. Both failures are usually caused by excess heat. Such heat may come from external sources or from power dissipated within the resistor. Sufficient heat burns the resistor until it becomes an open circuit.

Resistors can also fracture and become an open circuit as a result of physical shock. Contamination on or around a high-value resistor ($100\,k\Omega$ or more) can cause a change in value by providing a leakage path for current around a resistor. This contamination can occur on the resistor body, mounts or printed-circuit board. Resistors that have changed value should be replaced. Leakage is cured by cleaning the resistor body and surrounding area.

In addition to the problems of fixed-value resistors, potentiometers and rheostats can develop noise problems, especially in dc circuits. Dirt often causes intermittent contact between the wiper and resistive element. To cure the problem, spray electronic contact cleaner into the control, through holes in the case, and rotate the shaft a few times.

The resistive element in wire-wound potentiometers eventually wears and breaks from the sliding action of the wiper. In this case, the control needs to be replaced.

Replacement resistors should be of the same value, tolerance, type and power rating as the original. The value should stay within tolerance. Replacement resistors may be of a different type than the original, if the characteristics of the replacement are consistent with circuit requirements. (See the **Electrical Fundamentals** chapter for more information on resistor types.)

Substitute resistors can usually have a greater power rating than the original, except in high-power emitter circuits where the resistor also acts as a fuse or in cases where the larger size presents a problem.

Variable resistors should be replaced with the same kind (carbon or wire wound) and taper (linear, log, reverse log and so on) as the original. Keep the same, or better, tolerance and pay attention to the power rating.

In all cases, mount high-temperature resistors away from heat-sensitive components. Keep carbon composition and film resistors away from heat sources. This will extend their life and ensure minimum resistance variations.

26.2.6 Capacitors

Capacitors usually fail by shorting, opening or becoming electrically (or physically) leaky. They rarely change value. Capacitor failure is usually caused by excess current, voltage, temperature or aging of the dielectric or materials making up the capacitor. Leakage can be external to the capacitor (contamination on the capacitor body or circuit) or internal to the capacitor.

TESTS

If you do not have a multimeter with a capacitor test function or a component tester, the easiest way to test capacitors is out of circuit with an ohmmeter. In this test, the resistance of the meter forms a timing circuit with the capacitor to be checked. Capacitors from 0.01 µF to a few hundred µF can be tested with common ohmmeters. Set the meter to its highest range and connect the test leads across the discharged capacitor. When the leads are connected, current begins to flow. Current is high when the capacitor is discharged, but drops as the capacitor voltage builds up. This shows on the meter as a low resistance that builds, over time, toward infinity.

The speed of the resistance build-up corresponds to capacitance. Small capacitance values approach infinite resistance almost instantly. A 0.01 µF capacitor checked with a meter having an 11 MΩ input impedance would increase from zero to a two-thirds scale reading in 0.11 second, while a 1 µF unit would require 11 seconds to reach the same reading. If the tested capacitor does not reach infinity within five times the period taken to reach the two-thirds point, it has excess leakage. If the meter reads infinite resistance immediately, the capacitor is open. (Aluminum electrolytics normally exhibit high-leakage readings.)

Capacitance can also be measured for approximate value with a dip meter by constructing a parallel-resonant circuit using an inductor of known value. The formula for resonance is discussed in the **Electrical Fundamentals** chapter of this book.

It is good practice to keep a collection of known components that have been measured on accurate L or C meters. Alternatively, a standard value can be obtained by ordering 1 or 2% components from an electronics supplier. A 10% tolerance component can be used as a standard; however, the results will be known only to within 10%. The accuracy of tests made with any of these alternatives depends on the accuracy of the standard value component. Further information on this technique appears in Bartlett's article, "Calculating Component Values," in Nov 1978 *QST*.

Older capacitors can also be checked and the dielectric reformed, if necessary, with a capacitor checker of similar vintage. See this chapter's section on Restoration and Repair of Vintage Radios for more information about this technique.

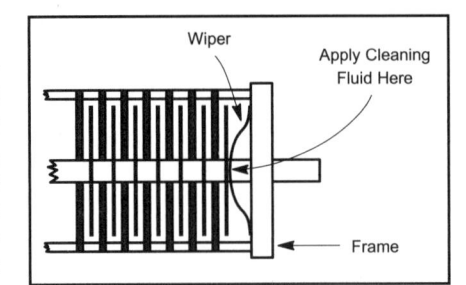

Figure 26.8 — Partial view of an air-dielectric variable capacitor. If the capacitor is noisy or erratic in operation, apply electronic cleaning fluid where the wiper contacts the rotor plates.

CLEANING

The only variety of common capacitor that can be repaired is the air-dielectric variable capacitor. Electrical connection to the moving plates is made through a spring-wiper arrangement (see **Figure 26.8**). Dirt normally builds on the contact area, and they need occasional cleaning. Before cleaning the wiper/contact, use gentle air pressure and a soft brush to remove all dust and dirt from the capacitor plates. Apply some electronic contact cleaning fluid. Do not lubricate the contact point. Rotate the shaft quickly several times to work in the fluid and establish contact. Use the cleaning fluid sparingly, and keep it off the plates except at the contact point.

Batteries and Tools

When working on equipment powered by a battery with a capacity of more than a few ampere-hours (Ah), take special care to avoid short circuits and always have a fuse or circuit-breaker in-line to the battery. If possible, fuse both the positive and negative connections. This is particularly important for vehicle batteries and mobile equipment. A short circuit can do thousands of dollars of damage to a vehicle's electrical power system in a matter of seconds! When working on mobile equipment, disconnect the battery's positive terminal or at least disconnect the circuit that powers the equipment by removing the fuse.

A tool that accidentally short-circuits the battery terminals can cause an instantaneous current flow of thousands of amps, often destroying both the battery and the tool and creating a significant fire and burn hazard.

REPLACEMENTS

Replacement capacitors should match the original in value, tolerance, dielectric, working voltage and temperature coefficient. Use only ac-rated capacitors for line service (capacitors connected directly to the ac line) to prevent fire hazards. If exact replacements are not available, substitutes may vary from the original part in the following respects: Bypass capacitors may vary from one to three times the capacitance of the original. Coupling capacitors may vary from one-half to twice the value of the original. Capacitance values in tuned circuits (especially filters) must be exact. (Even then, any replacement will probably require circuit realignment.)

If the same kind of capacitor is not available, use one with better dielectric characteristics. Do not substitute polarized capacitors for non-polarized parts. Capacitors with a higher working voltage may be used, although the capacitance of an electrolytic capacitor used significantly below its working voltage will usually increase with time.

The characteristics of each type of capacitor are discussed in the **Electrical Fundamentals** and **RF Techniques** chapters. Consider these characteristics if you're not using an exact replacement capacitor.

26.2.7 Inductors and Transformers

The most common inductor or transformer failure is a broken conductor. More rarely, a short circuit can occur across one or more turns of a coil. In an inductor, this changes the value. In a transformer, the turns ratio and resultant output voltage changes. In high-power circuits, excessive inductor current can generate enough heat to melt plastics used as coil forms.

Inductors may be checked for open circuit failure with an ohmmeter. In a good inductor, dc resistance rarely exceeds a few ohms. Shorted turns and other changes in inductance show only during alignment or inductance measurement.

The procedure for measurement of inductance with a dip meter is the same as that given for capacitance measurement, except that a capacitor of known value is used in the resonant circuit.

Replacement inductors must have the same inductance as the original, but that is only the first requirement. They must also carry the same current, withstand the same voltage and present nearly the same Q as the original part. Given the original as a pattern, the amateur can duplicate these qualities for many inductors. Note that inductors with ferrite or iron-powder cores are frequency sensitive, so the replacement must have the same core material.

If the coil is of simple construction, with the form and core undamaged, carefully count and write down the number of turns and their placement on the form. Also note how the coil leads are arranged and connected to the circuit. Then determine the wire size and insulation used. Wire diameter, insulation and turn spacing are critical to the current and voltage ratings of an inductor. (There is little hope of matching coil characteristics unless the wire is duplicated exactly in the new part.) Next, remove the old winding — be careful not to damage the form — and apply a new winding in its place. Be sure to dress all coil leads and connections in exactly the same manner as the original. Apply Q dope (a solution of polystyrene plastic) or a thin coating of plastic-based glue to hold the finished winding in place.

Follow the same procedure in cases where the form or core is damaged, except that a suitable replacement form or core (same dimensions and permeability) must be found.

Ready-made inductors may be used as replacements if the characteristics of the original and the replacement are known and compatible. Unfortunately, many inductors are poorly marked. If so, some comparisons, measurements and circuit analysis are usually necessary.

When selecting a replacement inductor, you can usually eliminate parts that bear no physical resemblance to the original part. This may seem odd, but the Q of an inductor depends on its physical dimensions and the permeability of the core material. Inductors of the same value, but of vastly different size or shape, will likely have a great difference in Q. The Q of the new inductor can be checked by installing it in the circuit, aligning the stage and performing the manufacturer's passband tests. Although this practice is all right in a pinch, it does not yield an accurate Q measurement. Methods to measure Q appear in the **Test Equipment and Measurements** chapter.

Once the replacement inductor is found, install it in the circuit. Duplicate the placement, orientation and wiring of the original. Ground-lead length and arrangement should not be changed. Isolation and magnetic shielding can be improved by replacing solenoid inductors with toroids. If you do, however, it is likely that many circuit adjustments will be needed to compensate for reduced coupling and mutual inductance. Alignment is usually required whenever a tuned-circuit component is replaced.

A transformer consists of two inductors that are magnetically coupled. Transformers are used to change voltage and current levels (this changes impedance also). Failure usually occurs as an open circuit or short circuit of one or more windings. Insulation failures can also occur that result in short circuits between windings or between windings and the core or case. It is also common for the insulated wire leads to develop cracks or abrasion where they come out of the case. This can be repaired easily by replacing the lead, or if the conducting wire strands are not burned or broken, by sliding an insulation sleeve over the wire to protect the insulation from further wear.

Amateur testing of power transformers is mostly limited to ohmmeter tests for open circuits and voltmeter checks of secondary voltage. Make sure that the power-line voltage is correct, then check the secondary voltage against that specified. There should be less than 10% difference between open-circuit and full-load secondary voltage. A test setup and procedure for evaluating power transformers is also provided in the **Power Sources** chapter.

Replacement transformers must match the original in voltage, volt-ampere (VA), duty cycle and operating-frequency ratings. They must also be compatible in size. (All transformer windings should be insulated for the full power supply voltage.)

When disconnecting a transformer for testing or repair, be sure to carefully record the color and connection for each of the transformer leads. In power transformers it is common for leads to be mostly one color but with a contrasting stripe or other pattern that can be overlooked. If in doubt, use tape or paper labels to note the connection for each lead. Recording transformer color codes and connections is a good use of the shack notebook.

26.2.8 Relays

Although relays have been replaced by semiconductor switching in low-power circuits, they are still used extensively in high-power Amateur Radio equipment for applications such as amplifier TR switching and in antenna systems or ac power control. Relay action may become sluggish. AC relays can buzz (with adjustment becoming impossible). A binding armature or weak springs can cause intermittent switching. Excessive use or hot switching ruins contacts and shortens relay life.

You can test relays with a voltmeter by measuring voltage across contacts (power on, in-circuit) or with an ohmmeter (out of circuit). Look for erratic readings across the contacts, open or short circuits at contacts or an open circuit at the coil. A visual inspection with a magnifying glass should show no oxidation or corrosion. Limited pitting is usually OK.

Most failures of simple relays can be repaired by a thorough cleaning. Clean the contacts and mechanical parts with a residue-free cleaner. Keep it away from the coil and plastic parts that may be damaged. Dry the contacts with lint-free paper, such as a business card; then burnish them with a smooth steel blade. Do not use a file to clean contacts because it will damage the contact surface.

Replacement relays should match or exceed the original specifications for voltage, current, switching time and stray impedance (impedance is significant in RF circuits only). Many relays used in transceivers are specially made for the manufacturer. Substitutes may not be available from any other source.

Before replacing a multi-contact relay, make a drawing of the relay, its position, the leads and their routings through the surrounding parts. This drawing allows you to complete the installation properly, even if you are distracted in the middle of the operation. (This is a good use of the shack notebook!)

26.2.9 Semiconductors

Testing diodes and transistors with the ohmmeter function of an analog VOM used to be the normal method. Today's inexpensive multimeters nearly always provide a forward and reverse junction voltage drop test function. This almost eliminates the need for resistance-based tests for functional troubleshooting with the attendant variability and dependence on meter circuits. However, it is occasionally useful to perform threshold and voltage-current testing to match components or troubleshoot a specialized circuit. In support of those tests, a short article "Diode and Transistor Test Circuits" containing test circuits and procedures for measuring leakage, gain, Zener point voltage and so forth is included with the downloadable supplemental content. This section will focus on simple go/no-go testing.

DIODES

The primary function of a diode is to pass current in one direction only. They can be easily tested with an ohmmeter, and most multimeters have a diode junction test function built-in as well.

Signal or switching diodes — The most common diode in electronics equipment, signal diodes are used to convert ac to dc, to detect RF signals or to take the place of relays to switch ac or dc signals within a circuit. Signal diodes usually fail open, although shorted diodes are not rare.

Power rectifiers — Most equipment contains a power supply, so power rectifier diodes are the second-most common diodes in electronic circuitry. They usually fail shorted, blowing the power-supply fuse.

Other diodes — Zener diodes are made with a predictable reverse-breakdown voltage and are used as voltage regulators. Varactor diodes are specially made for use as voltage controlled variable capacitors. (Any semiconductor diode may be used as a voltage-variable capacitance, but the value will not be as predictable as that of a varactor.) A diac is a special-purpose diode that passes only pulses of current in each direction.

Diode testing — There are several basic tests for most diodes. First, is it a diode? Does it conduct in one direction and block current flow in the other? A simple resistance measurement is suitable for this test in most cases.

Diodes should be tested out of circuit. Disconnect one lead of the diode from the circuit, then perform the test. We can also test diodes by measuring the voltage drop across the diode junction while the diode is conducting.

A functioning diode will show high resistance in one direction and low resistance in the other. A DMM with a diode-test function is the best instrument to use. If using an analog meter, make sure more than 0.7 V and less than 1.5 V is used to measure resistance. Use the highest resistance scale of the meter that gives a reading of less than full-scale. Check a known-good diode to determine the meter polarity if there is any question. Compare the forward and reverse resistance readings for a known-good diode to those of the diode being tested to determine whether the diode is good.

Diode junction forward voltage drops are measured by a multimeter's diode test function. Silicon junctions usually show about 0.6 V at typical test current levels, while germanium is typically 0.2 V. Junction voltage drop increases with current flow.

Multimeters measure the junction resistances at low voltage and are not useful for testing Zener diodes. A good Zener diode will not conduct in the reverse direction at voltages below its rating. See the article included with the downloadable supplemental content, and mentioned at the beginning of this section for procedures and a circuit to determine Zener diode performance.

Replacement diodes — When a diode fails, check associated components as well. Replacement rectifier diodes should have the same current and peak inverse voltage (PIV) as the original. Series diode combinations are often used in high-voltage rectifiers. (The resistor and capacitor networks used to distribute the voltage equally among the diodes are no longer required for new rectifiers but should be retained for older parts. See the **Power Sources** chapter for more information.)

Switching diodes may be replaced with diodes that have equal or greater current ratings and a PIV greater than twice the peak-to-peak voltage encountered in the circuit. Switching time requirements are not critical except in RF, logic and some keying circuits. Logic circuits may require exact replacements to assure compatible switching speeds and load characteristics. RF switching diodes used near resonant circuits must have exact replacements as the diode resistance and capacitance will affect the tuned circuit.

Voltage and capacitance characteristics must be considered when replacing varactor diodes. Once again, exact replacements are best. Zener diodes should be replaced with parts having the same Zener voltage and equal or higher power rating, and equal or lower tolerance. Check the associated current-limiting resistor when replacing a Zener diode.

BIPOLAR TRANSISTORS

Transistor failures occur as an open junction, a shorted junction, excess leakage or a change in amplification performance. Most transistor failure is catastrophic. A transistor that has no leakage and amplifies at dc or audio frequencies will usually perform well over its design range. For this reason, transistor tests need not be performed at the planned operating frequency. Tests are made at dc or a low frequency (usually 1000 Hz). The circuit under repair is the best test of a potential replacement part. Swapping in a replacement transistor in a failed circuit will often result in a cure.

A simple and reliable test of bipolar transistors can be performed with the transistor in a circuit and the power on. It requires a test lead, a 10 kΩ resistor and a voltmeter. Connect the voltmeter across the emitter/collector leads and read the voltage. Then use the test lead to connect the base and emitter (**Figure 26.9A**). Under these conditions, conduction of a good transistor will be cut off and the meter should show nearly the entire supply voltage across the emitter/collector leads. Next, remove the clip lead and connect the 10 kΩ resistor from the base to the collector. This should bias the transistor into conduction and the emitter/ collector voltage should drop (Figure 26.9B). (This test indicates transistor response to changes in bias voltage.)

Transistors can be tested (out of circuit) with an ohmmeter in the same manner as diodes or a multimeter with a transistor test function can be used. Before using the ohmmeter-transistor circuit, look up the device characteristics before testing and consider possible consequences of testing the transistor in this way. Limit junction current to 1 to 5 mA for small-signal transistors. Transistor destruction or inaccurate measurements may result from careless testing.

The reverse-to-forward resistance ratio for good transistors may vary from 30:1 to better than 1000:1. Germanium transistors — still occasionally encountered — sometimes show high leakage when tested with an ohmmeter. Bipolar transistor leakage may be specified from the collector to the base, emitter to base or emitter to collector (with the junction reverse biased in all cases). The specification may be identified as I_{cbo}, I_{bo}, collector cutoff current or collector leakage for the base-collector junction, I_{ebo}, and so on for other junctions. Leakage current increases with junction temperature. (See the **Circuits and Components** chapter for definitions of these and other transistor parameters.)

While these simple test circuits will identify most transistor problems, RF devices should be tested at RF. Most component manufacturers include a test-circuit schematic on

---

Cross-Reference Replacement Semiconductors

Semiconductors from older equipment, even ICs, may be available as a cross-reference generic replacement. The primary source for these devices is NTE Electronics (www.nteinc.com). Enter the part number of the device you are trying to replace in the "Cross-Reference" window. NTE also supplies cross-referenced replacements for ECG part numbers which were the original generic replacement parts.

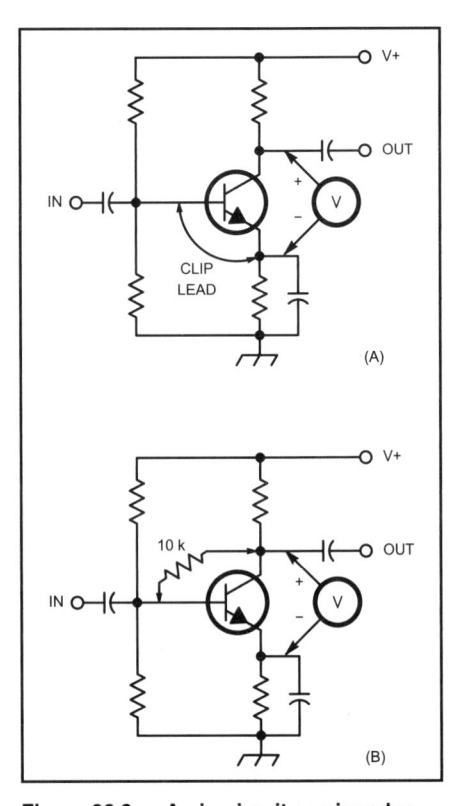

Figure 26.9 — An in-circuit semiconductor test with a clip lead, resistor and voltmeter. The meter should read V+ at (A). During test (B) the meter should show a decrease in voltage, ranging from a slight variation down to a few millivolts. It will typically cut the voltage to about half of its initial value.

the data sheet. The test circuit is usually an RF amplifier that operates near the high end of the device frequency range. If testing at RF is not possible, substitution of a known-good device is required.

Semiconductor failure is sometimes the result of environmental conditions. Open junctions, excess leakage (except with germanium transistors) and changes in amplification performance result from overload or excessive current.

Shorted junctions (low resistance in both directions) are usually caused by voltage spikes. Electrostatic discharge (ESD) or transients from lightning can destroy a semiconductor in microseconds.

Transistors rarely fail without an external cause. Check the surrounding parts for the cause of the transistor's demise, and correct the problem before installing a replacement.

JFETs

Junction FETs can be tested with a multimeter's diode junction test function in much the same way as bipolar transistors (see text and **Figure 26.10**). Reverse leakage should be several megohms or more. Forward resistance should be 500 to 1000 Ω if measured with an analog meter.

MOSFETs

Small-signal MOS (metal-oxide semiconductor) layers are extremely fragile. Normal body static is enough to damage them. Even gate protected (a diode is placed across the MOS layer to clamp voltage) MOSFETs may be destroyed by a few volts of static electricity. MOSFETs used for power circuits and RF amplifiers are much more resistant to damage. The manufacturer's sheet will specify any special static-protection measures that are required. (See the **Construction Techniques** chapter for more information about managing static at the workbench.)

When testing small MOSFETs make sure the power is off, capacitors discharged and the leads are shorted together before installing or removing it from a circuit. Use a voltmeter to be sure the chassis is near ground potential, then touch the chassis before and during MOSFET installation and removal. This assures that there is no difference of potential between your body, the chassis and the MOSFET leads. Ground the soldering-iron tip with a clip lead when soldering MOS devices. The FET source should be the first lead connected to and the last disconnected from a circuit. The insulating layers in MOSFETs prevent testing with an ohmmeter. Substitution is the only practical means for amateur testing of MOSFETs.

FET CONSIDERATIONS

Replacement FETs should be of the same

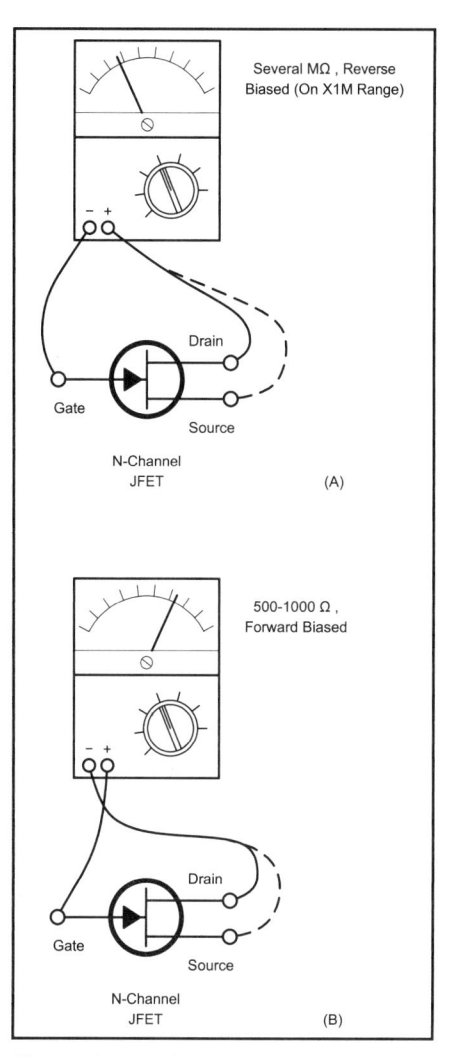

Figure 26.10 — Ohmmeter tests of a JFET. The junction is reverse biased at A and forward biased at B. (Analog meters are shown for convenience of illustration.)

type as the original part: JFET or MOSFET, P-channel or N-channel, enhancement or depletion. Consider the breakdown voltage required by the circuit. The breakdown voltage should be at least two to four times the power-supply and signal voltages in amplifiers. Allow for transients of 10 times the line voltage in power supplies. Breakdown voltages are usually specified as $V_{(BR)GSS}$ or $V_{(BR)GDO}$.

The gate-voltage specification gives the gate voltage required to cut off or initiate channel current (depending on the mode of operation). Gate voltages are usually listed as $V_{GS(OFF)}$, V_p (pinch off), V_{TH} (threshold) or $I_{D(ON)}$ or I_{TH}.

Dual-gate MOSFET characteristics are more complicated because of the interaction of the two gates. Cutoff voltage, breakdown voltage and gate leakage are the important traits of each gate.

INTEGRATED CIRCUITS

The basics of integrated circuits are covered in earlier chapters of this book. Amateurs seldom have the sophisticated equipment required to test ICs. Even a multi-channel oscilloscope can view only their simplest functions. We must be content to check every other possible cause, and only then assume that the problem lies with an IC. Experienced troubleshooters will tell you that — most of the time anyway — if a defective circuit uses an IC, it is the IC that is bad.

Linear ICs — There are two major classes of ICs: linear and digital. Linear ICs are best replaced with identical units. Original equipment manufacturers are the best source of a replacement; they are the only source with a reason to stockpile obsolete or custom-made items. If substitution of an IC is unavoidable, first try the cross-reference website of NTE mentioned in the sidebar. You can also look in manufacturers' websites and compare pin-outs and other specifications.

Digital ICs — It is usually not a good idea to substitute digital devices. While it may be okay to substitute an AB74LS00YZ from one manufacturer with a CD74LS00WX from a different manufacturer, you will usually not be able to replace an LS (low-power Schottky) device with an S (Schottky), C (CMOS) or any of a number of other families. The different families all have different speed, current-consumption, input and output characteristics. You would have to analyze the circuit to determine if you could substitute one type for another.

SEMICONDUCTOR SUBSTITUTION

In all cases try to obtain exact replacement semiconductors. Specifications vary slightly from one manufacturer to the next. Cross-reference equivalents such as NTE (**www.nteinc.com**) are useful, but not guaranteed to be an exact replacement. Before using an equivalent, check the specifications against those for the original part. When choosing a replacement, consider:

• Is it a PNP or an NPN?

• What are the operating frequency and input/output capacitance?

• How much power can it dissipate (often less than Vmax × Imax)?

• Will it fit the original socket or pad layout?

• Are there unusual circuit demands (low noise and so on)?

• What is the frequency of operation?

Remember that cross-reference equivalents are not guaranteed to work in every application. In cases where an absolutely exact replacement is required for an obsolete part, Rochester Electronics (**www.rocelec.com**) or 4 Star Electronics (**www.4starelectronics.com**) maintain extensive stocks, although the cost is likely to be rather high.

There may be cases where two dissimilar devices have the same part number, so it pays to compare the listed replacement specifications with the intended use. If the book says to use a diode in place of an RF transistor, it isn't going to work! Derate power specifications, as recommended by the manufacturer, for high-temperature operation.

26.2.10 Tubes

The most common tube failures in amateur service are caused by cathode depletion and gas contamination. Whenever a tube is operated, the coating on the cathode loses some of its ability to produce electrons. It is time to replace the tube when electron production (cathode current, I_c) falls to 50 to 60% of that exhibited by a new tube.

Gas contamination in a tube can often be identified easily because there may be a greenish or whitish-purple glow between the elements during operation. (A faint deep-purple glow is normal in most tubes.) The gas reduces tube resistance and leads to runaway plate current evidenced by a red glow from the anode, interelectrode arcing or a blown power supply fuse. Less common tube failures include an open filament, broken envelope and inter-electrode shorts.

The best test of a tube is to substitute a new one. Another alternative is a tube tester; these are sometimes available at hamfests or through antique radio or audiophile groups. You can also do some limited tests with an ohmmeter. Tube tests should be made out of circuit so circuit resistance does not confuse the results.

Use an ohmmeter to check for an open filament (remove the tube from the circuit first). A broken envelope is visually obvious, although a cracked envelope may appear as a gassy tube. Interelectrode shorts are evident during voltage checks on the operating stage. Any two elements that show the same voltage are probably shorted. (Remember that some inter-electrode shorts, such as the cathode-suppressor grid, are normal.)

Generally, a tube may be replaced with another that has the same type number. Compare the data sheets of similar tubes to assess their compatibility. Consider the base configuration and pinout, inter-electrode capacitances (a small variation is okay except for tubes in oscillator service), dissipated power ratings of the plate and screen grid and current limitations (both peak and average). For example, the 6146A may usually be replaced with a 6146B (heavy duty), but not vice versa.

In some cases, minor type-number differences signify differences in filament voltages, or even base styles, so check all specifications before making a replacement. (Even tubes of the same model number, prefix and suffix vary slightly, in some respects, from one supplier to the next.)

26.3 Getting Started

INSTINCTIVE OR SYSTEMATIC

A systematic approach to troubleshooting uses a defined process to analyze and isolate the problem. An instinctive approach relies on troubleshooting experience to guide you in selecting which circuits to test and which tests to perform.

When instinct is based on experience, searching by instinct may be the fastest procedure. If your instinct is correct, repair time and effort may be reduced substantially. As experience and confidence grow, the merits of the instinctive approach grow with them. However, inexperienced technicians who choose this approach are at the mercy of chance.

A systematic approach is a disciplined procedure that allows us to tackle problems in unfamiliar equipment with a reasonable hope of success. The systematic approach is usually chosen by beginning troubleshooters.

26.3.1 The Systematic Approach

Armed with a collection of test equipment, you might be tempted to immediately dig in and start looking for the problem. While it is sometimes obvious what piece of equipment or subassembly inside equipment is at fault, the many connections that make up nearly all ham stations today make it far more effective to begin troubleshooting by looking at the problem from the system perspective. By *system*, we mean more than one piece of equipment or subassemblies connected together — nothing fancier than that.

Amateur stations are full of systems: a digital mode system is made up of a radio, power supply, and PC. An antenna system consists of the antenna tuner, feed line, and antenna. Inside a radio there is a system made up of the power circuits, receiver, transmitter, control panel, and transmit-receive switching circuits. Connections between parts of the system need not be cables; wireless data links can also be part of a system.

In general, it's best to approach any problem — even the supposedly obvious problems — from the perspective of the system it affects. The first step is to determine the system with the smallest number of components that exhibits the problem. Then you can start looking for the problem in one of those components or the connection between them. We'll start with an example to illustrate the process.

Problem — After a year of trouble-free operation, when you transmit with more than 50 W of output power using PSK31, other stations now report lots of distortion products around your signal on the waterfall display, even though the ALC is not active at all and no software level settings have been changed. This could be RF interference, a problem with the digital interface between the PC and the radio, settings in the PC, settings in the radio, a bad connection...there are lots of possibilities.

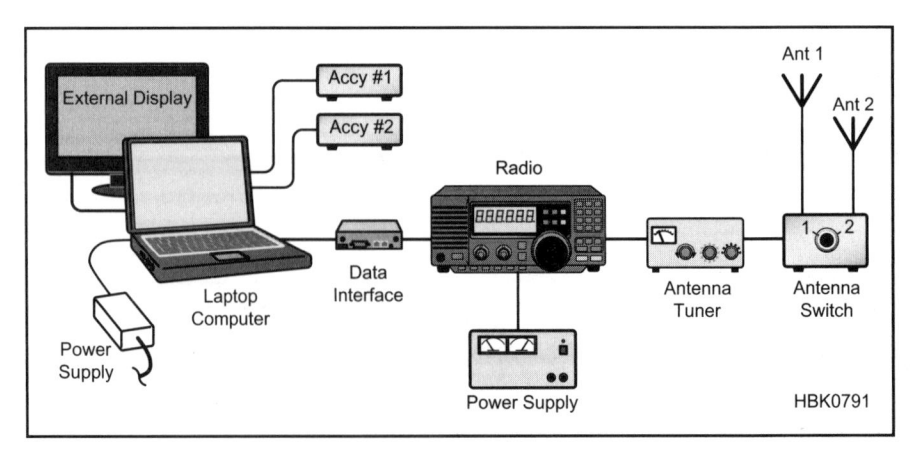

Figure 26.11 — The complete system of radio and power supply, data interface, laptop PC with a couple of accessories (Accy) and power supply, antenna tuner, antenna switch, antenna 1 and 2, and interconnecting cables.

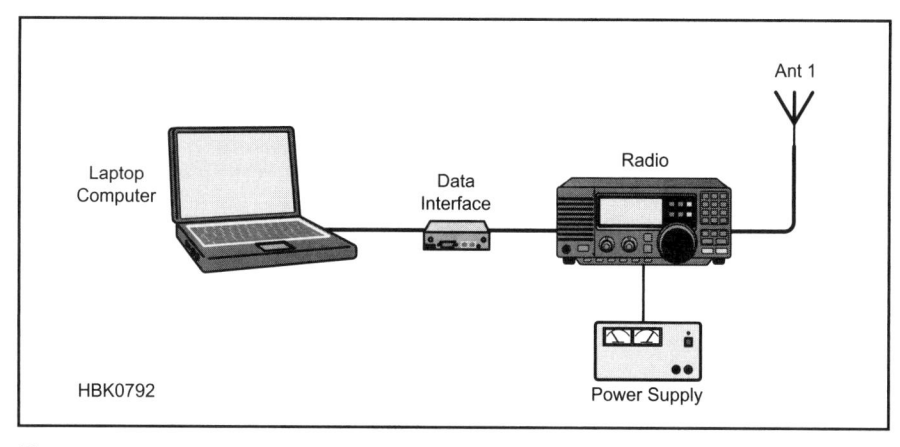

Figure 26.12 — The minimum system of radio and power supply, digital interface, laptop on battery power, antenna 1, and interconnecting cables.

Read the Manual!
Your equipment may be working as designed. Many electronic "problems" are caused by a switch or control in the wrong position, a misconfigured menu item, or a unit that is being asked to do something it was not designed to do. Before you open up your equipment for major surgery, make sure you are using it correctly. Most user's manuals have a procedure for setting up the equipment initially and for performing partial and full resets of microprocessor-controlled gear.

Get a pad of paper and sketch out the system that is exhibiting the problem, such as in **Figure 26.11**. Write down what the symptom(s) is(are) and the conditions under which they occur. Figure 26.11 shows that you have a system that has a lot of parts involved, including the interconnecting cables. Let's simplify that system! For this type of problem, it would be very helpful to have a friend available to listen on the air as you troubleshoot. To find the minimum system, start by removing any accessories that aren't being used from the radio and PC and trying to reproduce the problem, writing down each step and noting whether the problem changed. Not only will you simplify the problem but in the process you will have an excellent opportunity to inspect and check connections and configurations — perhaps even discovering the problem!

Let's say that the distortion persists with the mouse and external display disconnected and the laptop running from its internal battery. Then you were able to remove the antenna tuner and antenna switch, manually attaching just one antenna to the radio at a time, and found that the problem only occurred when using antenna 1. Removing any other part of the system makes it non-functional, so you have found the minimum system with the problem as shown in **Figure 26.12**.

Now it's time to start making small changes in the minimum system to observe the effect, again taking notes as you go. Changing the microphone gain a little bit up and down has hardly any effect. Changing the PC sound card output audio level a little bit also has hardly any effect. Reducing RF output power a little bit has a *big* effect: as power is reduced, so are the distortion products. Below 35 W, the problem was completely gone! This is an important clue, dutifully recorded on the pad of paper. Replacing antenna 1 with a dummy load had a similar effect — the problem disappeared according to your friend, who lives close enough to hear the weak signal leaking out of your greatly reduced antenna system. Putting antenna 1 back on the radio causes the problem to come back above 35 W, too.

The behavior of the problem points strongly to RF being picked up by a cable in your minimum system and interfering with the low-level digital audio. It's time for a close inspection of each remaining cable. Removing the radio's microphone connector shell and checking the wires inside didn't turn up anything — all of the connections were intact and only touching what they were supposed to touch. Looking at the cable between the digital interface and the sound card, though, you see that the shield of the cable at the PC end is badly frayed and barely making contact at all! In a few minutes, you've trimmed and re-soldered the cable, plugging it back into the PC. Testing even at full power output shows no distortion products on either antenna.

You fixed the problem by finding the minimum system and then inspecting one thing at a time until the root cause was found and eliminated.

What if the root cause didn't appear when you checked the cables? Then you would have to continue to test the system at the interfaces where the system components are connected together. You could measure signal levels with a sensitive voltmeter. You could add ferrite beads or cores on cables that might be picking up RF. You could check to see if the radio's power supply output is stable and clean as the transmitter power increases.

Another strategy would be to substitute known good components, one at a time, and see if the problem changes or disappears: You might swap in a different data interface. You could change the cables. Try a different power supply or radio or laptop.

Most systematic testing combines direct testing or inspection and a process of substitution. The goal is to either find the root cause or find the system component in which the root cause is hiding. Once you have a system component identified as the culprit, treat the component as a system itself and start the process all over again. Eventually, you'll find the problem.

Here are some guidelines to systematic troubleshooting in the ham shack:

1. Take the time to define and understand the system exhibiting the problem.

2. Remove system components one at a time.

3. Verify that the problem still exists. If not, restore that component.

4. Continue to remove components and test until the minimum system exhibiting the problem has been reached.

5. Inspect what is happening at each interface between system components by testing or substitution. In the example, you inspected the cables connecting the radio and other system components.

6. If a problem is identified, correct it and re-test.

7. Otherwise, continue to test or substitute each system component until the root cause has been identified or isolated to one component.

8. Treat that component as a new system and return to step 1.

Systematically reducing the number of components and testing each interface between them is almost always the fastest way to determine where the problem's root cause really lies. You may be a lucky guesser and sometimes a little plume of smoke is a dead giveaway, but in the long run, the system approach will save you time and money.

26.3.2 Assessing the Symptoms

An important part of the troubleshooting process is a careful definition of just what the symptoms of the problem really are. It is important to note exactly how the problem manifests itself and the conditions under which the problem occurs. Avoid vague descriptions such as "broken" and "not working." Train yourself to use precise descriptions such as "relay fails to activate" or "no speaker output."

Ask yourself these questions:

1. What functions of the equipment do not work as they should; what does not work at all?

2. What kind of performance can you realistically expect?

3. Has the trouble occurred in the past? (Keep a record of troubles and maintenance in the owner's manual, shack notebook or log book.)

Write down the answers to the questions. The information will help with your work, and it may help service personnel if their advice or professional service is required.

Question your assumptions and verify what you think you know. Are you *sure* that power supply output is OK under all conditions? Did you actually confirm that there is continuity at every position of the antenna switch? If there is any doubt, make a confirming measurement or inspection. Countless hours have been wasted because of unjustified assumptions!

Intermittent problems are generally harder to track down, so try to note the conditions under which the problem occurs — those are often important clues.

Troubleshooting is a good reason to do regular maintenance. Not only will you have fewer problems, but when something is just a little off or out of place, you are much likelier to notice it. Learn to listen to the little voice in your head noting something out of the ordinary. Don't discount the wild cards that occasionally cause problems.

Occasionally step away from the workbench and relax. Take a walk. Your mind will continue to think about the problem and you may surprise yourself when you sit back down to work!

If you can bounce ideas off a friend, try explaining the problem and letting the friend ask you questions. It's common for someone else with a different perspective to ask questions you haven't thought of.

26.3.3 External Inspection

Inspection is the easiest part of troubleshooting to do and careful, detailed inspection will often find the problem or a clue that leads to it. Make sure you have some paper to keep notes on as you go so when something occurs to you it can be recorded.

Try the easy things first. If you are able to solve the problem by replacing a fuse or reconnecting a loose cable, you might be able to avoid a lot of effort. Many experienced technicians have spent hours troubleshooting a piece of equipment only to learn the hard way that the on/off switch was set to OFF or the squelch control was set too high, or that they were not using the equipment properly.

Next, make sure that equipment is plugged in, that the ac outlet does indeed have power, that the equipment is switched on and that all of the fuses are good. If the equipment uses batteries or an external power supply, make sure they supply the right voltage under load.

Check that all wires, cables and accessories are working and plugged into the right connectors or jacks. In a system of components it is often difficult to be sure which component or subsystem is bad. Your transmitter may not work on SSB because the transmitter is bad, but it could also be a bad microphone.

Connector faults or misconnections are common. Consider them prime suspects in your troubleshooting detective work. Do a thorough inspection of the connections. Is the antenna connected? How about the speaker, fuses and TR switch? Are transistors and ICs firmly seated in their sockets? Are all interconnection cables sound and securely connected? Are any pins bent or is a connector inserted improperly? Many of these problems are obvious to the eye, so look around carefully.

While you are performing your inspection, don't forget to use all of your senses. Do you smell anything burnt or overheated? Is something leaking electrolyte or oil? Perhaps a component or connector looks overheated and discolored. Is mounting hardware secure?

Once you're done with your inspection, retest the equipment to be sure the problem is still there or note if it has changed in some way.

Newly Constructed Equipment

What if you built a piece of equipment and it doesn't work? In most repair work, the troubleshooter is aided by the knowledge that the circuit once worked so that it is only necessary to find and replace the faulty part(s). This is not the case with newly constructed equipment.

Repair of equipment with no working history is a special, and difficult, case. You may be dealing with a defective component, construction error or even a faulty design. Carefully checking for these defects can save you hours. This is a good reason to test homebrew equipment at each possible step and on a section-by-section basis, if possible. In that way, you'll know more about what does work if the completed project has a problem.

26.4 Inside the Equipment

At this point, you've determined that a specific piece of equipment has a problem. A visual inspection of all the operating controls and connections hasn't turned up anything, but the problem is still there. It is time to really dig in, take it apart, and fix it!

26.4.1 Documentation

In order to test any piece of equipment, you'll probably need at least a user's manual. If at all possible, locate a schematic diagram and service manual. It is possible to troubleshoot without a service manual, but a schematic is almost indispensable.

The original equipment manufacturer is the best source of a manual or schematic. However, many old manufacturers have gone out of business. Several sources of equipment manuals can be located by a web search or from one of the *QST* vendors that sell equipment needs. In addition K4XL's Boat Anchor Manual Archive (**www2.faculty.sbc.edu/kgrimm/boatanchor**) has hundreds of freely downloadable electronic copies of equipment manuals. If there is a user's group or email list associated with your equipment, a request to the group may turn up a manual and maybe even troubleshooting assistance.

If all else fails, you can sometimes reverse engineer a simple circuit by tracing wiring paths and identifying components to draw your own schematic. By downloading datasheets for the active devices used in the circuit, the pin-out diagrams and applications notes will sometimes be enough to help you understand and troubleshoot the circuit.

THE BLOCK DIAGRAM

An important part of the documentation, the block diagram is a road map. It shows the signal paths for each circuit function. These paths may run together, cross occasionally or not at all. Those blocks that are not in the paths of faulty functions can be eliminated as suspects. Sometimes the symptoms point to a single block and no further search is necessary. In cases where more than one block is suspect, several approaches may be used. Each requires testing a block or stage.

26.4.2 Disassembly

This seemingly simple step can trap the unwary technician. Most experienced service technicians can tell you the tale of the equipment they took apart and were unable to easily put back together. Don't let it happen to you.

Take photos and lots of notes about the way you take it apart. Take notes about each component you remove. Take a photo or make a sketch of complicated mechanical assemblies before disassembly and then record how you disassembled them. It is particularly important to record the position of shields and ground straps.

Write down the order in which you do things, color codes, part placements, cable routings, hardware notes, and anything else you think you might need to be able to reassemble the equipment weeks from now when the back-ordered part comes in.

Put all of the screws and mounting hardware in one place. A plastic jar with a lid works well; if you drop it the plastic is not apt to break and the lid will keep all the parts from flying around the work area (you will never find them all). It may pay to have a separate labeled container for each subsystem. Paper envelopes and muffin pans also work well.

26.4.3 Internal Inspection

Many service problems are visible, if you look for them carefully. Many a technician has spent hours tracking down a failure, only to find a bad solder joint or burned component that would have been spotted in careful inspection of the printed-circuit board. Internal inspections are just as important as external inspections.

It is time consuming, but you really need to look at every connector, every wire, every solder joint and every component. A low power magnifying glass or head-mounted magnifier enables you to quickly scan the equipment to look for problems. A connector may have loosened, resulting in an open circuit. You may spot broken wires or see a bad solder joint. Flexing the printed-circuit board or tugging on components a bit while looking at their solder joints will often locate a defective solder job. Look for scorched components.

Make sure all of the screws securing the printed-circuit board are tight and making good electrical contact. Check for loose screws on chassis-mounted connectors. (Do not tighten any electrical or mechanical adjusting screws or tuning controls, however!) See if you can find evidence of previous repair jobs; these may not have been done properly. Make sure that ICs are firmly seated in sockets if they are used. Look for pins folded underneath the IC rather than inserted into the socket. If you are troubleshooting a newly constructed circuit, make sure each part is of the correct value or type number and is installed correctly.

POWER SUPPLIES

If your careful inspection doesn't reveal anything, it is time to apply power to the unit under test and continue the process. Observe all safety precautions while troubleshooting equipment. There are voltages inside some equipment that can kill you. If you are not qualified to work safely with the voltages and conditions inside of the equipment, do not proceed. See Table 26.1 and the **Safety** chapter.

You may be able to save quite a bit of time if you test the power supply right away. If the power supply is not working at all or not working properly, no other circuit in the equipment can be expected to work properly either. Once the power supply has either been determined to be OK or repaired, you can proceed to other parts of the equipment. Power supply diagnosis is discussed in detail later in this chapter.

With power applied to the equipment, listen for arcs and look and smell for smoke or overheated components. If no problems are apparent, you can move on to testing the various parts of the circuit. For tube equipment, you may want to begin with ac power applied at a reduced voltage as described in the sections on repair of vintage equipment.

26.4.4 Signal Tracing and Signal Injection

There are two common systematic approaches to troubleshooting radio equipment at the block level. The first is signal tracing; the second is signal injection. The two techniques are very similar. Differences in test equipment and the circuit under test determine which method is best in a given situation. They can often be combined.

Both of these approaches are used on equipment that is designed to operate on a

---

Knowing When to Quit

It is common for experienced repair techs to be given "basket cases" — equipment that the original troubleshooter disassembled but then couldn't reassemble for whatever reason or couldn't find the problem. One of the most important decisions in the troubleshooting process is knowing when to quit. That is, realizing that you are about to go beyond your skills or understanding of the equipment.

If you proceed past this point, the chances of a successful outcome go down pretty quickly. It's far better to ask for help, work with a more knowledgeable friend, or carefully re-assemble the equipment and take it to a repair tech. Don't let your equipment wind up as a box full of partially connected pieces and mounting hardware under the table at the hamfest with a sign that says, "Couldn't fix — make offer!"

Block-Level Testing for DSP and SDR

More and more functions of today's radio equipment are implemented by microprocessor-based digital signal processing up to and including full SDR with direct digitization of RF signals very close to the antenna input. A look at the PC boards of such a radio show a few large, many-leaded ICs surrounded by control and interface components, power supply circuits, filtering, and transmitter power amplifiers. The individual stages of the classic superheterodyne architecture are nowhere to be seen. How do you troubleshoot such a radio?

Start with the same basic approach as for an older radio — begin at the input or output and work your way towards the "other end" of the radio. In a DSP-based radio however, you'll rapidly encounter the point at which the signal "goes digital" and disappears into the microprocessor or an analog/digital converter. Jump to the point where the signal returns to analog form on the "other side" of the microprocessor (or PC in the case of most SDR equipment) and resume testing. In this way you can simply treat the microprocessor as one very large stage in the radio. If the problem turns out to be in the surrounding circuitry or in the interface between a PC and the RF circuits, you can troubleshoot it as you would any other piece of equipment.

If the problem turns out to be in the microprocessor or analog/digital converter, in all probability you will have to get a replacement board from the manufacturer. It is possible to replace the converter or processor (if you can obtain the pre-programmed part) but most manufacturers treat the entire circuit board as the lowest-level replaceable component. This makes repair more expensive (or impossible if no replacements are available) but the positive tradeoff is that the microprocessors rarely fail by themselves, resulting in fewer repairs being required in the first place.

signal (RF or audio or data) in a sequence of steps. A transceiver based on the superheterodyne architecture is probably the best example of this type of equipment in the ham shack. Audio equipment is also built this way. More information about the signal injector and signal sources appears in "Some Basics of Equipment Servicing," from February 1982 *QST* (Feedback, May 1982).

Newer equipment that incorporates DSP and specialized or proprietary ICs is much less amenable to stage-by-stage testing techniques. (See the sidebar "Block-Level Testing for DSP and SDR") Nevertheless, the techniques of signal tracing and signal injection are still useful where the signal path is accessible to the troubleshooter.

SIGNAL TRACING

In signal tracing, start at the beginning of a circuit or system and follow the signal through to the end. When you find the signal at the input to a specific stage, but not at the output, you have located the defective stage. You can then measure voltages and perform other tests on that stage to locate the specific failure. This is much faster than testing every component in the unit to determine which is bad.

It is sometimes possible to use over-the-air signals in signal tracing, in a receiver for example. However, if a good signal generator is available, it is best to use it as the signal source. A modulated signal source is best.

Signal tracing is suitable for most types of troubleshooting of receivers and analog amplifiers. Signal tracing is the best way to check transmitters because all of the necessary signals are present in the transmitter by design. Most signal generators cannot supply the wide range of signal levels required to test a transmitter.

Equipment

A voltmeter with an RF probe is the most common instrument used for signal tracing. Low-level signals cannot be measured accurately with this instrument. Signals that do not exceed the junction drop of the diode in the probe will not register at all, but the presence, or absence, of larger signals can be observed.

A dedicated signal tracer can also be used. It is essentially an audio amplifier. (See the downloadable supplemental content for a project to build your own signal tracer.) An experienced technician can usually judge the level and distortion of the signal by ear. You cannot use a dedicated signal tracer to follow a signal that is not amplitude modulated (single sideband is a form of AM). A signal tracer is not suitable for tracing CW signals, FM signals or oscillators. To trace these, you will have to use a voltmeter and RF probe or an oscilloscope.

An oscilloscope is the most versatile signal tracer. It offers high input impedance, variable sensitivity, and a constant display of the traced waveform. If the oscilloscope has sufficient bandwidth, RF signals can be observed directly. Alternatively, a demodulator probe can be used to show demodulated RF signals on a low-bandwidth oscilloscope. Dual-trace scopes can simultaneously display the waveforms, including their phase relationship, present at the input and output of a circuit.

Procedure

First, make sure that the circuit under test and test instruments are isolated from the ac line by internal transformers, an isolation transformer, or operate from battery power. Set the signal source to an appropriate level and frequency for the unit you are testing. For a receiver, a signal of about 100 µV should be plenty. For other circuits, use the schematic, an analysis of circuit function and your own good judgment to set the signal level.

In signal tracing, start at the beginning and work toward the end of the signal path. Switch on power to the test circuit and connect the signal-source output to the test-circuit input. Place the tracer instrument at the circuit input and ensure that the test signal is present. Observe the characteristics of the signal if you are using a scope (see **Figure 26.13**). Compare the detected signal to the source signal during tracing.

Move the test instrument to the output of the next stage and observe the signal. Signal level should increase in amplifier stages and may decrease slightly in other stages. The signal will not be present at the output of a dead stage.

Low-impedance test points may not provide sufficient signal to drive a high-impedance signal tracer, so tracer sensitivity is

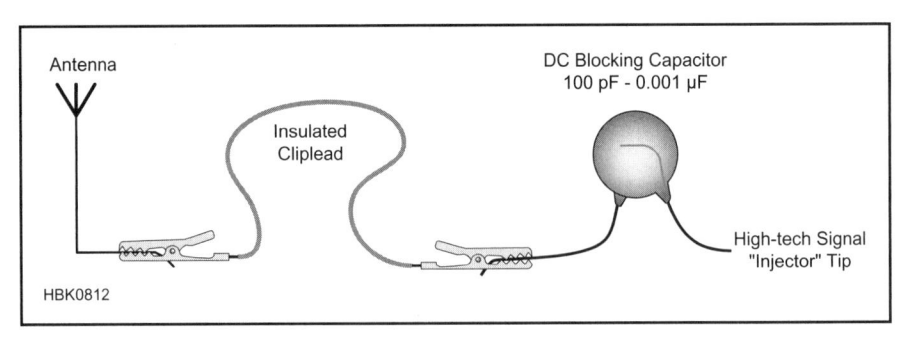

Figure 26.14 — A simple signal injector that uses an antenna to pick up signals to be applied to the circuit under test. [Courtesy Elecraft, www.elecraft.com]

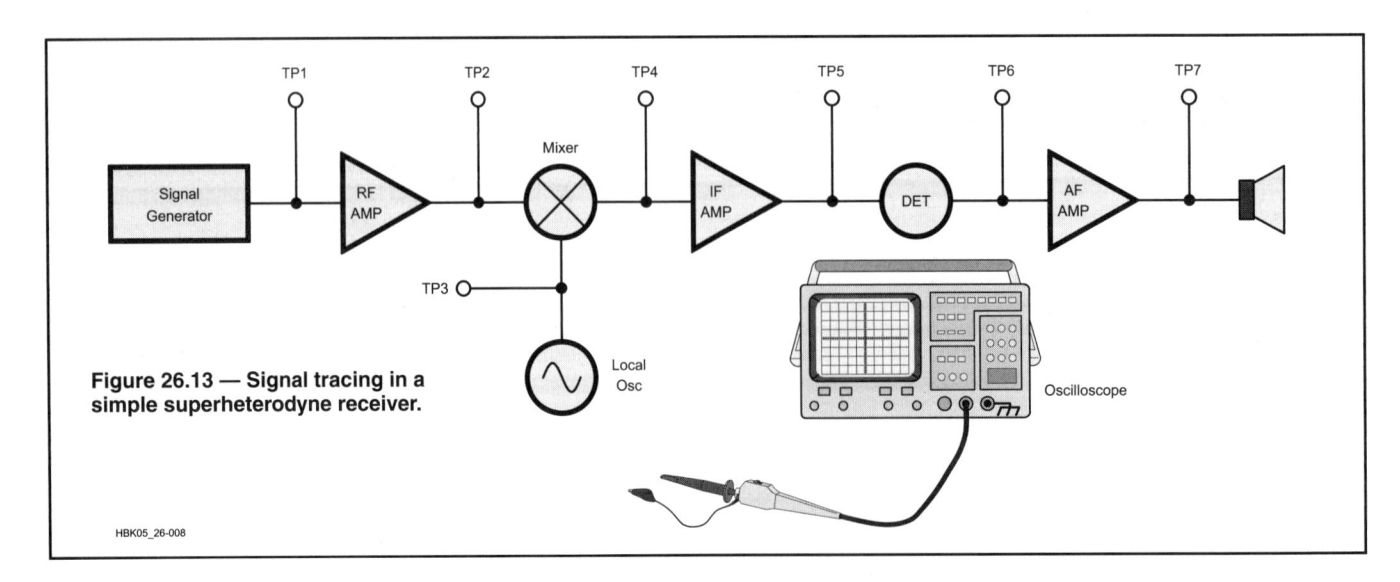

Figure 26.13 — Signal tracing in a simple superheterodyne receiver.

important. Also, in some circuits the output level appears low where there is an impedance change from input to output of a stage. For example, in a properly-working common-collector (emitter follower) circuit, the input (high-impedance) and output (low-impedance) signals are in phase and have roughly equal voltages. The voltages at TP1 and TP2 are approximately equal and in phase.

There are two signals — the test signal and the local oscillator signal — present in a mixer stage. Loss of either one will result in no output from the mixer stage. Switch the signal source on and off repeatedly to make sure that the test instrument reading varies (it need not disappear) with source switching.

SIGNAL INJECTION

Signal injection is a good choice for receiver troubleshooting because the receiver already has a detector as part of the design. If the detector is working or a suitable detector is devised (see the signal tracing section), a test signal can be injected at different points in the equipment until the faulty stage is discovered.

Equipment

Most of the time, your signal injector will be a signal generator. There are other injectors available, some of which are square-wave audio oscillators rich in RF harmonics (see Figure 26.5). These simple injectors do have their limits because you can't vary their output level or determine their frequency. They are still useful, though, because most circuit failures are caused by a stage that is completely dead.

Consider the signal level at the test point when choosing an instrument. The signal source used for injection must be able to supply appropriate frequencies and levels for each stage to be tested. For example, a typical superheterodyne receiver requires AF, IF and RF signals that vary from 6 V at AF, to 200 µV at RF. Each conversion stage used in a receiver requires a different IF from the signal source. When testing the signal path of an AM radio, such as a broadcast receiver, you'll need a modulated RF signal before the detector stage. Use an unmodulated RF signal to simulate the local oscillator.

The simple test circuit of **Figure 26.14** can be used as a quick-and-dirty signal injector for RF stages in a receiver. The antenna can be anything that will receive a signal at the stage's frequency of operation.

Procedure

If an external detector is required, set it to the proper level and connect it to the test circuit. Set the signal source for AF, and inject a signal directly into the signal detector to test operation of the injector and detector. Move the signal source to the input of the preceding stage, and observe the signal. Continue moving the signal source to the inputs of successive stages.

When you inject the signal source to the input of the defective stage, there will be no output. Prevent stage overload by reducing the level of the injected signal as testing progresses through the circuit. Use suitable frequencies for each tested stage.

Make a rough check of stage gain by injecting a signal at the input and output of an amplifier stage. You can then compare how much louder the signal is when injected at the input. This test may mislead you if there is a radical difference in impedance from stage input to output. Understand the circuit operation before testing.

Mixer stages present a special problem because they have two inputs, rather than one. A lack of output signal from a mixer can be caused by either a faulty mixer or a faulty local oscillator (LO). Check oscillator operation with an oscilloscope or by listening on another receiver. If none of these instruments are available, inject the frequency of the LO at the LO output. If a dead oscillator is the only problem, this should restore operation.

If the oscillator is operating, but off frequency, a multitude of spurious responses will appear. A simple signal injector that produces many frequencies simultaneously is not suitable for this test. Use a well-shielded signal generator set to an appropriate level at the LO frequency.

26.4.5 Microprocessor-Controlled Equipment

The majority of today's amateur equipment and accessories have at least one microprocessor and sometimes several. While reliability of this equipment is greatly improved over the older analog designs, troubleshooting microprocessor-based circuitry takes a different approach. While a tutorial on microprocessor troubleshooting is well outside the scope of this *Handbook*, the following basic guidelines will help determine whether the problem is inside the microprocessor (or its firmware) or in the supporting circuitry. In addition, the **Digital Basics** chapter contains lots of information about the operation of digital circuits.

1) Start by obtaining the microprocessor datasheet and identifying all of the power and control pins if they are not identified on the equipment schematic. Determine which state the control pins should be in for the device to run.

2) Test all power and control pins for the proper state (voltage). Verify that the microprocessor clock signal is active. If not, determine the reason and repair before proceeding.

3) If there is an address and data bus for external memory and input-output (I/O) devices (less common in newer equipment), use a logic probe or scope to verify that they are all active (changing state). If not, there is a program or logic fault.

4) Determine which pins are digital inputs or outputs of the microprocessor and verify that a valid digital logic level exists at the pin. If not, check the external circuit to which the pin is attached.

5) Determine which pins are analog inputs or outputs of the microprocessor. Analyze the external circuit to determine what constitutes a proper voltage into or out of the processor. If the voltage is not valid, check the external circuit to which the pin is attached. If an external voltage reference is used, verify that it is working.

6) External circuits can often be checked by disconnecting them from the microprocessor and either driving them with a temporary voltage source or measuring the signal they are attempting to send to the microprocessor.

7) If all control and power signals and the external circuitry checks out OK, it is likely that a microprocessor or firmware fault has occurred.

If you determine that the microprocessor is faulty, you will have to contact the manufacturer in most cases, since firmware is most often contained within the processor which must be programmed before it is installed. Older equipment in which the program and data memory are external to the microprocessor can be very difficult to repair due to obsolescence of the parts themselves and the requirement to program EPROM or PROM devices.

Divide and Conquer

If the equipment has a single primary signal path, the block-by-block search may be sped up considerably by testing between successively smaller groups of circuit blocks. Each test thus exercises some fraction of the remaining circuit.

This "divide and conquer" tactic cannot be used in equipment that splits the signal path between the input and the output. Test readings taken inside feedback loops are misleading unless you understand the circuit and the waveform to be expected at each point in the test circuit. It is best to consider all stages within a feedback loop as a single block during the block search.

Divide-and-conquer is a good tactic for those inclined to take the instinctive approach to troubleshooting. As you gain more experience, you'll find yourself able to quickly isolate problems this way. You can then test each block in more detail.

26.5 Testing at the Circuit Level

Once you have followed all of the troubleshooting procedures and have isolated your problem to a single defective stage or circuit, a few simple measurements and tests will usually pinpoint one or more specific components that need adjustment or replacement.

First, check the parts in the circuit against the schematic diagram to be sure that they are reasonably close to the design values, especially in a newly built circuit. Even in a commercial piece of equipment, someone may have incorrectly changed them during attempted repairs. A wrong-value part is quite likely in new construction, such as a homebrew or kit project.

26.5.1 Voltage Levels

Check the circuit voltages. If the voltage levels are printed on the schematic, this is easy. If not, analyze the circuit and make some calculations to see what the circuit voltages should be. Remember, however, that the printed or calculated voltages are nominal; measured voltages may vary from the calculations.

When making measurements, remember the following points:

• Make measurements at device leads, not at circuit-board traces or socket lugs.

• Use small test probes to prevent accidental shorts.

• Never connect or disconnect power to solid-state circuits with the switch on.

• Remember that voltmeters, particularly older analog meters may load down a high-impedance circuit and change the voltage, as will ×1 and low-impedance scope probes.

Voltages may give you a clue to what is wrong with the circuit. If not, check the active device. If you can check the active device in the circuit, do so. If not, remove it and test it, or substitute a known good device. After connections, most circuit failures are caused directly or indirectly by a bad active device. The experienced troubleshooter usually tests or substitutes these first. Analyze the other components and determine the best way to test each as described earlier.

There are two voltage levels in most analog circuits (V+ and ground, for example). Most component failures (opens and shorts) will shift dc voltages near one of these levels. Typical failures that show up as incorrect dc voltages include: open coupling transformers; shorted capacitors; open, shorted or overheated resistors and open or shorted semiconductors.

Digital logic circuits require that signals be within specific voltage ranges to be treated as a valid logic-low or logic-high value.

26.5.2 Noise

A slight hiss is normal in all electronic circuits. This noise is produced whenever current flows through a conductor that is warmer than absolute zero. Noise is compounded and amplified by succeeding stages. Repair is necessary only when noise threatens to obscure normally clear signals.

Semiconductors can produce hiss in two ways. The first is normal — an even white noise that is much quieter than the desired signal. Faulty devices frequently produce excessive noise. The noise from a faulty device is often erratic, with pops and crashes that are sometimes louder than the desired signal. In an analog circuit, the end result of noise is usually sound. In a control or digital circuit, noise causes erratic operation: unexpected switching and so on.

Noise problems usually increase with temperature, so localized heat may help you find the source. Noise from any component may be sensitive to mechanical vibration. Tapping various components with an insulated screwdriver may quickly isolate a bad part. Noise can also be traced with an oscilloscope or signal tracer.

Nearly any component or connection can be a source of noise. Defective components are the most common cause of crackling noises. Defective connections are a common cause of loud, popping noises.

Check connections at cables, sockets and switches. Look for dirty variable capacitor wipers and potentiometers. An arcing mica trimmer capacitor can create static crashes in received or transmitted audio. Test them by installing a series 0.01 µF capacitor. If the noise disappears, replace the trimmer.

Potentiometers are particularly prone to noise problems when used in dc circuits. Clean them with a spray contact cleaner and rotate the shaft several times.

Rotary switches may be tested by jumpering the contacts with a clip lead. Loose contacts may sometimes be repaired, either by cleaning, carefully rebending the switch contacts or gluing loose switch parts to the switch deck. Operate variable components through their range while observing the noise level at the circuit output.

26.5.3 Oscillations

Oscillations occur whenever there is sufficient positive feedback in a circuit that has gain. (This can even include digital devices.) Oscillation may occur at any frequency from a low-frequency "putt-putt" (often called *motorboating*) well up into the RF region.

Unwanted oscillations are usually the result of changes in the active device (increased junction or interelectrode capacitance), failure of an oscillation suppressing component (open decoupling or bypass capacitors or neutralizing components) or new feedback paths (improper lead dress or dirt on the chassis or components). It can also be caused by improper design, especially in home-brew circuits. A shift in bias or drive levels may aggravate oscillation problems.

Oscillations that occur in audio stages do not change as the radio is tuned because the operating frequency — and therefore the component impedances — do not change. RF and IF oscillations, however, usually vary in amplitude as operating frequency is changed.

Oscillation stops when the positive feedback is removed. Locating and replacing a defective (or missing) bypass capacitor may effect an improvement. The defective oscillating stage can be found most reliably with an oscilloscope.

26.5.4 Amplitude Distortion

Amplitude distortion is the product of nonlinear operation. The resultant waveform contains not only the input signal, but new signals at other frequencies as well. All of the frequencies combine to produce the distorted waveform. Distortion in a transmitter gives rise to splatter, harmonics and interference.

Figure 26.15 shows some typical cases of distortion. Clipping (also called flat-topping) is the consequence of excessive drive, a change in bias, or insufficient supply voltage to the circuit. The corners on the waveform show that harmonics are present. (A square wave contains the fundamental and all odd harmonics.) If this was a transmitter circuit, these odd harmonics would be heard well away from the operating frequency, possibly outside of amateur bands.

Harmonic distortion produces radiation at frequencies far removed from the fundamental; it is a major cause of electromagnetic interference (EMI). Harmonics are generated

---

Controlling Key Clicks

Key clicks are a special type of amplitude distortion caused by fast rising and falling edges of the output waveform or from abrupt disturbances in an otherwise smooth waveform. See the **Transmitting** chapter for more information about controlling key clicks. Most modern radios offer user configuration options to adjust keying rise and fall times. Older radios may require modification of a timing circuit that controls rise and fall time. Be a good neighbor to other operators and eliminate key clicks on your signal!

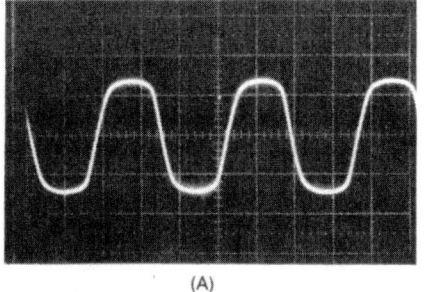

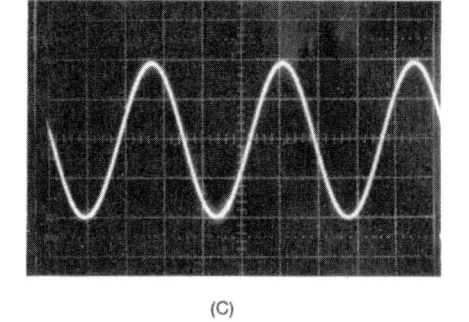

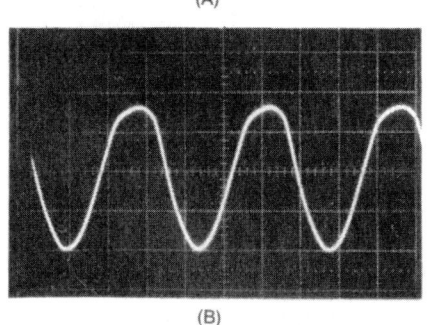

Figure 26.15 — Examples of distorted waveforms. The result of clipping is shown in A. Nonlinear amplification is shown in B. A pure sine wave is shown in C for comparison.

in nearly every amplifier. When they occur in a transmitter, they are usually caused by insufficient transmitter filtering (either by design, or because of filter component failure).

Anything that changes the proper bias of an amplifier can cause distortion. This includes failures in the bias components, leaky transistors or vacuum tubes with interelectrode shorts. In a receiver, these conditions may mimic AGC trouble. Improper bias of an analog circuit often results from a resistor that changed value or a leaky or shorted capacitor. RF feedback can also produce distortion by disturbing bias levels. Distortion is also caused by circuit imbalance in Class AB or B amplifiers.

Oscillations in an IF amplifier may produce distortion. They cause constant, full AGC action, or generate spurious signals that mix with the desired signal. IF oscillations are usually evident on the S meter, which will show a strong signal even with the antenna disconnected.

26.5.5 Frequency Response

Every circuit, even a broadband circuit, has a desired frequency response. Audio amplifiers used in amateur SSB circuits, for example, typically are designed for signals between 300 and 3000 Hz, more or less. A tuned IF amplifier may have a bandwidth of 50 to 100 kHz around the stage's center frequency. Any change in the circuit's frequency response can alter its effect on the signals on which it operates.

Frequency response changes are almost always a consequence of a capacitor or inductor changing value. The easiest way to check frequency response is to either inject a signal into the circuit and measure the output at several frequencies or use a spectrum analyzer or a signal generator's sweep function. In LC networks, it is relatively simple to lift one lead of the component and use a component checker to determine the value.

26.5.6 Distortion Measurement

A distortion meter is used to measure distortion of AF signals. A spectrum analyzer is the best piece of test gear to measure distortion of RF signals. If a distortion meter is not available, an estimation of AF distortion can sometimes be made with a function generator and an oscilloscope. Inject a square wave signal into the circuit with a fundamental frequency roughly in the middle of the expected frequency response.

Compare the input square wave to the output signal with an oscilloscope. **Figure 26.16** shows several effects on the square wave that are related to frequency response. These provide clues to what components or devices may be causing the problem. Severe distortion indicates some other problem besides frequency response changes.

26.5.7 Alignment

Alignment — the tuning or calibration of frequency sensitive circuits — is rarely the cause of an electronics problem with receiving or transmitting equipment, particularly modern equipment. Alignment does not shift suddenly and should be a last resort for treating sensitivity or frequency response problems. Do not attempt to adjust alignment without the proper equipment and alignment procedures. The process often requires steps to be performed exactly and in a specific order. Equipment misaligned in this way usually must be professionally repaired as a consequence.

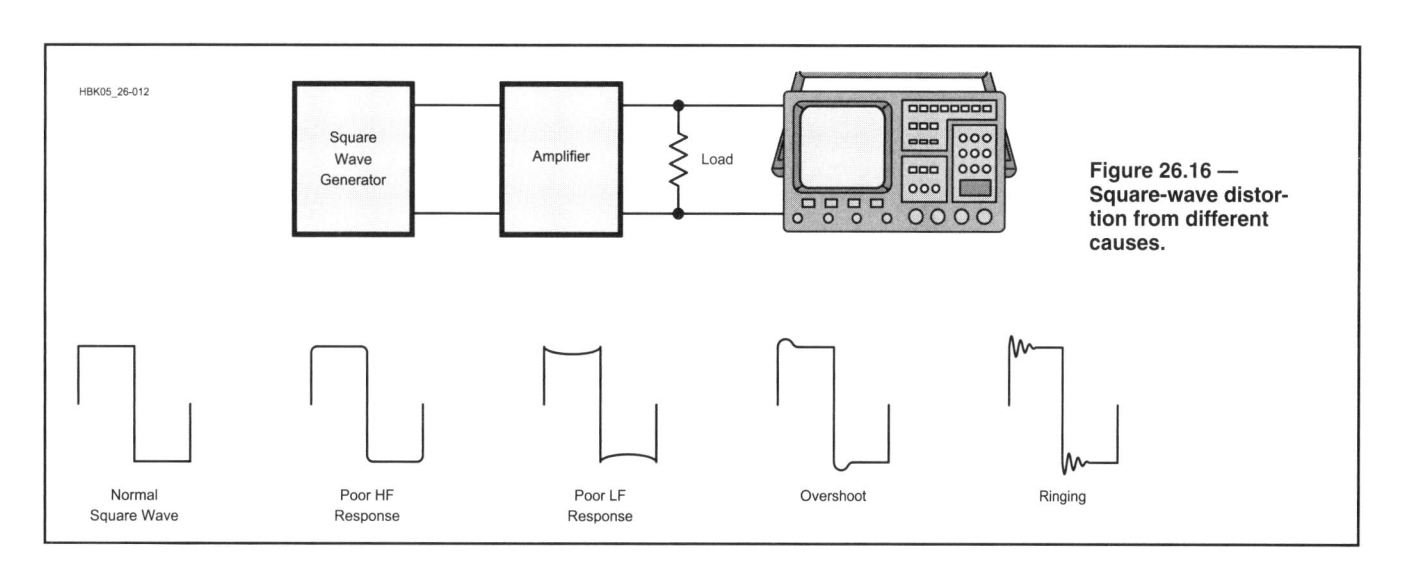

Figure 26.16 — Square-wave distortion from different causes.

Troubleshooting and Maintenance

26.5.8 Contamination

Contamination is another common service problem. Soda or coffee spilled into a piece of electronics is an extreme example (but one that does actually happen).

Conductive contaminants range from water to metal filings. Most can be removed by a thorough cleaning. Any of the residue-free cleaners can be used, but remember that the cleaner may also be conductive. Do not apply power to the circuit until the area is completely dry.

Keep cleaners away from variable-capacitor plates, transformers and parts that may be harmed by the chemical. The most common conductive contaminant is solder, either from a printed-circuit board solder bridge or a loose piece of solder deciding to surface at the most inconvenient time.

High-voltage circuits attract significant amounts of dust as described in the section on high-power amplifier maintenance later in this chapter. Cooling fans and ventilation holes also allow dust to accumulate, creating conductive paths between components. If not removed, the conductive paths gradually become lower in resistance until they begin to affect equipment performance. Vacuuming or blowing out the equipment is usually sufficient to clear away dust, although a carbon track may require a more thorough cleaning.

26.5.9 Solder Bridges

In a typical PC-board solder bridge, the solder that is used to solder one component has formed a short circuit to another PC-board trace or component. Unfortunately, they are common in both new construction and repair work. Look carefully for them after you have completed any soldering, especially on a PC-board. It is even possible that a solder bridge may exist in equipment you have owned for a long time, unnoticed until it suddenly decided to become a short circuit.

Related items are loose solder blobs, loose hardware or small pieces of component leads that can show up in the most awkward and troublesome places.

26.5.10 Arcing

Arcing is a serious sign of trouble. It may also be a real fire hazard. Arc sites are usually easy to find because an arc that generates visible light or noticeable sound also pits and discolors conductors.

Arcing is caused by component failure, dampness, dirt or lead dress. If the dampness is temporary, dry the area thoroughly and resume operation. Dirt may be cleaned from the chassis with a residue-free cleaner. Arrange leads so high-voltage conductors are isolated. Keep them away from sharp corners and screw points.

Arcing occurs in capacitors when the working voltage is exceeded. Air-dielectric variable capacitors can sustain occasional arcs without damage, but arcing indicates operation beyond circuit limits. Antenna tuners working beyond their ability may suffer from arcing. A failure or high SWR in an antenna circuit may also cause transmitter arcing. Prolonged, repeated, or high-power arcing can cause pits or deposits on capacitor plates that reduce capacitor voltage rating and lead to more arcing.

26.5.11 Digital Circuitry

Although every aspect of digital circuit operation may be resolved to a simple 1 or 0, or tristate (open circuit), the symptoms of their failure are far more complicated. The most common problems are false triggers or counts, digital inputs that do not respond to valid logic signals, and digital outputs stuck at ground or the supply voltage.

In most working digital circuitry the signals are constantly changing between low and high states, often at RF rates. Low-frequency or dc meters should not be used to check digital signal lines. A logic probe is often helpful in determining signal state and whether it is active or not. An oscilloscope or logic analyzer is usually needed to troubleshoot digital circuitry beyond simple go/no-go testing.

If you want to use an oscilloscope to give an accurate representation of digital signals, the scope bandwidth must be at least several times the highest clock frequency in the circuit in order to reproduce the fast rise and fall times of digital signals. Lower-bandwidth scopes can be useful in determining whether a signal is present or active but often miss short glitch signals (very fast transients) that are often associated with digital circuit malfunction.

LOGIC LEVELS

Begin by checking for the correct voltages at the pins of each IC. The correct logic voltages are specified in the device's datasheet, which will also identify the power pins (V_{cc} and ground). The voltages on the other pins should be a logic high, a logic low, or tristate (more on this later).

Most digital circuit failures are caused by a failed logic IC. IC failures are almost always catastrophic. It is unlikely that an AND gate will suddenly start functioning like an OR gate. It is more likely that the gate will have a signal at its input, and no signal at the output. In a failed device, the output pin will have a steady voltage. In some cases, the voltage is steady because one of the input signals is missing. Look carefully at what is going into a digital IC to determine what should be coming out. Manufacturers' datasheets describe the proper functioning of most digital devices.

TRISTATE DEVICES

Many digital devices are designed with a third logic state, commonly called tristate. In this state, the output of the device acts as an open circuit so that several device outputs can be connected to a common bus. The outputs that are active at any given time are selected by software or hardware control signals. A computer's data and address busses are good examples of this. If any device output connected to the bus fails by becoming locked or stuck in a 0 or 1 logic state, the entire bus becomes nonfunctional. Tristate devices can also be locked on by a failure of the signal that controls the tristate output status.

SIMPLE GATE TESTS

Most discrete logic ICs (collections of individual gates or other logic functions) are easily tested by in-circuit inspection of the input and output signals. The device's truth table or other behavior description specifies what the proper input and output signals should be. Testing of more complicated ICs requires the use of a logic analyzer, multi-trace scope or a dedicated IC tester. If a simple logic IC is found to be questionable, it is usually easiest to simply substitute a new device for it.

CLOCK SIGNALS

In clocked circuits, check to see if the clock signal is active. If the signal is found at the clock chip, trace it to each of the other ICs to be sure that the clock system is intact. Clock frequencies are rarely wrong but clock signals derived from a master clock can be missing or erratic if the circuitry that creates them is defective.

RF INTERFERENCE

If digital circuitry interferes with other nearby equipment, it may be radiating spurious signals. These signals can interfere with your Amateur Radio operation or other services. Computer networking and microprocessor-controlled consumer equipment generate a significant amount of noise due to RF being radiated from cables and unshielded equipment.

Digital circuitry can also be subject to interference from strong RF fields. Erratic operation or a complete lock-up is often the result. Begin by removing the suspect equipment from RF fields. If the symptoms stop when there is no RF energy present, apply common-mode chokes as described in the **RF Interference** chapter..

The ARRL RFI Book has a chapter on computer and digital interference to and from digital devices and circuits. The subject is also covered in the **RF Interference** chapter of this book.

26.5.12 Replacing Parts

If you have located a defective component within a stage, you need to replace it. When replacing socket mounted components, be sure to align the replacement part correctly. Make sure that the pins of the device are properly inserted into the socket. See the **Construction Techniques** chapter for guidance on working with SMT components.

Some special tools can make it easier to remove soldered parts. A chisel-shaped soldering tip helps pry leads from printed-circuit boards or terminals. A desoldering iron or bulb forms a suction to remove excess solder, making it easier to remove the component. Spring-loaded desoldering pumps are more convenient than bulbs. Desoldering wick draws solder away from a joint when pressed against the joint with a hot soldering iron.

Removing soldered ICs is a lot simpler if you simply clip its leads next to the IC body using fine-point wire cutters, although it does destroy the IC. Then melt the solder and lift out the pin with tweezers or the wire cutter. Use the desoldering pumps or wick to remove the solder. This works well for both through-hole and SMT components.

26.6 After the Repairs

Once you have completed your troubleshooting and repairs, it is time to put the equipment back together. Take a little extra time to make sure you have done everything correctly.

26.6.1 All Units

Give the entire unit a complete visual inspection. Look for any loose ends left over from your troubleshooting procedures — you may have left a few components temporarily soldered in place, forgotten to reattach a wire or cable, or overlooked some other repair error. Look for cold solder joints and signs of damage incurred during the repair. Double-check the position, leads and polarity of components that were removed or replaced.

Make sure that all ICs and connectors are properly oriented and inserted in their sockets. Test fuse continuity with an ohmmeter and verify that the current rating matches the circuit specification.

Look at the position of all of the wires and components. Make sure that wires and cables will be clear of hot components, screw points and other sharp edges. Make certain that the wires and components will not be in the way and pinched or crimped when covers are installed and the unit is put back together.

Separate the leads that carry dc, RF, input and output as much as possible. Plug-in circuit boards should be firmly seated with screws tightened and lock washers installed if so specified. Shields and ground straps should be installed just as they were on the original.

26.6.2 Transmitter Checkout

Since the signal produced by an HF transmitter can be heard the world over, a thorough check is necessary after any service has been performed. Do not exceed the transmitter duty cycle while testing. Limit transmissions to 10 to 20 seconds unless otherwise specified by the owner's manual.

1. Set all controls as specified in the operation manual, or at midscale.
2. Connect a dummy load and a power meter to the transmitter output.
3. Set the drive or carrier control for low output.
4. Switch the power on.
5. Transmit and quickly set the final-amplifier bias to specifications if necessary
6. For vacuum tube final amplifiers, slowly tune the output network through resonance. The current dip should be smooth and repeatable. It should occur simultaneously with the maximum power output. Any sudden jumps or wiggles of the current meter indicate that the amplifier is unstable. Adjust the neutralization circuit (according to the manufacturer's instructions) if one is present or check for oscillation. An amplifier usually requires neutralization whenever active devices, components or lead dress (that affect the output/input capacitance) are changed.
7. Check to see that the output power is consistent with the amplifier class used in the PA (efficiency should be about 25% for Class A, 50 to 60% for Class AB or B, and 70 to 75% for Class C). Problems are indicated by the efficiency being significantly low.
8. Repeat steps 4 through 6 for each band of operation from lowest to highest frequency.
9. Check the carrier balance (in SSB transmitters only) and adjust for minimum power output with maximum RF drive and no microphone gain.
10. Adjust the VOX controls.
11. Measure the passband and distortion levels if equipment (wideband scope or spectrum analyzer) is available.

26.6.3 Other Repaired Circuits

After the preliminary checks, set the circuit controls per the manufacturer's specifications (or to midrange if specifications are not available) and switch the power on. Watch and smell for smoke, and listen for odd sounds such as arcing or hum. Operate the circuit for a few minutes, consistent with allowable duty cycle. Verify that all operating controls function properly.

Check for intermittent connections by subjecting the circuit to heat, cold and slight flexure. Also, tap or jiggle the chassis lightly with an alignment tool or other insulator.

If the equipment is meant for mobile or portable service, operate it through an appropriate temperature range. Many mobile radios do not work on cold mornings, or on hot afternoons, because a temperature-dependent intermittent was not found during repairs.

26.6.4 Close It Up

After you are convinced that you have repaired the circuit properly, put it all back together. If you followed the advice in this book, you have all the screws and assorted doodads in a secure container. Look at the notes you took while taking it apart; put it back together in the reverse order. Don't forget to reconnect all internal connections, such as ac power, speaker or antenna leads.

Once the case is closed, and all appears well, don't neglect the final, important step — make sure it still works. Many an experienced technician has forgotten this important step, only to discover that some minor error, such as a forgotten antenna cable, has left the equipment nonfunctional.

26.7 Professional Repairs

Repairs that deal with very complex and temperamental circuits, or that require sophisticated test equipment, should be passed on to a professional. Factory authorized service personnel have a lot of experience. What seems like a servicing nightmare to you is old hat to them. There is no one better qualified to service your equipment than the factory.

If the manufacturer is no longer in business, check with your local dealer or look through Amateur Radio magazines and websites. You can usually find one or more companies or repair services that handle all makes and models. Your local club or a user's group may also be able to make a recommendation.

If you are going to ship your equipment somewhere for repair, notify the repair center first. Get authorization for shipping and an identification name or number for the package.

26.7.1 Packing Equipment

You can always blame shipping damage on the shipper, but it is a lot easier for all concerned if you package your equipment properly for shipping in the first place.

• Take photos of the equipment before packing it to document its condition before shipping. Additional photos during the packing steps might also be useful to show that you took the proper care in packing the equipment.

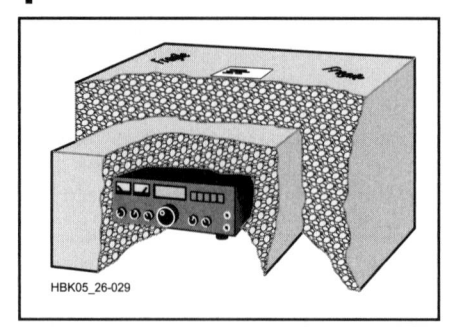

Figure 26.17 — Ship equipment packed securely in a box within a box.

• Firmly secure all heavy components, either by tying them down or blocking them off with shipping foam.
• Large transformers, such as for RF power amplifiers, should probably be removed and shipped separately.
• Large vacuum tubes should be wrapped in packing material or shipped separately.
• Make sure that all circuit boards and parts are firmly attached.

If you have the original shipping container, including all of the packing material, you should use that if the repair facility approves doing so. Otherwise use a box within a box for shipping. (See **Figure 26.17**). Place the equipment and some packing material inside a box and seal it with tape. Place that box inside another that is at least six inches larger in each dimension.

Don't forget to enclose a statement of the trouble, a short history of operation and any test results that may help the service technician. Include a good description of the things you have tried. Be honest! At current repair rates you want to tell the technician everything to help ensure an efficient repair. Place the necessary correspondence, statement of symptoms, and your contact information in a mailing envelope and place it just inside the top covers of the outer box or tape it to the top of the inner box.

Fill any remaining gaps with packing material, seal, address and mark the outer box. Choose a good freight carrier and insure the package. If available, get a tracking number for the package so you can tell when it was delivered.

Even if you tried to fix it yourself but ended up sending it back to the factory, you can feel good about your experience. You learned a lot by trying, and you have sent it back knowing that it really did require the services of a pro. Each time you troubleshoot and repair a piece of electronic circuitry, you learn something new. The down side is that you may develop a reputation as a real electronics whiz. You may find yourself spending a lot of time at club meetings offering advice, or getting invited over to a lot of shacks for a late-evening pizza snack. There are worse fates.

26.8 Typical Symptoms and Faults

26.8.1 Power Supplies

Many equipment failures are caused by power supply trouble. Fortunately, most power supply problems are easy to find and repair. This section focuses on the common linear power supply. Some notes are also made about switchmode supplies. Both types are discussed in detail in the **Power Sources** chapter, including projects with typical schematics.

LINEAR POWER SUPPLIES

The block diagram for a linear power supply is shown in **Figure 26.18**. First, use a voltmeter to measure output. Complete loss of output voltage is usually caused by an open circuit. (A short circuit draws excessive current that opens the fuse, thus becoming an open circuit.) If output voltage appears normal, apply a small load (1/10th supply capacity or smaller) and test output voltage again. If the small load causes voltage to drop, there is generally a problem in the regulator circuitry, often the pass transistors.

If the ac input circuit fuse is blown, that is usually caused by a shorted diode in the filter block, a failure of the output protection circuitry, or a short circuit in the device being powered by the supply. More rarely, one of the filter capacitors can short. If the fuse has opened, turn off the power, replace the fuse, and measure the load-circuit's dc resistance. The measured resistance should be consistent with the power-supply ratings. A short or open load circuit indicates a problem.

If the measured resistance is too low, troubleshoot the load circuit. (Nominal circuit resistances are included in some equipment manuals.) If the load circuit resistance is normal, suspect a defective regulator IC or problem in the rest of the unit.

IC regulators can oscillate, sometimes causing failure. The small-value capacitors on the input, output or adjustment pins of the regulator prevent oscillations. Check or replace these capacitors whenever a regulator has failed.

AC ripple (120 Hz buzz) is usually caused

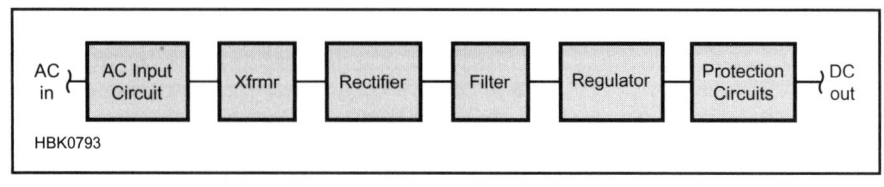

Figure 26.18 — Block diagram of a typical linear power supply.

by low-value filter capacitors in the power supply. Ripple can also become excessive due to overload or regulation problems. Look for a defective filter capacitor (usually open or low-value), defective regulator, or shorted filter choke if chokes are used (not common in modern equipment). In older equipment, the defective filter capacitor will often have visible leaking electrolyte: Look for corrosion residue at the capacitor leads. In new construction projects make sure RF energy is not getting into the power supply.

Here's an easy filter capacitor test: Temporarily connect a replacement capacitor (about the same value and working voltage) across the suspect capacitor. If the hum goes away, replace the bad component permanently.

Once the faulty component is found, inspect the surrounding circuit and consider what may have caused the problem. Sometimes one bad component can cause another to fail. For example, a shorted filter capacitor increases current flow and burns out a rectifier diode. While the defective diode is easy to find, the capacitor may show no visible damage.

If none of these initial checks find the problem, here are the usual systematic steps to locate the part of the supply with a problem:

• Check the input ac through switches and fuses to the transformer primary.

• Verify that the transformer secondary outputs ac of the right voltage. Disconnect the output leads, if necessary.

• Check the rectifiers for shorted diodes. Disconnect the rectifier output and test for output with a resistor load.

• Reconnect the filter and disconnect the regulator. Verify that the right dc voltage is present at the filter output.

• Reconnect the regulator and in the regulator IC or circuit, test every pin or signal, especially enable/disable/soft-start and the voltage reference.

• Disconnect any output protective circuitry and verify that the pass transistors are working with a resistor load.

• Reconnect and test the output protective circuitry.

SWITCHMODE POWER SUPPLIES

Switchmode or switching power supplies are quite different from conventional supplies. In a switcher, the regulator circuit is based on a switching transistor and energy storage inductor instead of a pass transistor to change power from one dc level to another that can be higher or lower than the input voltage. Switching frequencies range from 20-120 kHz for most supplies and up to the MHz range for miniature dc-dc converter modules.

Switchmode supplies operating from the ac line have similar input circuits to linear supplies. The transformer that supplies isolation is then located in the low-voltage, high frequency section.

Apply the same input and output block-level tests as for linear supplies. The regulator circuitry in a swichmode supply is more complex than for a linear supply, but it usually is implemented in a single regulator IC. Failure of the regulator IC, transistor switch, or feedback path usually results in a completely dead supply. While active device failure is still the number one suspect, it pays to carefully test all components in the regulator subsystem.

HIGH-VOLTAGE POWER SUPPLIES

Obviously, testing HV supplies requires extreme caution. See the safety discussion at the beginning of this chapter, the **Safety** chapter of this book, and the discussion of HV supplies in the **Power Sources** chapter. If you do not feel comfortable working on HV supplies, then don't. Ask for help or hire a professional repair service to do the job.

Most HV supplies used in amateur equipment are linear supplies with the same general structure as low voltage supplies. A typical supply is presented as a project in the **Power Sources** chapter and the same basic steps can be applied — just with a lot more caution.

Components in a string, such as rectifiers or filter capacitors, should all be tested if any are determined to have failed. This is particularly true for capacitors which can fail in sequence if one capacitor in the string shorts. Voltage equalizing resistors are not required for rectifier diodes available today such as the 1N5408. Consider replacing older rectifier strings with new rectifiers as a preventive maintenance step.

Interlocks rarely fail but verify that they are functioning properly before assuming they are in good working order.

26.8.2 Amplifier Circuits

Amplifiers are the most common circuits in electronics. The output of an ideal amplifier would match the input signal in every respect except magnitude: No distortion or noise would be added. Real amplifiers always add noise and distortion. Typical discrete and op-amp amplifier circuits are described in the **Analog Basics** chapter.

AMPLIFIER GAIN

Amplifier failure usually results in a loss of gain or excessive distortion at the amplifier output. In either case, check external connections first. Is there power to the stage? Has the fuse opened? Check the speaker and leads in audio output stages, the microphone and push-to-talk (PTT) line in transmitter audio sections. Excess voltage, excess current or thermal runaway can cause sudden failure of semiconductors. The failure may appear as either a short circuit or open circuit of one or more PN junctions.

Thermal runaway occurs most often in bipolar transistor circuits. If degenerative feedback (the emitter resistor reduces base-emitter voltage as conduction increases) is insufficient, thermal runaway will allow excessive current flow and device failure. Check transistors by substitution, if possible. If not, voltage checks as described below usually turn up the problem.

Faulty coupling components can reduce amplifier output. Look for component failures that would increase series impedance, or decrease shunt impedance, in the coupling network. Coupling faults can be located by signal tracing or parts substitution. Other passive component defects reduce amplifier output by shifting bias or causing active-device failure. These failures are evident when the dc operating voltages are measured.

If an amplifier is used inside a feedback loop, faults in the feedback loop can force a transistor into cutoff or saturation or force an op amp's output to either power supply rail. In a receiver, the AGC subsystem is such a feedback loop. Open the AGC line to the device and substitute a variable voltage for the AGC signal. If amplifier action varies with voltage, suspect the AGC-circuit components; otherwise, suspect the amplifier.

In an operating amplifier, check carefully for oscillations or noise. Oscillations are most likely to start with maximum gain and the amplifier input shorted. Any noise that is due to 60 Hz sources can be heard, or seen with an oscilloscope triggered by the ac line.

Unwanted amplifier RF oscillations should be cured with changes of lead dress or circuit components. Separate input leads from

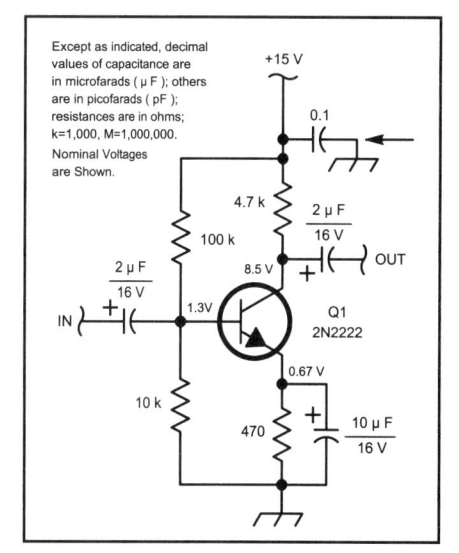

Figure 26.19 — The decoupling capacitor in this circuit is designated with an arrow.

output leads; use coaxial cable to carry RF between stages; neutralize inter-element or junction capacitance. Ferrite beads on the control element of the active device often stop unwanted oscillations.

Low-frequency oscillations (motorboating) indicate poor stage isolation or inadequate power supply filtering. Try a better lead-dress arrangement and/or check the capacitance of the decoupling network (see **Figure 26.19**). Use larger capacitors at the power supply leads; increase the number of capacitors or use separate decoupling capacitors at each stage. Coupling capacitors that are too low in value can also cause poor low-frequency response. Poor response to high frequencies is usually caused by circuit design.

COMMON-EMITTER AMPLIFIER

The common-emitter circuit (or common-source using an FET) is the most widely used configuration. It can be used as an amplifier or as a switch. Both are analyzed here as an example of how to troubleshoot transistor amplifier circuits. Other types of circuit can be analyzed similarly

Figure 26.20 is a schematic of a common-emitter transistor amplifier. The emitter, base and collector leads are labeled e, b and c, respectively. Important dc voltages are measured at the emitter (V_e), base (V_b) and collector (V_c) leads. V+ is the supply voltage.

First, analyze the voltages and signal levels in this circuit. The junction drop is the potential measured across a semiconductor junction that is conducting. It is typically 0.6 V for silicon and 0.2 V for germanium transistors.

This is a Class-A linear circuit. In Class-A circuits, the transistor is always conducting some current. R1 and R2 form a voltage divider that supplies dc bias (V_b) for the transistor. Normally, V_e is equal to V_b less the emitter-base junction drop. R4 provides degenerative dc bias, while C3 provides a low-impedance path for the signal. From this information, normal operating voltages can be estimated.

The bias and voltages will be set up so that the transistor collector voltage, V_c, is somewhere between V+ and ground potential. A good rule of thumb is that V_c should be about one-half of V+, although this can vary quite a bit, depending on component tolerances. The emitter voltage is usually a small percentage of V_c, say about 10%.

Any circuit failure that changes collector current, I_c, (ranging from a shorted transistor or a failure in the bias circuit) changes V_c and V_e as well. An increase of I_c lowers V_c and raises V_e. If the transistor shorts from collector to emitter, V_c drops to about 1.2 V, as determined by the voltage divider formed by R3 and R4.

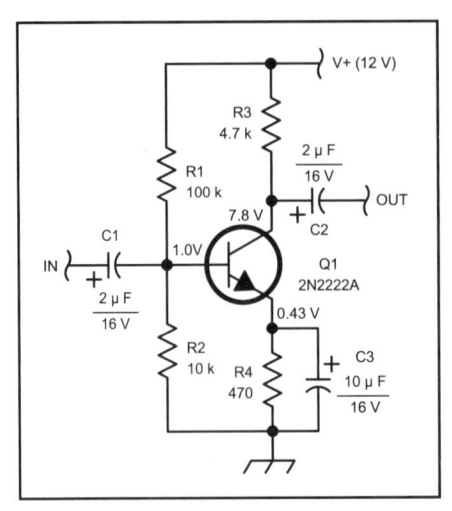

Figure 26.20 — A typical common-emitter audio amplifier.

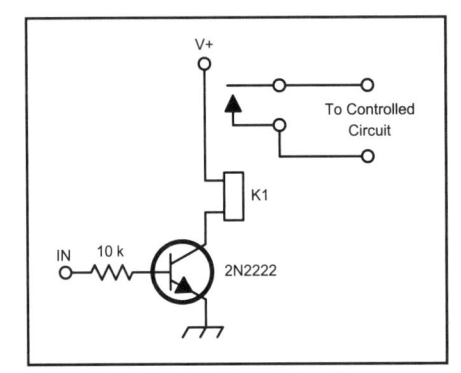

Figure 26.21 — A typical common-emitter switch or driver.

You would see nearly the same effect if the transistor were biased into saturation by collector-to-base leakage, a reduction in R1's value or an increase in R2's value. All of these circuit failures have the same effect. In some cases, a short in C1 or C2 could cause the same symptoms.

To properly diagnose the specific cause of low V_c, consider and test all of these parts. It is even more complex; an increase in R3's value would also decrease V_c. There would be one valuable clue, however: if R3 increased in value, I_c would not increase; V_e would also be low.

Anything that decreases I_c increases V_c. If the transistor failed open, R1 increased in value, R2 were shorted to ground or R4 opened, then V_c would be high.

COMMON-EMITTER SWITCH

A common-emitter transistor switching circuit is shown in **Figure 26.21**. This circuit functions differently from the circuit shown in Figure 26.20. A linear amplifier is designed so that the output signal is a faithful reproduction of the input signal. Its input and output may have any value from V+ to ground.

The switching circuit of Figure 26.21, however, is similar to a digital circuit. The active device is either on or off, 1 or 0, just like digital logic. Its input signal level should either be 0 V or positive enough to switch the transistor on fully (saturate). Its output state should be either full off (with no current flowing through the relay), or full on (with the relay energized). A voltmeter placed on the collector will show either approximately +12 V or 0 V, depending on the input.

Understanding this difference in operation is crucial to troubleshooting the two circuits. If V_c were +12 V in the circuit in Figure 26.20, it would indicate a circuit failure. A V_c of +12 V in the switching circuit is normal when V_b is 0 V. (If V_b measured 0.8 V or higher, V_c should be low and the relay energized.)

DC-COUPLED AMPLIFIERS

In dc-coupled amplifiers, the transistors are directly connected together without coupling capacitors. They comprise a unique troubleshooting case. Most often, when one device fails, it destroys one or more other semiconductors in the circuit. If you don't find all of the bad parts, the remaining defective parts can cause the installed replacements to fail immediately. To reliably troubleshoot a dc coupled circuit, you must test every semiconductor in the circuit and replace them all at once.

26.8.3 Oscillators

In many circuits, a failure of the oscillator will result in complete circuit failure. A transmitter will not transmit, and a superheterodyne receiver will not receive if you have an internal oscillator failure. (These symptoms do not always mean oscillator failure, however.)

Whenever there is weakening or complete loss of signal from a radio, check oscillator operation and frequency. There are several methods:

• Use a receiver with a coaxial probe to listen for the oscillator signal.

• A dip meter can be used to check oscillators by tuning to within ±15 kHz of the oscillator, couple it to the circuit, and listen for a beat note in the dip-meter headphones.

• Look at the oscillator waveform on a scope. The operating frequency can't be determined with great accuracy, but you can see if the oscillator is working at all. Use a low capacitance (10×) probe for oscillator observations.

Many modern oscillators are phase-locked loops (PLLs). Read the **Oscillators and Synthesizers** chapter of this book in order to learn how PLLs operate.

To test for a failed LC oscillator, use a dip meter in the active mode. Set the dip meter to the oscillator frequency and couple it to the oscillator output circuit. If the oscillator is dead, the dip-meter signal will take its place and temporarily restore some semblance of normal operation.

STABILITY

Drift is caused by variations in the oscillator. Poor voltage regulation and heat are the most common culprits. Check regulation with a voltmeter (use one that is not affected by RF). Voltage regulators are usually part of the oscillator circuit. Check them by substitution.

Chirp is a form of rapid drift that is usually caused by excessive oscillator loading or poor power-supply regulation. The most common cause of chirp is poor design. If chirp appears suddenly in a working circuit, look for component or design defects in the oscillator or its buffer amplifiers. (For example, a shorted coupling capacitor increases loading drastically.) Also check for new feedback paths from changes in wiring or component placement (feedback defeats buffer action).

Frequency instability may also result from defects in feedback components. Too much feedback may produce spurious signals, while too little makes oscillator start-up unreliable.

Sudden frequency changes are frequently the result of physical variations. Loose components or connections are probable causes. Check for arcing or dirt on printed-circuit boards, trimmers and variable capacitors, loose switch contacts, bad solder joints or loose connectors.

FREQUENCY ACCURACY

In manually tuned LC oscillators, tracking at the high-frequency end of the range is controlled by trimmer capacitors. A trimmer is a variable capacitor connected in parallel with the main tuning capacitor (see **Figure 26.22**). The trimmer represents a higher percentage of the total capacitance at the high end of the tuning range. It has relatively little effect on tuning characteristics at the low-frequency end of the range.

Low-end range is adjusted by a series trimmer capacitor called a *padder*. A padder is a variable capacitor that is connected in series with the main tuning capacitor. Padder capacitance has a greater effect at the low-frequency end of the range. The padder capacitor is often eliminated to save money. In that case, the low-frequency range is set by adjusting the main tuning coil.

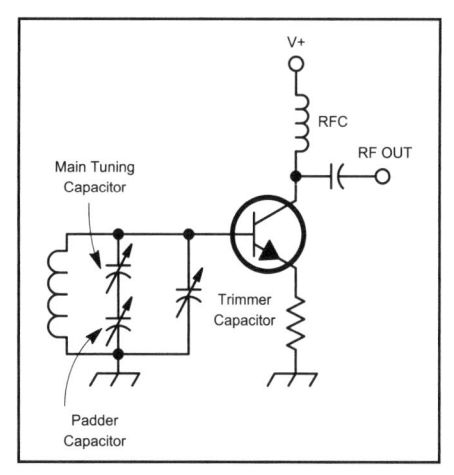

Figure 26.22 — A partial schematic of a simple oscillator showing the locations of the trimmer and padder capacitors.

26.8.4 Transmit Amplifier Modules

Most VHF/UHF mobile radios and many small HF radios use commercial amplifier modules as the final amplifier instead of discrete transistors. These modules are quite reliable and can withstand various stresses such as disconnected antennas. However, replacement units are rarely available more than a few years after a particular radio model goes out of production. You may be able to find a damaged radio of the same model to scavenge for parts, but once the modules fail, you are usually out of luck. User's groups are often good sources of information about common failure modes of certain radios and possibly even sources of replacement parts.

The usual failure mode of an amplifier module is caused by thermal cycling that eventually leads to an internal connection developing a crack. The module becomes intermittent and then eventually fails completely. If you can open the module, you can sometimes identify and repair such a problem by soldering over the crack.

When reinstalling or replacing an amplifier module, be very careful to attach it to the heat sink as it was at the factory. Do not use excessive amounts of thermal compound or grease and make sure the mounting screws are secure. If you can find a datasheet for the module, check to see if there are recommendations for mounting screw torque and any other installation procedures. (See the **RF Power Amplifiers** chapter for guidelines on mounting power transistors.)

26.9 Radio Troubleshooting Hints

Tables 26.2, **26.3**, **26.4** and **26.5** list some common problems and possible cures for older radios that are likely to have developed problems with some later-model equivalents. These tables are not all-inclusive. They are a collection of hints and shortcuts that may save you some troubleshooting time. If you don't find your problem listed, continue with systematic troubleshooting.

Remember that many problems are caused by improper setting of a switch, a control, or a configuration menu item. Before beginning a troubleshooting session, be sure you've checked the operating manual for proper control settings and checked through the manual's troubleshooting guide. If possible, obtain a service manual with its detailed procedures, measurements, and schematics.

26.9.1 Receivers

A receiver can be diagnosed using any of the methods described earlier, but if there is not even a faint sound from the speaker, signal injection is not a good technique. If you lack troubleshooting experience, avoid following instinctive hunches. Begin with power supply tests and proceed to signal tracing.

SELECTIVITY

Failure of control or switching circuits that determine the signal path and filters can cause selectivity problems. In older equipment, tuned transformers or the components used in filter circuits may develop a shorted turn, capacitors can fail and alignment is required occasionally. Such defects are accompanied by a loss of sensitivity. Except in cases of catastrophic failure (where either the filter passes all signals, or none), it is difficult to spot a loss of selectivity. Bandwidth and insertion-loss measurements are necessary to judge filter performance.

SENSITIVITY

A gradual loss of sensitivity results from gradual degradation of an active device or long-term changes in component values. Sudden partial sensitivity changes are usually the result of a component failure, usually in the RF or IF stages. Excessive signal levels

Table 26.2
Symptoms and Their Causes for All Electronic Equipment

Symptom — *Cause*

Power Supplies

Symptom	Cause
No output voltage	Open circuit (usually a fuse, pass transistor, or transformer winding)
Hum or ripple	Faulty regulator, capacitor or rectifier, low-frequency oscillation

Amplifiers

Symptom	Cause
Low gain	Transistor, coupling capacitors, emitter-bypass capacitor AGC component
Noise	Transistors, coupling capacitors, resistors
Oscillations	Dirt on variable capacitor or chassis, shorted op-amp input
Oscillations, untuned (oscillations do not change with frequency)	Audio stages
Oscillations, tuned	RF, IF and mixer stages
Static-like crashes	Arcing trimmer capacitors, poor connections
Static in FM receiver	Faulty limiter stage, open capacitor in ratio detector, weak RF stage, weak incoming signal
Intermittent noise	All components and connections, band-switch contacts, potentiometers (especially in dc circuits), trimmer capacitors, poor antenna connections
Distortion (constant)	Oscillation, overload, faulty AGC, leaky transistor, open lead in tab-mount transistor, dirty potentiometer, leaky coupling capacitor, open bypass capacitors, imbalance in tuned FM detector, IF oscillations, RF feedback (cables)
Distortion (strong signals only)	Open AGC loop
Frequency change	Physical or electrical variations, dirty or faulty variable capacitor, broken switch, loose compartment parts, poor voltage regulation, oscillator tuning (trouble when switching bands)

No Signals

Symptom	Cause
All bands	Dead VFO or LO, PLL won't lock
One band only	Defective crystal, oscillator out of tune, band switch
No function control	Faulty switch or control, poor connection to front panel subassembly

Table 26.3
Receiver Problems

Symptom	Cause
Low sensitivity	Semiconductor degradation, circuit contamination, poor antenna connection
Signals and calibrator heard weakly	
(low S-meter readings)	RF chain
(strong S-meter readings)	AF chain, detector
No signals or calibrator heard, only hissing	RF oscillators

Distortion

Symptom	Cause
On strong signals only	AGC fault
AGC fault	Active device cut off or saturated
Difficult tuning	AGC fault
Inability to receive	Detector fault
AM weak and distorted	Poor detector, power or ground connection
CW/SSB unintelligible	BFO off frequency or dead
FM distorted	Open detector diode

or transients can damage input RF switching, amplifier, or mixing circuits. Complete and sudden loss of sensitivity is caused by an open circuit anywhere in the signal path or by a dead oscillator.

AGC

AGC failure usually causes distortion that affects only strong signals. All stages operate at maximum gain when the AGC influence is removed. An S meter can help diagnose AGC failure because it is operated by the AGC loop. If the S meter does not move at all or remains at full scale, the AGC system has a problem.

In DSP radios, the AGC function is often controlled by software which you cannot troubleshoot but inputs to the software such as signal level detectors may be causing a problem instead.

In analog receivers, an open bypass capacitor in the AGC amplifier causes feedback through the loop. This often results in a receiver squeal (oscillation). Changes in the loop time constant affect tuning. If stations consistently blast, or are too weak for a brief time when first tuned in, the time constant is too fast. An excessively slow time constant makes tuning difficult, and stations fade after tuning. If the AGC is functioning, but the timing seems wrong, check the large-value capacitors found in the AGC circuit — they usually set the AGC time constants. If the AGC is not functioning, check the AGC-detector circuit. There is often an AGC voltage that is used to control several stages. A failure in any one stage could affect the entire loop.

DETECTOR PROBLEMS

Detector trouble usually appears as complete loss or distortion of the received signal. AM, SSB and CW signals may be weak and unintelligible. FM signals will sound distorted. Look for an open circuit in the detector circuit. If tests of the detector parts indicate no trouble, look for a poor connection in the detector's power supply or ground connections. A BFO that is dead or off frequency prevents SSB and CW reception. In modern rigs, the BFO frequency is usually derived from the main VFO system.

26.9.2 Transmitters

Many potential transmitter faults are discussed in several different places in this chapter. There are, however, a few techniques used to ensure stable operation of RF amplifiers in transmitters that are not covered elsewhere.

RF final amplifiers often use parasitic chokes to prevent instability. Older parasitic chokes usually consist of a 51- to 100-Ω non-inductive resistor with a coil wound around the body and connected to the leads. It is

Table 26.4
Transmitter Problems

Symptom	Cause
Key clicks	Keying filter, distortion in stages after keying, ALC overshoot or instability

Modulation Problems

Symptom	Cause
Loss of modulation	Broken cable (microphone, PTT, power), open circuit in audio chain, defective modulator
Distortion on transmit	Defective microphone, RF feedback, modulator imbalance, bypass capacitor, improper bias, excessive drive
Arcing	Dampness, dirt, improper lead dress
Low output	Incorrect control settings, improper carrier shift (CW signal outside of passband) audio oscillator failure, transistor or tube failure, SWR protection circuit

Antenna Problems

Symptom	Cause
Poor SWR	Damaged antenna element, matching network, feed line, balun failure (see below), resonant conductor near antenna, poor connection at antenna
Balun failure	Excessive SWR, weather or cold-flow damage in coil choke, broken wire or connection
RFI	Arcing or poor connections anywhere in antenna system or nearby conductors

Table 26.5
Transceiver Problems

Symptom	Cause
Inoperative S meter	Faulty TR switching or relay
PA noise in receiver	Faulty TR switching or relay
Excessive current on receive	Faulty TR switching or relay
Arcing in PA	Faulty TR switching or relay
Reduced signal strength on transmit and receive	IF failure
Poor VOX operation	VOX amplifiers
Poor VOX timing	Adjustment, component failure in VOX timing circuits or amplifiers
VOX consistently tripped by receiver audio	AntiVOX circuits or adjustment

used to prevent VHF and UHF oscillations in a vacuum-tube amplifier. The suppressor is placed in the plate lead, close to the plate connection.

In recent years, problems with this style of suppressor have been discovered. See the **RF Power Amplifiers** chapter for information about suppressing parasitics. If parasitic suppressors are present in your transmitter, continue to use them as the exact layout and lead dress of the RF amplifier circuitry may require them to avoid oscillation. If they are not present, do not add them. When working on RF power amplifiers, take care to keep leads and components arranged just as they were when they left the factory.

Parasitic chokes often fail from excessive current flow. In these cases, the resistor is charred. Occasionally, physical shock or corrosion produces an open circuit in the coil. Test for continuity with an ohmmeter.

Transistor amplifiers are protected against parasitic oscillations by low-value resistors or ferrite beads in the base or collector leads. Resistors are used only at low power levels (about 0.5 W), and both methods work best when applied to the base lead. Negative feedback is used to prevent oscillations at lower frequencies. An open component in the feedback loop may cause low-frequency oscillation, especially in broadband amplifiers.

KEYING

The simplest form of modulation is on/off keying. Although it may seem that there cannot be much trouble with such an elementary form of modulation, two very important transmitter faults are the result of keying problems.

Key clicks are produced by fast rise and times of the keying waveform (see the previous sidebar, "Controlling Key Clicks"). Most transmitters include components in the keying circuitry to prevent clicks. When clicks are experienced, check the keying filter components first, then the succeeding stages. An improperly biased power amplifier, or a Class C amplifier that is not keyed, may produce key clicks even though the keying waveform earlier in the circuit is correct. Clicks caused by a linear amplifier may be a sign of low-frequency parasitic oscillations. If they occur in an amplifier, suspect insufficient power-supply decoupling. Check the power-supply filter capacitors and all bypass capacitors.

The other modulation problem associated with on/off keying is called backwave. Backwave is a condition in which the signal is heard, at a reduced level, even when the key is up. This occurs when the oscillator signal feeds through a keyed amplifier. This usually indicates a design flaw, although in some cases a component failure or improper keyed-stage neutralization may be to blame.

LOW OUTPUT POWER

Check the owner's manual to see if the condition is normal for some modes or bands, or if there is a menu item to set RF output power. Check the control settings. Solid-state transmitters require so little effort from the operator that control settings are seldom noticed. The CARRIER (or DRIVE) control may have been bumped. Remember to adjust tuned vacuum tube amplifiers after a significant change in operating frequency (usually 50 to 100 kHz). Most modern transmitters are also designed to reduce power if there is high (say 2:1) SWR. Check these obvious external problems before you tear apart your rig.

Power transistors may fail if the SWR protection circuit malfunctions. Such failures occur at the weak link in the amplifier chain: It is possible for the drivers to fail without damaging the finals. An open circuit in the reflected side of the sensing circuit leaves the transistors unprotected; a short shuts them down.

Low power output in a transmitter may also spring from a misadjusted carrier oscillator or a defective SWR protection circuit. If the carrier oscillator is set to a frequency well outside the transmitter passband, there may be no measurable output. Output power will increase steadily as the frequency is moved into the passband.

26.9.3 Transceivers

SWITCHING

Elaborate switching schemes are used in transceivers for signal control. Many transceiver malfunctions can be attributed to relay or switching problems. Suspect the switching controls when:

• The S meter is inoperative, but the unit otherwise functions. (This could also be a bad S meter or a consequence of a configuration menu item.)

• There is arcing in the tank circuit. (This could also be caused by a fault in the antenna system.)

• There is excessive broadband PA noise in the receiver.

Since transceiver circuits are shared, stage defects frequently affect both the transmit and receive modes, although the symptoms may change with mode. Oscillator problems usually affect both transmit and receive modes, but different oscillators, or frequencies, may be used for different emissions. Check the block diagram.

VOX

Voice operated transmit (VOX) controls are another potential trouble area. If there is difficulty in switching to transmit in the VOX mode, check the VOX-SENSITIVITY and ANTI-VOX control settings. Next, see if the PTT and manual (MOX) transmitter controls work. If the PTT and MOX controls function, examine the VOX control circuits. Test the switches, control lines and control voltage if the transmitter does not respond to other TR controls.

VOX SENSITIVITY and ANTI-VOX settings should also be checked if the transmitter switches on in response to received audio. Suspect the ANTI-VOX circuitry next. Unacceptable VOX timing results from a poor VOX-delay adjustment, or a bad resistor or capacitor in the timing circuit or VOX amplifiers.

26.9.4 Amplifiers

While this section focuses on vacuum-tube amplifiers using high-voltage (HV) supplies, it also applies to solid-state amplifiers that operate at lower voltages and generally have fewer points of failure. Amplifiers are simple, reliable pieces of equipment that respond well to basic care, regular maintenance, and common sense. A well-maintained amplifier will provide reliable service and maximum tube lifetime. (The complete version of a *QST* article on amplifier repair is included with the downloadable supplemental content.)

The key to finding the trouble with your amplifier (or any piece of sophisticated equipment) is to be careful and methodical, and to avoid jumping to false conclusions or making random tests. The manufacturer's customer service department will likely be helpful if you are considerate and have taken careful notes detailing the trouble symptoms and any differences from normal operation. There may be helpful guidelines on the manufacturer's web pages or from other Internet resources. Sometimes there is more than one problem — they work together to act like one very strange puzzle. Just remember that most problems can be isolated by careful, step-by-step tests.

SAFETY FIRST

It is important to review good safety practices. (See the **Safety** and **Power Sources** chapters for additional safety information.) Tube amplifiers use power supply voltages well in excess of 1 kV and the RF output can be hundreds of volts, as well. Almost every voltage in a vacuum-tube amplifier can be lethal! Take care of yourself and use caution!

Power Control — Know and control the state of both ac line voltage and dc power supplies. Physically disconnect line cords and other power cables when you are not working on live equipment. Use a lockout on circuit breakers. Double-check visually and with a meter to be absolutely sure power has been removed.

Interlocks — Unless specifically instructed by the manufacturer's procedures to do so, never bypass an interlock. This is rarely required except in troubleshooting and should only be done when absolutely necessary. Interlocks are there to protect you.

The One-Hand Rule — Keep one hand in your pocket while making any measurements on live equipment. The hand in your pocket removes a path for current to flow through you. It's also a good idea to wear shoes with insulating soles and work on dry surfaces. Current can be lethal even at levels of a few mA — don't tempt the laws of physics.

Test Equipment Rating — Be sure your test equipment is adequately rated for the voltages and power levels encountered in amplifiers! This is particularly important in handheld equipment in which there is no metal enclosure connected to an ac safety ground. Excessive voltage can result in a *flashover* to the user from the internal electronics, probes, or test leads, resulting in electric shock. Know and respect this rating.

If you are using an external high voltage probe, make sure it is in good condition with no cracks in the body. The test lead insulation should be in good condition — flexible and with no cracks or wire exposed. If practical, do not make measurements while holding the probe or meter. Attach the probe with the voltage discharged and then turn the power on. Turn power off and discharge the voltage before touching the probe again. Treat high voltage with care and respect!

Patience — Repairing an amplifier isn't a race. Take your time. Don't work on equipment when you're tired or frustrated. Wait several minutes after turning the amplifier off to open the cabinet — capacitors can take several minutes to discharge through their bleeder resistors. On most amplifiers, the meter switch has a HV position — wait until it is at zero before opening the cabinet. Some amplifiers have a safety interlock that shorts the high voltage to ground — if the capacitor bank has not discharged, this can be quite spectacular — and destroy power supply components.

A Grounding Stick — Make the simple safety accessory shown in the High Voltage section of the **Power Sources** chapter and use it whenever you work on equipment in which hazardous voltages have been present. The ground wire should be heavy duty (#12 AWG or larger) due to the high peak currents (hundreds of amperes) present when discharging a capacitor or tripping a circuit breaker. When equipment is opened, touch the tip of the stick to every exposed component and connection that you might come in contact with. Assume nothing — accidental shorts and component failures can put voltage in places it shouldn't be.

The Buddy System and CPR — Use the buddy system when working around any equipment that has the potential for causing serious injury. The buddy needn't be a ham, just anyone who will be nearby in case of trouble. Your buddy should know how to remove power and administer basic first aid or CPR.

CLEANLINESS

The first rule in taking good care of an amplifier is cleanliness. Amplifiers need not be kept sparkling new, but their worst enemy is heat. Excess heat accelerates component aging and increases stress during operation.

Outside the amplifier, prevent dust and obstructions from blocking the paths by which heat is removed. This means keeping all ventilation holes free of dust, pet hair and insects. Fan intakes are particularly susceptible to inhaling all sorts of debris. Use a vacuum cleaner to clean the amplifier and surrounding areas. Keep liquids well away from the amplifier.

Keep papers or magazines off the amplifier — even if the cover is solid metal. Paper acts as an insulator and keeps heat from being radiated through the cover. Amplifier heat sinks must have free air circulation to be effective. There should be at least a couple of inches of free space surrounding an amplifier on its sides and top. If the manufacturer recommends a certain clearance, mounting orientation or air flow, follow those recommendations.

Inside the amplifier, HV circuits attract

Figure 26.23 — A small paintbrush and a vacuum cleaner crevice attachment make dust removal easy.

dust that slows heat dissipation and will eventually build up to where it arcs or carbonizes. Use the vacuum cleaner to remove any dust or dirt. If you find insects (or worse) inside the amp, try to determine how they got in and plug that hole. Window screening works fine to allow airflow while keeping out insects. While you're cleaning the inside, perform a visual inspection as described in the next section.

Vacuuming works best with an attachment commonly known as a crevice cleaner. **Figure 26.23** shows a crevice cleaning attachment being used with a small paintbrush to dislodge and remove dust. The brush will root dust out of tight places and off components without damaging them or pulling on connecting wires. Don't use the vacuum cleaner brush attachment; they're designed for floors, not electronics. Some vacuums also have a blower mechanism, but these rarely have enough punch to clean as thoroughly as a brush. Blowing dust just pushes the dust around and into other equipment.

If you can't get a brush or attachment close enough, a spray can of compressed air will usually dislodge dust and dirt so you can vacuum it up. If you use a rag or towel to wipe down panels or large components, be sure not to leave threads or lint behind. Never use a solvent or spray cleaner to wash down components or flush out crevices unless the manufacturer advises doing so — it might leave behind a residue or damage the component.

Cigarette smoke causes its own set of unique problems as tar and nicotine accumulate along with dust and dirt. Removal is difficult at best; commercial solvents such as *Krud Kutter* can be thinned 4-to-1 and will remove the gummy deposits. In extreme cases, disassemble the amplifier (remove tube(s), power transformer and meters), and wash it in a sink with soap and water. Be careful to protect or remove meters and other components that can be damaged by water. Thoroughly dry the amplifier in warm air. Re-lubricate variable capacitors, variable inductors, and any rotary controls.

INSPECTION

Remove any internal covers or access panels and...stop! Get out the grounding stick (see the **Power Sources** chapter), clip its ground lead securely to the chassis, and touch every exposed connection. Now, using a strong light and possibly a magnifier, look over the components and connections. Use all of your senses to analyze the interior — smell, look, listen.

Amplifiers have far fewer components than transceivers, so look at every component and insulator. Look for cracks, signs of arcing, carbon traces (thin black lines), discoloration, loose connections, melting of plastic, and anything else that doesn't look right. This is a great time to be sure that mounting and grounding screws are tight. Does anything smell burnt? Learn the smells of overheated components. Make a note of what you find, repair or replace — even if no action is required. If the amplifier was recently powered up, an infrared thermometer can spot components that were running hot. Or you may hear a crackling or sizzling noise from heat — not a good sign! Try to isolate the source of the noise.

ELECTRICAL COMPONENTS

Let's start with the power supply. There are three basic parts to amplifier power supplies — the ac transformer and line devices, the rectifier/filter, and the metering/regulation circuitry. (See the **Power Sources** chapter for more information.) Transformers need little maintenance except to be kept cool and be mounted securely, but inspect for overheating, discoloration, or seepage from insulation or tar. Line components such as switches, circuit breakers and fuses, if mechanically sound and adequately rated, are usually electrically okay, as well. Check fuses and switches with a multimeter.

Rectifiers and HV filter capacitors require occasional cleaning. Look for discoloration around components mounted on a printed circuit board (PCB) and make sure that all wire connections are secure. HV capacitors are generally electrolytic or oil and should show no signs of leakage, swelling or outgassing around terminals.

Components that perform metering and regulation of voltage and current can be affected by heat or heavy dust. If there has been a failure of some other component in the amplifier — such as a tube — these circuits can be stressed severely. Resistors may survive substantial temporary overloads, but may show signs of overload such as discoloration or swelling — and change value. Verify the correct value with a multimeter against the color code; if it is not readable or reads erratically, replace the component.

Amplifiers contain two types of relays — control and RF. Control relays switch ac and dc voltages and do not handle input or output RF energy. The usual problem encountered with control relays is oxidation or pitting of their contacts. A burnishing tool can be used to clean relay contacts. In a pinch a strip of ordinary paper can be pulled between contacts gently held closed. Avoid the temptation to over-clean silver-plated relay and switch contacts. It is easy to remove contact plating with excessive polishing and while silver-plated relay and switch contacts may appear to be dark in color, oxidized silver (black) is still a good conductor. Once the silver's gone,

Figure 26.24 — The band switch section on the left clearly shows the signs of destructive arcing.

and reseated once or twice to clear oxide on contact surfaces.

Carefully inspect any connector that seems loose. Be especially careful with connectors and cables in amplifiers with power supplies in separate enclosures from the RF deck. Those interconnects are susceptible to both mechanical and electrical stress and you don't want an energized HV cable loose on the operating desk. Check the electrical integrity of those cables and make sure they are tightly fastened.

As with relays, switches found in amplifiers either perform control functions or route RF signals. Adequately rated control switches, if mechanically sound, are usually okay. Band switches are the most common RF switch — usually a rotary phenolic or ceramic type. A close visual inspection should show no pitting or oxidation on the wiper (the part of the switch that rotates between contacts) or the individual contacts. Arcing or overheating will quickly destroy rotary switches. **Figure 26.24** shows a heavy-duty band switch that has suffered severe damage from arcing.

Slight oxidation is acceptable on it's gone; contact erosion will then be pervasive. If visual inspection shows heavy pitting or discoloration or resistance measurements show the relay to have intermittent contact quality, it should be replaced.

If the resting current is too high or intermittent, check power relays for good contact from the bias supply. On some older amplifiers, the relay coil is used as a resistor to create a voltage drop that cuts off the tube. If the relay coil covering is discolored, measure the resistance of the coil and possibly replace it.

RF relays are used to perform transmit/receive (TR) switching and routing of RF signals through or around the amplifier circuitry. Amplifiers designed for full break-in operation will usually use a high-speed vacuum TR relay. Vacuum relays are sealed and cannot be cleaned or maintained. When you replace RF relays, use a direct replacement part or one rated for RF service with the same characteristics as the original.

If the SWR measured between the transceiver and the amplifier suddenly increases, is erratic, or QSK (break-in) stays in the transmit state or is just open in receive, check the RF relay contacts.

Cables and connectors are subjected to heavy heat and electrical loads in amplifiers. Plastics may become brittle and connections may oxidize. Cables should remain flexible and not be crimped or pinched if clamped or tied down. Gently wiggle cables while watching the connections at each end for looseness or bending. Connectors can be unplugged

Wafer Switch Repair

Because they are often custom parts, replacements for individual wafers and contacts for rotary switches can be difficult or impossible to find. You may be able to find switches with the same size contacts, however. These can serve as replacements for contacts on the damaged switch. Save pieces of the damaged switch, since it can be used for parts.

Start by disassembling the damaged switch. If it is on a shaft there are usually two threaded rods holding it together. Save all pieces. Note the order in which flat and lock washers are used. Taking a close-up photo or making a careful drawing is a good idea. Take care to save all the parts. Place the damaged wafer on your work surface with the hollow-side of the rivet facing up. Use a drill bit just a bit larger than the rivet. Drill-out the rivet at low speed, using just enough pressure to cut off the lip of the rivet – do not drill into the contact itself. Remove the burned contacts first to get a "feel" for how to do it without damaging the contact.

Now disassemble the switch to be used for part replacement and once again, save all the parts for future use. Once the wafers are in-hand, inspect them and pick the best ones to be used as replacements. Remove the replacement contacts in the same way as the damaged contacts were removed.

Now replace the damaged contacts with the replacements using #2-56 screws and nuts (smaller switches may require even smaller hardware), being careful not to over tighten the screws and crack the ceramic or phenolic wafer; "just tight" is good enough. Use a dab of LockTite Red (or paint or fingernail polish) to secure. **Figure 26.A1** shows a wafer that has been repaired using this technique.

Figure 26.A1 — Five contacts starting at the 4:30 position on the wafer have been replaced using contacts removed from another switch and #2-56 hardware. [Photo courtesy of Matt Kastigar, N9ES]

26.30   Chapter 26

silver-plated switches. Phosphor-bronze contacts can sometimes be cleaned with a light scrub from a pencil eraser, but plating can be easily removed, so use caution with this method and be sure to remove any eraser crumbs. Rotary switch contacts cannot be replaced easily although individual wafer sections may be replaced if an exact matching part can be obtained. (See sidebar.)

When replacing capacitors and resistors, be sure to use adequately rated parts. Voltage and power-handling ratings are particularly important, especially for components handling high RF currents. An RF tank capacitor replacement should be checked carefully for adequate RF voltage and current ratings, not just dc. HV resistors are generally long and thin to prevent arcing across their surfaces. Even if a smaller (and cheaper) resistor has an equivalent power rating, resist the temptation to substitute it. In a pinch, a series string of resistors of the appropriate combined value can be used to replace one HV unit. Don't use carbon resistors for metering circuits, use metal or carbon film types. The carbon composition types are too unstable. Electrolytic capacitors also have a temperature rating, usually 85 or 105 °C; use the higher rating if available.

If you are repairing or maintaining an old amplifier and manufacturer-specific parts are no longer available, the ham community has many sources for RF and HV components. Fair Radio Sales (**www.fairradio.com**) and Surplus Sales of Nebraska (**www.surplus-sales.com**) are familiar names. Hamfests and websites often have amplifier components for sale. (See the **RF Power Amplifiers** chapter's sidebar on using surplus or used parts for amplifiers.) You might consider buying a non-working amplifier of the same model for parts. MFJ (**www.mfjenterprises.com**) sells some parts that are used in the Ameritron brand of amplifiers — you may be able to substitute.

TUBES

Good maintenance starts with proper operation of the amplifier. Follow the manufacturer's instructions for input drive levels, duty cycles, tuning and output power level. Frequently check all metered voltages and current to be sure that the tubes are being operated properly and giving you maximum lifetime. The manufacturer spent time and effort to develop the manual — read it! If you do not have one, do a web search (or call the manufacturer) and get one. It is time well-spent. Penta Labs' "Tube Maintenance & Education" (**www.pentalaboratories.com/maintenance.asp**) is an excellent web page on maintaining power tubes.

The internal mechanical structures of tubes generally do not deal well with mechanical shock and vibration, so treat them gently. The manufacturer may also specify how the amplifier is to be mounted, so read the operating manual. Tubes generate a lot of heat, so it's important that whatever cooling mechanism employed is kept at peak efficiency. Airways should be clean, including between the fins on metal tubes. All seals and chimneys should fit securely and be kept clean. Wipe the envelope of glass tubes clean after handling them — fingerprints should be removed to prevent baking them into the surface. On metal tubes that use finger-stock contacts, be sure the contacts are clean and make good contact all the way around the tube. Partial contact or dirty finger stock can cause asymmetric current and heating inside the tube, resulting in warping of internal grids and possibly cause harmonics or parasitics.

Plate cap connections and VHF parasitic suppressors should be secure and show no signs of heating. Overheated parasitic suppressors may indicate that the neutralization circuit is not adjusted properly. Inspect socket contacts and the tube pins to be sure all connections are secure, particularly high-current filament connections. Removing and inserting the tubes once or twice will clean the socket contacts.

While the tubes are removed, check the pins for melted solder — this is common on over-heated 3-500Z tubes. If needed, resolder with silver solder, and be careful not to use too much solder that might expand the diameter of the pin.

Adjustments to the neutralizing network, which suppresses VHF oscillations by negative feedback from the plate to grid circuit, are rarely required except when you are replacing a tube or after you do major rewiring or repair of the RF components. The manufacturer will provide instructions on making these adjustments. If symptoms of VHF oscillations occur without changing a tube, then perhaps the tube characteristics or associated components have changed. Parasitic oscillations in high-power amplifiers can be strong enough to cause arcing damage. Perform a visual inspection prior to readjusting the neutralizing circuit.

Metering circuits rarely fail on their own, but they play a key part in maintenance. By keeping a record of normal voltages and currents, you will have a valuable set of clues when things go wrong. Record tuning settings, drive levels, and tube voltages and currents on each band and with every antenna. When settings change, you can refer to the notebook instead of relying on memory.

MECHANICAL

The most common faults appear with the moving parts: connectors, relays and switches. Thermal cycling and heat-related stresses can result in mechanical connections loosening over time or material failures. Switch shafts, shaft couplings (especially if they are plastic) and panel bearings all need to be checked for tightness and proper alignment. All mounting hardware needs to be tight, particularly if it supplies a grounding path. Examine all panel-mounted components, particularly RF connectors, and be sure they're attached securely. BNC and UHF connectors mounted with a single nut in a round panel hole are notorious for loosening with repeated connect/disconnect cycles. Rubber and plastic parts are particularly stressed by heat. If there are any belts, gears or pulleys, make sure they're clean and that dust and lint are kept out of their lubricant. Loose or slipping belts should be replaced. Check O-rings, grommets and sleeves to be sure they are not brittle or cracked. If insulation sleeves or sheets are used, check to be sure they are covering what they're supposed to. Never discard them or replace them with improperly sized or rated materials.

Enclosures and internal shields should all be fastened securely with every required screw in place. Watch out for loosely overlapping metal covers. If a sheet metal screw has stripped out, either drill a new hole or replace the screw with a larger size, taking care to maintain adequate clearance around and behind the new screw. Or, if space permits, a "speed" or clip nut can sometimes be used. These are available from auto parts or home improvement stores, usually in the "specialty hardware" section.

Tip the amplifier from side to side while listening for loose hardware or metal fragments, all of which should be removed.

Clean the front and back panels to protect the finish. If the amplifier cabinet is missing a foot or an internal shock mount, replace it. A clean unit with a complete cabinet will have a significantly higher resale value, so it's in your interest to keep the equipment looking good.

SHIPPING

When you are traveling with an amplifier or shipping it, some care in packing will prevent damage. Improper packing can also result in difficulty in collecting on an insurance claim, should damage occur. The original shipping cartons are a good method of protecting the amplifier for storage and sale, but they were not made to hold up to frequent shipping. If you travel frequently, it is best to get a sturdy shipping case made for electronic equipment. Pelican (**www.pelican-shipping-cases.com**) and Anvil (**www.anvilsite.com**) make excellent shipping cases suitable for carrying amplifiers and radio equipment.

Some amplifiers require the power transformer to be removed before shipping. Check your owner's manual or contact the manufacturer to find out. Failure to remove it before shipping can cause major structural damage to the amplifier's chassis and case.

Tubes should also be removed from their sockets for shipment. It may not be necessary to ship them separately if they can be packed in the amplifier's enclosure with adequate plastic foam packing material. If the manufacturer of the tube or amplifier recommends separate shipment, however, do it!

CLEANING AND MAINTENANCE PLAN

For amateur use, there is little need for maintenance more frequently than once per year. Consider the maintenance requirements of the amplifier and what its manufacturer recommends. Review the amplifier's manuals and make up a checklist of what major steps and tools are required.

TROUBLESHOOTING

A benefit of regular maintenance will be familiarity with your amplifier should you ever need to repair it. Knowing what it looks (and smells) like inside will give you a head start on effecting a quick repair.

The following discussion is intended to illustrate the general flow of a troubleshooting effort, not be a step-by-step guide. Before starting on your own amplifier, review the amplifier manual's "Theory of Operation" section and familiarize yourself with the schematic. If there is a troubleshooting procedure in the manual, follow it. **Figure 26.25** shows a general-purpose troubleshooting flow chart. Do not swap in a known-good tube or tubes until you are sure that a tube is actually defective. Installing a good tube in an amplifier with circuit problems can damage a good tube.

Many "amplifier is dead" problems turn out to be simply a lack of ac power. Before even opening the cabinet of an unresponsive amplifier, be sure that ac is really present at the wall socket and that the fuse or circuit breaker is really closed. If ac power is present at the wall socket, trace through any internal fuses, interlocks and relays all the way through to the transformer's primary terminals. If the amplifier operates from 240-V circuits, be sure you check both hot wires. (See the **Safety** chapter for more information about ac wiring practices.)

Hard failures in a high-voltage power supply are rarely subtle, so it's usually clear if there is a problem. When you repair a power supply, take the opportunity to check all related components. If all defective components are not replaced, the failures may be repeated when the circuit is re-energized.

Rectifiers may fail open or shorted — test them using a DMM diode checker. An open rectifier will result in a drop in the high-voltage output of 50% or more but will probably not overheat or destroy itself. A shorted rectifier failure is usually more dramatic and may cause additional rectifiers or filter capacitors to fail. If one rectifier in a string has failed, it may be a good idea to replace the entire string as the remaining rectifiers have been subjected to a higher-than-normal voltage.

High-voltage filter capacitors usually fail shorted, although they will occasionally lose capacitance and show a rise in ESR (equivalent series resistance). Check the rectifiers and any metering components — they may have been damaged by the current surge caused from a short circuit.

Power transformer failures are usually due to arcing in the windings, insulation failures, or overheating. high-voltage transformers can be disassembled and rewound by a custom transformer manufacturer.

Along with the plate supply, tetrode screen supplies occasionally fail, too. The usual cause is the regulation circuit that drops the voltage from the plate level. Operating without a screen supply can be damaging to a tube, so be sure to check the tube carefully after repairs.

If the power supply checks out okay and the tube's filaments are not lit, check the tube socket and the pins on the tube itself — overheating can cause solder to flow and

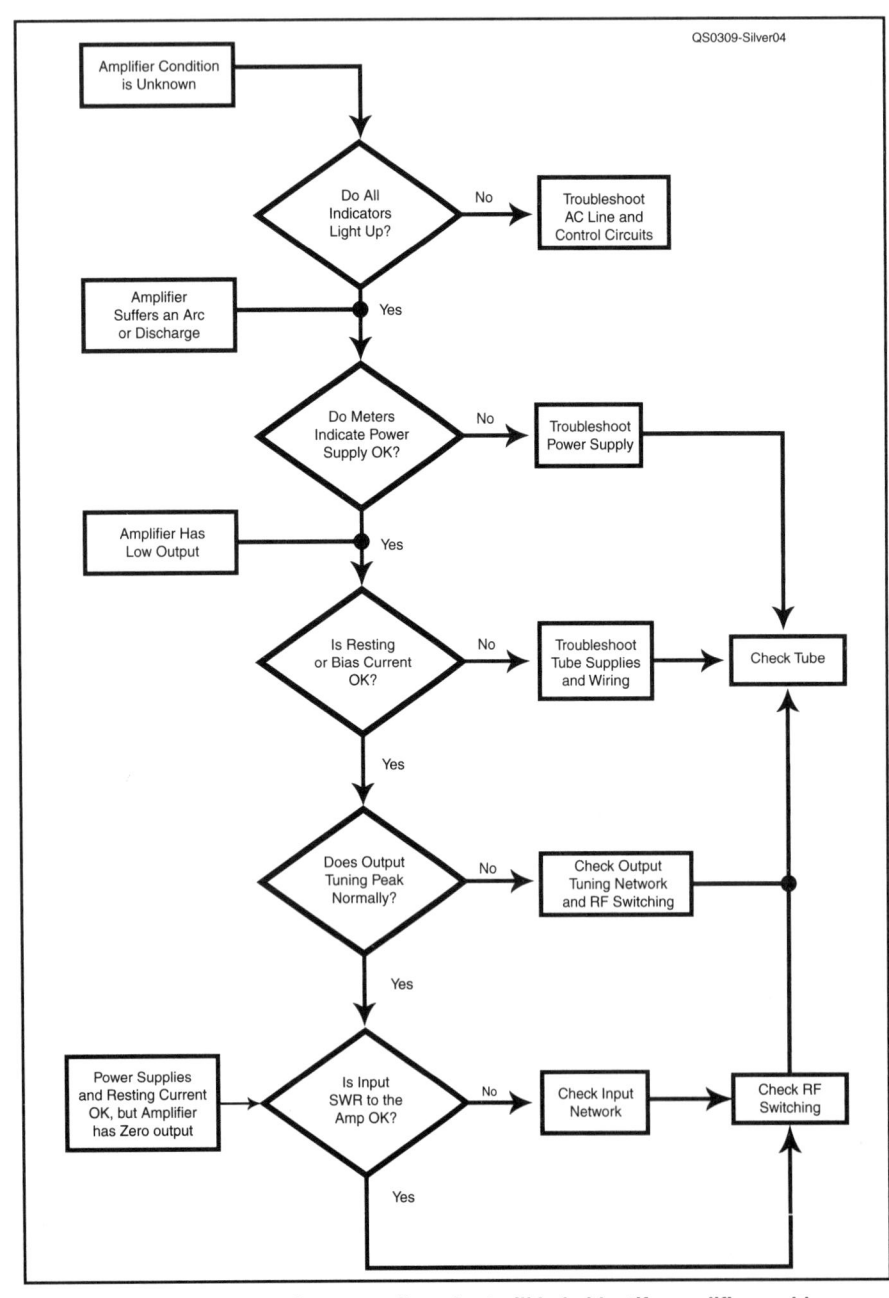

Figure 26.25 — This general-purpose flow chart will help identify amplifier problems. For solid-state units, substitute "Check Output Transistors" for "Check Tube."

intermittent failure. If the tube's filament is lit, check the resting or bias current. If it is excessive or very low, check all bias voltages and dc current paths to the tube, such as the plate choke, screen supply (for tetrodes) and grid or cathode circuits.

If you do not find power supply and dc problems, check the RF components or RF deck. Check the input SWR to the amplifier. If it has changed then you likely have a problem in the input circuitry (overheated coil, shorted capacitor or bad switch contact) or one or more tubes have failed. Perform a visual check of the input circuitry and the band switch, followed by an ohmmeter check of all input components. Use an SWR analyzer or a dip oscillator to see if the input tuning has changed, indicating a possible bad tuning network component in the input circuits. If input SWR is normal and applying drive does not result in any change in plate current, you may have a defective tube, tube socket or connection between the input circuits and the tube.

Check the TR control circuits and relay. If plate current changes, but not as much as normal, try adjusting the output tuning circuitry. If this has little or no effect, the tube may be defective or a connection between the tube and output circuitry may have opened. If retuning has an effect, but at different settings than usual, the tube may be defective or there may be a problem in the tuning circuitry. A visual inspection and an ohmmeter check are in order.

SOLID STATE AMPLIFIERS

Almost all diagnostic techniques used for tube amplifiers are also applicable to solid state amplifiers. Input and output circuits are very similar. Power supplies are usually lower voltage (but high current).

Power supplies typically can be checked with a multimeter for voltage but current will require reading the voltage drop across a low-value, high-wattage resistor (this can cause problems from the voltage drop) or use a clamp-on current probe. Bias adjustments typically are made with a potentiometer on a voltage regulator circuit (you'll need the schematic or user's manual) and resting current needs to be checked and verified against the manufacturer's specifications.

As with tubes, heat is the enemy. Keep all ventilation openings clear and clean. Check fans for proper operating and speed. Remove any dust or dirt buildup, especially on heat sinks and transistor packages.

Bipolar transistors can be checked with a multimeter (see the **Component Data and References** chapter), as can MOSFETS which are now more common in RF amplifiers. Replacements will require de-soldering the old part, cleaning-up the PC board, and installation of the new part. If the transistors are mounted against a heat sink, use a thin, bubble-free film of heat sink compound between the transistor and heat sink. Make sure all screws are in-place and tight. If shoulder washers are used to insulate screws, be sure they are used when the amplifier is reassembled.

POWERING UP OLD AMPLIFIERS

When a piece of equipment has been idle for a long period of time, proper care must be taken to "revive" it. DO NOT just "plug it in" and "power it up" — the results will most likely be smoke and sparks! This is especially true for amplifiers with high-voltage power supplies.

First, examine the device for physical damage such as bent sheet metal or dents. Clean metal work and panels is usually a good sign. Assuming it is ac-powered, look at the line cord for cuts, scuffs, or cracks, then bend it between your fingers and listen for "cracking." If it is dried out or brittle, replace it before proceeding. If the line cord is okay, tie a piece of wire through the plug's pins so that it cannot be plugged-in to a receptacle. Make sure the plug is the right one for the input voltage (120 or 240 V). Check the fuses (if present) — a good indication of condition when last used.

Open the cabinet, remove the tube(s) and store in a safe place. Look closely for any irregularities such as dark PC board areas, discolored resistors, breached, swollen, or leaky capacitors, disconnected wires, loose components or screws, or cracked components or hardware. Begin with these and replace as required. Verify that all of the power supply connections are in order, including that power transformer connections are configured for the proper voltage.

Typically, old electrolytic capacitors, even if otherwise good, have dried-out and need attention. They can be tested with a multimeter for shorts (or open), or with an ESR meter if available. These are best replaced if the amplifier is really old or if they don't charge up properly in the power-up test (see below and this chapter's section on repairing vintage equipment.)

Use a multimeter to test for shorts to ground in the power supply section. With the power switch in the ON position (still not attached to ac power), measure resistance across the pins of the ac plug. It should read 4 to 5 Ω if it is connected to the primary of a transformer and open when the power switch is OFF. If you measure anything other than an open circuit, check for decoupling capacitors on the ac line that might be leaky. Check the secondary resistance of the transformer — it will be higher in resistance. Then work your way to the rectifier and filter capacitors and any chokes.

Check the resistance across the input and output RF connectors. They should be open or nearly open depending on the input or output network type. (Some amplifiers have an RF choke across the output connector which will present a low resistance.) Check the resistance of the HV plate connections of the tubes to ground — it should be open (the plate capacitors may be observed charging up).

If all looks good, and it is possible to do so, disconnect the rectifier board or assembly and check the transformer output windings. Then check any interlock components that might have to be closed or opened (depending on function).

Before starting power-up tests, *make sure* your multimeter is rated for the voltage. If not, don't use it as the meter could be destroyed or an arc through the meter or its leads (called *flashover*) can present a severe shock hazard.

Using a variable transformer (such as a Variac), bring up input power slowly to about 25% of rated input voltage. The secondary voltage of the transformer should be 25% of the recommended output. (Make high voltage measurements either hands-free or with one hand not touching anything.) Because full output voltage will exceed the maximum rating of most multimeters, disconnect the multimeter unless you are using a high-voltage probe. Increase the voltage slowly to full input while watching the transformer — it should not get hot or make noise. Use an infrared thermometer to avoid direct contact but verify the transformer does not get hot without a load.

Next, power down and reconnect the rectifier / filter board or assemblies. Using the variable transformer, start at 25% input voltage again. If the amplifier has a meter with an HV or B+ position, look for about 25% of the normal voltage reading. Dial lights might just barely light. Leave the power supply to "cook" for a few hours, monitoring it closely. Initially, there will be a high current surge that will slowly drop after the electrolytic filter capacitors start to reform their dielectric layer. When the current drops, bump the voltage up 10 to 20 V, wait a half hour, then turn it up again, monitoring the power supply with each increase. Continue until you have reached full input voltage.

When full power supply high voltage has been achieved, the electrolytic caps should be reformed and the dial lights should be at full brightness. If, at any time there is smoke, crackling noise or sparks, disconnect at once, discharge the capacitors, and investigate the issue(s).

Once the power supply is up and running, disconnect the plate B+ lead from the output of the rectifier / filter. In order to check filament voltage, solder temporary wires to the filament socket pins and route them out of the amplifier cabinet. Insert the tube(s), close the cabinet (checking the interlock safety switches), and power up. Quickly verify the filament voltage — it should be within 5% of the specified voltage; if not, power off and investigate. Check the fan(s) for proper operation and air flow.

Tubes get gassy and may arc internally when first powered up after a long period of storage; leave the B+ disconnected and let the tubes "cook" for a few hours. If the tube has a "getter" this may activate it to remove gas. Not all power tubes have a getter — check the data sheet for your tube.

Using lots of caution and a high-voltage probe, check that there is no dc voltage at the output RF connector — if the plate coupling capacitor is shorted, there may be full B+ on the amplifier output!

Power down, wait for the HV / B+ to read zero, and open the cabinet. Use a grounding stick to *be sure* the B+ is at zero, then reconnect it (see the **Power Sources** chapter for safety tips on working with high-voltage power supplies). Put the plate caps on, reattach the cover, and power it up. Listen and watch (if you can see the tubes) for any issues. If you notice anything unusual, stop at once and investigate (after discharging the high voltage, of course). If all is well, monitor the amp and let it cook for a few hours.

After a thorough test, power the amp off, let it sit overnight, then power up the next day. Check the idling current for the recommended value once again.

Connect the amp to a dummy load that can handle full power output. Put the amp in transmit mode. The idling current should be the recommended value. Switch to standby. Connect a transmitter set for low output (about 20 W), and drive the amplifier. At low drive, the output should be proportional to the input times the gain. If all goes well, apply more drive until full output is achieved. At this point, if the tube is bad, it may fail to reach full power or it may arc. Listen and carefully verify all operations.

26.10 Antenna Systems

This section is an abbreviated version of the Antenna System Troubleshooting chapter of the *ARRL Antenna Book* that was added to the 22nd edition. Because of the enormous variety of antenna systems, general guidelines must be presented, but the successful troubleshooting process usually follows a systematic approach just as for any other radio system.

26.10.1 Basic Antenna System Troubleshooting

Start with an inventory of the antenna system. Any of these can be the cause of your problem: supports, insulators, elements, feed point, balun (if any), feed line, grounding or transient protectors, impedance matching and switching equipment, RF jumper cables at any point. As with any troubleshooting process, be alert for mistaken or loose connections, loose or disconnected power and control cables, wires touching each other that shouldn't be, and so forth. Reduce the antenna system to the simplest system with the problem and it will likely look something like the system in **Figure 26.26**.

It is particularly important to remember that your station ground is often part of the antenna system. The length of the connection between the equipment ground bus and the ground rod is usually several feet at minimum and that can be an appreciable fraction of a wavelength on the higher HF bands. This can greatly affect tuning if there is common-mode current on the feed line or if a random-wire or end-fed type of antenna is being used. If touching equipment enclosures or the ground wire affects SWR or impedance readings, that will affect your antenna measurements as well.

DUMMY-LOAD TESTING

Begin by replacing components of your antenna system with a dummy load, starting at the output of the radio using a known-good jumper cable. Verify that the radio works properly into a 50 Ω load using a known-good directional wattmeter. Then move the dummy load to the output side of any antenna tuning or switching equipment, one component at a time until you have replaced the antenna

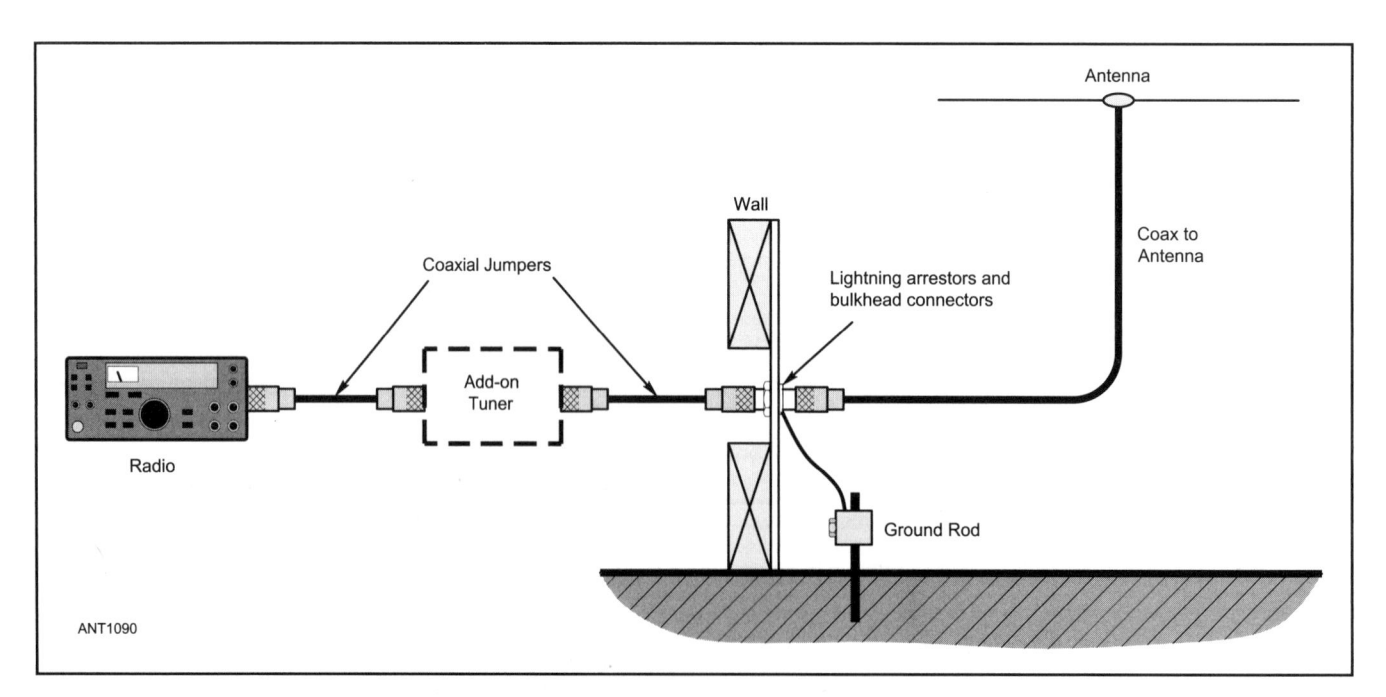

Figure 26.26 — A typical simple antenna system. An add-on antenna tuner is likely to be used if one is not built-in to the radio. More complex antenna systems have all of the same components plus some switching equipment.

feed line with the dummy load. If everything checks OK to this point, the problem is in the feed line or antenna. Don't forget to verify that the problem with the antenna is still present after each dummy load test. If the problem was a loose or intermittent connection, it is likely that swapping the dummy load in and out changed or eliminated the problem.

ANTENNA VISUAL INSPECTION

Now it is time to perform a visual inspection of the feed line and antenna itself. Start with the feed line connector at the last point where the dummy load was swapped in. Disassemble the connector and inspect it for damage from water or corrosion. If either are present, replace the connector and check the condition of the cable before proceeding. Note that if water can get into the cable at the antenna's elevated feed point, it is not unknown for it to flow downward through the braid both by gravity and by capillary action all the way to the shack! If the cable braid is wet at both ends, the cable must be replaced.

If you have a wire antenna, lower it and make a visual inspection of all the pieces.

• Cut away the waterproofing around the coax termination and inspect for water and/or corrosion.

• On the insulators at each end, there is no possibility of contact between the antenna wire and the supporting wire/ropes.

• If there are any splices in the wire elements, they are well crimped or soldered.

• At the center insulator, there is no possibility of contact between the element wires.

• At the balun or coax connection the element connections are soldered or firmly connected.

If you have a Yagi or vertical antenna, similar steps are required. Carefully check any feed point matching assembly, such as a gamma match, hairpin, or stub and make sure connections are clean and tight.

ANTENNA TEST

Assuming any mechanical problems have been rectified, proceed to retest the antenna and feed line. Replace the antenna with a dummy load and check the feed line loss with a wattmeter or antenna analyzer at the antenna end of the feed line. If the feed line checks out OK, the problem must be in the antenna. Reattach the feed line to the antenna and verify that the problem remains. Note that for wire antennas lowered to near ground level, the resonant point will change — this is to be expected.

If the problem is still present, repeat the visual inspection at a closer level of detail. Check all dimensions and connections. Double-check any telescoping sections of tubing, transmission line stubs, in-line coax connectors, clamped connections between wires and between wires and tubing. If possible, give joints and connections a good shake while watching for intermittent readings on the wattmeter or antenna analyzer. If you cannot see inside a component or assembly, perform resistance tests for continuity. Remember to identify your signals since you are testing on the air at this point in the process.

The next step is to reinstall or raise the antenna at least ¼-wavelength off the ground and verify that the problem remains. If you have repaired the antenna, perform a re-check at this point to be sure everything is in good working order before returning the antenna to full height. Once you have re-installed the antenna, including full weatherproofing of any coaxial cable terminations or connectors, record in the shack notebook your measurements of the antenna along with what the problem was discovered to be and how you repaired it.

26.10.2 General Antenna System Troubleshooting

Think of the following topics as a kind of toolbox for troubleshooting. Many of them assume you are testing some type of Yagi or other beam antenna, but the general guidelines apply to all types of antennas

It is important to remember this simple rule for adjustments and troubleshooting: Do the simplest and easiest adjustment or correction *first*, and only *one* at a time.

When making on-air comparisons, select signals that are at the margin and not pushing your receiver well over S9 where it can be difficult to measure differences of a few dB. Terrain has a lot to do with performance as well. If you are comparing with a large station, keep in mind that its location was probably selected carefully and the antennas were placed exactly where they should be for optimum performance on the property.

TEST MEASUREMENTS

A) Test the antenna at a minimum height of 15 to 20 feet. (See **Figure 26.27**.) This will move the antenna far enough away from the ground (which acts to add capacitance to the antenna) and enable meaningful measurements. Use sawhorses *only* for construction purposes.

• 15 to 20 feet above ground does not mean 5 feet above a 10 to 15 foot high roof, it means

---

AM Broadcast Interference to Antenna Analyzers

Living or testing within a couple of miles of an AM broadcast station can create a lot of problems for the sensitive RF detectors in portable antenna analyzers. This type of RFI usually appears as values of SWR and impedance that don't change with frequency or that change in unexpected ways or an upscale meter reading that varies with the station modulation. The analyzer SWR reading will not agree with SWR measured by using a directional wattmeter and more than a few watts of power. The solution is sometimes to use a broadcast-rejection filter (available from analyzer manufacturers) although this tends to color measurements a bit and typically can't be used for measurements on 160 meters because it is so close to the AM broadcast band. In cases where the station is nearby or on 160 meters, directional wattmeters or analyzers with narrow-band tuned inputs must be used.

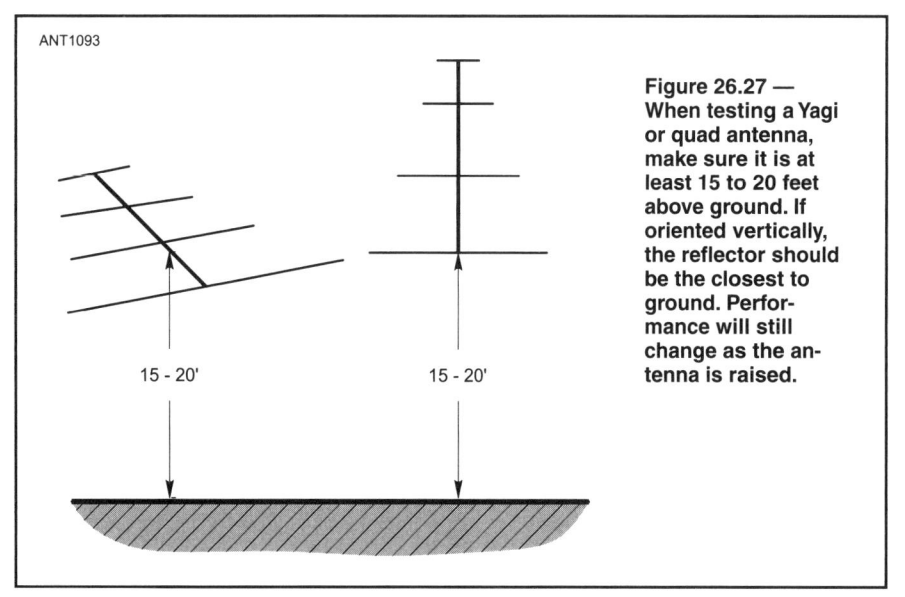

Figure 26.27 — When testing a Yagi or quad antenna, make sure it is at least 15 to 20 feet above ground. If oriented vertically, the reflector should be the closest to ground. Performance will still change as the antenna is raised.

above ground with nothing in between;
- Antenna resonant frequency will shift upward as it is raised;
- Feed point impedance will change with a change in height and this applies to both horizontal and vertical antennas;
- Some antennas are more sensitive to proximity to ground than others;
- Some antennas are more sensitive to nearby conductive objects (such as other antennas) than others.

B) Aiming the antenna upward with the reflector on the ground might coincide with some measurements on rare occasions, but there are no guarantees with this method. The reflector is literally touching a large capacitor (earth) and the driver element is very close, too. Raise the antenna at least 15 to 20 feet off the ground.

C) When using a hand-held SWR analyzer you are looking for the dip in SWR, not where the impedance or resistance meter indicates 50 Ω. (Dip = frequency of lowest SWR value, or lowest swing on the meter.) On the MFJ-259/269 series, the left-hand meter (SWR) is the one you want to watch, not the right-hand meter (Impedance).

D) Does the SWR and frequency of lowest dip change when the coax length is changed? If so, the balun might be faulty, as in not isolating the load from the coax feed line.

Additionally, with an added length of coax and its associated small (hopefully small) amount of loss :
- The value of SWR is expected to be lower with the additional coax and,
- The width of the SWR curve is expected to be wider with the additional coax , when measured at the transmitter end of the coax.

E) Be sure you are watching for the right dip, as some antennas can have a secondary resonance (another dip). It is quite possible to see a Yagi reflector's resonant frequency, or some other dip caused by interaction with adjacent antennas.

MECHANICAL

A. Are the dimensions correct? Production units should match the documentation (within reason). When using tubing elements, measure each *exposed* element section during assembly and the element *half-length* (the total length of each half of the element) after assembly. Measuring the entire length is sometimes tricky, depending on the center attachment to the boom on Yagis, as the element can bow, or the tape might not lay flat along the tubing sections. Self-designed units might have a taper error.

B. Making the average taper diameter larger will make the equivalent electrical element longer. This makes the antenna act as if the physical element is too long.

C. Making the average taper diameter smaller will make the equivalent electrical element shorter. This makes the antenna act as if the physical element is too short.

D. If the element is a mono-taper (tubing element is the same for the entire length), larger diameter elements will be physically shorter than smaller diameter mono-taper elements to give the same electrical performance at the same frequency.

E. The type of mounting of the element to the boom affects the element length, whether it is attached directly to the boom, or insulated from the boom. Incorrect mounting/mounting plate allocation will upset the antenna tuning:
- A mounting plate 4 × 8 inches has an equivalent diameter of approximately 2.5 inches and 4 inches in length for each element half.
- A mounting plate that is 3 × 6 inches has an equivalent diameter of about 1.8 inches and a length of 3 inches for each element half.
- The mounting plate equivalent will be the first section in a model of the element half.

F. In a Yagi, if the elements are designed to be touching, are the elements touching the boom in the correct locations?

G. In a Yagi, if the elements are designed to be insulated, are the elements insulated from the boom in the correct locations?

H. The center of hairpin matching devices (i.e. on a Yagi) can be grounded to the boom.

I. The boom is neutral, but it is still a conductor! The center of a dipole element is also neutral and can be touched while tuning without affecting the reading. With a hairpin match , the center of the hairpin can also be touched while tuning and touching the whole hairpin might not affect the readings much at all.

PROXIMITY

A. What else is near-by (roof, wires, guy lines, gutters)? If it can conduct at all, it can and probably will couple to the antenna!

B. Does the SWR change when the antenna is rotated? If so, this indicates interaction. Note that in some combinations of antennas, there can be destructive interaction even if the SWR does not change. Computer models can be useful here.

C. What is within ¼ wavelength of the antenna? Imagine a sphere (like a big ball) with the antenna in question at the center of the sphere, with the following as a radius, depending on frequency. Think in three dimensions like a sphere — up and down and front and rear. Any resonant conductor (antenna or not) with the following radii will couple to and probably affect the antenna you are testing or installing.

160 meters = 140 feet
80 meters = 70 feet
40 meters = 35 feet
20 meters = 18 feet
15 meters = 12 feet
10 meters = 9 feet

D. Interaction occurs whether or not you are transmitting on the adjacent antennas. When receiving, it simply is not as apparent as when transmitting.

E. Wire antennas under a Yagi can easily affect it. This includes inverted V dipoles for the low bands and multi-band dipoles. The wire antennas are typically for lower frequency band (s) and will not be affected by the Yagi(s), as the Yagis are for the higher bands.

FEED SYSTEM

The feed system includes:
- the feed line,
- switching mechanisms,
- pigtails from the feed point on the antenna to the main feed line or switch and,
- all feed lines inside the radio room.

The feed system is the *entire connection* between the radio and the feed point of the antenna.

A. Is the feed line (coax) known to be good? (Start with the easiest first.) Check the dc resistance across the cable with the far end open and shorted. Is there water in the coax? This can give strange readings, even frequency-dependent ones. If there is any question, swap the feed line for a known good one and re-test.

B. Are the connectors installed properly? Has a connector been stressed (pulled)? Is the rotation loop done properly to not stress the coax? Is it an old existing loop or a new one? Usually it's alright if new. Type N connectors (especially the older type) are prone to having the center conductor pull out due to the weight of the coax pulling down on the connector. Connectors are easy to do, using the right technique.

C. Is there a barrel connector (a PL-258 dual-SO-239 adapter) in the feed line anywhere? Has a new or different barrel been inserted? These are a common failure point, even with new barrels. The failures range from micro-bridges across the face of the barrel shorting out the center and shield, to resistance between the two ends of the barrel. Have the new barrels been tested in a known feed system? Always test them before installing. Use only quality RF adapters as these are common system failure points.

D. Is the coax intact and not frayed such that the shield can come into contact with anything? This can cause intermittent problems as the coax shield touches the tower, such as on rotation loops and coax on telescoping towers.

E. Is the tuner OFF on the radio? This is often overlooked when adding a new antenna.

F. Are there any new devices in the line? It might be a good idea to remove everything but the essential items when troubleshooting.

G. Is there a remote antenna switch? Swap to another port.

H. Is there a low pass filter in the line? The filter can be defective, especially on 10 meters, causing strange SWR readings

26.11 Repair and Restoration of Vintage Equipment

When purchasing a classic receiver or transmitter, unless you absolutely know otherwise, assume the radio will need work. Often you can get a top-of-the-line radio needing a bit of repair or clean-up inexpensively. Don't worry — these radios were designed to be repaired by their owners — and curiously, except for cosmetic parts such as cabinets and knobs, parts are much easier to find for 60-year-old radios than a 20-year-old imported transceiver!

Chances are the radio has gone for years without use. Even if it has been recently used, don't completely trust components that might be 60 or more years old. Don't start by plugging in your new acquisition! To do so might damage a hard-to-replace power transformer, or cause a fire.

Instead, if the radio didn't come with its owner's manual, get one. Several *QST* vendors sell old manuals in good condition. K4XL's Boat Anchor Manual Archive (**www2.faculty.sbc.edu/kgrimm/boat anchor**) is probably *the* best free resource for these manuals. Armed with the manual, remove the radio from its cabinet. You very likely will find evidence of unsightly repairs, modifications, or even dangling wires. While modifications aren't necessarily bad, they can certainly add some drama to any necessary subsequent troubleshooting. It's up to you to reverse or remove them.

Another option for working with vintage equipment is to refer to editions of the *ARRL Handbook* published around the time that the equipment was in common use. The circuit design and construction practices described in the *Handbook* are likely to be representative of those in the radio and may provide guidance for troubleshooting, repair, and adjustment. Similarly, the troubleshooting sections and chapters in previous editions provide valuable guidance for working with equipment of the same or earlier vintages.

26.11.1 Component Replacement

Correct any obvious problems such as dangling components. Replace the line cord with a three-wire, grounded plug, if not a transformerless "ac/dc" type as discussed below. If the radio is one with a live chassis, you should operate it from an isolation transformer for safety. If you don't have an isolation transformer, use a voltmeter to determine the orientation of the ac plug that places the chassis at ground potential. Avoid teaching touching the chassis and do not use knobs with set screws that contact metal control shafts. It's also a good idea to add a fuse, if the radio doesn't originally have one. Are we ready to give it the smoke test? Not so fast!

CAPACITOR RATINGS

Obviously, aged components deteriorate and capacitors are particularly prone to developing leakage or short-circuits with age. There are as many opinions on capacitor replacement as there are radio collectors, but *at the very least* you should replace the electrolytic filter capacitors. Here's why: they *will* short circuit sometime, and when they do, they'll probably take the rectifier tube and the power transformer with them. Modern high voltage electrolytic capacitors are reliable and much smaller than their classic counterparts. Old paper-wax and black plastic tubular capacitors should also be replaced. Again, a short circuit in one of them could take out other components, too. Modern film capacitors of the appropriate voltage are great replacements. Opinions vary as to whether all should be replaced, but replacements are cheap and you have the radio apart now, so why not? If keeping the original components is important, follow the procedure for using a variable transformer to reform electrolytics as described below.

You can mount the new capacitors under the chassis by mounting a new terminal strip (do *not* just wire them to the old capacitor terminals), you can re-stuff an old electrolytic capacitor's can with new capacitors, or you can buy a new can from places such as **www.hayseedhamfest.com** or Antique Electronics Supply (**www.tubesandmore.com**). In any event, follow the manufacturer's schematic — don't assume that the – (minus) end of the capacitor goes to ground, as in some radios the ground path is through a resistor so as to develop bias for the audio output stage or RF gain circuit. Observe the polarity or you'll soon be cleaning up a stinky mess!

TESTING OLD CAPACITORS

All capacitors have a voltage rating written on the side of the cap unless it is a small disc. Surplus stores often have bins full of capacitors of unmarked voltage rating. Don't assume they are a high enough voltage to use — check them with a capacitor checker. There are many models out there by Knight Kit, Lafayette, Sencore, and Eico, but the best were the Heathkit IT-11 or IT-28. They are basically the same model but different colors. Both use a 6E5 Magic Eye tube to indicate the status of the capacitor. A selectable voltage from 3 to 600 V dc can be applied to check for leakage and operation. These are good for small disc or paper caps and large electrolytics.

Take the unknown voltage cap and place it in the test terminals. Advance the voltage control from minimum until the eye tube shows it breaking down. You now know what voltage it is good to.

If the capacitor tests good through the 600 V dc range, it probably is a 1000 V dc capacitor. It is best, though, to know for sure the rating of the cap. In tube equipment, most capacitors should be 500 or 1000 V rated. Mouser (**www.mouser.com**) and Digikey (**www.digikey.com**) do still sell caps for those voltage ranges, but they have become very expensive. You could also find new old stock (NOS) capacitors of the correct voltage rating at surplus stores.

REFORMING ELECTROLYTIC CAPACITORS

The best idea is to replace old electrolytic capacitors with a new unit. They are available cheaply in the voltage ranges required and more compact and reliable than the original electrolytic caps. If necessary, however, old electrolytics can often be revived by reforming the dielectric using a capacitor checker.

Disconnect the wires attached to the capacitor under test and connect it to the capacitor checker. Start at the lowest voltage rating and let it charge up the capacitor. You will know when it is charged by viewing the eye tube: if it is wide open, the cap is charged; if it is closed, the capacitor is either shorted or still charging. Advance gradually to the next voltage rating and wait until the eye fully opens—take plenty of time for the capacitor to stabilize. Continue on through the voltage ranges; each time it will take longer for the eye to open. The dielectric is being reformed. Finally, when you reach the voltage range of the capacitor and the eye is fully open, the cap has been fully revived and is ready for use.

The same process can be performed with a variable autotransformer (Variac) by advancing it a few volts at a time over several hours, but that is a coarse and unreliable process. A diode must be placed in series with the transformer to convert the ac voltage to dc. Monitor the voltage across the capacitor with a meter. If it suddenly jumps to zero, the capacitor has shorted and is now useless. Usually the capacitor can be revived successfully and will work just fine.

RESISTORS

Over time, carbon resistors in older radios can change value significantly, which can affect circuit operation. Disconnect one end of the questionable resistor and measure it with an accurate ohmmeter. If it is out of tolerance, replace it. Most resistors in the tube era were ½ W or greater. Most circuits today use ¼ W or smaller resistors, which will not dissipate the power tubes produce.

Carbon composition resistors are becoming rarer but there are still ample quantities of NOS in surplus stores. Be careful about power rating. Use metal oxide resistors if needed. Remember that wirewound resistors are very inductive and not good for RF circuits. They are excellent for power supply circuits and are usually found in the 1 to 25 W range.

REPLACING DIODES

Many old tube radios use rectifier tubes. It is not a good idea to replace these with solid-state rectifiers, as a shorted diode can take out the transformer. Selenium rectifiers, however, are good candidates to replace with a silicon diode. The 1N400x series of diode are usually fine for use and very cheap. For higher voltage supplies, be sure to use 1N4007 or higher rated diodes. This may result in higher ouput voltage from the supply. Add a series dropping resistor if necessary to reduce voltage.

TRANSFORMER REPLACMENT

The best bet is to find another radio of the same variety from which you can harvest the transformer. This is especially common in transmitters like the Heathkit DX-35 and DX-40 which frequently had transformers fail. Replacement transformers are generally no longer available. Some companies will rewind transformers, but that is usually prohibitively expensive. Output voltages are quite critical in the design of tube radios, so it is not a good idea to replace a 400 V ac transformer with a 600 V ac unit. It may be best to find a donor radio for a replacement transformer.

WIRE REPLACEMENT

Power cords should be replaced at the first sign of hardening and cracking. It is often a good idea to replace the two-wire power cords with three-wire cords, but this *cannot* be done on ac/dc transformerless radios in which one side of the ac line is connected directly to the chassis! Those must retain the two-wire cords. As noted previously, operating these radios with an isolation transformer is the safest option. If replacing the cord with a two-wire version, the neutral (larger blade) must be connected to the chassis.

Pre-WWII vintage radios often used a cotton covered power cord. To keep the radio as authentic as possible, cotton covered power cords and matching plugs can be found at suppliers such as Antique Radio Supply.

Many early radios had a two-pin power plug with fuses in the plug (the radio has no internal fusing). These are made by Elmeco and are still available (check eBay). Standard 3AG type fuses go in the power plug. Usually a 1 or 2 A fast-blow fuse will work fine except for a higher powered transmitter.

For using PVC-covered wire with terminal strips, solid wire is easier to attach before soldering than stranded wire, although stranded is very usable. You can also use Teflon covered wire that doesn't burn when the soldering iron hits the insulation.

TUBE REPLACEMENT

The sidebar "Using a Tube Tester" explains what a tube tester does. Watch swap meets and garage sales for tube substitution books. Many tubes are interchangeable or similar in purpose. Be sure to document any tube substitutions you make on a vintage radio. Remember that a new tube in the circuit may require re-peaking of the tuned circuits associated with it.

If a tube has a loose tube cap on top, you can easily repair it. Unsolder the cap and make sure that ample wire is still coming from the tube glass envelope. The tube cap should have a tiny hole in the center of the top which the wire will pass through. Mix a small amount of JB Weld epoxy (**www.jbweld.com**) and glue the tube cap back in place. Make sure the wire is sticking out of the hole. After the epoxy has hardened, solder the wire back onto the tube top. Don't let a loose tube cap break it off.

One might be anxious to wipe off the tube and clean it up. Be careful, as you might wipe off the tube number, and then you won't have any idea what the tube is. Many tubes have been lost because they have become unidentifiable. If you do decide to clean up the tube, make sure you steer well clear of the tube number.

Tube sockets and tube pins easily become oxidized which result in radios not working or being intermittent. It is a good idea to pull each tube and spray the socket with DeoxIT or tuner cleaner. Re-insert the tube and wiggle it around in the socket to rub away any oxidation remaining.

REMOVING AND REPLACING COMPONENTS

Replacing capacitors and/or other components isn't difficult, unless they are buried under other components. The Hallicrafters SX-28 and SX-42 receivers are examples of receivers that have extremely difficult-to-reach components. There are different schools of thought on the proper component replacement method. You can use solder wick and/or a desoldering tool to remove the solder from a terminal, unwrap the wires, and install the new component by wrapping the lead around the terminal and soldering it securely. The proponents of this method point out that this is the preferred military and commercial method. I find it often will needlessly damage other components such as tube sockets and create solder droplets inside of the radio.

Back in the day, radio repairmen clipped out a component leaving a short stub of wire, made little coils in the new lead, then soldered the coiled lead to the old stub. This is a much faster, easier and neater method. Refer to books and websites on repairing vintage equipment for other useful tips and tricks.

26.11.2 Powering Up the Equipment

Get out your volt-ohm meter and measure the resistance from the B+ line to ground. Filter capacitors will cause an initial low-resistance reading that increases as the capacitors charge. If the resistance stays low or does not increase beyond tens of kΩ, find the short circuit before you proceed. Now it's time to plug in the radio. It's best to use a variable transformer such as a Variac and ramp up the voltage slowly, or use a "dim bulb tester" (a 100 W light-bulb wired in series with one leg of the ac power). Turn on the radio, and watch for any sparking, flashing

---

Using a Tube Tester

Vacuum-tube testers are scarce but can be located through antique or vintage radio associations, audiophile groups, and sellers of tubes.

Most simple tube testers measure the cathode emission of a vacuum tube. Each grid is shorted to the plate through a switch and the current is observed while the tube operates as a diode. By opening the switches from each grid to the plate (one at a time), we can check for opens and shorts. If the plate current does not drop slightly as a switch is opened, the element connected to that switch is either open or shorted to another element. (We cannot tell an open from a short with this test.) The emission tester does not necessarily indicate the ability of a tube to amplify.

Other tube testers measure tube gain (transconductance). Some transconductance testers read plate current with a fixed bias network. Others use an ac signal to drive the tube while measuring plate current.

Most tube testers also check inter-element leakage. Contamination inside the tube envelope may result in current leakage and shorts between elements. The paths can have high resistance, and may be caused by gas or deposits inside the tube. Tube testers use a moderate voltage to check for leakage. Leakage can also be checked with an ohmmeter using the ×1M range, depending on the actual spacing of tube elements.

or a red glow from the plates of the rectifier tube, or smoke. If any of these occur, immediately remove power and correct the problem. Observe that the tube filaments should light (although you won't see the glow from metal tubes, you should be able to feel them warm up). Again, any tubes that fail to light should be replaced before you continue.

Now hook up a speaker and antenna, and test the radio. With any luck you'll be greeted by a perfectly-performing radio. Seldom, however, is that the case. You may encounter any number of problems at this point. Dirty bandswitches and other controls manifest themselves by intermittently cutting out; they can be cleaned by DeoxIT contact cleaner applied with a cotton swab (don't spray the switch directly!). Scratchy volume or RF gain controls can be cleaned with some DeoxIT; in some cases you might need to remove the control and uncrimp the cover to reveal the carbon element inside.

If a receiver is totally dead at this point but the filaments and dial lights are lit, double-check to see that the Receive-Standby switch is in the receive position, and any battery plug or standby switch jumpers (as described in the manual) are in their correct place.

Although comprehensive troubleshooting is covered elsewhere in this chapter, the next step is comparing voltages with those stated in the user manual. If the manual doesn't have a voltage table denoting the expected voltage at each tube pin, expect between 200-350 V at the tube plate terminals, a few volts at the cathode (unless it's directly grounded), 70-200 V at the screen, and slightly negative voltage at the grid. If you're faced with this situation and a newcomer to troubleshooting vintage gear, help can be found at **http://amfone.net**, **www.antiqueradios.com**, or other forums that cater to boat-anchors and/or vintage radio repair and restoration.

26.11.3 Alignment

Over the years hams have been cautioned that alignment is usually the *last* thing that should be attempted to repair a radio. In general this is true — but it's also a certainty that a 50 year old radio *will* need alignment in order for it to perform at its best. In any case, replace the capacitors and any other faulty components before you attempt alignment — it'll never be right if it still has bad parts! You'll need a good signal generator and a volt-ohm-meter or oscilloscope. Follow the manufacturer's instructions, and with care you'll be rewarded with a radio that performs as good as it did when it was new.

RECEIVER ALIGNMENT

One last caution — alignment should not be attempted by the novice technician or if you do not have the proper equipment or experience. That said alignment may be justified under the following conditions:

• The set is very old and has not been adjusted in many years.

• The circuit has been subject to abusive treatment or environment.

• There is obvious misalignment from a previous repair.

• Tuned-circuit components or crystals have been replaced.

• An inexperienced technician attempted alignment without proper equipment.

• There is a malfunction, but all other circuit conditions are normal. (Faulty transformers can be located because they will not tune.)

Even if one of the above conditions is met, do not attempt alignment unless you have the proper equipment. Receiver alignment should progress from the detector to the antenna terminals. When working on an FM receiver, align the detector first, then the IF and limiter stages and finally the RF amplifier and local oscillator stages. For an AM receiver, align the IF stages first, then the RF amplifier and oscillator stages.

Both AM and FM receivers can be aligned in much the same manner. Always follow the manufacturer's recommended alignment procedure. If one is not available, follow these guidelines:

1. Set the receiver RF gain to maximum, BFO control to zero or center (if applicable to your receiver) and tune to the high end of the receiver passband.

2. Disable the AGC.

3. Set the signal source to the center of the IF passband, with no modulation and minimum signal level.

4. Connect the signal source to the input of the IF section.

5. Connect a voltmeter to the IF output.

6. Adjust the signal-source level for a slight indication on the voltmeter.

7. Peak each IF transformer in order, from the meter to the signal source. The adjustments interact; repeat steps 6 and 7 until adjustment brings no noticeable improvement.

8. Remove the signal source from the IF section input, reduce the level to minimum, set the frequency to that shown on the receiver dial and connect the source to the antenna terminals. If necessary, tune around for the signal — if the local oscillator is not tracking, it may be off.

9. Adjust the signal level to give a slight reading on the voltmeter.

10. Adjust the trimmer capacitor of the RF amplifier for a peak reading of the test signal. (Verify that you are reading the correct signal by switching the source on and off.)

11. Reset the signal source and the receiver tuning for the low end of the passband.

12. Adjust the local-oscillator padder for peak reading.

13. Steps 8 through 11 interact, so repeat them until the results are as good as you can get them.

26.11.4 Using Vintage Receivers

Connect a speaker, preferably the same impedance as the output impedance of the receiver. Some receivers have a 600 Ω and 3.2- or 4 Ω output. An 8 Ω speaker is fine — connect it to the low impedance output. Do not operate the receiver without a speaker, however, as the audio output transformer could be damaged by high voltage transients with no load. Alternatively, plug in a pair of headphones, keeping in mind that old receivers usually have high impedance headphone outputs and new headphones are usually low impedance. They'll work fine, but the volume may be considerably lower with the newer headphones.

If you're going to use the receiver in conjunction with a transmitter, you need to be able to mute the receiver while you're transmitting — otherwise, you'll end up with copious feedback from the receiver. Most receivers have mute terminals — some mute with a closed switch, others mute on open. Figure out which method your receiver and transmitter use. You'll need a relay if the receiver mute arrangement doesn't match that of the transmitter.

Some receivers — such as the older Hammarlund Super Pros and pre-WWII Hallicrafters models — use the mute terminals to open the B+ when putting the receiver in standby mode. This is extremely dangerous with 300 V or so on exposed terminals! An easy modification will save you from an almost certain shock. Open up the receiver and remove the wires from the standby terminals. Solder them together and insulate the connection with electrical tape or a wire nut. Better, solder them to an unused, ungrounded terminal if there's one handy. Next, examine the RF gain control and notice that one terminal is probably grounded. Cut this wire and solder a 47 kΩ resistor between ground and the RF gain control terminal. Connect a pair of wires from the terminals of the mute connection across the 47 kΩ resistor just installed. Now, with the mute terminals open the RF gain is all the way down so the receiver is essentially muted. Short the terminals to receive. The voltage here is low and not dangerous.

Next, connect an antenna and antenna relay in the same manner and tune the bands. You'll find that the best fidelity from the receiver occurs at its maximum bandwidth. The crystal filter, if fitted, can help notch out heterodynes as can tuning the receiver slightly higher or lower. The bandspread control can be used to fine tune. Now, just enjoy using your classic, vintage equipment!

26.11.5 Plastic Restoration

Sometimes an old radio has a meter lens or dial face that is badly damaged. If it is cracked, there isn't much you can do but find a replacement. If it is just scratched, you have a good chance at fully restoring it.

First, remove the meter lens from the meter movement if possible. Most just snap on. To avoid damaging the very delicate needle and meter movement, place it in a protected area and be sure metal filings cannot get to the movement's magnet.

Make sure the scratch hasn't gone all the way though the plastic to become a crack, although even a deep scratch can be buffed out. You will need various grades of wet/dry sandpaper. Obtain sheets of 320, 400 and 600 grit (600 is the finest). One sheet will last a long time. Cut a piece about ½ inch by 2 inches and fold it in half. Start with 320 and gently sand in *one* direction only, over the scratch. This is very tedious and will take a while before you sand away enough plastic to get through the scratch.

Once the scratch is removed, it is time to start reconditioning the plastic. Again sanding in one direction, use the 400 and finally the 600 to completely remove all traces of the earlier sanding scratches. The 600 should leave almost a powdered effect but the plastic will still be hazy and opaque. Sand a little more with the 600 just to be sure all traces of any sanding scratches are gone completely.

To remove the haze you will need a polishing compound called Novus #2 (**www.novuspolish.com** or hobby stores) and another compound called Novus #1, which is a plastic shiner and static remover. This will be important to remove the static on the meter cases when you finish. Static causes the needle to react strangely and erratically.

Start with just a drop of NOVUS #2 and a soft cloth such as the disposable shop towels found at auto parts stores for polishing. Cut a 2 inch by 3 inch piece and start polishing. Continue for a long time and bit by bit the haze will disappear — you will be left with a perfectly clear lens.

FRONT PANEL RESTORATION

The most important part of a radio restoration, cosmetically, is the front panel. The case should also look good, but the front panel is the highlight of the radio and needs the most attention. Usually, paint on a radio from the 50s and 60s is well oxidized and there may be some fine scratches as well.

Scratches can be touched up by using enamel model car paint. Buy a bottle of gloss white, gloss black, and the color closest to the panel you have. Into a small paper cup put a drop or two of the stock color. Using the white or the black, stirring in a small drop at a time, lighten or darken the color until it most closely matches the panel. Use a model paint brush with the finest tip you can find to fill just the scratch and not get it on the rest of the paint. Remove excess with a Q-tip. Let it dry completely.

Remove the panel completely, if possible, or at least remove all the knobs. You will work on them individually later. If the panel was originally a gloss panel, you are in luck. If it is a wrinkle finish or flat, this technique might not work for you — those will be addressed later.

Use the Novus #2 compound to remove a few microns of paint — just the oxidized layer. Place a drop on the panel, and with a soft cloth or shop towel, start working the Novus into the paint. You just want to remove the oxidation, so don't rub too hard. Be careful when working on paint that is a second layer above a base paint. It can be very thin and removed with the Novus. After a small amount of gentle polishing, get another cloth or towel and wipe off the panel which should appear just as it did when it came from the factory.

If your panel is a wrinkle finish, you cannot use the Novus. Use a gentle soapy type cleaner and carefully brush the ridges and peaks of the finish to remove layers of dirt and smoke. Sometimes cleaners like 409 and Simple Green will work very well, but be cautious that it doesn't take off the lettering. Be very carefully around the lettering. One way to work it in is with a plumber's acid brush with the bristles cut very short. The bristles will get down into the crevices of the wrinkle finish and clean it. Once the panel is clean, it can be shined up a bit with some WD-40. This also works very well on wrinkle finish cabinets. Just lightly brush it on and remove it with a rag. This can collect dust but gives a nice wet finish to the wrinkle finish paints.

KNOBS

Most knobs are plastic or have metal plates around the bottom. Use the Novus #2 to shine up the flat parts of the knob. Knobs with flutes on the sides are very tedious to clean, but look beautiful once restored. Take a fine pick and drag it down each flute to scrape out the accumulated dirt. Once cleaned, the Novus can be used to shine up the flutes as well. On knobs with metalized bases, the bases are also shined up with the Novus. Make sure you don't polish off any markings on the trim bases. Sometimes the knobs will have white or red lines in the tops. Those can be filled with model paint to restore them to full beauty.

HOLES IN FRONT PANELS

It may be most disconcerting to find someone has drilled a hole in the panel for one reason or another. Extra holes greatly devalue the rig because to properly restore it, you have to find a replacement panel. Panels with wrong holes can be salvaged with quite nice results by using JB Weld epoxy metal filler (**www.jbweld.com**).

First remove the panel. If the hole is a considerable distance from the other knobs, repairs can be done on the radio but it is not advised. You will need a special tape called Kapton tape. This is a high temperature polymide film tape that is widely available but not cheap. A little tape lasts a long time.

You will need a piece of tape slightly larger than the hole. Other types of tape may work but won't give as smooth a finish. If the panel is wrinkle finished, you may want a rough finish tape such as masking tape. The key is a tight fit to the front of the panel. Place a piece of tape across the hole on the front of the panel and seal it securely all around the hole.

Lay the panel on a flat surface tape-down so the tape will be held flat and not bulge at all. Mix a suitable amount of the JB Weld epoxy and flow it into the hole from the rear of the panel. Stir it while it is still very wet and pliable to make sure no air bubbles are in the hole. Let it cure securely overnight so the hole will be filled and rock hard.

Flip the panel over and remove the tape. If you have secured the tape well enough, none of the epoxy will have been drawn out onto the front surface. There should be a flat filled area exactly level with the rest of the panel.

Now you can touch up the repaired hole with an exact match of spray paint. Mask off the rest of the panel so you don't get any on the lettering. You can also use the model paint method, described for scratch repair Once painted, the offending hole should be virtually invisible.

BROKEN PLASTIC

Sometimes a microphone or other item will have a chunk of the plastic broken out of it. It is most unsightly and usually is the reason for discarding the item. But, using our repair technology, it can be saved and fully restored as in this example of repairing a damaged microphone case. This procedure will work well on broken Bakelite cases, too.

Once again, we will use JB Weld Epoxy and Kapton tape. Remove the microphone elements and switch from the case along with the cord and anything else not plastic. Clean the area around the broken part well. With the Kapton tape, make a backing area on the inside of the case to form a backing for the epoxy. The tape will hold it well and not deform.

Mix some JB Weld and pour it into the space around the break. Fill *higher* than the surrounding plastic. This will be difficult as the fill area will not be level. It may take a couple of fills to build up the area high enough to build up past the level of the surrounding plastic. Once cured and very hard (wait at least 24 hours), you now can begin to file the epoxy. File it down until it is nearly level with the plastic and then switch to sandpaper. Carefully sand the epoxy so it is exactly flush with the original plastic, and make sure the shape is correct. You can always add more JB Weld if too much is filed off.

Once sanded flush, finish the sanding with fine sandpaper (400 and 600 grade). The JB Weld will shine just like the original plastic, but will be the wrong color. Spray paint the entire case with a color close to the original. Once painted, the repair will be virtually undetectable!

26.12 References and Bibliography

J. Bartlett, "Calculating Component Values," *QST*, Nov 1978, pp 21-28.

J. Carr, *How to Troubleshoot and Repair Amateur Radio Equipment* (TAB Books, 1980).

D. DeMaw, "Understanding Coils and Measuring their Inductance," *QST*, Oct 1983, pp 23-26.

M. Eiselman, "Troubleshooting Radios," *QST*, May 2009, pp 30-33.

R. Goodman, *Practical Troubleshooting with the Modern Oscilloscope* (TAB Books, 1979).

A. Haas, *Oscilloscope Techniques* (Gernsback Library, 1958).

J. Lenk, *Handbook of Electronic Test Procedures* (Prentice-Hall, 1982).

J. Lenk, *Encyclopedia of Circuits and Troubleshooting Guide, Vol 1-4* (McGraw-Hill, 1993-1997).

G. Loveday, and A. Seidman, *Troubleshooting Solid-State Circuits* (John Wiley and Sons, 1981).

C. Smith, *Test Equipment for the Radio Amateur*, 4th edition (RSGB, 2011).

D. DeMaw, "Some Basics of Equipment Servicing — Part 1," *QST*, Dec 1981, pp 11-14.

G. Collins, "Some Basics of Equipment Servicing — Part 2," *QST*, Jan 1982, pp 38-41.

G. Collins, "Some Basics of Equipment Servicing — Part 3," *QST*, Feb 1982, pp 40-44, Feedback May 1982, p 43.

N. Bradshaw, "Some Basics of Equipment Servicing — Part 4," *QST*, Mar 1982, pp 40-44.

Contents

27.1 Managing Radio Frequency Interference
    27.1.1 Responsibility for Radio Frequency Interference
    27.1.2 Proper Station Operation
    27.1.3 Personal Diplomacy
    27.1.4 Interference to Your Station
    27.1.5 Interference to a Neighbor's Equipment
27.2 FCC Rules and Regulations
    27.2.1 FCC Part 97 Rules
    27.2.2 FCC Part 15 Rules
27.3 Elements of RFI
    27.3.1 Source-Path-Victim
    27.3.2 Differential-Mode vs Common-Mode Signals
    27.3.3 Types of RFI
    27.3.4 Fundamental Overload
    27.3.5 Spurious Emissions
    27.3.6 External Noise Sources
    27.3.7 Intermodulation Distortion
    27.3.8 Ground Connections
27.4 Identifying the Type of RFI Source
    27.4.1 Identifying Noise from Part 15 Devices
    27.4.2 Identifying Power-line and Electrical Noise
    27.4.3 Identifying Intermodulation Distortion (IMD)
27.5 Locating Sources of RFI
    27.5.1 Locating Noise Sources Inside Your Home
    27.5.2 Locating Noise Sources Outside Your Home
    27.5.3 Approaching Your Neighbor
    27.5.4 Radio Direction Finding

27.6 Power-Line Noise
    27.6.1 Before Filing a Complaint
    27.6.2 Filing a Complaint
    27.6.3 Techniques for Locating Power-line Noise Sources
    27.6.4 Amateur Power-line Noise Locating Equipment
    27.6.5 Signature or Fingerprint Method
    27.6.6 Locating the Source's Power Pole or Structure
    27.6.7 Pinpointing the Source on a Pole or Structure
    27.6.8 Common Causes of Power-line Noise
    27.6.9 The Cooperative Agreement
27.7 Elements of RFI Control
    27.7.1 Differential- and Common-Mode Signal Control
    27.7.2 Shields and Filters
    27.7.3 Common-Mode Chokes
27.8 Troubleshooting RFI
    27.8.1 General RFI Troubleshooting Guidelines
    27.8.2 Transmitters
    27.8.3 Television Interference (TVI)
    27.8.4 Cable TV
    27.8.5 DVD and Video Players
    27.8.6 Non-Radio Devices
27.9 Automotive RFI
    27.9.1 Before Purchasing a Vehicle
    27.9.2 Transceiver Installation Guidelines
    27.9.3 Diagnosing Automotive RFI
    27.9.4 Eliminating Automotive RFI
    27.9.5 Electric and Hybrid-Electric Vehicles
    27.9.6 Automotive RFI Summary
27.10 RFI Projects
    27.10.1 Project: RF Sniffer
27.11 RFI Glossary
27.12 References and Bibliography

Chapter 27

RF Interference

This chapter has been reviewed and updated for current practices by an experienced team composed of the ARRL Lab Staff and supporters of the *Handbook*. Reviewers include Jim Brown, K9YC and Frank Hass, KB4T. We appreciate their many contributions.

Mike Gruber, W1MG —
ARRL Lab General RFI Management and Troubleshooting, FCC Regulations and Responsibilities

Ron Hranac, NØIVN –
Cable and Digital TV

Mark Steffka, WW8MS and Jeremy Campbell, KC8FEI –
 Automotive RFI

Chapter 27 — Downloadable Supplemental Content

Files
- "What To Do if You Have an Electronic Interference Problem" — *CEA Handbook*
- TV Channel, Amateur Band and Harmonic Chart

Projects
- "A Home-made Ultrasonic Power Line Arc Detector and Project Update" by Jim Hanson, W1TRC (SK)
- "A Simple TRF Receiver for Tracking RFI" by Rick Littlefield, K1BQT
- "Active Attenuator for VHF-FM" by Fao Eenhoorn, PAØZR (article and template)
- "Simple Seeker" by Dave Geiser, W5IXM
- "Tape Measure Beam for Power Line Hunting" by Jim Hanson, W1TRC

Amateurs live in an increasingly crowded technological environment. As our lives become filled with technology, every lamp dimmer, garage-door opener or other new technical "toy" contributes to the electrical noise around us. Many of these devices also "listen" to that growing noise and may react to the presence of their electronic siblings. The more such devices there are, the higher the likelihood that the interactions will be undesirable.

What was once primarily a conversation about "interference" has expanded to include power systems, shielding, intentional and unintentional radiators, bonding and grounding, and many other related topics and phenomena. These are all grouped together under the general label of *electromagnetic compatibility (EMC)*. The scope of EMC includes all the ways in which electronic devices interact with each other and their environment.

The general term for interference caused by signals or fields is *electromagnetic interference* or *EMI*. This is the term you'll encounter in the professional literature and standards. The most common term for EMI involving amateur signals is *radio frequency interference (RFI)* and when a television or video display is involved, *television interference (TVI)*. RFI is the term used most commonly by amateurs. Whether it's called EMI, RFI or TVI, unwanted interaction between receivers and transmitters has stimulated vigorous growth in the field of electromagnetic compatibility! (This chapter will use the term RFI to refer to all types of interference to or from amateur signals, except where noted.)

This chapter begins with an overview of dealing with interference and includes relevant FCC regulations. This section is an excellent resource when you are confronted with an interference problem and are wondering "What do I do now?" The information here is based on the experiences of ARRL Lab staff in assisting amateurs with RFI problems.

The second part of this chapter is a discussion on identifying and locating RFI-related noise and signal sources then presents some effective ways of resolving the problem. A glossary of RFI terminology concludes the chapter.

The material in this chapter may provide enough information for you to solve your problem, but if not, the ARRL website offers extensive resources on RF interference at **www.arrl.org/radio-frequency-interference-rfi**. Many topics covered in this chapter are covered in more detail in the *ARRL RFI Book* from a practical amateur perspective.

Throughout this chapter you'll also find references to "Ott," meaning the book *Electromagnetic Compatibility Engineering* by EMC consultant Henry Ott, WA2IRQ. EMC topics are treated in far greater depth in Ott's book than is possible in this *Handbook*. Readers interested in the theory of EMC, analysis of EMC mechanisms, test methodology and EMC standards may be able to find a copy through a library or can purchase a copy through the ARRL Publication Sales department or the ARRL website.

27.1 Managing Radio Frequency Interference

Sooner or later, nearly every Amateur Radio operator will have a problem with RFI, but temper your dismay. Most cases of interference can be cured! Before diving into the technical aspects of interference resolution, consider the social aspects of the problem. A combination of "diplomacy" skills and standard technical solutions are the most effective way to manage the problem so that a solution can be found and applied. This section discusses the overall approach to solving RFI problems. Specific technical causes and solutions are described in subsequent sections.

27.1.1 Responsibility for Radio Frequency Interference

When an interference problem occurs, we may ask "Who is to blame?" The ham and the other party often have different opinions. It is natural (but unproductive) to assign blame instead of fixing the problem.

No amount of wishful thinking (or demands for the "other guy" to solve the problem) will result in a cure for interference. Each party has a unique perspective on the situation and a different degree of understanding of the personal and technical issues involved. On the other hand, each party has certain responsibilities and should be prepared to address them fairly. Given the realities of amateur operation, one of the parties is likely to be a neighbor to the amateur and so the term "neighbor" is used in this chapter, including businesses or other owners of equipment that might cause or experience RFI. The power utility is covered in a separate section dealing with power-line noise.

Always remember that every interference problem has two components — the equipment that is involved and the people who use it. A solution requires that we deal effectively with both the equipment and the people. The ARRL recommends that the hams and their neighbors cooperate to find solutions. The FCC also shares this view. It is important therefore to define the term "interference" without emotion.

27.1.2 Proper Station Operation

A radio operator is responsible for the proper operation of the radio station. This responsibility is spelled out clearly in Part 97 of the FCC regulations. If interference is caused by a spurious emission from your station, you must correct the problem there.

Fortunately, most cases of interference are not the fault of the transmitting station. If an amateur signal is the source of interference, the problem is usually caused by fundamental overload — a general term referring to interference caused by the intended, fundamental signal from a transmitter. If the amateur station is affected by interference, electrical noise is most often the culprit. Typical sources include power lines and consumer devices.

27.1.3 Personal Diplomacy

Whether the interference is to your station or from your station, what happens when you first talk to your neighbor (or the utility or business) sets the tone for all that follows. Any technical solutions cannot help, for example, if you are not allowed in your neighbor's house to explain them! If the interference is not caused by spurious emissions from your station, however, you should be a locator of solutions, not a provider of solutions.

Your neighbor will probably not understand all of the technical issues — at least not at first. Understand that, regardless of fault, interference is annoying whether your signals are causing interference to the neighbor or a device owned by the neighbor is causing interference to you.

Let your neighbor know that you want to help find a solution and that you want to begin by talking things over. Talk about some of the more important technical issues, in non-technical terms. Explain that you must also follow technical rules for your signal, such as for spurious emissions, and that you will check your station, as well.

27.1.4 Interference to Your Station

POWER-LINE NOISE (PLN)

A very common source of RFI to an amateur station is from ac power lines and associated equipment. It is so common that there is an entire section of this chapter devoted to identifying power-line noise (PLN), locating sources of it, and dealing with the utility to resolve it. Remember that you are not authorized to do any more than locate possible sources of PLN and refer them to the utility. See the section on PLN for further information on this common source of RFI.

RFI FROM A NEIGHBOR'S EQUIPMENT

Your neighbor is probably completely unaware that his or her equipment can interfere with your operation. You will have to explain that some home electronics equipment can generate radio signals many times stronger than the weak signals from a distant transmitter. Also explain that there are a number of ways to prevent those signals from being radiated and causing interference. If the equipment causing the problem can be identified, the owner's manual or manufacturer of the device may provide information on the potential for RFI and for its elimination.

Explain that your intent is to help find a solution. Without further investigation it is premature to assume that the neighbor's equipment is at fault or that FCC regulations require the neighbor to perform any corrective action. Working together to find a mutually acceptable solution is the best strategy.

27.1.5 Interference to a Neighbor's Equipment

Your transmitted signals can be the source of interference to a neighbor's equipment. Assure your neighbor that you will check your station thoroughly and correct any problems. You should also discuss the possible susceptibility of consumer equipment. You may want to print a copy of the RFI information found on the ARRL website at **www.arrl.org/information-for-the-neighbors-of-hams**. (This document, "What To Do if You Have an Electronic Interference Problem," is also included in this book's downloadable supplemental information.)

As with interference appearing to be caused by your station, your neighbor will probably feel much better if you explain that you will help find a solution, even if the interference is not your fault. This offer can change your image from neighborhood villain to hero, especially if the interference is not caused by your station. (This is often the case.)

Here is a good analogy: If you tune your TV to channel 3, and see channel 8 instead, you would likely decide that your TV set is broken. Now, if you tune your TV to channel 3, and see your local shortwave radio station (quite possibly Amateur Radio), you shouldn't blame the shortwave station without some investigation. In fact, many televisions respond to strong signals outside the television bands. They may be working as designed, but require added filters and/or shields to work properly near a strong, local RF signal.

PREPARING TO TROUBLESHOOT RFI

In order to troubleshoot and cure RFI to someone else's non-amateur equipment, you need to learn more than just the basics. This is especially important when dealing with your neighbor. If you visit your neighbor's house and try a few dozen things that don't work (or make things worse), your neighbor may lose confidence in your ability to help cure the problem. If that happens, you may be asked to leave.

Start by carefully studying the technical sources and cures for RFI in this book and in other references, such as the *ARRL RFI*

Warning: Performing Repairs

You are the best judge of a local situation, but the ARRL strongly recommends that you do not work on your neighbor's equipment. The minute you open up a piece of equipment, you may become liable for problems. Internal modifications to your neighbor's equipment may cure the interference problem, but if the equipment later develops some other problem, you may be blamed, rightly or wrongly. In some states, it is even *illegal* for you to do *any* work on electronic equipment other than your own.

Book. Review some of the ARRL Technical Information Service and *QST* articles about interference. If you are unfamiliar with any of the terms in this chapter, refer to the glossary.

LOCAL HELP

If you are not an expert (and even experts can use moral support), you should find some local help. Fortunately, such help is often available from your ARRL Section's Technical Coordinator (TC). The TC knows of any local RFI committees and may have valuable contacts in the local utility companies. Even an expert can benefit from a TC's help. The easiest way to find your TC is through your ARRL Section Manager (SM). There is a list of SMs on the ARRL website or in any recent *QST*. He or she can quickly put you in contact with the best source of local help.

Even if you can't secure the help of a local expert, a second ham can be a valuable asset. Often a second party can help defuse any hostility. When evaluating and solving RFI problems involving your station, it is very important for two hams to be part of the process. One can operate your station and the other can observe symptoms, and, when appropriate, try solutions.

PREPARE YOUR HOME AND STATION

The first step toward curing the problem is to make sure your own signal is clean and that devices in your home are not causing any problems. Eliminate all interference issues in your own home to be sure your station is operating properly and that your own electronic equipment is not being interfered with or causing interference to your station!

This is also a valuable troubleshooting tool for situations in which your station is suspected of being the source of interference: If you know your signals are "clean," you have cut the size of the problem in half! If the FCC ever gets involved, you can demonstrate that you are not interfering with your own electronics.

Apply RFI cures to your own consumer electronics and computer equipment. What you learn by identifying and eliminating interference in your own home will make you better prepared to do so in your neighbor's home. When your neighbor sees your equipment working well, it also demonstrates that filters work and cause no harm.

To help build a better relationship, you may want to show your station to your neighbor. A well-organized and neatly-wired station inspires confidence in your ability to solve the RFI problem. Clean up your station and clean up the mess! A rat's nest of cables, unsoldered connections and so on can contribute to RFI.

Grounding and bonding in your station is also important for lightning safety and to help manage RF currents and voltages picked up by the wiring and cables. This is typically not a cure for RFI, but proper grounding will improve lightning safety. Bonding and proper cable management can greatly reduce hum and buzz from power systems. Make sure cable shields are connected properly and that RF current picked up from your transmitted signal by audio and power wiring is minimized.

Install a low-pass or band-pass transmit filter. (In the unlikely event that the FCC becomes involved, they will ask you about filtering.) Show your neighbor that you have installed the necessary filter on your transmitter. Explain that if there is still interference, it is necessary to try filters on the neighbor's equipment, too.

Operating practices and station-design considerations can cause interference to TV and FM receivers. Don't overdrive a transmitter or amplifier; that can increase its harmonic output. Make sure an amplifier or impedance-matching unit is tuned properly.

Along with applying some of the interference-reducing solutions in this chapter, you can also consider steps to reduce the strength of your signal at the victim equipment. This includes raising, moving, or re-orienting the antenna, or reducing transmit power. The use of a balun and properly balanced feed line will minimize radiation from your station feed line. (See the **Transmission Lines** chapter.) Changing antenna polarization may help, such as if a horizontal dipole is coupling to a cable TV service drop. Using different modes, such as CW or FM, may also change the effects of the interference. Although the goal should be for you to operate as you wish with no interference, be flexible in applying possible solutions.

CONTACTING YOUR NEIGHBOR

Now that you have learned more about RFI, located some local help (we'll assume it's the TC) and done all of your homework, make contact with your neighbor. First, arrange an appointment convenient for you, the TC and your neighbor. After you introduce the TC, allow him or her to explain the issues to your neighbor. Your TC will be able to answer most questions, but be prepared to assist with support and additional information as required.

Invite the neighbor to visit your station. Show your neighbor some of the things you do with your radio equipment. Point out any test equipment you use to keep your station in good working order. Of course, you want to show the filter you have installed on your transmitter's output.

Next, have the TC operate your station on several different bands while you show your neighbor that your home electronics equipment is working properly when your station is transmitting. Point out the filters or chokes you have installed to correct any RF susceptibility problems. If the interference is coming from the neighbor's home, show it to the neighbor and explain why it is a problem for you.

At this point, tell your neighbor that the next step is to try some of the cures seen in your home and station on his or her equipment. This is a good time to emphasize that the problem is probably not your fault, but that you and the TC will try to help find a solution anyway.

Study the section on Troubleshooting RFI before deciding what materials and techniques are likely to be required. You and the TC should now visit the neighbor's home and inspect the equipment installation.

AT YOUR NEIGHBOR'S HOME

Begin by asking when the interference occurs, what equipment is involved, and what frequencies or channels are affected, if appropriate. The answers are valuable clues.

The next step should be opening the neighbor's home's main breaker to test whether the RFI is coming from equipment in the neighbor's home. Have the neighbor open their main breaker to see if the noise goes away - then further isolate the source by having them open individual circuit breakers. The ARRL references two downloadable resources that a ham can provide his or her neighbor to help explain the process. The first on opening the breaker is available at **www.rfiservices.com/tips.doc** and the second explaining RFI in layman's term for the neighbor is available at **www.arrl.org/information-for-the-neighbors-of-hams** .

Next, the TC should operate your station while you observe the effects. Try all bands and modes that you use. Ask the neighbor to demonstrate the problem. Seeing your neighbor's interference firsthand will help all parties feel more comfortable with the outcome of the investigation.

If it appears that your station is involved, note all conditions that produce interference. If no transmissions produce the problem, your station *may* not be the source. (It's possible that some contributing factor may have been missing in the test.) Have your neighbor keep notes of when and how the interference appears: what time of day, what channels or device was being interfered with, what other equipment was in use, what was the weather? You should do the same whenever you operate. If you can readily reproduce the problem, you can start to troubleshoot the problem. This process can yield important clues about the nature of the problem.

The tests may show that your station isn't involved at all. A variety of equipment

Product Review Testing and RFI

The ARRL Laboratory mostly considers RFI as an outside source interfering with the desired operation of radio reception. Power line noise, power supplies, motor controls and light dimmers are all *outside* a radio receiver and antenna system and can be a major annoyance that distracts from the pleasure of operating. Have you ever considered RFI generated *inside* your own receiver or by another legally operating Amateur Radio station?

Harmonics

RFI is just that: radio frequency interference. For instance, a harmonic from another radio amateur's transmitter could be interfering with the desired signal you're tuned to. One might think in this day and age, harmonics are minimal and do not cause interference. I ask you to reconsider.

The maximum spurious output of a modern amateur transmitter must be 43 dB lower than the output on the carrier frequency at frequencies below 30 MHz. While that figure may be "good enough" for an FCC standard, it's not good enough to eliminate the possibility of causing interference to other radio amateurs or possibly other services. Here at the ARRL Laboratory, the measurement of harmonic emission level is a measurement I make of RFI generated *outside* your receiver.

A radio amateur contacted me, concerned about a report that he was causing interference to operators on the 80 meter CW band while operating at full legal limit power during a 160 meter CW contest. Knowing FCC rule part 97.307, he made the effort to measure his 80 meter harmonic. Easily meeting FCC standards at 50 dB below carrier output on 160, he wondered how his transmitter could cause interference.

Here's a breakdown of power output and signal reduction:
0 dB down from 1500 W = 1500 W
10 dB down from 1500 W = 150 W
20 dB down from 1500 W = 15 W
30 dB down from 1500 W = 1.5 W
40 dB down from 1500 W = 150 mW
43 dB down from 1500 W = 75.2 mW (this is the FCC legal limit)
50 dB down from 1500 W = 15 mW

While 15 mW may seem too low of a power to cause interference, it wasn't in this case; the interfering signal was reported to be S9. QRP enthusiasts know that at 15 mW, signals can propagate well with the right conditions. Using a single band, resonant antenna will reduce interference caused by harmonics located on other bands, but today many stations employ antennas resonant on more than one ham band. (In this case, the use of a bandpass filter designed for 160 meters would significantly attenuate the harmonic on 80 meters, eliminating the interference.)

Signals Generated in the Receiver

What about RFI generated *inside* the receiver you're operating? You're tuning across the 15 meter band when, all of a sudden, you hear what seems to be an AM broadcast station. Is it a jammer? It is definitely interference — radio frequency interference — caused by two strong shortwave stations! In this particular case, a Midwest radio amateur experienced interference on 15 meters and figured out what was happening. One station was transmitting near 6 MHz and another transmitting above 15 MHz. These two strong stations added up to created a second order IMD (intermodulation distortion) product at the 1st IF stage, and this unwanted signal was passed along to subsequent stages and to the speaker. The RFI in this case was caused by insufficient receiver performance (second order IMD dynamic range) where the frequencies of the two stations added up to exactly the frequency that the operator was tuned to. Third-order IMD products from strong in-band signals are another form of RFI created within a radio receiver.

Nearby stations transmitting at or near the IF frequency will cause interference not because the transmitter is at fault, but because of a receiver's insufficient IF rejection. The same interference will be heard if a nearby transmitter is operating at an image frequency.

Power Supplies

RFI can also be created from another part of a radio system, such as an external power supply. In addition to transmitter and receiver testing, the Lab also measures the conducted emission levels of power supplies. This is an indication of the amount of RF at given frequencies conducted onto power lines from a power supply as described in this chapter.

Through our published Product Review test results in *QST* magazine, readers can compare the above figures of modern HF transceivers when considering the purchase of a new or used transceiver. Our published data tables spawn friendly competition between radio manufacturers who in turn, strive to perfect their circuit designs. The result is a better product for the manufacturer and a better product for you, the radio amateur. — *Bob Allison, WB1GCM, ARRL Test Engineer*

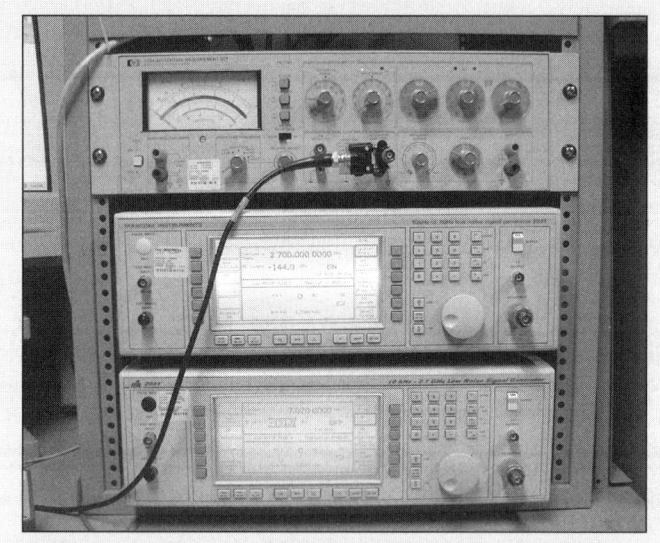

The Lab uses these signal generators to test receivers for internally generated intermodulation distortion, as well as other key performance parameters.

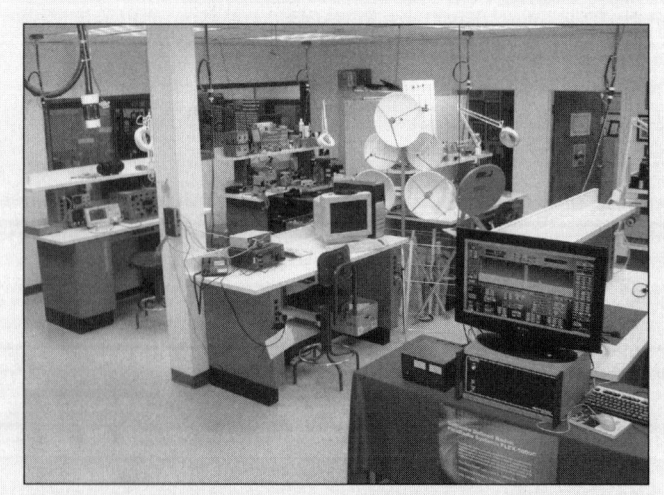

The ARRL Lab maintains a complete set of up-to-date equipment as well as an RF-tight screen room for Product Review testing. [Bob Allison, WB1GCM, photo]

malfunctions or external noise can look like interference. Some other nearby transmitter or noise source may be causing the problem. You may recognize electrical noise or some kind of equipment malfunction. If so, explain your findings to the neighbor and suggest that he or she contact appropriate service personnel.

If the interference is to your station from equipment that may be in the neighbor's home, take along a portable receiver. A familiar AM broadcast band receiver is a good choice. You will need to visit when the noise is occurring. Show that the noise is present but there is no need to make it so loud as to be offensive. Describe when you are receiving the interference and what pattern it seems to have (continuous, pulsed, intermittent, certain times of day, and so on). Show that the problem is what you are experiencing and that you need the neighbor's help.

Begin with the main breaker test as described earlier in this section. Then proceed to individual circuits. Once you have identified the circuit powering the equipment, physically unplug it, turn it off, or remove the batteries as required while you or the TC observe at your station. (Remember that turning a piece of equipment OFF with its ON/OFF switch may not cause the equipment to completely power down.) Removing cables from a powered-up piece of equipment may serve to further isolate the problem.

At this point, the action you take will depend on the nature of the problem and its source. Techniques for dealing with specific interference issues are discussed in the following sections of the chapter. If you are unable to determine the exact nature of the problem, develop a plan for continuing to work with the neighbor and continue to collect information about the behavior of the interference.

Some Common Reported Problems — A Few Statistics

The ARRL has nearly 20 years of RFI complaint data. During that time we've found that the vast majority of reported sources are either power line noise or a consumer device. They fall within one of three categories under the FCC rules. Although a small percentage of reports may come from other sources it is generally recommended to start a typical RFI search with the assumption that it probably falls into one of these categories. Excluding unknown sources, here is a rough breakdown:

Part 15 Incidental Radiators

These sources do not intentionally create or radiate RF energy but do so as an incidental part of their intended operation. Typically these are non-electronic sources and the RF is generated by sparking or arcing. Excluding unknown source complaints, approximately one third of the interference reports received by the ARRL are power line noise. This is by far the most common RFI problem caused by incidental radiators. Other common sources in this category include bad doorbell transformers and arcing electric fences.

Part 15 Unintentional Radiators

These sources intentionally create RF energy but do not intentionally radiate it. (RF in this case is defined as a frequency above 9 kHz.) These are typically electronic consumer devices such as computers, televisions and radio receiving equipment. By far the most common unintentional radiator at the heart of an RFI problem is the ubiquitous switching mode power supply. Switchers are in many consumer devices these days, including lighting devices and battery chargers. They are often easy to identify by their regular and repeating pattern of noise peaks and nulls as you tune across the spectrum. The peaks are usually around 50 kHz apart, but a spacing anywhere between 40 and 80 kHz is common. Less common are lower and higher spacings ranging from 20 to 120 kHz. The peaks will often drift with respect to time.

Part 18 RF Lighting Devices

Part 18 of the FCC rules covers Industrial, Medical and Industrial (ISM) devices. Some consumer devices, however, also fall under Part 18. These devices concert RF directly into some other form of energy such as heart or light. Devices in this category include microwave ovens, some ultrasonic jewelry cleaners and lighting devices that use RF to ionize gas molecules. Once again, the RF must be greater than 9 kHz. Part 18 also prohibits the RF from being used to communicate intelligence or data of any kind.

So far, the only problematic Part 18 consumer devices at the heart of an RFI problem have been lighting devices, including CFLs, electronic fluorescent light ballasts, and grow lights. Particularly noteworthy have been grow lights which have been measured to be as much as 58 dB over the applicable FCC limits. — *by Mike Gruber, W1MG, ARRL Test Engineer*

27.2 FCC Rules and Regulations

In the United States most unlicensed electrical and electronic devices are regulated by Part 15 of the FCC's rules. These are referred to as "Part 15 devices." Most RFI issues reported to the ARRL involve a Part 15 device. Some consumer equipment, such as certain wireless and lighting devices, is covered under FCC Part 18 which pertains to ISM (Industrial, Scientific and Medical) devices.

The Amateur service is regulated by FCC Part 97. (Part 97 rules are available downloadable at **www.arrl.org/part-97-amateur-radio.** See also the sidebar "RFI-related FCC Rules and Definitions.") To be legal, the amateur station's signal must meet all Part 97 technical requirements, such as for spectral purity and power output.

As a result, it isn't surprising that most interference complaints involve multiple parts of the FCC rules. (The FCC's jurisdiction does have limits, though — ending below 9 kHz.) It is also important to note that each of the three parts (15, 18 and 97) specifies different requirements with respect to interference, including absolute emissions limits and spectral purity requirements. The FCC does not specify *any* RFI immunity requirements. Most consumer devices therefore receive no FCC protection from a legally licensed transmitter, including an amateur transmitter operating legally according to Part 97.

Licensed services are protected from interference to their signals, even if the interference is generated by another licensed service transmitter. For example, consider TVI from an amateur transmitter's spurious emissions, such as harmonics, that meet the requirements of Part 97 but are still strong enough to be received by nearby TV receivers. The TV receiver itself is not protected from interference under the FCC rules. However, within its service area the licensed TV broadcast signal is protected from harmful interference caused by spurious emissions from other licensed transmitters. In this case, the amateur transmitter's interfering spurious emission would have to be eliminated or reduced to a level at which harmful interference has been eliminated.

27.2.1 FCC Part 97 Rules

While most interference to consumer devices may be caused by a problem associated with the consumer device as opposed to the signal source, all amateurs must still comply with Part 97 rules. Regardless of who is at fault, strict conformance to FCC requirements, coupled with a neat and orderly station appearance, will go far toward creating a good and positive impression in the event of an FCC field investigation. Make sure your

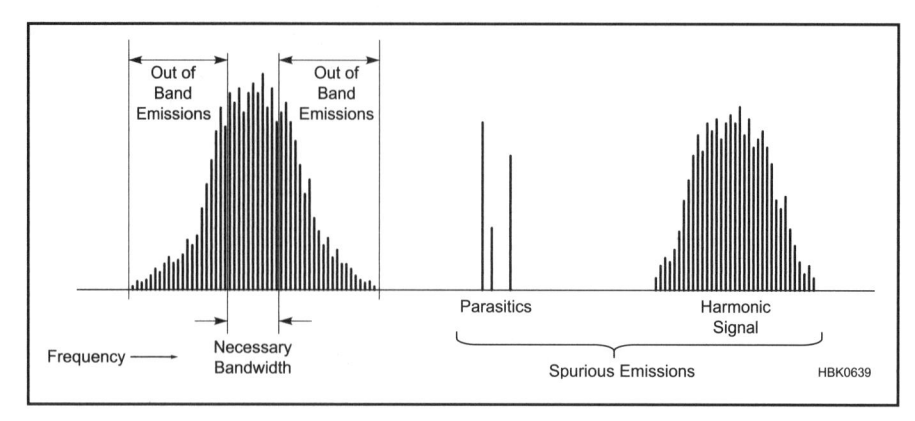

Figure 27.1 — An illustration of out-of-band versus spurious emissions. Some of the modulation sidebands are outside the necessary bandwidth. These are considered out-of-band emissions, not spurious emissions. The harmonic and parasitic emissions shown here are considered spurious emissions; these must be reduced to comply with §97.307.

What If the Police Are Called?

Many amateurs have had a similar experience. You are enjoying some time in front of the radio when the doorbell rings. When you answer the door, you find an irate neighbor has called the police about your transmissions interfering with their stereo (or cordless telephone or other home electronics). The officer tells you that you are interfering with your neighbor and orders you to stop transmissions immediately.

The bad news is you are in the middle of a bad situation. The good news is that most cases of interference can be cured! The proper use of "diplomacy" skills to communicate with a neighbor and standard technical cures will usually solve the problem. Even more good news is that if you are operating in accordance with your license and employing good engineering practices, the law and FCC rules are on your side.

Most RFI is caused by the unfortunate fact that most consumer equipment lacks the necessary filtering and shielding to allow it to work well near a radio transmitter. The FCC does not regulate the immunity of equipment, however, so when interference is caused by consumer-equipment fundamental overload, there is no FCC rules violation, and licensed stations have no regulatory responsibility to correct interference that may result.

Further, in 1982, Congress passed Public Law 97-259. This law is specific and reserves exclusive jurisdiction over RFI matters to the Federal Communications Commission. This national law preempts any state or local regulations or ordinances that attempt to regulate or resolve RFI matter. This is a victory for amateurs (and other services operating with the legal and technical provisions of their licenses).

Simply put, 97-259 says that cities and towns may not pass ordinances or regulations that would prohibit someone from making legal radio transmissions. But what do you do when your neighbor (or the police) confront you about RFI to their consumer electronics? First and foremost, remain calm. In all likelihood the officer or your neighbor has probably never heard of 97-259. Don't get defensive and get drawn into an argument. Don't make comments that the problem is with the neighbor's "cheap" equipment. While inexpensive radios are usually big culprits, any home electronics are potential problems due to inadequate technical designs.

Begin by listening to the complaint. Explain that while you understand, you are operating your equipment within its technical specifications. If your equipment doesn't interfere with your own home electronics, offer to demonstrate that to the officer. Also explain the basics of PL 97-259. If the officer (or neighbor) continues to insist that regardless of the law that you cease, consider temporarily complying with his or her request, with the understanding that you are doing so until the matter is resolved.

Work with your neighbors to understand that steps can be taken that should help resolve the problems (for example, placing toroids and filters on the consumer electronics). The ARRL website has lots of helpful information as you work to resolve the problems. If your club has a local RFI committee or ARRL Technical Specialist, get them involved — their expertise can really be helpful. But above all, remember that when you practice easy, level-headed "diplomacy" you can usually keep the situation from escalating. — *Dan Henderson, N1ND, ARRL Regulatory Information*

station and signal exhibit good engineering and operating practices.

The bandwidth of a signal is defined by §97.3(a)(8) while the paragraphs of §97.307 define the technical standards amateur transmissions must meet. Paragraph (c) defines the rules for interference caused by spurious emissions. As illustrated in **Figure 27.1**, modulation sidebands outside the necessary bandwidth are considered *out-of-band* emissions, while harmonics and parasitic signals are considered *spurious emissions*. Paragraphs (d) and (e) specify absolute limits on spurious emissions, illustrated in **Figure 27.2**. Spurious emissions must not exceed these levels, whether or not the emissions are causing interference. If spurious emissions from your transmitter are causing interference, it's your responsibility to clean them up.

Strict observance of these rules can not only help minimize interference to the amateur service, but other radio services and consumer devices as well.

27.2.2 FCC Part 15 Rules

In the United States, most unlicensed devices are regulated by Part 15 of the FCC's rules. While understanding these rules doesn't necessarily solve an RFI problem, they do provide some important insight and background on interference to and from a Part 15 device. (Part 18 devices and rules are similar in some respects) and will not be discussed separately — see the sidebar.)

There are literally thousands of Part 15 devices with the potential to be at the heart of an RFI problem. A Part 15 device can be almost anything not already covered in another

FCC Part 18, Consumer Devices

Some consumer devices are regulated by Part 18 of the FCC Rules which pertains to the Industrial, Scientific and Medical (ISM) bands. These devices convert RF energy directly into some other form of energy, such as heat, light or ultrasonic sound energy. Some common household Part 18 devices therefore include microwave ovens, electronic fluorescent light ballasts, CFLs, and ultrasonic jewelry cleaners. (Note that LED bulbs are covered under Part 15 because of the process by which they generate light.) Recently, indoor grow light ballasts and related equipment have been causing a lot of RFI. Those sold to consumers are required to be certified under Part 18 rules, while those sold to industrial and commercial customers are not. There have been reports of non-Part 18 devices being sold at home-improvement and other consumer outlets. The ARRL is working with the FCC and manufacturers to resolve this issue.

Consumer Part 18 devices are generators of RF — but not for communications purposes — and can cause interference in some cases. However, there are no rules that protect them from interference. The purpose of Part 18 is to permit those devices to operate and to establish rules prohibiting interference.

From the standpoint of an RFI problem, Part 18 rules aren't much different from Part 15. As with a Part 15 device, a Part 18 device is required to meet specified emissions limits. Furthermore, it must not cause harmful interference to a licensed radio service.

Part 18 Rules and the 33 cm Band

Part 18 specifies a number of bands for ISM (industrial, scientific, and medical) devices. The so-called ISM bands in some cases overlap amateur spectrum. For example, the entire 33 cm band from 902 to 928 MHz is both an amateur and ISM band. And, as the following rule from Part 97 indicates, the amateur service is not protected from ISM devices operating in this or any other ISM band:

§97.303 (e) Amateur stations receiving in the 33 cm band, the 2400-2450 MHz segment, the 5.725-5.875 GHz segment, the 1.2 cm band, the 2.5 mm band, or the 244-246 GHz segment must accept interference from industrial, scientific, and medical (ISM) equipment.

Additional restrictions apply in some areas of the country when using the 33 cm band.

• Amateurs located in some parts of Colorado and Wyoming may not transmit in some parts of this band.
• Amateurs located in some parts of Texas and New Mexico are prohibited from using this band.
• Amateurs located within 150 miles of White Sands Missile Range are limited to 150 W PEP.

Amateurs in these areas are responsible for knowing the boundaries of these areas and observing all applicable rules. See the latest edition of the *ARRL Repeater Directory* for more information and boundary details.

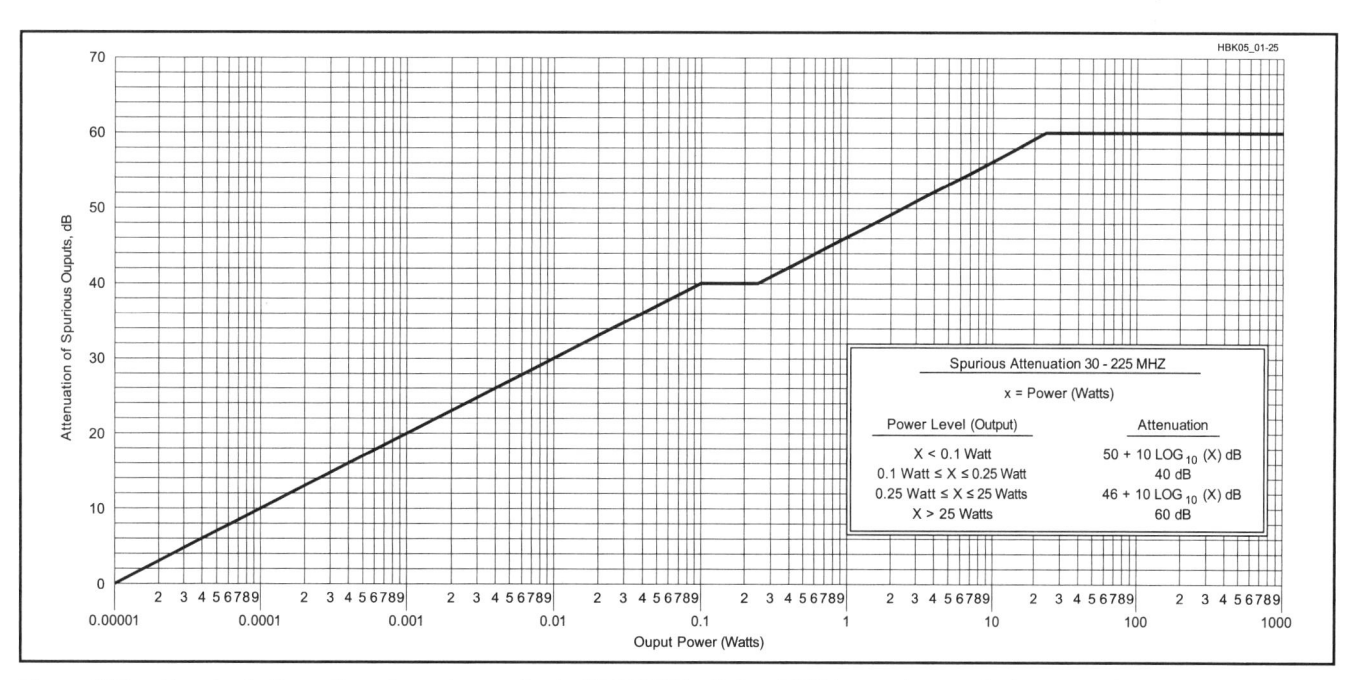

Figure 27.2 — Required attenuation of spurious outputs, 30-225 MHz. Below 30 MHz, spurious emissions must be suppressed by 43 dB for amateur transmitters installed after January 1, 2003.

Part of the FCC rules. In fact, many Part 15 devices may not normally even be associated with electronics, RF or in some cases, electricity. While televisions, radios, telephones and even computers obviously constitute a Part 15 device, the rules extend to anything that is capable of generating RF, including electric motors and consumer devices such as baby monitors, wireless microphones and intercoms, RF remote controls, garage door openers, etc. With so many Part 15 consumer devices capable of generating and responding to RF, it isn't surprising therefore that most reported RFI problems involving Amateur Radio also involve a Part 15 device.

TYPES OF PART 15 DEVICES

Part 15 describes three different types of devices that typically might be associated with an RFI problem. A fourth type of device, called a *carrier current device*, uses power lines and wiring for communications purposes. As we'll see, the rules are different for each type.

Intentional Emitters — Intentionally generate RF energy and radiate it. Examples include garage door openers, cordless phones and baby monitors.

Unintentional Emitters — Intentionally generate RF energy internally, but do not intentionally radiate it. Examples include computers and network equipment, superheterodyne receivers, switchmode power supplies and TV receivers.

Incidental Emitters — Generate RF energy only as an incidental part of their normal operation. Examples include power lines, arcing electric fence, arcing switch contacts, dc motors and mechanical light switches.

Carrier Current Devices — Intentionally generate RF and conduct it on power lines and/or house wiring for communications purposes. Examples include Powerline and X.10 networks, Access or In-House Broadband-Over-Power-Line (BPL), campus radio-broadcast systems, and other powerline communications devices.

PART 15 SUMMARY

FCC's Part 15 rules pertain to unlicensed devices and cover a lot of territory. Although reading and understanding Part 15 can appear rather formidable — especially at first glance — the rules pertaining to RFI can be roughly summarized as follows:

• Part 15 devices operate under an unconditional requirement to not cause harmful interference to a licensed radio service, such as Amateur Radio. If such interference occurs, the operator of the Part 15 device is responsible for eliminating the interference.

• Part 15 devices receive no protection from interference from a licensed radio service. There are no FCC rules or limits with regard to Part 15 device RFI immunity.

When is the operator of a licensed transmitter responsible for interference to a Part 15 device?

• The rules hold the transmitter operator responsible if interference is caused by spurious emissions such as a harmonic. An example would be a harmonic from an amateur's transmitter interfering with a cordless telephone. In this case, the transmitter is generating harmful RF energy beyond its permitted bandwidth. A cure must be installed at the transmitter.

• The transmitter operator is not responsible when a Part 15 device is improperly responding to a legal and intentional output of the transmitter. An example of this case would be interference to a cordless telephone operation by the strong-but-legal signal from a nearby amateur transmitter. In this case, the Part 15 device is at fault and the cure must be installed there. It is important to note that

---

RFI-Related FCC Rules and Definitions

Here are some of the most important rules and definitions pertaining to RFI and the Amateur Radio Service. Definitions in Part 2 are used in regulations that apply to all radio services.

§2.1 Definitions

Harmful Interference. Interference which endangers the functioning of a radionavigation service or of other safety services or seriously degrades, obstructs, or repeatedly interrupts a radiocommunication service operating in accordance with [the ITU] Radio Regulations.

Interference. The effect of unwanted energy due to one or a combination of emissions, radiations, or inductions upon reception in a radiocommunication system, manifested by any performance degradation, misinterpretation, or loss of information which could be extracted in the absence of such unwanted energy.

Out-of-band Emission. Emission on a frequency or frequencies immediately outside the necessary bandwidth which results from the modulation process, but excluding spurious emissions. Band does not mean "amateur band" here.

§97.3 Definitions

(a) The definitions of terms used in Part 97 are:

(8) Bandwidth. The width of a frequency band outside of which the mean power of the transmitted signal is attenuated at least 26 dB below the mean power of the transmitted signal within the band.

(23) Harmful interference. (see the previous Part 2 definition)

(42) Spurious emission. An emission, on frequencies outside the necessary bandwidth of a transmission, the level of which may be reduced without affecting the information being transmitted.

§97.307 Emission standards

(a) No amateur station transmission shall occupy more bandwidth than necessary for the information rate and emission type being transmitted, in accordance with good amateur practice.

(b) Emissions resulting from modulation must be confined to the band or segment available to the control operator. Emissions outside the necessary bandwidth must not cause splatter or key-click interference to operations on adjacent frequencies.

(c) All spurious emissions from a station transmitter must be reduced to the greatest extent practicable. If any spurious emission, including chassis or power line radiation, causes harmful interference to the reception of another radio station, the licensee of the interfering amateur station is required to take steps to eliminate the interference, in accordance with good engineering practice.

(d) For transmitters installed after January 1, 2003, the mean power of any spurious emission from a station transmitter or external RF amplifier transmitting on a frequency below 30 MHz must be at least 43 dB below the mean power of the fundamental emission. For transmitters installed on or before January 1, 2003, the mean power of any spurious emission from a station transmitter or external RF power amplifier transmitting on a frequency below 30 MHz must not exceed 50 mW and must be at least 40 dB below the mean power of the fundamental emission. For a transmitter of mean power less than 5 W installed on or before January 1, 2003, the attenuation must be at least 30 dB. A transmitter built before April 15, 1977, or first marketed before January 1, 1978, is exempt from this requirement.

(e) The mean power of any spurious emission from a station transmitter or external RF power amplifier transmitting on a frequency between 30-225 MHz must be at least 60 dB below the mean power of the fundamental. For a transmitter having a mean power of 25 W or less, the mean power of any spurious emission supplied to the antenna transmission line must not exceed 25 µW and must be at least 40 dB below the mean power of the fundamental emission, but need not be reduced below the power of 10 µW. A transmitter built before April 15, 1977, or first marketed before January 1, 1978, is exempt from this requirement.

this situation is typical of most interference to Part 15 devices.

Even though the causes and cures for these situations are different, the common element for all three situations is the need for personal diplomacy in resolving the problem.

PART 15 MANUFACTURER REQUIREMENTS

Under FCC rules, both device manufacturers and operators of those devices share responsibility for addressing an RFI problem. The rules for manufacturers are primarily designed to reduce the possibility of harmful interference. They do not however completely eliminate the possibility of an RFI problem. If and when interference does occur, the rules are designed to minimize and confine the scope of problems such that they can be addressed on a case by case basis. Responsibility then falls on the device operator to correct the problem or cease using the device.

Manufacturers are subject to requirements that they use good engineering practice to help minimize the potential for interference. In addition, they must meet certain absolute conducted and radiated emissions limits for intentional and unintentional emitters. (See the sidebar for limits on conducted and radiated emissions.) These limits are high enough

---

Part 15 Absolute Emissions Limits for Unintentional Emitters

§15.107 Conducted limits

(a) Except for Class A digital devices, for equipment that is designed to be connected to the public utility (ac) power line, the radio frequency voltage that is conducted back onto the ac power line on any frequency or frequencies within the band 150 kHz to 30 MHz shall not exceed the limits in the following table, as measured using a 50 µH/50 ohms line impedance stabilization network (LISN). Compliance with the provisions of this paragraph shall be based on the measurement of the radio frequency voltage between each power line and ground at the power terminal. The lower limit applies at the band edges.

Conducted Limits — Non Class-A Digital Devices

Frequency of emission (MHz)	Conducted limit (dBµV) Quasi-peak	Average
0.15–0.5	66 to 56*	56 to 46*
0.5–5	56	46
5–30	60	50

*Decreases with the logarithm of the frequency.

(b) For a Class A digital device that is designed to be connected to the public utility (ac) power line, the radio frequency voltage that is conducted back onto the ac power line on any frequency or frequencies within the band 150 kHz to 30 MHz shall not exceed the limits in the following table, as measured using a 50 µH/50 ohms LISN. Compliance with the provisions of this paragraph shall be based on the measurement of the radio frequency voltage between each power line and ground at the power terminal. The lower limit applies at the boundary between the frequency ranges.

Conducted Limits — Class-A Digital Devices

Frequency of emission (MHz)	Conducted limit (dBµV) Quasi-peak	Average
0.15–0.5	79	66
0.5–30	73	60

(c) The limits shown in paragraphs (a) and (b) of this section shall not apply to carrier current systems operating as unintentional radiators on frequencies below 30 MHz. In lieu thereof, these carrier current systems shall be subject to the following standards:

(1) For carrier current systems containing their fundamental emission within the frequency band 535-1705 kHz and intended to be received using a standard AM broadcast receiver: no limit on conducted emissions.

(2) For all other carrier current systems: 1000 µV within the frequency band 535–1705 kHz, as measured using a 50 µH/50 ohms LISN.

(3) Carrier current systems operating below 30 MHz are also subject to the radiated emission limits in §15.109(e).

(d) Measurements to demonstrate compliance with the conducted limits are not required for devices which only employ battery power for operation and which do not operate from the ac power lines or contain provisions for operation while connected to the ac power lines. Devices that include, or make provision for, the use of battery chargers which permit operating while charging, ac adaptors or battery eliminators or that connect to the ac power lines indirectly, obtaining their power through another device which is connected to the ac power lines, shall be tested to demonstrate compliance with the conducted limits.

§ 15.109 Radiated emission limits

(a) Except for Class A digital devices, the field strength of radiated emissions from unintentional radiators at a distance of 3 meters shall not exceed the following values:

Radiated Limits — Non Class-A Digital Devices

Frequency of emission (MHz)	Field Strength (µV/meter)
30–88	100
88–216	150
216–960	200
Above 960	500

(b) The field strength of radiated emissions from a Class A digital device, as determined at a distance of 10 meters, shall not exceed the following:

Radiated Limits — Class-A Digital Devices

Frequency of emission (MHz)	Field Strength (µV/meter)
30–88	90
88–216	150
216–960	210
Above 960	300

(c) In the emission tables above, the tighter limit applies at the band edges. Sections 15.33 and 15.35 which specify the frequency range over which radiated emissions are to be measured and the detector functions and other measurement standards apply.

(d) For CB receivers, the field strength of radiated emissions within the frequency range of 25–30 MHz shall not exceed 40 microvolts/meter at a distance of 3 meters. The field strength of radiated emissions above 30 MHz from such devices shall comply with the limits in paragraph (a) of this section.

(e) Carrier current systems used as unintentional radiators or other unintentional radiators that are designed to conduct their radio frequency emissions via connecting wires or cables and that operate in the frequency range of 9 kHz to 30 MHz, including devices that deliver the radio frequency energy to transducers, such as ultrasonic devices not covered under part 18 of this chapter, shall comply with the radiated emission limits for intentional radiators provided in §15.209 for the frequency range of 9 kHz to 30 MHz. As an alternative, carrier current systems used as unintentional radiators and operating in the frequency range of 525 kHz to 1705 kHz may comply with the radiated emission limits provided in §15.221(a). At frequencies above 30 MHz, the limits in paragraph (a), (b), or (g) of this section, as appropriate, apply.

RFI-related Part 15 FCC Rules and Definitions

The FCC's Part 15 rules are found in Title 47 section of the Code of Federal Regulations (CFR). They pertain to unlicensed devices. Here are some of the more important Part 15 rules and definitions pertaining to RFI.

§15.3 Definitions.

(m) **Harmful interference.** Any emission, radiation or induction that endangers the functioning of a radionavigation service or of other safety services or seriously degrades, obstructs or repeatedly interrupts a radio communications service operating in accordance with this chapter.

(n) **Incidental radiator.** A device that generates radio frequency energy during the course of its operation although the device is not intentionally designed to generate or emit radio frequency energy.

(o) **Intentional radiator.** A device that intentionally generates and emits radio frequency energy by radiation or induction.

(z) **Unintentional radiator.** A device that intentionally generates radio frequency energy for use within the device, or that sends radio frequency signals by conduction to associated equipment via connecting wiring, but which is not intended to emit RF energy by radiation or induction.

(t) **Power line carrier systems.** An unintentional radiator employed as a carrier current system used by an electric power utility entity on transmission lines for protective relaying, telemetry, etc. for general supervision of the power system. The system operates by the transmission of radio frequency energy by conduction over the electric power transmission lines of the system. The system does not include those electric lines which connect the distribution substation to the customer or house wiring.

(ff) **Access Broadband over Power Line (Access BPL).** A carrier current system installed and operated on an electric utility service as an unintentional radiator that sends radio frequency energy on frequencies between 1.705 MHz and 80 MHz over medium voltage lines or over low voltage lines to provide broadband communications and is located on the supply side of the utility service's points of interconnection with customer premises. Access BPL does not include power line carrier systems as defined in §15.3(t) or In-House BPL as defined in §15.3(gg).

(gg) **In-House Broadband over Power Line (In-House BPL).** A carrier current system, operating as an unintentional radiator, that sends radio frequency energy by conduction over electric power lines that are not owned, operated or controlled by an electric service provider. The electric power lines may be aerial (overhead), underground, or inside the walls, floors or ceilings of user premises. In-House BPL devices may establish closed networks within a user's premises or provide connections to Access BPL networks, or both.

Some of the most important Part 15 rules pertaining to radio and television interference from unintentional and incidental radiators include:

§15.5 General conditions of operation.

(b) Operation of an intentional, unintentional, or incidental radiator is subject to the conditions that no harmful interference is caused and that interference must be accepted that may be caused by the operation of an authorized radio station, by another intentional or unintentional radiator, by industrial, scientific and medical (ISM) equipment, or by an incidental radiator.

(c) The operator of the radio frequency device shall be required to cease operating the device upon notification by a Commission representative that the device is causing harmful interference. Operation shall not resume until the condition causing the harmful interference has been corrected.

§15.13 Incidental radiators.

Manufacturers of these devices shall employ good engineering practices to minimize the risk of harmful interference.

§15.15 General technical requirements.

(c) Parties responsible for equipment compliance should note that the limits specified in this part will not prevent harmful interference under all circumstances. Since the operators of Part 15 devices are required to cease operation should harmful interference occur to authorized users of the radio frequency spectrum, the parties responsible for equipment compliance are encouraged to employ the minimum field strength necessary for communications, to provide greater attenuation of unwanted emissions than required by these regulations, and to advise the user as to how to resolve harmful interference problems (for example, see Sec. 15.105(b)).

§15.19 Labeling requirements.

(a) In addition to the requirements in part 2 of this chapter, a device subject to certification, notification, or verification shall be labeled as follows:

(3) All other devices shall bear the following statement in a conspicuous location on the device:

This device complies with part 15 of the FCC Rules. Operation is subject to the following two conditions: (1) This device may not cause harmful interference, and (2) this device must accept any interference received, including interference that may cause undesired operation.

And the following requirements apply for consumer and residential Class B digital devices. Different requirements apply for Class A digital devices which can only be used in industrial and similar environments:

§15.105 Information to the user.

(b) For a Class B digital device or peripheral, the instructions furnished the user shall include the following or similar statement, placed in a prominent location in the text of the manual:

This equipment has been tested and found to comply with the limits for a Class B digital device, pursuant to part 15 of the FCC Rules. These limits are designed to provide reasonable protection against harmful interference in a residential installation. This equipment generates, uses and can radiate radio frequency energy and, if not installed and used in accordance with the instructions, may cause harmful interference to radio communications. However, there is no guarantee that interference will not occur in a particular installation. If this equipment does cause harmful interference to radio or television reception, which can be determined by turning the equipment off and on, the user is encouraged to try to correct the interference by one or more of the following measures:

Reorient or relocate the receiving antenna.

Increase the separation between the equipment and receiver.

Connect the equipment into an outlet on a circuit different from that to which the receiver is connected.

Consult the dealer or an experienced radio/TV technician for help.

that S9+ interference levels can occur nearby, depending on frequency, distance and other factors. In fact, most reported Part 15 consumer products causing harmful interference to Amateur Radio are legal and meet these required limits. Therefore, the fact that a particular device is causing harmful interference is not in itself evidence or proof of a rules violation with regard to emissions limits.

With the exception of intentional emitters and carrier-current devices, there are no absolute radiated emissions limits below 30 MHz. The size of a Part 15 device is usually small relative to the wavelength at these frequencies. It is typically too small to be an effective antenna at these longer wavelengths. Therefore, under the FCC rules, only conducted emissions are specified below 30 MHz. (Note that cables and wiring connected to the devices are often effective at radiating signals and are frequent sources of radiated RFI.)

In general, radiated emissions limits are specified only at frequencies above 30 MHz. At the shorter wavelengths above 30 MHz, the device itself is large enough to be a radiator. Wiring connected to it can also be an effective antenna for radiating noise.

Although incidental radiators do not have any absolute emissions limits, as for all Part 15 devices, manufacturers must still employ good engineering practice to minimize the potential for interference.

The FCC also requires manufacturers to add information as a label to most Part 15 devices or as text in the device's operating manual. This information attests to the potential for interference and to the responsibility of the device operator. It must be placed in a conspicuous location on the device or in the manual and contain the following statement:

This device complies with part 15 of the FCC Rules. Operation is subject to the following two conditions: (1) This device may not cause harmful interference, and (2) this device must accept any interference received, including interference that may cause undesired operation.

Owners of Part 15 devices are frequently unaware of this information and surprised to find it on the device or in its manual. Reading this label can be an important step in resolving RFI issues. Additional details regarding labeling requirements can be found in the sidebar on Part 15 Rules.

FCC EMISSION LIMITS

While the FCC's rules impose absolute emissions limits for most electronic consumer devices, it is a common misconception that they will protect nearby receivers from interference. The reality is that these limits are high — high enough to cause harmful interference to a ham even if the source is in a nearby residence. Once manufacturers meet these limits, the device can be legally marketed and sold in the United States as described in the next section. However, if and when harmful interference occurs from an otherwise legal device, the burden to correct it falls on the operator of the device causing it. In most cases, this is either the ham or a neighbor.

The rules for unintentional radiators are summarized by the ubiquitous Part 15 label that follows. It should also be noted that Part 18 devices such as electronic fluorescent light ballasts and CFLs have a similar provision:

This device complies with part 15 of the FCC Rules. Operation is subject to the following two conditions: (1) This device may not cause harmful interference, and (2) this device must accept any interference received, including interference that may cause undesired operation.

In addition, many non-electronic sources are classified as "incidental radiators" under Part 15. These devices typically generate RF by a spark or arcing and are classified as "incidental radiators." There are no emissions limits for incidental radiators – only a provision that they not cause harmful interference to licensed radio services. Once again, the burden to correct any harmful interference caused by these devices falls on the operator of the device.

EQUIPMENT AUTHORIZATION

FCC regulations do not require Part 15 devices to be tested by the FCC. In fact, very few devices must actually undergo FCC testing. In most cases, the requirements are met by the manufacturer testing the device and the test results either kept on file or sent to the FCC, depending on the type of device involved. Here is some general information concerning various FCC approval processes for RF devices:

• *Certification:* Requires submittal of an application that includes a complete technical description of the product and a measurement report showing compliance with the FCC technical standards. Certification procedures have now largely replaced the once familiar Type Acceptance, which is no longer used by the FCC. Devices subject to certification include: low-power transmitters such as cordless telephones, security alarm systems, scanning receivers, super-regenerative receivers, Amateur Radio external HF amplifiers and amplifier kits, and TV interface devices such as DVD players.

• *Declaration of Conformity (DoC)*: Is a declaration that the equipment complies with FCC requirements. A DoC is an alternative to certification since no application to FCC is required, but the applicant must have the device tested at an accredited laboratory. A Declaration of Conformity is the usual approval procedure for Class B personal computers and personal computer peripherals.

• *Notification*: Requires submittal to the FCC of an abbreviated application for equipment authorization which does not include a measurement report. However, a measurement report showing compliance of the product with the FCC technical standards must be retained by the applicant and must be submitted upon request by the Commission. Devices subject to notification include: point-to-point microwave transmitters, AM, FM and TV broadcast transmitters and other receivers (except as noted elsewhere).

• *Verification*: Verification is a self-approval process where the applicant performs the necessary tests and verifies that they have been done on the device to be authorized and that the device is in compliance with the technical standards. Verified equipment requires that a compliance label be affixed to the device as well as information included in the operating manual regarding the interference potential of the device. Devices subject to verification include: business computer equipment (Class A); TV and FM receivers; and non-consumer Industrial, Scientific and Medical Equipment.

PART 15 OPERATOR REQUIREMENTS

All Part 15 devices are prohibited from causing harmful interference to a licensed radio service — including the Amateur Radio Service. This is an absolute requirement without regard to the emitter type or a manufacturer's conformance to emissions limits or other FCC technical standards. It is important to note that the manufacturer's requirements are not sufficient to prevent harmful interference from occurring under all circumstances. If and when a Part 15 device generates harmful interference, it becomes the responsibility of the device operator to correct the problem. Upon notice from the FCC, the device operator may also be required to cease using the device until such time as the interference has been corrected.

PART 15 INTERFERENCE IMMUNITY

Licensed radio services, including Amateur Radio, are guaranteed absolute protection from harmful interference caused by Part 15 devices. There is a similar provision for Part 18 devices unless the affected amateur frequency happens to also be an ISM band (such as the 902 MHz band.) So what's the problem?

First, the emissions limits for most electronic consumer equipment are not low enough to protect nearby radio receivers from harmful interference. The only way to know for sure is to test the device that is causing the problem, which is expensive and not practical. Even then, most of the reported interference sources tested at the ARRL Laboratory actually meet the emissions limits.

As a result, most RFI cases are actually argued on basis of harmful interference as opposed to exceeding the specified emission limits. The rules place the burden to correct the interference on device operator — not manufacturer. Typically the operator is either the ham or a neighbor.

So, if the source is found to be in the ham's residence, he or she is responsible for fixing the problem. (The FCC historically is not sympathetic if you own the device.) And if the operator proves to be a neighbor, the problem can become even worse. The ham is now confronted with a potentially awkward and difficult situation with his neighbor, often stretching his or her diplomacy skills to their limit. Should the neighbor refuse to cooperate, the case can drag on for a considerable period of time, even with FCC intervention.

Another potential issue for the ham centers on the meaning of "harmful interference." Paraphrasing, the FCC rules (both Parts 2 and 15) define harmful interference as a repeated disruption of intended radio communications. If and when an RFI complaint results in an FCC field investigation, this determination is made by the agent conducting the investigation. The ham and agent may not agree as to whether or not his or her problem meets the FCC's definition to be considered harmful. (In fact, the ARRL has seen one case in which a particular case in which it went both ways for the ham. There were two investigations about a year apart. Each investigator came to a different conclusion concerning the same case — and both were from the same field office.)

Finally, it is important to emphasize that the rules don't specify who must actually find the noise source(s). The FCC doesn't have the resources to do RFI locating, at least in a timely and consistent fashion. The reality in the case of consumer a device is that the burden to find it falls on the affected ham. In the case of power line noise, the utility is responsible for finding and fixing the problem. However, many utilities lack the necessary personnel and equipment to locate noise sources in a timely manner. The ARRL has seen cases some such cases drag on for years.

RF Interference and the FCC

by Riley Hollingsworth, K4ZDH (retired Special Counsel to the FCC Enforcement Bureau)

Since 1999, the FCC has worked with the ARRL in a cooperative agreement whereby the staff at the ARRL Lab takes the first cut at resolving RFI. The lab works with the complainant to make sure that the noise is narrowed down to the most probable source. The success rate with this program has been very high, and in many cases — perhaps most — the ARRL and the complainant solve the problem without any FCC involvement.

The lab can help you with the proper testing you need to do in your shack and with the documentation you need in the event the matter is referred to the FCC. I was always amazed at the number of situations in which noise that at first seemed to be power line related, was in fact (these are real examples) a nearby electric fence, a battery charger for a golf cart, an Ethernet adapter, a paper shredder or a circuit board in a brand new clothes washer in a room adjacent to the radio shack.

Don't assume anything. Test every possibility and document your testing. Not only will you learn a lot about the devices in your house and what causes noise and what doesn't, but good documentation will make your case stronger and easier to work. Follow to the letter the ARRL articles and website tutorials on tracking down noise in and around your shack. You can even hear noise samples on the website.

The documentation requirement is especially important if it is power line related and you have to start dealing with the power company. Take notes of every call you make, who you talked to and when. This helps not only the power company but also the FCC in the unfortunate event that FCC action is required. In many cases, power company staff has a lot of experience running down such noise and they take pride in locating it. In other cases, the power company has been bought, sold, merged or whatever and does not have staff with a lot of experience in these matters. Sometimes its staff has no experience.

The cost of the equipment required to track down power line noise is less than that of two employees and a bucket truck for a day. Often the source of power line noise is a simple piece of equipment that is loose or about to fail, so finding the source helps the power company maintain its system. Keep in mind, though, that some areas are just not suitable for Amateur Radio. If you live next to an old substation, or a conglomeration of old poles and transformers, or an industrial area, your situation is tenuous. Whether it's our roads or power grids, lots of the infrastructure in this country is just plain old and out of date.

You must test diligently and document thoroughly. Never go to the FCC with a situation when you have not already worked with the ARRL and the power company.

27.3 Elements of RFI

27.3.1 Source-Path-Victim

All cases of RFI involve a *source* of radio frequency energy, a device that responds to the electromagnetic energy (*victim*), and a transmission *path* that allows energy to flow from the source to the victim. Sources include radio transmitters, receiver local oscillators, computing devices, electrical noise, lightning and other natural sources. Note that receiving unwanted electromagnetic energy does not necessarily cause the victim to function improperly.

A device is said to be *immune* to a specific source if it functions properly in the presence of electromagnetic energy from the source. In fact, designing devices for various levels of immunity is one aspect of electromagnetic compatibility engineering. Only when the victim experiences a *disturbance* in its function as a consequence of the received electromagnetic energy does RFI exist. In this case, the victim device is *susceptible* to RFI from that source.

There are several ways that RFI can travel from the source to the victim: *radiation*, *conduction*, *inductive coupling* and *capacitive coupling*. *Radiated RFI* propagates by electromagnetic radiation from the source through space to the victim. *Conducted RFI* travels over a physical conducting path between the source and the victim, such as wires, enclosures, ground planes, and so forth. Inductive coupling occurs when two circuits are magnetically coupled. Capacitive coupling occurs when two circuits are coupled electrically through capacitance. Typical RFI problems you are likely to encounter often include multiple paths, such as conduction and radiation. (See the section Shields and Filters, also Ott, sections 2.1-2.3.)

Many instances of RFI are a combination of radiated and conducted RFI. Conducted RFI exits the source as current on one or more conductors connected to the source. The conductors act as transmitting antennas for the common-mode current which creates radiated signals. A conductor connected to the victim then picks up the radiated signal where the resulting common-mode current is conducted to the victim.

27.3.2 Differential-Mode vs Common-Mode Signals

The path from source to victim almost always includes some conducting portion, such as wires or cables. RF energy can be conducted directly from source to victim, be conducted onto a wire or cable that acts as an antenna where it is radiated, or be picked up by a conductor connected to the victim that acts like an antenna. When the noise signal is traveling along the conducted portion of the path, it is important to understand the differences between *differential-mode* and *common-mode* conducted signals (see **Figure 27.3**).

Differential-mode signals usually have two easily identified conductors. In a two-wire transmission line, for example, the signal leaves the generator on one wire and returns on the other. When the two conductors are in close proximity, they form a transmission line and the two signals have opposite polarities as shown in Figure 27.3A. Most desired signals, such as the TV signal inside a coaxial cable or an Ethernet signal carried on CAT5 network cable, are conducted as differential-mode signals.

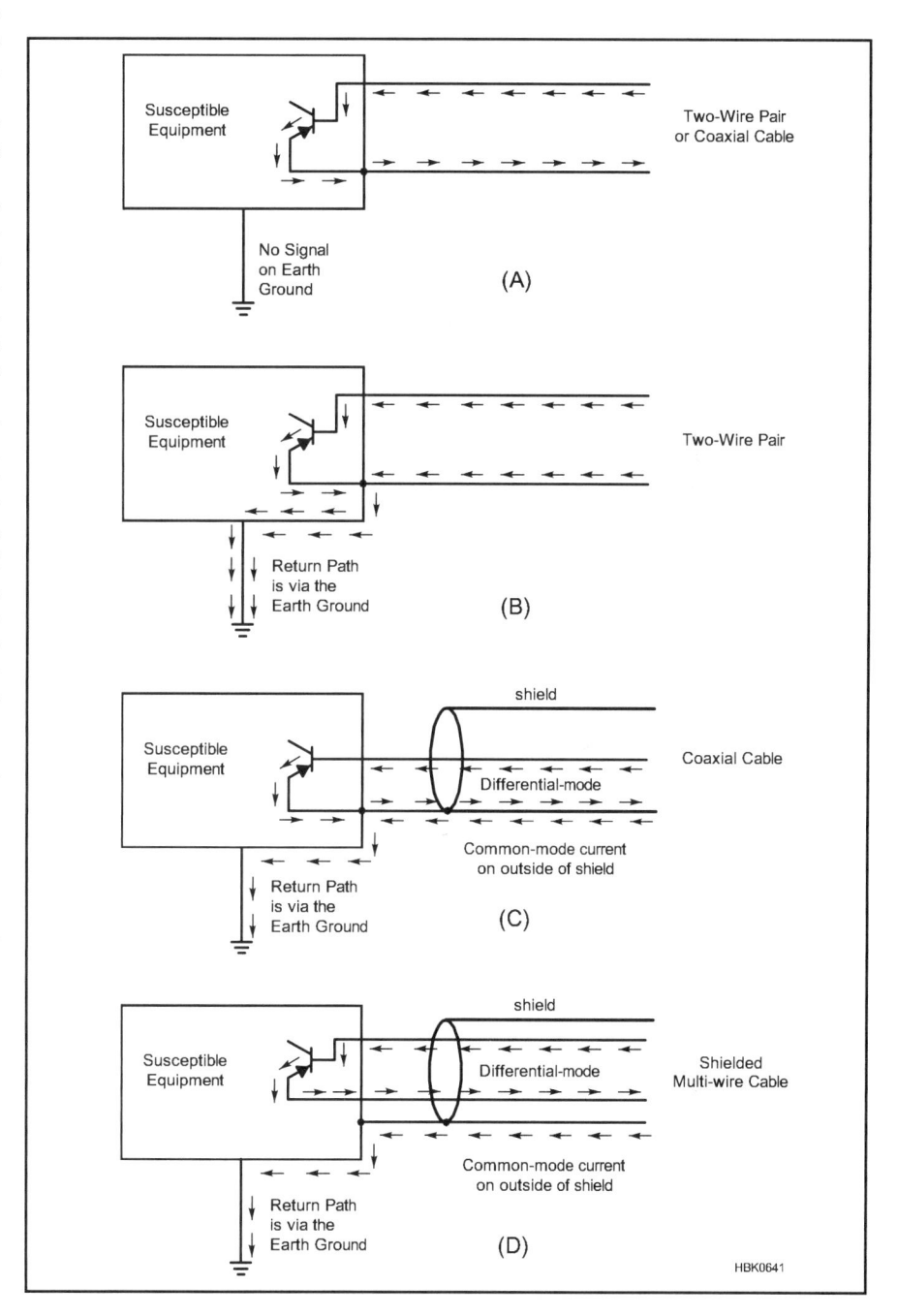

Figure 27.3 — Typical configurations of common-mode and differential-mode current. The drawing in A shows the currents of a differential-mode signal while B shows a common-mode signal with currents flowing equally on all of the source wires. In C, a common-mode signal flows on the outside of a coaxial cable shield with a differential-mode signal inside the cable. In D, the differential-mode signal, such as a data signal with a dedicated return circuit, flows on the internal wires while a common-mode signal flows on the outside of the cable shield.

A common-mode circuit consists of two or more wires in a multi-wire cable acting as if they were a single signal path as in Figure 27.3B. Common-mode circuits also exist when the outside surface of a cable's shield acts as a conductor as in Figures 27.3C and 27.3D. (See the chapter on **Transmission Lines** for a discussion about isolation between the shield's inner and outer surfaces for RF signals.) The return path for a common-mode signal often involves earth ground. Common-mode currents are the net result of currents for which there is not an equal-and-opposite current in the same conductors or group of conductors

Figure 27.3D illustrates the case for a signal and its return path both enclosed in a separate shield. This is a common arrangement for digital data or control signals in a multiconductor cable with a dedicated signal return or signal ground wire. The cable shield should be kept separate from all data and data return connections.

External noise generated by electronic equipment and RFI caused to electronic equipment is often associated with common-mode current on a cable shield that is improperly connected. For example, consider what happens when the cable shield in Figures 27.3C and 27.3D is not connected to the enclosure but enters the device before connecting to a circuit's common or ground connection. In this case, any noise generated by the circuit has a path out of the enclosure and on to the surface of the cable shield where it is then radiated. Similarly, any noise or signals picked up by the cable shield are conducted into the equipment where it is connected to the circuit and can disrupt normal operation or interfere with the desired signals. This is discussed more in this chapter's section Elements of RFI Control.

COMMON-MODE AND POWER WIRING

There is an important difference between the preceding definition and what ac power companies consider common-mode. Corcom is a major manufacturer of power line RFI filters and related components. (See **www.te.com/usa-en/products/emi-filters/power-line-filters.html**.) Common-mode is defined in their Product Guide's appendix on "Understanding Insertion Loss," as "signals present on both sides of the line (hot and neutral) referenced to ground." The RF definition of common-mode in this book includes signals on the ground conductor, as well.

What this means is that a typical ac-line filter may be ineffective against common-mode RF flowing on the ground conductor. The ground connection is typically carried through a power-line RFI filter as a direct connection. To block RF on the ground conductor of a three-wire ac power cord or cable, the usual remedy is to wind the cord on a ferrite core. This places an impedance in all three conductors, not just hot and neutral. (See the sidebar "Differential-Mode and Common-Mode Current and RFI Filtering" by W1RFI in the section Elements of RFI Control.)

Power Inverters and Conducted Emissions Limits

Some electronic devices intentionally generate internal RF but do not intentionally radiate it. For example, the RF generated by computers, televisions, radio receivers, and switch-mode power supplies (SMPS) is intentional and necessary for such devices to function. Although the RF is intentionally generated by these devices, they do *not* intentionally radiate it. Under Part 15 of the FCC rules, these are defined as *unintentional emitters*.

Like all Part 15 devices, unintentional emitters must not cause harmful interfere to a licensed radio service. In addition, Part 15 rules further establish the following two types of absolute limits for unintentional emitters:

• *Conducted emissions* — emissions conducted onto the house wiring and power lines via the device power cord. Part 15 provides absolute limits for conducted emissions from 150 kHz to 30 MHz. There are no conducted emissions limits above 30 MHz, in part because power lines are not particularly good transmission lines at these higher frequencies. In addition, most Part 15 devices are small relative to the longer wavelengths below 30 MHz. Conducted emissions therefore become the primary problem when a physically larger RFI "antenna" is required at HF and lower frequencies.

• *Radiated emissions* — emissions radiated by the device itself. The absolute limits in this case are specified at 30 MHz and higher frequencies. It's important to note that there are no radiated emissions limits below 30 MHz. Since power lines are relatively inefficient "transmission lines" at VHF and higher frequencies, radiated emissions now become the primary problem. The relatively shorter wavelengths now start to approach the physical size of a typical Part 15 device at 30 MHz.

Conducted emissions rules and limits normally only apply to devices that plug into house wiring. Inverters, however, convert dc power from batteries and solar panels into ac power. In this case, inverters *are* the ac power source, and as such, not connected to house wiring and power lines. Emissions from power inverters are therefore not considered "conducted emissions" as defined by the FCC rules.

Although the usual limits don't apply in this case, they are conducted emissions in every other respect. Fortunately the shorter power lines typically associated with inverters reduce the potential for interference from conducted emissions. Using one to power an amateur station, however, can be a particularly demanding application. For this reason, the ARRL Lab staff felt typical Part 15 conducted emissions testing, using standard procedures and instruments, would be useful when evaluating inverters. The data correlates directly with other unintentional emitters and the FCC limits.

At the ARRL Laboratory we use a LISN (Line Impedance Stabilization Network) and a calibrated Rohde & Schwarz ESH-3 EMC receiver to measure conducted emissions. Normally, the device under test is plugged into the LISN, which separates the unwanted RF from the desired 60 Hz ac power. The conducted emissions are then measured by the special Rohde & Schwarz receiver using quasi-peak detection (AM, 9 kHz bandwidth, designed to access the effect of interference of a received signal to the human ear). In the case of power inverters, however, the LISN is plugged into the power inverter. In order to accomplish this, we used a set of adapter cables to reverse the LISN input and output. In the case of the power inverter test, we used the LISN as described in ANSI Standard C63.4-2003, page 10, Figure 2.

The table below lists the Part 15 conducted emissions limits. Note that the limits are expressed in dBµV, or dB relative to a microvolt. In this case, 1000 µV of signal equals +60 dBµV.

Frequency	dBµV, quasi-peak detection
0.150 – 0.5 MHz	66 to 56*
0.5 – 5.0	56
5.0 – 30.0	60
>30.0	None

*Decreases with the logarithm of the frequency.

It is important to note that these limits are not low enough to eliminate the possibility of interference but rather localize it. With power inverters, one may hear a buzzing sound across the LF, MF and HF spectrum. Besides conducted emissions levels, the severity of the interference can also depend upon such things as the placement and characteristics of the power cords and distance from the antenna. The lower the conducted emissions level, the better. — *Bob Allison, WB1GCM, ARRL Laboratory Assistant Manager*

27.3.3 Types of RFI

There are four basic types of RFI that apply to Amateur Radio. The first two occur in the following order of likelihood when the interfering source is the transmitted signal from an amateur transmitter:

1) *Fundamental Overload* — Disruption or degradation of a device's function in the presence of a transmitter's fundamental signal (the intended signal from the transmitter). This can happen because the fundamental is simply too strong for the victim device's circuitry to reject — a true overload situation. It can also happen because of *common-mode ingress* in which the strong signal is picked up as common-mode current on an external cable which is then conducted into the victim device's circuitry. A third variation is *direct pickup* or *direct detection* in which the interfering signal is picked up by the victim device's internal wiring. The appropriate remedy must be used for each mechanism.

2) *Spurious Emissions* — Reception of a radio signal interfered with by spurious emissions from the transmitter as defined in the previous section on Part 97 definitions and Figure 27.1.

The second two types of RFI occur, again in order of likelihood, when the reception of a desired signal is interfered with by RF energy received along with the desired signal.

3) *External Noise Sources* — Reception of a radio signal interfered with by RF energy transmitted incidentally or unintentionally by a device that is not a licensed transmitter

4) *Intermodulation* — Reception of a radio signal interfered with by intermodulation distortion (IMD) products generated inside or outside of the receiver

As an RFI troubleshooter, start by determining which of these is involved in your interference problem. Once you know the type of RFI, selecting the most appropriate cure for the problem becomes much easier.

27.3.4 Fundamental Overload

Most cases of interference caused by an amateur transmission are due to *fundamental overload*. The world is filled with RF signals. Properly designed radio receivers of any sort should be able to select the desired signal, while rejecting all others. Unfortunately, because of design deficiencies such as inadequate shields or filters, some radio receivers are unable to reject strong out-of-band signals. Electronic equipment that is not a radio receiver can also suffer from fundamental overload from similar design shortcomings. Both types of fundamental overload are common in consumer electronics.

A strong signal can enter equipment in several different ways. Most commonly, it is conducted into the equipment by connecting wires and cables. Possible RFI conductors include antennas and feed lines, interconnecting cables, power cords, and ground wires. TV antennas and feed lines, telephone or speaker wiring and ac power cords are the most common points of entry.

If the problem is a case of fundamental overload, significant improvement can often be observed just by moving the victim equipment's antenna and the signal source farther away from each other. The effect of an interfering signal is directly related to its strength, diminishing with the square of the distance from the source. If the distance from the source doubles, the strength of the electromagnetic field decreases to one-fourth of its power density at the original distance from the source. An attenuator is often a weapon of choice when encountering this type of problem. Reducing the level of the offending strong signal returns the receiver to normal operation and causes the undesirable effects to disappear. This characteristic can often be used to help identify an RFI problem as fundamental overload. If reducing the strength of the signal source causes the same effect that is also a signature of fundamental overload.

27.3.5 Spurious Emissions

All transmitters generate some (hopefully few) RF signals that are outside their intended transmission bandwidth — out-of-band emissions and spurious emissions as illustrated in Figure 27.1. Out-of-band signals result from distortion in the modulation process or consist of broadband noise generated by the transmitter's oscillators that is radiated along with the intended signal. Harmonics, the most common spurious emissions, are signals at integer multiples of the operating (or fundamental) frequency.

Transmitters may also produce broadband noise and/or parasitic oscillations as spurious emissions. (Parasitic oscillations are discussed in the **RF Power Amplifiers** chapter.) Overdriving an amplifier often creates spurious emissions. Amplifiers not meeting FCC certification standards but sold illegally are frequent sources of spurious emissions.

Regardless of how the unwanted signals are created, if they cause interference, FCC regulations require the operator of the transmitter to correct the problem. The usual cure is to adjust or repair the transmitter or use filters at the transmitter output to block the spurious emissions from being radiated by the antenna.

27.3.6 External Noise Sources

Most cases of interference to the Amateur Service reported to the FCC are eventually determined to involve some sort of external noise source, rather than signals from a radio transmitter. Noise in this sense means an RF signal that is not essential to the generating device's operation.

The most common external noise sources are electrical, primarily power lines. Motors and switching equipment can also generate electrical noise. Noise radiated by switch-mode systems such as power supplies, digital equipment, and variable-speed drives is increasingly common.

External noise can also come from unlicensed Part 15 RF sources such as computers and networking equipment, video games, appliances, and other types of consumer electronics.

Regardless of the source, if you determine the problem to be caused by external noise, elimination of the noise must take place at the source. As an alternative, several manufacturers also make noise canceling devices that can help in some circumstances.

27.3.7 Intermodulation Distortion

As discussed in the chapter on **Receiving**, intermodulation distortion (IMD) is caused by two signals combining in such a way as to create *intermodulation products* — signals at various combinations of the two original frequencies. The two original signals may be perfectly legal, but the resulting *intermodulation distortion products* may occur on the frequencies used by other signals and cause interference in the same way as a spurious signal from a transmitter. Depending on the nature of the generating signals, "intermod" can be intermittent or continuous. IMD can be generated inside a receiver by large signals or externally by signals mixing together in non-linear junctions or connections.

27.3.8 Ground Connections

An electrical ground is not a huge sink that somehow swallows noise and unwanted signals. Ground is a *circuit* concept, whether the circuit is small, like a radio receiver, or large, like the propagation path between a transmitter and AM/FM receiver. Ground forms a universal reference point between circuits.

While grounding is not a cure-all for RFI problems, ground is an important safety component of any electronics installation. It is part of the lightning protection system in your station and a critical safety component of your house wiring. Any changes made to a grounding system must not compromise these important safety considerations. Refer to the **Safety** chapter for important information about grounding. The ARRL book *Grounding and Bonding for the Radio Amateur* also goes into detail about ground systems for electrical safety, lightning protection, and managing RF voltages and currents.

Many amateur stations have several connections referred to as "grounds"; the required safety ground that is part of the ac wiring system, another required connection to earth for lightning protection, and perhaps another shared connection between equipment for RFI control. These connections can interact with each other in ways that are difficult to predict. Rearranging the station ground connections may cure some RFI problems in the station by changing the RF current distribution so that the affected equipment is at a low-impedance point and away from RF "hot spots." It is better to address the problem by implementing proper bonding within the station and to the station's ground system.

BONDING

Bonding refers to a connection intended to minimize potential (voltage) differences. The purpose of bonding in the amateur station is to minimize the potential difference between equipment and all elements of the ground system — ground rods, entry wiring for electrical power, telephone or data systems, cable or satellite TV systems, and amateur antennas. This minimizes voltage differences in the event of lightning surges. It also minimizes hum and buzz and reduces RFI resulting from voltage differences between pieces of equipment.

Creating a low-impedance connection between your station's equipment is easy to do and will help reduce voltage differences (and current flow) between pieces of equipment. Bonding is also discussed in this book's **Safety** chapter.

Bonding also reduces voltage differences between the ends of cable shields that are connected to different pieces of equipment. This voltage difference is effectively in series with the cable shield and can be added to the desired signals carried by the cable. The voltage difference can be at ac power, audio, or RF so bonding helps reduce RFI across a wide frequency range.

The conductors used for bonding should be heavy enough to have low inductance and resistance. The standard for commercial and military facilities is solid copper strap but heavy stranded or solid wire (bare or insulated) works well. Flat woven braid will also work if kept dry. Braid removed from coaxial cable is not recommended but is often used with good results.

Equipment enclosures should be connected either directly together as in **Figure 27.5** or by using a bonding bus or ground reference plane as shown in the chapter on **Assembling a Station**. Amateur Radio and home entertainment equipment usually has a ground screw or terminal. Chassis connections for many computers can be found at the shell of video or data connectors.

LENGTH OF GROUND CONNECTIONS

The required ground connection for lightning protection between the station equipment and an outside ground rod is at least several feet long in most practical installations. (See the **Safety** chapter for safety and lightning protection ground requirements.)

In general, however, a long connection to earth should be considered as part of an RFI problem only to the extent that it is part of the antenna system. For example, should a long-wire HF antenna end in the station, a ground connection of *any* length is a necessary and useful part of that antenna and will radiate RF.

At VHF a ground wire can be several wavelengths long — a very effective antenna for any harmonics that could cause RFI! For example, in **Figure 27.4**, signals radiated from the required safety ground wire could very easily create an interference problem in the downstairs electronic equipment.

GROUND LOOPS, HUM, AND BUZZ

A *ground loop* is created by a continuous conductive path around a series of equipment enclosures. While this does create an opportunity for lightning and RFI susceptibility, the ground loop itself is rarely a cause of problems at RF. Problems created by loops

Figure 27.4 — An earth ground connection can radiate signals that might cause RFI to nearby equipment. This can happen if the ground connection is part of an antenna system or if it is connected to a coaxial feed line carrying RF current on the outside of the shield.

RFI and End-Fed Antennas

An end-fed antenna brought directly into the station is often adjusted to produce a current-maximum (low-impedance point) at the feed point. The feed point is often the output of an antenna tuner so the feed point is actually *in* the station. If a resonant counterpoise is not attached to the tuner, the resulting current will couple to and flow on whatever conductors happen to be connected to or close to the enclosures of the transmitter and tuner, including ground system and signal connections. Common-mode current on the outside of an antenna feed line can act in the same way. To address this situation, make sure equipment is bonded together properly, as well as the ground system, and provide the necessary counterpoise for the end-fed wire or a common-mode choke for the antenna feed line (see the **Transmission Lines** chapter).

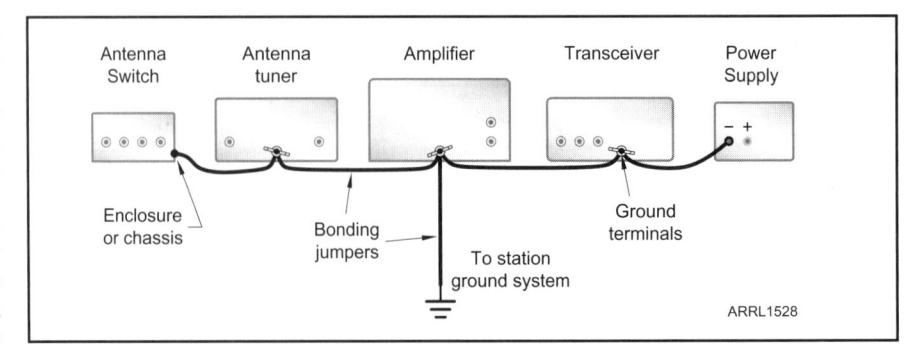

Figure 27.5 — Direct equipment-to-equipment bonding. Use heavy wire or strap connected to a single ground terminal or enclosure screw on each piece of equipment, including computers and related gear. The same approach can be used in home entertainment systems or with computers and accessories.

picking up RF signals are addressed by proper bonding of equipment and by minimizing the loop area formed by cables and wiring.

Ground loops are usually associated with audio hum caused by coupling to power-frequency magnetic fields from transformers or motors and sometimes from coupling to high-current power wiring. The hum appears as a nearly-pure sine wave at the frequency of the ac power system, 50 or 60 Hz. To avoid low-frequency ground-loop issues, use short cables that are the minimum length required to connect the equipment and bundle them together to minimize the area of any enclosed loop. Moving the cables away from the source of the magnetic field or reorienting the source or cables can reduce hum. Bonding equipment together to short-circuit a loop is sometimes effective.

Audio "buzz" is caused primarily by currents at harmonics of the ac power frequency. The current results from leakage in ac-powered equipment with rectifiers or switching circuits that conduct during parts of the ac power waveform. Buzz is addressed by bonding and by insuring the ac power ground connections have a minimum of these voltages on them.

27.4 Identifying the Type of RFI Source

It is useful to recognize an offending noise source as one of several broad categories at the early stages of any RFI investigation. Since locating and resolution techniques can vary somewhat for each type of noise, the process of locating and resolving RFI problems begins with identifying the *general* type of RFI source. It is not useful, however, to go farther and attempt to identify a particular type of equipment or device at the beginning of the search. The purpose of this section is to help you determine the general category of the noise being received and choose the right set of tools and methods to locate the source of the noise.

It is often impossible to identify the exact type of device generating the RFI from the sound of the interference. Because there are many potential sources of RFI, it is often more important to obtain and interpret clues from the general noise characteristics and the patterns in which it appears.

A source that exhibits a repeatable pattern during the course of a day or week, for example, suggests something associated with human activity. A sound that varies with or is affected by weather suggests an outdoor source. Noise that occurs in a regular and repeating pattern of peaks and nulls as you tune across the spectrum, every 50 kHz for example, is often associated with a switch-mode power supply or similar pulsed-current devices. A source that exhibits fading or other sky wave characteristics suggests something that is not local. A good ear and careful attention to detail will often turn up some important clues. A detailed RFI log can often help, especially if maintained over time.

BROADBAND AND NARROWBAND NOISE

Noise can be characterized as broadband or narrowband — another important clue. *Broadband noise* is defined as noise having a bandwidth much greater than the affected receiver's operating bandwidth and is reasonably uniform across a wide frequency range. Noise from arcs and sparks, such as power-line noise, tend to be broadband. *Narrowband noise* is defined as noise having a bandwidth less than the affected receiver's bandwidth. Narrowband noise is present on specific, discrete frequencies or groups of frequencies, with or without additional modulation. In other words, if you listened to the noise on an SSB receiver, tuning would cause its sound to vary, just like a regular signal. Narrowband noise often sounds like an unmodulated carrier with a frequency that may drift or suddenly change. Microprocessor clock harmonics, oscillators and transmitter harmonics are all examples of narrowband noise.

27.4.1 Identifying Noise from Part 15 Devices

The most common RFI problem reported to the ARRL comes from an unknown and unidentified source. Part 15 devices and other consumer equipment noise sources are ubiquitous. Although the absolute signal level from an individual noise source may be small, their increasing numbers makes this type of noise a serious problem in many suburban and urban areas. The following paragraphs describe several common types of electronic noise sources.

Electronic devices containing oscillators, microprocessors, or digital circuitry produce RF signals as a byproduct of their operation. The RF noise they produce may be radiated from internal wiring as a result of poor shielding. The noise may also be conducted to external, unshielded or improperly shielded wiring as a common-mode signal where it radiates noise. Noise from these devices is usually narrowband that changes characteristics (frequency, modulation, on-off pattern) as the device is

---

Common Mistake — What Is It?

When someone has an unusual RFI problem, the first question he or she almost always asks is: What is it? That's an interesting question, and you may need to ask it during the troubleshooting process, but it is not the first question you should ask. Even if someone were to say that it's a Model XYZ Panashibi switching power supply, what would that tell you? You would still have to go into the world and find it. It could be useful, though, to know whether you are searching for a switching power supply, DSL or cable leakage, or a plasma TV. But be general, not specific, because you don't want to be misled. — *Ed Hare, W1RFI, ARRL Lab Manager* (An extended version of this sidebar is available on this book's supplemental material online.)

Keeping an RFI Log

The importance of maintaining a good and accurate RFI log cannot be overstated. Be sure to record time and weather conditions. Correlating the presence of the noise with periods of human activity and weather often provide very important clues when trying to identify power-line noise. It can also be helpful in identifying noise that is being propagated to your station via sky wave. A log showing the history of the noise can also be of great value should professional services or FCC involvement become necessary at some point.

used in different ways. HF and lower frequency problems are typically caused by conducted emissions although they may travel to the victim as radiated signals. As we'll see, the cure in these cases usually involves common-mode chokes and filters. At VHF and higher frequencies, the probable cause is radiated emissions from the source device. In these cases, shielding is often the solution of choice.

Another major class of noise source is equipment or systems that control or switch large currents. Among them are variable-speed motors in products as diverse as washing machines, elevators, and heating and cooling systems. Charging regulators and control circuitry for battery and solar power systems are a prolific source of RF noise. So are switchmode power supplies for computers and low-voltage lighting. This type of noise is only present when the equipment is operating.

Switchmode supplies, solar controllers and inverters often produce noise signals every N kHz, with N typically being from 5 to 50 or more kHz, the frequency at which current is switched. This is different from noise produced by spark or arc sources that is uniform across a wide bandwidth. This pattern is often an important clue in distinguishing switching noise from power-line or electrical noise.

Wired computer networks radiate noise directly from their unshielded circuitry and from network and power supply cables. The noise takes two forms — broadband noise and modulated carriers at multiple frequencies within the amateur bands. As an example, Ethernet network interfaces often radiate signals heard on a receiver in CW mode. 10.120, 14.030, 21.052 and 28.016 MHz have been reported as frequencies of RFI from Ethernet networks. Each network interface uses its own clock, so if you have neighbors with networks you'll hear a cluster of carriers around these frequencies, ±500 Hz or so.

In cable TV systems video signals are converted to RF across a wide spectrum and distributed by coaxial cable into the home. Some cable channels overlap with amateur bands, but the signals should be confined within the cable system. No system is perfect, and it is common for a defective coax connection to allow leakage to and from the cable. When this happens, a receiver outside the cable will hear RF from the cable and the TV receiver may experience interference from local transmissions. Interference to and from cable TV signals is discussed in detail later in this chapter.

27.4.2 Identifying Power-line and Electrical Noise

POWER-LINE NOISE

Next to external noise from an unknown source, the most frequent cause of an RFI problem reported to the ARRL involving a known source is power-line noise. (For more information on power-line noise, see the book *AC Power Interference Handbook*, by Marv Loftness, KB7KK.) Virtually all power-line noise originating from utility equipment is caused by spark or arcing across some hardware connected to or near a power line. A breakdown and ionization of air occurs and current flows across a gap between two conductors, creating RF noise as shown in **Figure 27.6**. Such noise is often referred to as "gap noise" in the utility power industry. The gap may be caused by broken, improperly installed or loose hardware. Typical culprits include insufficient and inadequate hardware spacing such as a gap between a ground wire and a staple. Contrary to common misconception, corona discharge is almost never a source of power-line noise.

While there may not be one single conclusive test for power-line noise, there are a number of important tell-tale signs. On an AM or SSB receiver, the characteristic raspy buzz or frying sound, sometimes changing in intensity as the arc or spark sputters a bit, is often the first and most obvious clue.

Power-line noise is typically a broadband type of interference, relatively constant across a wide spectrum. Since it is broadband noise, you simply can't change frequency to eliminate it. Power-line noise is usually, but not always, stronger on lower frequencies. It occurs continuously across each band and up through the spectrum. It can cause interference from below the AM broadcast band through UHF, gradually tapering off as frequency increases. If the noise is not continuous across all of an amateur band, exhibits a pattern of peaks and nulls at different frequencies, or repeats at some frequency interval, you probably do not have power-line noise.

The frequency at which power-line noise diminishes can also provide an important clue as to its proximity. The closer the source, the higher the frequency at which it can be received. If it affects VHF and UHF, the source is relatively close by. If it drops off just above or within the AM broadcast band, it may be located some distance away — up to several miles.

Power-line noise is often affected by weather if the source is outdoors. It frequently changes during rain or humid conditions, for example, either increasing or decreasing in response to moisture. Wind may also create fluctuations or interruptions as a result of line and hardware movement. Temperature effects can also result from thermal expansion and contraction.

Another good test for power-line noise requires an oscilloscope. Remember that power-line noise occurs in bursts most frequently at a rate of 120 bursts per second and sometimes at 60 bursts per second. Observe the suspect noise from your radio's audio output. (Note: The record output jack works best if available). Use the AM mode with wide filter settings and tune to a frequency without a station so the noise can be heard clearly. Use the LINE setting of the oscilloscope's trigger subsystem to synchronize the sweep to the line. Power-line noise bursts will remain stable on the display and should repeat every 8.33 ms (a 120-Hz repetition rate) or less commonly, 16.67 ms (60 Hz), if the gap is only arcing once per cycle. (This assumes the North American power-line frequency of 60 Hz.) See **Figure 27.7** for an explanation. If

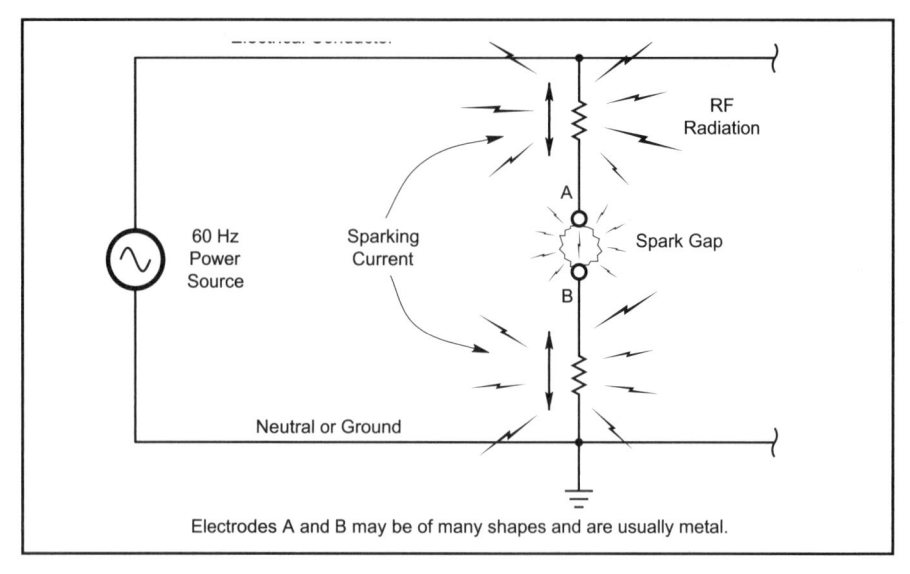

Figure 27.6 — The gap noise circuit on a power line — simplified. (From Loftness, *AC Power Interference Handbook*)

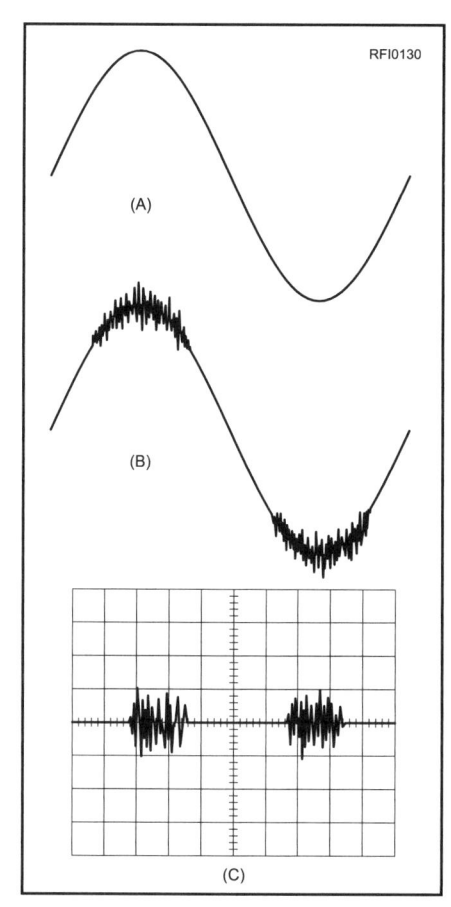

Figure 27.7 — The 60-Hz signal found on quiet power lines is almost a pure sine wave, as shown in A. If the line, or a device connected to it, is noisy, this will often add visible noise to the power-line signal, as shown in B. This noise is usually strongest at the positive and negative peaks of the sine wave where line voltage is highest. If the radiated noise is observed on an oscilloscope, the noise will be present during the peaks, as shown in C.

a noise does not exhibit either of these characteristics, it is probably not power-line noise.

If a local TV station is transmitting analog TV signals on a lower VHF channel (very few remain as of early 2018), additional clues may be obtained by viewing the noise pattern on an analog TV set (if you still have one) using an antenna (not a cable TV connection). Power-line noise usually appears as two horizontal bars that drift slowly upward on the screen through the picture. (This is due to the difference between the NTSC signal's 59.94 Hz field rate and the 60 Hz power-line frequency.) As one bar rolls off the screen at the top of the display, a new one simultaneously forms at the bottom. In cases where the noise is occurring at 60 bursts per second, there will be only one bar on the display. In addition, the power-line noise bursts may have slightly different characteristics at the positive and negative peaks. This can cause each half of the cycle to have a slightly different pattern on the screen.

ELECTRICAL NOISE

Electrical noise sounds like power-line noise, but is generally only present in short bursts or during periods when the generating equipment or machinery is in use. Noise that varies with the time of day, such as daytime-only or weekends-only, usually indicates some electrical device or appliance being used on a regular basis and not power-line noise. Unless it is associated with climate control or HVAC system, an indoor RFI source of electrical noise less likely to be affected by weather than power-line noise.

ELECTRIC FENCES

A special type of electrical noise that is easy to identify is the "pop…pop…pop" of an electric fence. High voltage is applied to the fence about once a second by a charging unit. Arcs will occur at corroded connections in the fence, such as at a gate hook or splice. If brush or weeds touch the fence, the high-voltage will cause an arc at those points until the vegetation burns away (the arc will return when the vegetation re-grows). Each arc results in a short burst of broadband noise, received as a "tick" or "pop" in an HF receiver.

27.4.3 Identifying Intermodulation Distortion (IMD)

IMD products generated from the mixing of two strong signals in a non-linear junction or circuit appear at frequencies that are combinations of the two signal frequencies. The process of combination can occur outside or inside the receiver. The resulting IMD product signals include the modulation of both signals. For example, intermodulation from two SSB or FM voice signals produces somewhat distorted signals with the modulating signals of both stations. Since the two signals are not synchronized, the intermodulation products come and go unpredictably, existing only when both of the external signals are present.

IMD GENERATED OUTSIDE A RECEIVER

Mixing of signals can occur in any non-linear junction where the original signals are both strong enough to cause current to flow in the junction. This is a particular problem at multi-transmitter sites, such as broadcast facilities and industrial or commercial communications sites. Non-linear junctions can be formed by loose mechanical contacts in metal hardware, corroded metal junctions, and by semiconductor junctions connected to wires that act as antennas for the strong signals. Non-linear junctions also detect or demodulate RF signals to varying degrees, creating interfering audio or dc signals in some cases. IMD products generated externally cannot be filtered out at the receiver and must be eliminated where the original signals are being combined.

An intermodulation product generated externally to a receiver often appears as an intermittent transmission, similar to a spurious emission. (See the **Receiving** chapter for more information on intermodulation.) It is common for strong signals from commercial paging or dispatch transmitters sharing a common antenna installation to combine and generate short bursts of voice or data signals. AM broadcast transmissions can combine to produce AM signals with the modulation from both stations audible.

An amateur station itself can be the source of strong signals that are picked up on various cables and wiring. The RF is then conducted into the station where it can encounter many types of diodes and transistors that act as the non-linear junctions. The resulting IMD product signals can then be conducted and radiated by the same cables and wiring that picked up the RF in the first place.

IMD can also be created in a broadcast FM or TV receiver or preamplifier. The solution is to add suitable filters or reduce overall signal levels and gain so that the strong interfering signal or signals can be processed linearly.

IMD GENERATED INSIDE A RECEIVER

Since the products are generated internally to the receiver, the strong signals must be filtered out or attenuated before they can enter the receiver circuits in which IMD products are generated. Like external intermodulation products, those generated by a receiver acting non-linearly appear as combinations of two

---

Common Mistake — The Source Must Be Illegal Because It's So Loud

The FCC limits for consumer electronics are not sufficient to protect against interference to nearby receivers. In a typical suburban neighborhood, the interference can be loud even from a neighboring residence. Proving they meet the applicable limits, these devices can be legally marketed and sold. If and when interference occurs, the burden then fall on the operator of the device to correct the problem.

Conclusion: Don't automatically assume that the device illegally exceeds the FCC limits just because it is causing harmful interference, even if it seems excessive. — *Mike Gruber, W1MG*

or more strong external signals. Intermodulation generated within a receiver can often be detected simply by activating the receiver's incoming signal attenuator. If attenuating the incoming signals causes the intermodulation product to by reduced in strength by a greater amount than that of the applied attenuation, intermodulation in the receiver is a strong possibility. Since receivers vary in their IMD performance, differences in the interfering signal strength between receivers is also an indication of intermodulation.

The following simple "attenuator test" can be used to identify an IMD product, even in cases where it appears similarly in multiple receivers. This procedure applies mainly to superheterodyne receivers with analog circuitry in the sensitive front-end stages. SDR receivers respond to strong signals somewhat differently, with a more abrupt transition between linear and non-linear operation.

• If your receiver does not have one, install a step attenuator at its RF input. If you use an attenuator internal to your receiver, it must attenuate the RF at the receiver's input.

• Tune the receiver to the suspected intermod product with the step attenuator set to 0 dB. Note the signal level.

• Add a known amount of attenuation to the signal. Typically 10 or 20 dB makes a good starting point for this test.

• If the suspect signal drops by more than the amount of added attenuation, the suspect signal is an IMD product. For example, if you add 10 dB of attenuation, and the signal drops by 30 dB, you have identified an IMD product.

• You can also compare the reduction in signal level between the suspect IMD product and a known genuine signal with and without the added attenuation. Use a known genuine signal that is about the same strength as the suspect signal with no added attenuation. If the suspect signal drops by the same as the added attenuation, it is not an IMD product.

Intermodulation distortion can be cured in a number of ways. The goal is to reduce the strength of the signals causing IMD so that the receiver circuits can process them linearly and without distortion.

If IMD is occurring in your receiver, filters that remove the strong unwanted signals causing the IMD while passing the desired signal are generally the best approach since they do not compromise receiver sensitivity. (The chapter on **Receiving** discusses how to add additional filtering to your receiver.) Turning off preamplifiers, adding or increasing the receiver's attenuation, and reducing its RF gain will reduce the signal strength in your receiver. Antenna tuners and external band-pass filters can also act as a filter to reduce IMD from out-of-band signals. Directional beams and antennas with a narrower bandwidth can also help, depending on the circumstances of your particular problem.

Common Mistake – Radiated vs. Conducted Emissions

The FCC does not impose radiated emissions limits below 30 MHz. There are only conducted emissions below 30 MHz. Specifically, the FCC requirements are for the RF conducted on the ac power connection, a power cord for most consumer devices. The limits in the case are expressed in terms of a voltage from both the phase (or "hot") conductor and neutral conductor to the ground conductor.

Note: Typical consumer devices are too small to be an effective antenna at HF. While the device may generate the RF, it doesn't radiate it. The actual radiation takes place from the wires and cables connected to the source device. The FCC rules in this regard only address the connection to ac power.

Above 30 MHz, the situation is reversed. There are no limits for conducted emissions — only for radiated emissions. The limits in this case are expressed as a field strength at a specified distance from the device. — *Mike Gruber, W1MG, ARRL Test Engineer*

27.5 Locating Sources of RFI

Once you have determined the *general* nature of the noise, it's time to find out where it's coming from. "Pinpoint the source precisely and you will know what it is." Good advice! There is no need to know exactly what the source is until it is found or narrowed down to a few possibilities. So the proper first question is, "How do I locate the source?"

Along with the material in this chapter, the Radio Direction Finding chapter of *The ARRL RFI Book*, describes the many methods available to locate sources. There are numerous websites with information about direction finding at all frequencies. This information helps educate the amateur that locating the source is the first step rather than speculating about what it might be.

Locating an offending device or noise source might sometimes seem like trying to find a needle in a haystack. With a little patience and know-how, it is often possible to find the source of a problem in relatively short order. RF detective work is often required and some cases require a little more perseverance than others. In any case, armed with some background and technique, it is often easier to find an offending source than the first-time RFI investigator might expect. Once the source is pinpointed and its exact nature is known, proper treatment can be applied to eliminate the RFI.

PREPARING TO FIND A SOURCE OF RFI

Consider the following questions:

1) First and foremost, does the searcher have an open mind? This kind of search is not a visual search until the structure containing the source is located. Even then, equipment must still be relied upon to pinpoint the source. An open mind means a willingness to trust the equipment and not waste time guessing or deviating from the search path to pursue something seen or guessed at.

2) Is the searcher equipped to produce useful results? A battery operated AM-FM-SW-VHF receiver with a useful signal strength indicator and a directional antenna suitable for a walking search that receives fairly well at the highest relevant frequency is essential. See the Power-line Noise section for examples of what works for that type of source. Handheld SDR receivers are now available that can act as a portable spectrum analyzer, as well.

3) Does the searcher know how to direction-find? The type of power lines or potential sources in the area is irrelevant at this point. Finding the structure that contains the source is the only objective. Only by trusting your equipment and using it correctly to lead you to the source will the job get done with a minimum of wasted time and effort.

Prospecting for RFI

By using several types of radios at the same time, you can characterize a wide area. For example, RFI professional KB4T uses the following radios when driving; the vehicle AM/FM radio tuned to 1710 kHz AM, an IC-7000 mobile HF transceiver tuned to 15 MHz AM (WWV), and an IC-2820 VHF receiver tuned to 121.500 MHz in AM mode. All three are operated unsquelched with the volume turned down so only a slight hiss is heard. A noise source will be very apparent on one or more of the radios when approached or passed.

---

4) Has the searcher done enough listening and record keeping to have a good idea when the source is active, the best (highest?) frequency at which to listen to hear and track the source. Information includes:
- Signal strength
- Highest frequency at which each source can be heard
- A simple description of each source's character
- Any other descriptive data
- Brief notes about weather conditions

If you can record the noise for a long period of time that shows the time as well as the noise, that will provide a lot of information about the source, as well.

5). Can it be decided what tools are best to locate the source? (Receiver, antenna, attenuator) Even if the right tools are in hand, mastery of them is essential. Make sure you know how to interpret the measurements or work with an experienced user to learn how.

NOISE SOURCE SIGNATURES

Be wary of assuming too much about a source based on what the interference "sounds like" on a receiver or even "looks like" on an oscilloscope or spectrum analyzer. At the beginning of the search, "keep it simple" by not making too many assumptions about the nature of the source. Once the location of a source has been determined, then you can begin to narrow the search based on the source's "fingerprint" or signature.

Keep an open mind, be deliberate in your search, and don't act on assumptions about what a source is or isn't until you have exhausted the search techniques. Much time has been wasted in looking for sources of RFI because of assuming a location or type of source at the beginning.

MULTIPLE NOISE SOURCES

Consider that the source may be more than a single piece of equipment! You might have power-line noise combined with switchmode power supply noise, for example. Trying to find the source based on the combination of noise signatures will be frustrating at best. Most suburban and urban locations have multiple noises active at any time. Survey the area to see if different sources are stronger in different areas.

Take careful notes about the nature and behavior of the source, then let your location-finding equipment lead you to each source in turn. It is often most productive to work on the strongest noise source first. Be prepared to discover there are multiple levels of noise sources — after dealing with the top-level source, you may find additional (and equally objectionable) sources remain. Be patient!

VERIFY NOISE IS EXTERNAL TO THE RADIO

Whenever an unknown source of interference becomes an issue, you can begin the process of identifying the source by verifying that the problem is external to your radio. This advice might not sound very useful but it can save you a lot of wasted time. Start by removing the antenna connection. If the noise disappears, the source is external to your radio and you are ready to begin hunting for the noise source.

27.5.1 Locating Noise Sources Inside Your Home

Professional RFI investigators and the experiences of the ARRL RFI desk confirm that most RFI sources are ultimately found to be in the complainant's home. Furthermore, locating an in-house source of RFI is so simple it that it makes sense to start an investigation by simply turning off your home's main circuit breaker while listening to the noise with a battery-powered portable radio.

Remember that battery-powered equipment may also be a noise source — turn off or disable battery-powered consumer devices, as well. If you have a UPS (uninterruptable power supply) it will continue to operate with ac power removed. It may be necessary to actually disconnect the UPS battery to shut it completely down.

If the noise goes away, you know the source is in your residence. After resetting the breaker, you can further isolate the source by turning off individual breakers one at a time. Once you know the source circuit, you can then unplug devices on that circuit to find it.

CAUTION: *Do not attempt to remove cartridge fuses or operate exposed or open-type disconnects if it is possible to make physical contact with exposed electrical circuits.*

27.5.2 Locating Noise Sources Outside Your Home

It is often possible to locate a noise source outside your home with a minimum of equip-

---

Hunting Noise with an SDR

SDR receivers are increasingly common and can be very good tools for locating noise sources and characterizing them. Portable SDRs are also available, potentially replacing the time-honored battery-powered AM radio. Dave Cole, NK7Z uses the SDRPlay (10 kHz – 2 GHz) with SDR software on a PC to characterize noise. (**nk7z.net/sdr-for-rfi-survey-p1**) The PC can also store data over an extended period — he captures 24 hours of noise across multiple bands as a "site survey." This provides information about when the noise source is active, which is often key to locating and identifying one source of many possibilities.

Common Mistake — It's Everywhere, Joe Even Hears It Across Town!

RFI from a typical otherwise legal consumer device usually only propagates for a few hundred feet or less. However, the ARRL often receives reports of non-power line noise RFI covering an extraordinarily wide area. In this case – multiple hams hear a noise at opposite ends of a town, across a state wide area, or in some cases, even a multi-state region.

The fact of the matter is that RFI is a very common problem. And if you look hard enough, noise from a consumer devices can probably be heard in most suburban neighborhoods these days. Many of them sound alike, so much so that they can easily be mistaken for each other.

Conclusion: Don't rely on RFI reported by hams in other locations as being the same RFI at your location. Before concluding that the RFI covers a widespread area, always make sure that an RFI source is not local and nearby.

Note: While power-line noise at 80 or 40 meters can propagate for miles, it won't propagate much more than that. Most power-line noise sources can sound alike so beware. Power-line noise will not propagate across state or multi-state-wide regions. In this case, the ARRL recommends the use of signature analysis to determine which source or sources are contributing to an RFI problem before making unnecessary repairs. See the section on Power-Line Noise for more information on signature analysis.
— *Mike Gruber, W1MG, ARRL Test Engineer*

ment and effort. The following process will help you determine whether the noise is radiated directly to your equipment or conducted, most frequently by power lines or wiring which then radiate the noise signal themselves.

Because of Part 15's absolute emissions limits, most noise sources that are compliant with Part 15 are within a few hundred feet of the complainant's antenna. They are also often on the same power transformer secondary system as the complainant if the noise is conducted. This typically reduces the number of possible residences to relatively few.

If the noise source is not compliant with Part 15 limits, it may be blocks, or in some rare cases, even thousands of feet from your station. The ballasts of grow lights, for example, have been known to exceed the FCC limits by a considerable margin and have been heard for over ½ mile. Some Part 15 devices, battery chargers for electric scooters and wheelchairs, for example, are well-known for exceeding Part 15 absolute emissions limits on conducted noise.

Electrical noise sources in a home, such as an arcing thermostat or a noisy washing machine controller, can also be tracked down in the same way as noise from consumer electronic devices. Electrical noise from an incidental emitter, such as a power line, can propagate much farther than noise from an otherwise legal unintentional emitter.

The following procedure can be used to trace a noise source to a private home, town house, apartment, or condominium. The number of homes that could be host to a source generating noise could make searching house by house impractical. In such cases, use noise tracking techniques discussed in the following sections to narrow the search to a more reasonable area.

1) Verify that the noise is active before attempting to locate it. Don't forget this all-important first step. You cannot find the source when it's not present.

2) If possible, use a beam to record bearings to the noise before leaving your residence. Walk or drive through the neighborhood with particular emphasis in the direction of the noise, if known. Try to determine the rough geographic area over which the noise can be heard. If the geographic area over which you can hear the noise is confined to a radius of several hundred feet or less, or it diminishes quickly as you leave your neighborhood, this confirms you are most likely dealing with a Part 15 consumer device.

3) Since the noise will be strongest at an electrical device connected to the residence containing the source, you want to measure the noise at a device common to the exterior of all the potential homes. Suitable devices include electric meters, main service breakers (whether outside or in a utility room), front

Common Mistake — It's Not Me, I've Already Eliminated My House as the Source

Consumer devices are by far one of the most common sources of RFI. And once found, a surprisingly high percentage of them are actually in the complainant's home. For this reason, that we recommend that hams affected by noise open the main breaker to their residence while listening with a battery-powered radio. (See the text's caution about making sure battery-powered devices are off, as well.) If the noise goes away, you can further isolate the source by tripping the individual circuit breakers.

While all this sounds simple enough, many hams actually skip this step. Unplugging or turning off suspect sources is not the same as tripping the main breaker. Another mistake is to conclude that the source could not be in your home because you haven't bought or changed anything. Even though quiet when new, devices that fail or otherwise break down can become a source of RFI.

Conclusion: When it comes to consumer devices, do not assume that a noise source is not in your home until you open the main breaker. This is a simple and easy test to perform. Many hams have spent months – even years – searching for a noise that they could have easily found with simple breaker test. Why skip it? — *Mike Gruber, W1MG, ARRL Test Engineer*

Common Mistake — Nothing In My Home Could Cause Noise Like That

One of the most common sources of RFI is the ubiquitous switching mode power supply. They are found in almost everything these days. Devices such as "wall warts," many light bulbs, computers, battery chargers, televisions and various other appliances all may and probably do include switchers capable of causing RFI. In addition, many other electronic devices have clocks and other oscillators that can cause RFI.

Despite this reality, it is surprising how many hams are convinced that the source of an RFI problem could not possibly be located in their home. They are often proven wrong.

Conclusion: Do not automatically that nothing in your home could cause an RFI problem. Almost every electronic device in a home can be suspect. Furthermore, a typical home these days can contain hundreds of potential RFI sources.— *Mike Gruber, W1MG, ARRL Test Engineer*

Common Mistake — I Don't Have the Equipment

Most consumer devices actually meet the FCC emission limits so the RFI problem is usually limited to about 300 feet or less. They are also often in the complainant's residence, and if not, frequently in a home connected to the same power transformer secondary system as the complainant.

With this in mind, a simple portable (battery powered) shortwave radio capable of hearing the noise is all you typical need to find it. Opening the main breaker of your home will locate many of the problems. And if it's not in your home, it's likely in an adjacent or nearby residence. By collapsing or removing the antenna, adding a step attenuator, or reducing the RF gain of the locating receiver, you can often reduce the area in which you search for the source. Reducing the signal level to something at or below the receiver's AGC threshold (or turning AGC off) can often help.

An approach that often works is to find the loudest power pole. Next, look to see what houses are connected to that pole. And finally, if possible, hold the radio a short distance from the power meters at each house. Always be sure to minimize signal levels but do not make any adjustments when making comparisons between the different meters. If access to the power meters is not possible, you can use lawn lights or similar for this. The house with the highest noise level will be the one containing the source.

Please note that spectrum analyzers are not needed. In fact, in many cases, a spectrum analyzer can add to confusion, especially if there are other sources at other frequencies.

Conclusion: Finding noisy consumer devices is often easier than most people think. Furthermore, it does not require specialized equipment. A cheap battery powered shortwave radio will often do the job. — *Mike Gruber, W1MG, ARRL Test Engineer*

porch lights, electric lamp posts, outside air conditioner units, or doorbell buttons. Whatever radiator you choose, it should be accessible at each home. The device you select to test as the noise radiator will be referred to in these instructions as the "radiator." Using the same type of device as a test point at each home helps obtain consistent results.

4) You are now ready to compare the relative signal strengths at the radiator on each of the potential source residences. Use a detector suitable to receive the noise, typically a battery-powered receiver. Preferably, the receiver should have a variable RF gain control. An external step attenuator will also work if the antenna is external to the radio. If the antenna can be removed, a probe can also be made from a small piece of wire or paper clip to reduce the receiver's sensitivity. Start by holding the detector about two inches from the radiator at the residence where the noise source may be located. Turn the detector's RF gain control down to a point where you can just barely hear the noise. Alternately, increase the attenuation if using an external step attenuator. Record the RF gain or attenuator setting for each test. Because any wiring connected to a portable receiver becomes part of the receiver's antenna, including headphones, external battery, even the operator's hands and body, keep the configuration the same as you evaluate each potential source.

5) Proceed to the next residence. Again hold the detector approximately two inches from the radiator. (The detector should be placed at the same location at each residence, as much as is practical.) Since you had previously set the detector to just barely hear the noise at the residence having the interference problem, you can move on to the next residence if you do not hear the noise. Remember, in order for your detector to hear the noise at the next house, the noise level will have to be the same or higher than the previous location. If you need to increase the detector's sensitivity to be able to hear the noise, you are moving away from the noise source.

6) When you reach the next residence, if the level is lower or not heard, you're moving further from the source. Continue your search to residences in other directions or across the street. If the level is higher, then you're headed in the right direction. Be sure to turn the gain control down to the point of just barely hearing the noise as its strength increases.

7) Continue on to the next house, repeating the previous steps as necessary. The residence with the source will be the one with the strongest noise at the radiator.

Depending on the circumstances of a particular situation, it may be possible to first isolate the power pole to which the source residence is connected. Walk or drive along the power lines in the affected area while listening to the noise with a battery-powered radio. Continue to decrease the receiver's RF gain as the noise gets louder, thus reducing the area over which you can hear it. Finally, isolate the loudest pole by reducing the RF gain to a point at which you can hear it at only one pole. Once the pole has been isolated, look to see which houses are connected to its transformer. Typically this will reduce the number of potential residences to a very small number.

Be aware that not all power poles have a grounding conductor (a wire running down the side of the pole into the ground). This wire will carry currents from the entire section of the power system for that pole. A receiver held close to that wire will hear more noise than at poles without a ground wire. This may create a "false positive" with respect to homes fed from that pole — the actual noise source may be in any home connected to that section of the power system. Follow up by checking the power drop to the home and, if possible, at the meter before identifying that residence as the source of the noise. Noise on power lines can travel a long way and it is easy to be fooled by where it is heard.

CAUTION: *Always observe good safety practices! Only qualified people familiar with the hazards of working around energized electrical equipment should inspect power-line or other energized circuitry.*

When attempting to isolate the pole, it is often best to use the highest frequency at which you can hear the noise. Noise can exhibit peaks and nulls along a power line that are a function of its wavelength. Longer wavelengths can therefore make it difficult to pinpoint a particular point along a line. Furthermore, longer wavelength signals typically propagate further along power lines. You can often reduce your search area by simply increasing the frequency at which you look for the noise.

In some cases, tuning upward in frequency can also be used to attenuate noise. This can be especially helpful in cases where your receiver does not have an RF gain control. As mentioned previously, switchmode power supplies typically generate noise that exhibits a regular and repeating pattern of peaks and nulls across the spectrum. While a typical interval might be every 50 kHz or so, the noise will often start to diminish at the highest frequencies. The peaks in some cases might drift over time, but tuning to the highest frequency at which you can hear the noise will often attenuate it enough to help locate it. If the peak drifts however, be sure to keep your receiver set on the peak as you attempt to locate the source.

Under FCC rules, the involved utility is responsible for finding and correcting harmful interference that is being generated by its own equipment. In cases where a utility customer is using an appliance or device that generates noise, the operator of the device is responsible for fixing it — even if the noise is conducted and radiated by the power company's power lines.

27.5.3 Approaching Your Neighbor

Once you identify the source residence and approach your neighbor, the importance of personal diplomacy simply cannot be overstated. The first contact regarding an RFI problem between a ham and a neighbor is often the most important; it is the start of all future relations between the parties. The way you react and behave when you first discuss the problem can set the tone for everything that follows. It is important, therefore, to use a diplomatic path from the very start. A successful outcome can depend upon it!

Common Mistake — It Must Be The XYZ Company — They Were Just Here

Many hams might notice activity in their neighborhood by a cable, power or telephone company. Other variations include an installation of something electrical at an adjacent or nearby residence. Typical examples might include a swimming pool pump, broadband, satellite TV or an alarm system. So far, so good...

The problem, however, will become apparent a few days later when he or she turns on their radio. Interference now plagues the amateur bands! The ham may now erroneously conclude that the interference is a result of the activity he saw in his neighborhood several days prior. In some cases, the ham is so convinced of the source that they fail to take even the most rudimentary steps to confirm their suspicions. This often leads to significant delays in resolving their problem.

The reality in a typical suburban neighborhood is that there could easily be over a thousand devices in range of an amateur's antenna if those sources are all at the legal limit. This RFI environment is also constantly in transition as family members and nearby neighbors buy or turn on electronic devices and other appliances.

Conclusion: Do not automatically assume that you know what the source of an interference problem is based on activity that you've seen in the neighborhood. Always verify the source to the best extent possible. — *Mike Gruber, W1MG, ARRL Test Engineer*

A self-help guide for the consumer published jointly by the ARRL and the Consumer Electronics Association (CEA) often proves helpful when discussing an interference problem with a neighbor. Entitled *What To Do if You Have an Electronic Interference Problem*, it may be printed and distributed freely. It is available on the ARRL website at **www.arrl.org/information-for-the-neighbors-of-hams** and also in the downloadable supplemental information accompanying this book. Be sure to download and print a copy for your neighbor before you approach him or her.

With the noise active and with a copy of the pamphlet handy, approach your neighbor with a radio in hand, preferably an ordinary AM broadcast or short-wave receiver. Let them hear it but not so loud that it will be offensive. Tell them this is the problem you are experiencing and you believe the source may be in their home. Don't suggest what you think the cause is. If you're wrong, it often makes matters worse. Give them the pamphlet and tell them it will only take a minute to determine whether the source is in their home. Most neighbors will agree to help find the source, and if they agree to turn off circuit breakers, it can be found very quickly. Start with the main breaker to verify you have the correct residence, then the individual breakers to find the circuit. The procedure then becomes the same as described for your own residence.

27.5.4 Radio Direction Finding

Radio direction finding (RDF) can be a highly effective method to locate an RFI source although it requires more specialized equipment than other methods. RDF techniques can be used to find both broadband and single-signal, narrowband noise sources. Professional interference investigators almost always use radio direction finding techniques to locate power-line noise sources. See the **Antennas** chapter for more information on direction finding antennas. The following recommendations are most effective in locating noise from a broadband source. For narrow-band, single-signal sources, regular RDF techniques are the most effective way to determine a source's location.

A good place to start, whenever possible, is at the affected station. Use an AM receiver, preferably one with a wide IF bandwidth. An RF gain control is particularly helpful but an outboard step attenuator can be a good substitute. If there is a directional beam capable of receiving the noise, use it on highest frequency band at which the noise can be heard using the antenna. If you can hear the noise at VHF or UHF, you'll typically want to use those frequencies for RDF.

Select a frequency at which no other stations or signals are present and the antenna can discern a directional peak in the noise. Rotate the beam as required to get a bearing on the noise, keeping the RF gain at a minimum. Repeat with a complete 360° sweep using the minimum RF gain possible to hear the noise in its loudest direction. Try to decrease the RF gain to a point at which the noise clearly comes from one and only one direction. You can simultaneously increase the AF gain as desired to hear the noise.

Distant sources, including power-line noise, are generally easier to RDF at HF than nearby sources. Whenever possible, it's almost always better to use VHF or UHF when in close proximity to a source. Tracking a source to a specific residence by RDF at HF is sometimes possible. Such factors as balance and geometry of a home's internal wiring, open switch circuits and distance, may cause the residence to appear somewhat as a point source.

If the search is being conducted while mobile or portable, VHF and UHF are typically the easiest and most practical antennas. Small handheld Yagi antennas for 2 meters and 440 MHz are readily available and can serve double duty when operating portable. Many handheld receivers can be configured to receive AM on the VHF bands. Be sure to check your manual for this feature. VHF Aircraft band or "Air band" receivers are also a popular choice since they receive AM signals.

Using RDF to locate an HF noise source while in motion presents significant challenges. Conducted emissions are typical from a consumer device or appliance. In this case, the emissions can be conducted outside the residence and on to the power line. The noise can then propagate along neighborhood distribution lines, which in turn acts as an antenna. The noise can often exhibit confusing peaks and nulls along the line, and if in the vicinity of a power line radiating it, RDF can be extremely difficult, if not impossible. Depending on the circumstances, you could literally be surrounded by the near field of an antenna! You would generally want to stay away from power lines and other potential radiators when searching at HF.

Antennas for HF RDF while walking typically include small loops and ferrite rod antennas. In some cases, a portable AM broadcast radio with a ferrite rod antenna can be used for direction finding. An HF dipole made from a pair of whip antennas may be able to be used to get an approximate bearing toward the noise. Mount the dipole about 12 feet above ground (remembering to watch out for overhead conductors!) and rotate to null out the noise. For all three types of antenna, there will be two nulls in opposite directions. Note the direction of the null. Repeat this procedure from another location then triangulate to determine the bearing to the noise.

27.6 Power-Line Noise

This chapter's section "Identifying RFI Source Types" describes power-line noise, its causes, and methods to identify it. Power-line noise is a unique problem in several respects. First and foremost, the offending source is never under your direct control. You can't just simply "turn it off" or unplug the offending device. Nor will the source be under the direct control of a neighbor or someone you are likely to know. In the case of power-line noise, the source is usually operated by a company, municipality, or in some cases, a cooperative. Furthermore, shutting down a power line is obviously not a practical option.

Another unique aspect of power-line noise is that it almost always involves a defect of some sort. The cure for power-line noise is to fix the defect. This is almost always a utility implemented repair and one over which you do not have any direct control.

FCC rules specify that that the operator of a device causing interference is responsible for fixing it. Whenever encountering a power-line noise problem, you will be dealing with a utility and won't have the option of applying a relatively simple technical solution to facilitate a cure, as you would if the device were located in your home. Utilities have a mixed record when it comes to dealing with power-line noise complaints. In some cases, a utility will have a budget, well-trained personnel, and equipment to quickly locate and address the problem. In other cases, however, the utility is simply unable to effectively deal with power-line noise complaints or even denies their equipment can cause RFI.

What does this mean for an amateur with a power-line noise complaint? Utilities can be of any size from large corporations to local cooperatives or city-owned systems. Regardless of the category in which your utility may fall, it must follow Part 15 of the FCC rules. Dealing with a company, coop or municipality, however, as opposed to a device in your home, or a nearby neighbor that you know personally, can present its own set of unique challenges. Multiple parties and individuals are often involved, including an RFI investigator, a line crew and associated management. In some cases, the utility may never have received an RFI complaint before yours.

27.6.1 Before Filing a Complaint

Obviously, before filing a complaint with your local utility, it is important to verify the problem as power-line noise as best as possible and verify that it is not caused by a problem with electrical equipment in your home. Other sources, such as lighting devices and motors, can mimic power-line noise, especially to an untrained ear. Don't overlook these important steps. Attempting to engage your utility in the resolution of an RFI problem can not only waste time but can be embarrassing if the source is right in your own home!

Utilities are not responsible for noise generated by customer-operated devices — *even if the noise is being radiated by the power lines*. They are responsible for fixing only that noise which is being generated by their equipment.

27.6.2 Filing a Complaint

Once you have verified the problem to be power-line noise (see this chapter's section on Identifying Power-line and Electrical Noise) and that it is not coming from a source in your home or a nearby residence, contact your utility's customer service department. In addition to your local phone book, customer service phone numbers are included on most power company websites.

It is important to maintain a log during this part of the process. Be sure to record any "help ticket" numbers that may be assigned to your complaint as well as names, dates and a brief description of each conversation you have with electric company personnel. If you identify specific equipment or power poles as a possible noise source, record the address and any identifying numbers on it.

Hopefully, your complaint will be addressed in a timely and professional manner. Once a noise source has been identified, it is up to the utility to repair it within a reasonable period. You and the utility may not agree on what constitutes a reasonable period, but attempt to be patient. If no action is taken after repeated requests, reporting the complaint to the ARRL and requesting assistance may be in order. (Before contacting the ARRL review The Cooperative Agreement, a section of this chapter.)

It is also important to cooperate with utility personnel and treat them with respect. Hostile and inappropriate behavior is almost always counter-productive in these situations. Remember, you want utility and other related personnel to help you — not avoid you. Even if the utility personnel working on your case seem unqualified, hostile behavior has historically never been a particularly good motivator in these situations. In fact, most protracted power-line noise cases reported to the ARRL began with an altercation in the early stages of the resolution process. In no case did it help or expedite correction of the problem.

27.6.3 Techniques for Locating Power-line Noise Sources

Radio direction finding (RDF) techniques

Common Mistake — It's Coming From That Pole!

RFI problems from consumer devices, especially below 30 MHz, frequently involve conducted emissions. The RF in this cases is generated by a consumer device in a home. It is then conducted by the house wiring, where it is radiated. In some cases, the RF can also be conducted to the service entrance of the home and out to a utility pole. In this case, the noise will peak at the pole and appear to be the source of the interference. It is not. The real source of the problem is in a residence connected to the pole.

Always verify that the actual source is not in a home connected to that pole. Frequently, the source residence will be connected to the power transformer secondary system on that pole. Also keep in mind that the hardware on a pole can also make for a better "antenna." This means that noise tends to peak at poles in general. Noise also tends to peak at about every half wavelength as you traverse along a power line. Be sure to use higher frequencies (i.e., shorter wavelengths) whenever possible.

Conclusion: Don't automatically assume that the source of an RFI problem is on a pole where the noise peaks. This is a common mistake made by many beginners! — *Mike Gruber, W1MG, ARRL Test Engineer*

---

typically offer the best and most efficient approach to locating most power-line noise sources. It is the primary method of choice used by professionals. While RDF is usually the most effective method, it also requires some specialized equipment, such as a hand-held beam antenna. Although specialized professional equipment is available for RDF, hams can also use readily available amateur and homebrew equipment successfully. The downloadable supplemental information for this *Handbook* includes some power-line noise locating equipment projects you can build. This includes a simple and easy to build RDFing antenna, an ultrasonic dish, and attenuators.

Although it is the utility's responsibility to locate a source of noise emanating from its equipment, many companies simply do not possess the necessary expertise or equipment to do so. As a practical matter, many hams have assisted their utility in locating noise sources. In some cases, this can help expedite a speedy resolution.

There is a significant caveat to this approach however. Should you mislead the power company into making unnecessary repairs, they will become frustrated. This expense and time will be added to their repair list. Do not make a guess or suggestions if you don't know what is causing the noise. While some power companies might know less about the locating process than the affected ham, indiscriminate replacement of hardware almost always makes the problem worse. Nonetheless, depending on your level of expertise and the specifics of your situation, you may be able to facilitate a speedy resolution by locating the RFI source for the utility.

27.6.4 Amateur Power-line Noise Locating Equipment

Additional information on the equipment, antennas, and techniques used to locate power line noise are also discussed in the *ARRL Antenna Book's* material on Direction Finding. Before discussing how to locate power-line noise sources, here are a few additional equipment guidelines.

Receiver — You'll need a battery-operated portable radio capable of receiving VHF or UHF in the AM mode. Ideally, it should also be capable of receiving HF frequencies, especially if the interference is a problem at HF and not VHF. Some amateurs also use the aircraft band from 108 to 137 MHz. The lower frequencies of this band can sometimes enable an RFI investigator to hear the noise at greater distances than on 2 meters or 70 cm. An RF gain control is essential but an outboard step attenuator can be used as a substitute. A good S-meter is also required.

Attenuator — Even if your receiver has an RF gain control, an additional outboard step attenuator can often be helpful. It can not only minimize the area of a noise search but also provide added range for the RF gain control. As with other RFI sources — you'll need to add more and more attenuation as you approach the source.

VHF/UHF Antennas — You'll need a hand-held directional beam antenna. A popular professional noise-locating antenna is an eight-element Yagi tuned for 400 MHz. Since power-line noise is a broadband phenomenon, the exact frequency is not important. Either a 2 meter or 70 cm Yagi are capable of locating a power-line noise source on a specific power pole.

Although professional grade antennas can cost several hundred dollars, some hams can build their own for a lot less. See this book's downloadable supplemental information for the article, "Adapting a Three-Element Tape Measure Beam for Power-line Noise Hunting," by Jim Hanson, W1TRC. This low cost and easy to build antenna for locating power-line noise can be adapted for a variety of frequencies and receivers. Commercial 2 meter and 70 cm antennas for portable use are also suitable if a handle is added, such as a short length of PVC pipe.

Before using an antenna for power-line noise locating, determine its peak response frequency. Start by aiming the antenna at a known power-line noise source. Tune across its range and just beyond. Using minimum RF gain control, find its peak response. Label the antenna with this frequency using a piece of tape or marking pen. When using this antenna for noise locating, tune the receiver to this peak response frequency.

If you don't have a VHF or UHF receiver that can receive AM signals, see the CD-ROM accompanying this book for the article, "A Simple TRF Receiver for Tracking RFI," by Rick Littlefield, K1BQT. It describes the combination of a simple 136 MHz beam and receiver for portable RFI tracking.

HF Antennas — Depending on the circumstances of a particular case, a mobile HF whip such as a 7 or 14 MHz model can be helpful. Magnet-mount models are acceptable for temporary use. An RFI investigator can typically get within VHF range by observing the relative strength of the noise from different locations. Driving in a circle centered on the affected station will typically indicate the general direction in which the noise is strongest. As with beam antennas, determine the peak response frequency for best results.

Ultrasonic Pinpointer — Although an ultrasonic pinpointer is not necessary to locate the pole or structure containing the source, some hams prefer to go one more step by finding the offending noise source on that structure. Guidelines for the use of an ultrasonic device are described later in this section.

Professional-grade ultrasonic locators are often beyond the budget of the average ham. Home brewing options however, can make a practical ultrasonic locator affordable in most situations — and make a great weekend project too. See the downloadable supplemental information accompanying this book for "A Home-made Ultrasonic Power Line Arc Detector" by Jim Hanson, W1TRC.

Oscilloscope — A battery-powered portable oscilloscope is only required for signature analysis. See the next section, Signature or Fingerprint Method, for details.

Thermal/Infrared Detectors and Corona Cameras — This equipment is not recommended for the sole purpose of locating power-line noise sources. It is rare that an RFI source is even detectable using infrared techniques. Although these are not useful tools for locating noise sources, many utilities still use them for such purposes with minimal or no results. Not surprisingly, ARRL experience has shown that these utilities are typically unable to resolve interference complaints in a timely fashion.

27.6.5 Signature or Fingerprint Method

Each sparking interference source exhibits a unique pattern. By comparing the characteristics between the patterns taken at the affected station with those observed in the field, it becomes possible to conclusively identify the offending source or sources from the many that one might encounter. It therefore isn't surprising that a pattern's unique characteristic is often called its "fingerprint" or "signature." See **Figure 27.8** for an example.

This is a very powerful technique and a real money saver for the utility. Even though there may be several different noise sources in the field, this method helps identify only those sources that are actually causing the interference problem. The utility need only correct the problem(s) matching the pattern of noise affecting your equipment.

You as a ham can use the signature method by observing the noise from your radio's audio output with an oscilloscope. Record the pattern by drawing it on a notepad or taking a photograph of the screen. Take the sketch or photograph with you as you hunt for the source and compare it to signatures you might observe in the field.

Professional interference-locating receivers, such as the Radar Engineers Model 243 shown in Figure 27.8, have a built in time-domain display and waveform memory similar to a digital oscilloscope. This is the preferred method used by professional interference investigators. These receivers provide the ability to switch between the patterns saved at the affected station and those from sources located in the field.

Once armed with the noise fingerprint taken at the affected station, you are ready to begin the hunt. If you have a directional beam, use it to obtain a bearing to the noise. If multiple sources are involved, you'll need to record the bearings to each one. Knowing how high in frequency a particular noise can be heard also provides a clue to its proximity. If the noise can be heard at 440 MHz, for example, the source will typically be within walking distance. If it diminishes beginning 75 or 40 meters, it can be up to several miles away.

Since each noise source will exhibit unique characteristics, you can now match this noise "signature" with one from the many sources you may encounter in the investigation. Compare such characteristics as the duration of each noise burst, pulse shape, and number of pulses. Be wary of assuming that all devices have similar signatures when arcing. The fingerprint of a particular piece of hardware arcing may be quite different even for the same device on another pole.

If you have a non-portable oscilloscope,

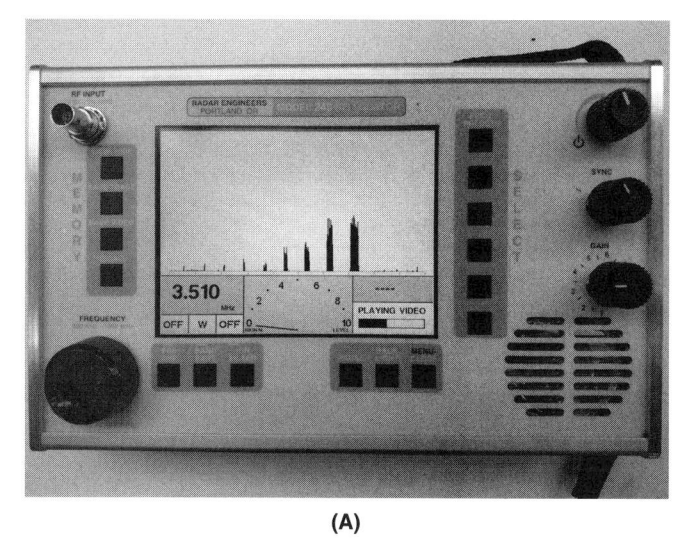

Figure 27.8 — The spectrum of an unknown noise source is shown on the display of a Model 243 RFI locating receiver (A) along with a typical noise receiving antenna (B). During the RFI investigation, noise signatures not matching this pattern can be ignored. Once the matching signature originally shown in A is found, the offending noise source has been located.

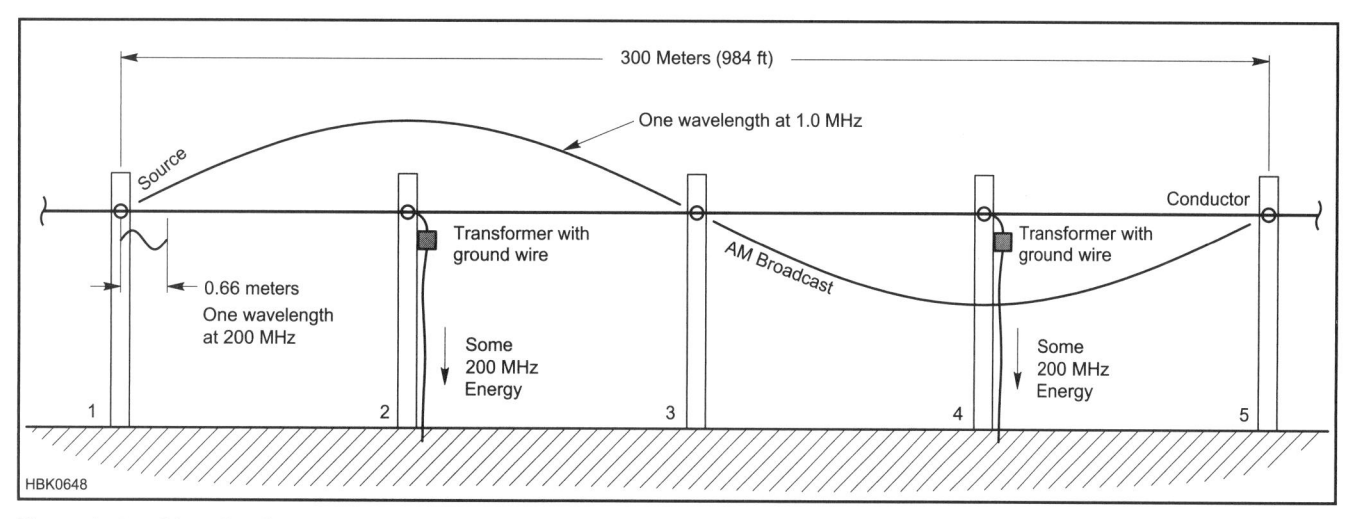

Figure 27.9 — Listening for noise signals on a power distribution line at 1 MHz vs 200 MHz can result in identification of the wrong power pole as the noise source. (From Loftness, *AC Power Interference Handbook*)

you may still be able to perform signature matching by using an audio recorder. Make a high quality recording of the noise source at your station and at each suspected noise source in the field, using the same receiver if possible. Replay the sounds for signature analysis.

27.6.6 Locating the Source's Power Pole or Structure

Start your search in front of the affected station. If you can hear the noise at VHF or UHF, begin with a handheld beam suitable for these frequencies. As discussed previously, the longer wavelengths associated with the AM broadcast band and even HF, can create misleading "hotspots" along a line when searching for a noise source as shown in **Figure 27.9**.

As a general rule, only use lower frequencies when you are too far away from the source to hear it at VHF or UHF. Generally work with the highest frequency at which the noise can be heard. As you approach the source, keep increasing the frequency to VHF or UHF, depending on your available antennas. Typically, 2 meters and 70 cm are both suitable for isolating a source down to the pole level.

If you do not have an initial bearing to the noise and are unable to hear it with your portable or mobile equipment, start traveling in a circular pattern around the affected station, block-by-block, street-by-street, until you find the noise pattern matching the one recorded at the affected station.

Once in range of the noise at VHF or UHF, start using a handheld beam. You're well on your way to locating the structure containing the source. In many cases, you can now continue your search on foot. *Again, maintain minimum RF gain to just barely hear the noise over a minimum area.* This is important step is crucial for success. If the RF gain is too high, it will be difficult to obtain accurate bearings with the beam.

Power-line noise will often be neither vertically nor horizontally polarized but somewhere in between. Be sure to rotate the beam's polarization for maximum noise response. Maintain this same polarization when comparing poles and other hardware.

27.6.7 Pinpointing the Source on a Pole or Structure

Once the source pole has been identified, the next step becomes pinpointing the offending hardware on that pole. A pair of binoculars

RF Interference 27.27

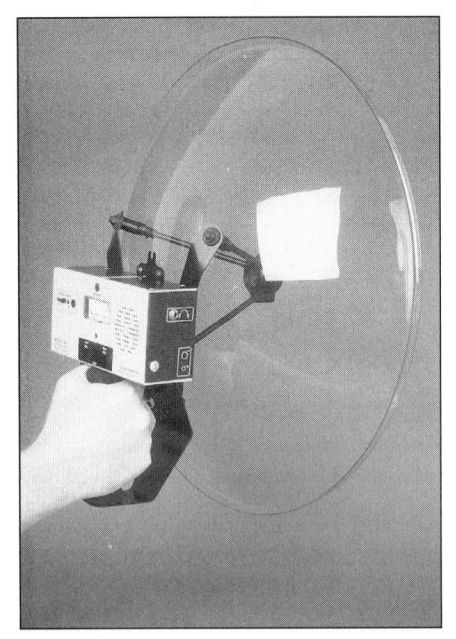

Figure 27.10 — The clear plastic parabolic dish is an "ear" connected to an ultrasonic detector that lets utility personnel listen for the sound of arcs.

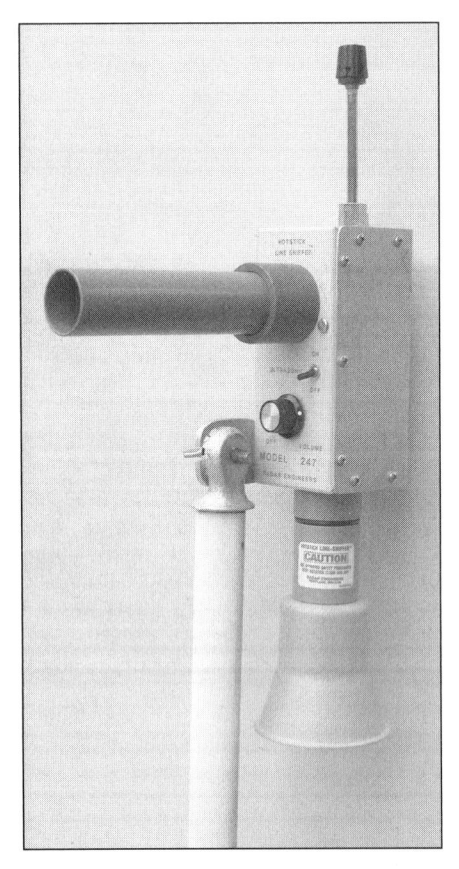

Figure 27.11 — The Radar Engineers Model 247 Hotstick Line Sniffer is an RF and ultrasonic locator. It is used by utility workers to pinpoint the exact piece of hardware causing a noise problem. Mounted on a hotstick, the sniffer is used from the ground or from a bucket.

on a dark night may reveal visible signs of arcing and in some cases you may be able to see other evidence of the problem from the ground. These cases are rare. More than likely, a better approach will be required. Professional and utility interference investigators typically have two types of specialized equipment for this purpose:

• An ultrasonic dish or pinpointer. The RFI investigator, even if not a lineman, can pinpoint sources on the structure down to a component level from the ground using this instrument. See **Figure 27.10**.

• An investigator can instruct the lineman on the use of a hot stick-mounted device used to find the source. This method is restricted to only qualified utility personnel, typically from a bucket truck. See **Figure 27.11**.

Both methods are similar but hams only have one option — the ultrasonic pinpointer.

CAUTION — *Hot sticks and hot stick mounted devices are not for hams! Do not use them. Proper and safe use of a hot stick requires specialized training. In most localities, it is generally unlawful for anyone unqualified by a utility to come within 10 feet of an energized line or hardware. This includes hot sticks.*

Remember that it may be interesting to you to determine what piece of equipment is generating noise but it is the utility's job to positively complete the identification and then work on the equipment. Once you have identified the noise as coming from a particular location, be prepared to step back and let the professionals do their job.

ULTRASONIC PINPOINTER TIPS

An ultrasonic dish is the tool of choice for pinpointing the source of an arc from the ground. While no hot stick is required, an unobstructed direct line-of-sight path is required between the arc and the dish. This is not a suitable tool for locating the structure containing the source. It is only useful for pinpointing a source once its pole or structure has been determined.

Caveat: Corona discharge, while typically not a source of RF power-line noise, can and often is a significant source of ultrasonic sound. It can often be difficult to distinguish between the sound created by an arc and corona discharge. This can lead to mistakes when trying to pinpoint the source of an RFI problem with an ultrasonic device.

The key to success, just as with locating the structure, is using gain control effectively. Use minimum gain after initially detecting the noise. If the source appears to be at more than one location on the structure, reduce the gain. In part, this will eliminate any weaker noise signals from hardware not causing the problem.

27.6.8 Common Causes of Power-line Noise

The following are some of the more common power-line noise sources. They're listed in order from most common to least common. Note that some of the most common sources are not connected to a primary conductor. This in part is due to the care most utilities take to ensure sufficient primary conductor clearance from surrounding hardware. Note, too, that power transformers do not appear on this list:

• Loose staples on ground conductor
• Loose pole-top pin
• Ground conductor touching nearby hardware
• Corroded slack span insulators
• Guy wire touching neutral
• Loose hardware
• Bare tie wire used with insulated conductor
• Insulated tie wire on bare conductor
• Loose cross-arm braces
• Lightning arrestors

27.6.9 The Cooperative Agreement

While some cases of power-line noise are resolved in a timely fashion, the reality is that many cases can linger for an extended period of time. Many utilities simply do not have the expertise, equipment or motivation to properly address a power-line noise complaint. There are often no quick solutions. Patience can often be at a premium in these situations. Fortunately, the ARRL has a Cooperative Agreement with the FCC that can help. While the program is not a quick or easy solution, it does offer an opportunity and step-by-step course of action for relief. It emphasizes and provides for voluntary cooperation without FCC intervention.

Under the terms of the Cooperative Agreement, the ARRL provides technical help and information to utilities in order to help them resolve power-line noise complaints. It must be emphasized that the ARRL's role in this process is strictly a technical one — it is not in the enforcement business. In order to participate, complainants are required to treat utility personnel with respect, refrain from hostile behavior, and reasonably cooperate with any reasonable utility request. This includes making his or her station available for purposes of observing and recording noise signatures. The intent of the Cooperative Agreement is to solve as many cases as possible before they go to the FCC. In this way, the FCC's limited resources can be allocated where they are needed the most — enforcement.

As the first step in the process, the ARRL sends the utility a letter advising of pertinent Part 15 rules and offering assistance. The FCC then requires a 60-day waiting period before the next step. If by the end of 60 days the utility has failed to demonstrate a good faith effort to correct the problem, the FCC then issues an advisory letter. This letter allows the utility another 60-day window to correct the problem.

A second FCC advisory letter, if necessary, is the next step. Typically, this letter provides another 20- or 30-day window for the utility to respond. If the problem still persists, a field investigation would follow. At the discretion of the Field Investigator, he or she may issue an FCC Citation or Notice of Apparent Liability (NAL). In the case of an NAL, a forfeiture or fine can result.

It is important to emphasize that the ARRL Cooperative Agreement Program does not offer a quick fix. There are several built-in waiting periods and a number of requirements that a ham must follow precisely. It does however provide a step-by-step and systematic course of action under the auspices of the FCC in cases where a utility does not comply with Part 15. Look for complete details, including how to file a complaint, in the ARRL's Powerline Noise FAQ web page at **www.arrl.org/power-line-noise-faq-page**.

27.7 Elements of RFI Control

27.7.1 Differential- and Common-Mode Signal Control

As shown in **Figure 27.12**, the path from source to victim almost always includes some conducting portion, such as wires or cables. RF energy can be conducted directly from source to victim, be conducted onto a wire or cable that acts as an antenna where it is radiated, or be picked up by a conductor connected to the victim that acts like an antenna. When the energy is traveling along the conducting portion of its path, it is important to understand whether it is a differential- or common-mode signal.

Removing unwanted signals that cause RFI is different for each of these conduction modes. Differential-mode cures (a high-pass filter, low-pass filter, or a capacitor across the ac power line, for example) do not attenuate common-mode signals. Similarly, a common-mode choke will not affect interference resulting from a differential-mode signal.

It's relatively simple to build a differential-mode filter that passes desired signals and blocks unwanted signals with a high series impedance or presents a low-impedance to a signal return line or path. The return path for common-mode signals often involves earth ground, or even the chassis of equipment if it is large enough to form part of an antenna at the frequency of the RFI. A differential-mode filter is not part of this current path, so it can have no effect on common-mode RFI. Note that in practice, conducted emissions problems are more likely to be the result of common-mode than differential-mode signals.

In either case, an exposed shield surface is a potential antenna for RFI, either radiating or receiving unwanted energy, regardless of the shield's quality. In this way, a coaxial cable can act as an antenna for RFI if the victim device is unable to reject common-mode signals on the cable's shield. This is why it is important to connect cable shields in such a way that common-mode currents flowing on the shields are not allowed to enter the victim device. (See the section below on Cable Shield Connections.)

27.7.2 Shields and Filters

Breaking the path between source and victim is often an attractive option, especially if either is a consumer electronics device. Remember, the path will involve one or more of three possibilities — radiation, conduction, and inductive or capacitive coupling. Breaking the path of an RFI problem can require

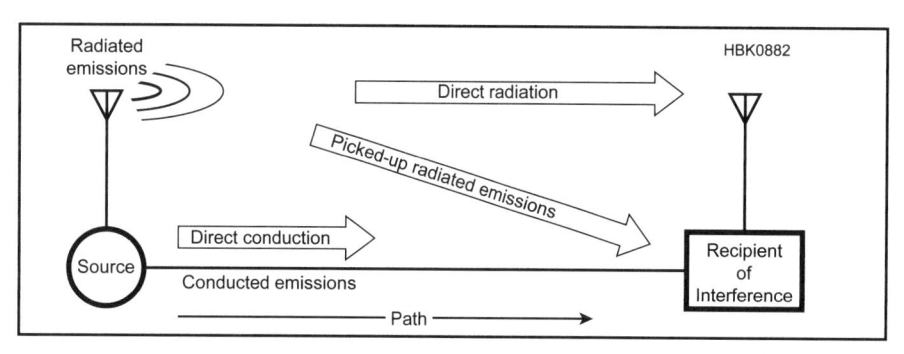

Figure 27.12 — A block diagram showing every RFI problem involves three elements – a source, path and a victim. Fixing the problem requires removing one or more of them.

RFI Email Reflector

A good source of information and help is the RFI email reflector maintained on the contesting.com website (**http://lists.contesting.com/mailman/listinfo/RFI**). Simply subscribing in digest form provides a daily dose of RFI discussion. Before asking your question, however, be sure to check the reflector's searchable archives to see if your topic has been covered recently.

analysis and experimentation in some cases. Obviously you must know what the path is before you can break it. While the path may be readily apparent in some cases, more complex situations may not be so clear. Multiple attempts at finding a solution may be required.

ENCLOSURE SHIELDING

Shielding can be used to control radiated emissions — that is, signals radiated by wiring inside the device — or to prevent radiated signals from being picked up by signal leads in cables or inside a piece of equipment. Shielding can also be used to reduce inductive or capacitive coupling, usually by acting as an intervening conductor between the source and victim.

Shields are used to set boundaries for radiated energy and to contain electric and magnetic fields. Thin conductive films, copper braid and sheet metal are the most common shield materials for the electric field (capacitive coupling), and for electromagnetic fields (radio waves). At RF, the small skin depth allows thin shields to be effective at these frequencies. Thicker shielding material is needed for magnetic field (inductive coupling) to minimize the voltage caused by induced current. At audio frequencies and below, the higher skin depth of common shield materials is large enough (at 60 Hz, the skin depth for aluminum is 0.43 inches) that high-permeability materials such as steel or mu-metal (a nickel-iron alloy that exhibits high magnetic permeability) are required.

Maximum shield effectiveness usually requires solid sheet metal that completely encloses the source or susceptible circuitry or equipment. While electrically small holes generally do not affect shield effectiveness (fine-mesh screening makes good shielding at VHF and below, for example) seams can act as a slot antenna if they are a significant fraction of a wavelength long. In addition, mating surfaces between different parts of a shield must be conductive. To ensure conductivity, file or sand off paint or other nonconductive coatings on mating surfaces.

The effectiveness of a shield is determined by its ability to reflect or absorb the undesired energy. Reflection occurs at a shield's surface. In this case, the shield's effectiveness is independent of its thickness. Reflection is typically the dominant means of shielding for radio waves and capacitive coupling, but is ineffective against magnetic coupling. Most RFI shielding works, therefore, by reflection. Any good conductor will serve in this case, even thin plating.

Magnetic material is required when attempting to break a low-frequency inductive coupling path by shielding. A thick layer of high permeability material is ideal in this case. Although the near field of low frequency magnetic fields can extend for long distances, magnetic fields generally have their greatest effect at relatively short range. Simply increasing the distance between the source and victim may help avoid the expense and difficulty of implementing a shield.

Adding shielding may not be practical in many situations, especially with many consumer products, such as a television. Adding a shield to a cable can minimize capacitive coupling and RF pickup, but it has no effect on magnetic coupling. Replacing parallel-conductor cables (such as zip cord) with twisted-pair is quite effective against magnetic coupling and also reduces electromagnetic coupling.

Additional material on shielding may be found in Chapter 2 of Ott.

FILTERS

Many RFI problems are caused by conducted emissions which leave the noise source as common-mode signals on wiring connected to the source. The noise may travel directly from the source to the victim or it might be radiated by the wiring and picked up by wiring connected to the victim. The same design or production problems that enable conducted emissions can also work in reverse, allowing the noise that has been picked up to be conducted into the victim where it causes the interference.

Filters and chokes can be very effective in dealing with a conducted emissions problem by blocking or suppressing the noise. Fortunately, filters and chokes are simple, economical and easy to try. As we'll see, use of common-mode chokes alone can often solve many RFI problems, especially at HF when common-mode current is more likely to be the culprit. In many cases, filters and chokes can also be applied externally to the victim device, avoiding the need to open an enclosure. Solving an RFI problem without having to alter a device's internal wiring is almost always preferable to the alternative.

A primary means of separating signals relies on their frequency difference. Filters offer little opposition to signals with certain frequencies while blocking or shunting others. Filters vary in attenuation characteristics, frequency characteristics and power-handling capabilities. The names given to various filters are based on their uses. (More information on filters may be found in the **Analog and Digital Filtering** chapter.)

Low-pass filters pass frequencies below some cutoff frequency, while attenuating frequencies above that cutoff frequency. A typical low-pass filter curve is shown in **Figure 27.13A**. A schematic is shown in Figure 27.13B. These filters are can be difficult to construct properly so many hams choose to buy them. Many retail Amateur Radio stores that advertise in *QST* stock low-pass filters.

High-pass filters pass frequencies above some cutoff frequency while attenuating frequencies below that cutoff frequency. A typical high-pass filter curve is shown in **Figure 27.14A**. Figure 27.14B shows a schematic of a typical high-pass filter. Again, it is best to buy one of the commercially available filters.

Bypass capacitors can be used to cure differential-mode RFI problems by providing a low-impedance path for RF signals away from the affected lead or cable. A bypass capacitor is usually placed between a signal or power

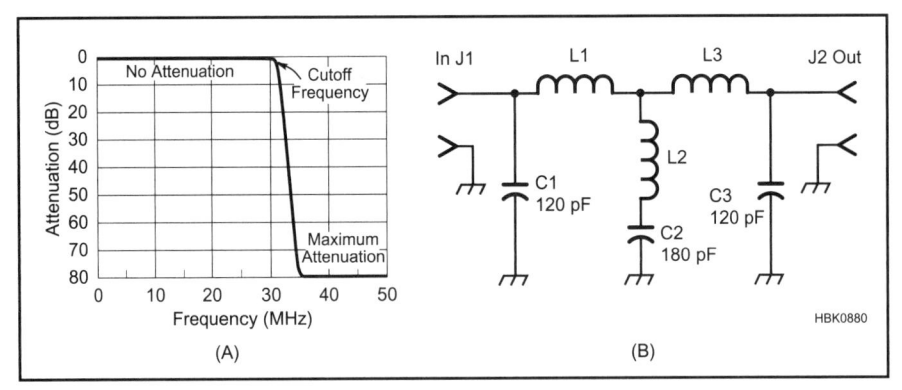

Figure 27.13 — (A) An example of a low-pass filter's response curve. (B) A low-pass filter schematic for amateur transmitting use. Complete construction information appears in the Transmitters chapter of *The ARRL RFI Book*. A high-performance 1.8-54 MHz filter project can be found in the Analog and Digital Filtering chapter of this *Handbook*.

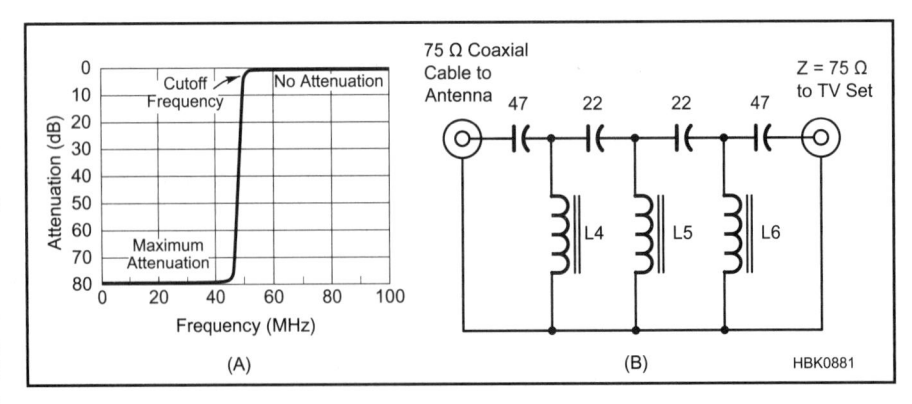

Figure 27.14 — (A) An example of a high-pass filter's response curve. (B) A differential-mode high-pass filter for 75-Ω coaxial cable. It rejects HF signals picked up by a TV antenna or that leak into a cable-TV system. All capacitors are high-stability, low-loss, NP0 ceramic disc components. Values are in pF. The inductors are all #24 AWG enameled wire on T-44-0 toroid cores. L4 and L6 are each 12 turns (0.157 µH) and L5 is 11 turns (0.135 µH).

27.30   Chapter 27

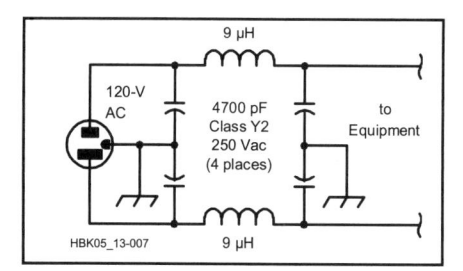

Figure 27.15 — A "brute-force" ac-line filter. Note there is no filtering on the chassis ground connections. See the sidebar "Differential-Mode and Common-Mode Currents and RFI."

lead and the equipment chassis. If the bypass capacitor is attached to a shielded cable, the shield should also be connected to the chassis. Bypass capacitors for HF signals are usually 0.01 µF, while VHF bypass capacitors are usually 0.001 µF. Leads of bypass capacitors should be kept short, particularly when dealing with VHF or UHF signals.

AC-line filters, sometimes called "brute-force" filters, are used to remove RF energy from ac power lines. A typical schematic is shown in **Figure 27.15**. Note that no filtering is performed on the ground or common connection. (See the Elements of RFI section for the definition for common-mode by utilities and ac power systems.)

Products from Corcom (**www.corcom.com**) and Delta Electronics (**www.deltaww.com**) are widely available and well documented on their websites. Morgan Manufacturing (**www.morganmfg.us**) sells stand-alone ac-line filters with ac plugs and sockets, such as the M-473 and M-475 series of AC Line Protectors.

AC-line filters come in a wide variety of sizes, current ratings, and attenuation. In general, a filter must be physically larger to handle higher currents at lower frequencies. The Corcom 1VB1, a compact filter small enough to fit in the junction box for many low voltage lighting fixtures, provides good common-mode attenuation at MF and HF (only on the hot and neutral lines) and its 1 A at 250 V ac rating is sufficient for many LV lighting fixtures. In general, you will get more performance from a filter that is physically small if you choose the filter with the lowest current rating sufficient for your application. (Section 13.3 of Ott covers ac-line filters.)

The best location for an ac line filter is at the enclosure of the equipment. Filter modules can be bonded to the enclosure through the case of the filter (best) or via a bonding jumper to the enclosure. Bond the enclosure of the filter to the enclosure of the equipment by the shortest possible path. Many enclosures are painted which defeats the bonding of either a filter case, terminal, or solder lug. Clean the paint off the enclosure wherever a bonding connection is made.

Some commercial filters are built with an integral IEC power socket, and can replace a standard IEC connector if there is sufficient space behind the panel. (IEC is the International Electrotechnical Commission, an international standards organization that has created specifications for power plugs and sockets. See the **Safety** chapter for a drawing of an IEC connector.) The case of such a filter is bonded to the enclosure and interconnecting leads are shielded by the enclosure, optimizing its performance.

AC-line filters connected externally to equipment through a cord require extra attention. Any wiring between a filter and the equipment being filtered acts as an antenna and forms an inductive loop that degrades the performance of the filter. All such wiring should be as short as possible, and should be twisted. As described above, they do not apply filtering to the ground conductor which remains active for RFI. Wind several turns of the wiring on a ferrite core to block common-mode RF current on the ground conductor.

AC-line capacitors — A capacitor between line and neutral or between line and ground at the noise source or at victim equipment can solve some RFI problems. ("Ground" in this sense is not "earth," it is the power system equipment ground — the green wire — at the equipment.) Power lines, cords, and cables are often subjected to short-duration spikes of very high voltage (4 kV). Ordinary capacitors are likely to fail when subjected to these voltages, and the failure could cause a fire. Only Type X1, X2, Y1 and Y2 capacitors should be used on power wiring. AC-rated capacitors can safely handle being placed across an ac line along with the typical voltage surges that occur from time to time. Type X1 and X2 capacitors are rated for use between line and neutral, and are available in values between

Differential-Mode and Common-Mode Currents and RFI

Ed Hare, ARRL Lab Manager

Most RFI problems involve a combination of differential-mode and common-mode signals or noise. (See the definition of these terms in the section Elements of RFI and Figures 27.3 and 27.16.) It is important to understand the difference between these two types of signals because generally, a filter designed to filter one type of signal will not be effective against the other type.

A common-mode filter is designed to not affect the differential-mode signals inside of the wiring being filtered. The result is that a common-mode choke would not attenuate any differential-mode noise carried by the wires being filtered. As another example, a differential-mode filter does not usually filter the ground lead in a 3-wire ac cord or cable (see Figure 27.15), so any common-mode signals or noise present on the ground conductor of the ac wiring would be coupled directly through the filter.

In many cases, a noisy device creates both differential-mode and common-mode currents, due to various imbalances in the device and the wiring it is connected to. A susceptible device experiencing interference from a nearby transmitter can be the result of both common-mode and differential-mode signals being picked up on its wiring. Imbalance in ac or signal wiring usually results in both types of signals being created and coupled into and out of devices. For this reason, in many cases, both common-mode and differential-mode filtering may be required.

If an amateur decides on filtering the ac line supplying equipment belonging to a neighbor, it is often best to resolve that problem as quickly and efficiently as possible. Experimenting to find out which type of filter is needed often leads to frustration on the part of the neighbor, who may quickly lose confidence in the ham's ability to resolve the problem. For this reason, it is usually advisable to install both common-mode and differential-mode filtering on a neighbor's device as shown in **Figure 27.A1**, resolving the interference that is present and making future interference less likely.

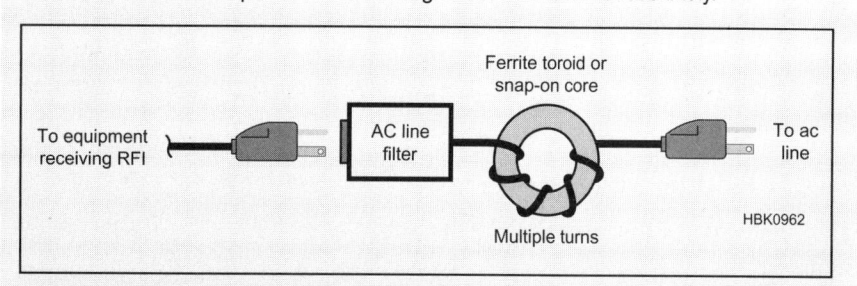

Figure 27.A1 — An ac line filter and a ferrite RF choke combined in the ac line to the affected equipment block both differential- and common-mode current. The line filter can be a standalone model with plugs and receptacles or a module in a grounded metal enclosure. The ferrite mix should be type 31 (for HF) or type 43 (for middle HF through VHF). Either a toroid or clamp-on core can be used if multiple turns can be wound on the core to create sufficient choking impedance.

0.1 µF and 1 µF. Type X2 capacitors are tested to withstand 2.5 kV, type X1 capacitors are tested to 4 kV. Type Y1 and Y2 capacitors are rated for use between line and ground; Y1 capacitors are impulse tested to 8 kV; Type Y2 to 5 kV. Note that 4700 pF is the largest value permitted to be used between line and ground — larger values can result in excessive leakage currents.

CABLE SHIELD CONNECTIONS

In this chapter's prior discussion of common-mode and differential-mode signals, the need for proper connection of cable shields was introduced. Improperly connected shields on audio, RF, and data cables are an important source of radiated and conducted emissions. In addition, they provide a path into equipment for common-mode RF that has been picked up on a cable shield as common-mode current. Either way, an improperly connected shield is a likely cause of RFI.

Figure 27.16 describes the basic reasoning as to how cable shields should be connected. This is a very simplified overview to illustrate the basic concepts. Figure 27.16A shows a metal enclosure and an internal circuit, usually on a PC board. In the circuit itself, there is a common connection that could be a ground plane or point-to-point wiring or traces. Either way, there is some small impedance between any two points in the circuit's ground system. This is shown by the resistor symbols. Current flowing in the ground system is shown as i_G.

The usual practice is to connect the ground system to the enclosure (chassis ground) through a wire or hardware. That, too, has some impedance, shown as a resistor.

The actual voltage applied to the cable connection, V_{DM}, is not equal to V_{OUT}. The ground currents flowing through the ground system impedances create small voltages. So does the ground current flowing through the connection between the circuit ground system and the enclosure. All of these voltages combine to create V_G, which then combines with the amplifier output voltage, V_{OUT}, to create V_{DM}.

Outside the enclosure, a coaxial cable is terminated in an RF connector, such as a PL-259, BNC, Type N, or even a shielded, metal phono plug. The differential-mode signal currents inside the cable (shown as i_{DM}) flow on the cable's center conductor and the *inside* of the cable shield. If a signal is picked up by the cable the resulting common-mode current (shown as i_{CM}) flows on the *outside* of the cable shield. Due to the skin effect, the inside and outside of the cable shield are independent conductors for RF currents.

On the inside of the mating connector (such as an SO-239) a cable or wire pair connect the i_{DM} currents to the circuit. In Figure 27.16A, the center conductor in the cable is connected to some kind of amplifier output (V_{OUT}) and the enclosure-connected part of the connector to the circuit's common or ground terminal. If the connector and shield are attached properly, there is no path between the circuit's differential-mode common terminal and the outside, common-mode surface of the cable shield. Similarly, whatever current i_{DM} is flowing inside the cable, it cannot flow to the outside of the cable where it would become common-mode current and radiate an unwanted signal — a radiated emission.

Figure 27.16B shows what happens when the shield connection goes through the enclosure and is connected directly to the inner circuit ground system. The common-mode current path is now open to i_G that flows in the connection from the circuit ground system to the enclosure. This allows noise and signals from the circuit to escape the enclosure as a

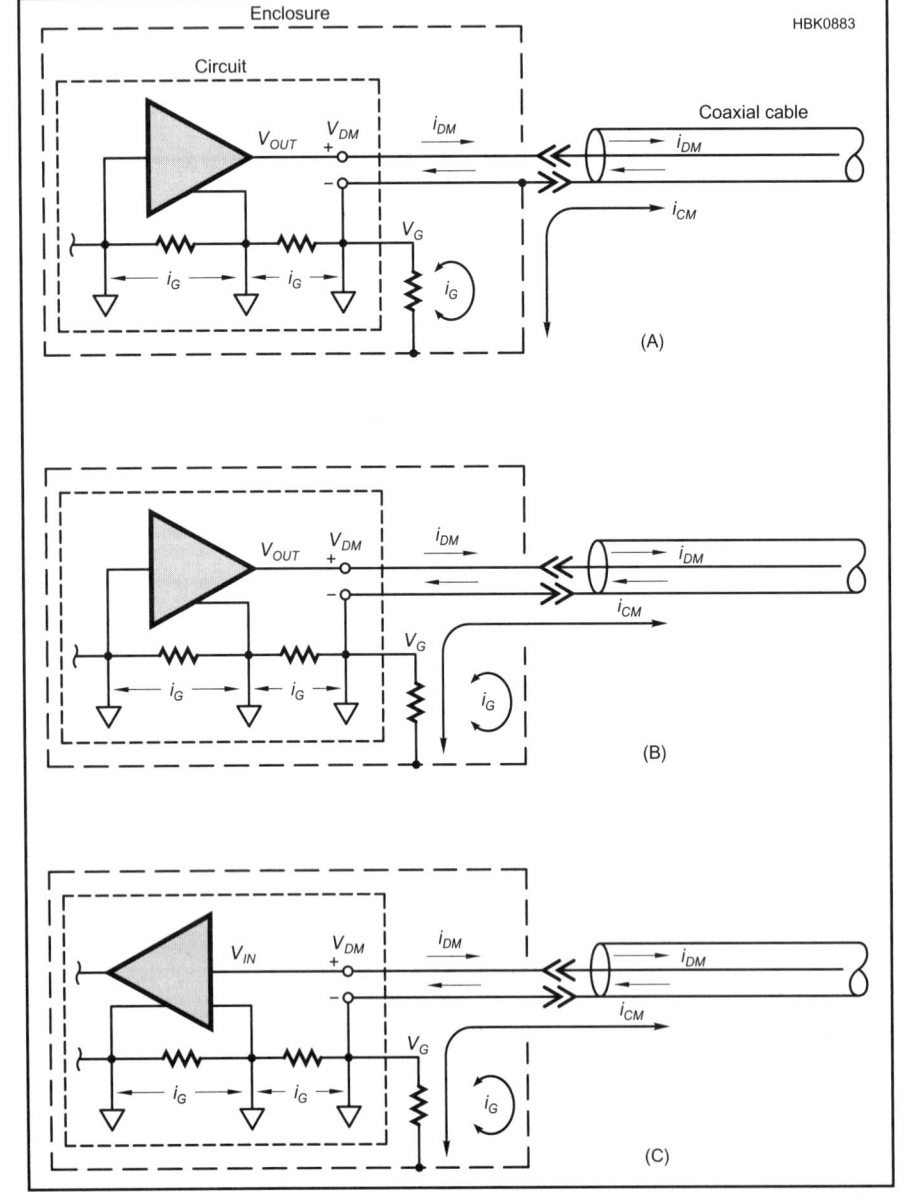

Figure 27.16 — Properly (A) and improperly (B,C) connected shields showing undesired paths for common-mode current into and out of equipment. Improperly connected shields create an ingress and egress path for RF common-mode current. See the text for discussion.

> **Warning: Bypassing Speaker Leads**
>
> Older amateur literature might suggest connecting a 0.01-µF capacitor across an amplifier's speaker output terminals to cure RFI from common mode signals on speaker cables. *Don't do this!* Doing so can cause some modern solid-state amplifiers to break into a destructive, full-power, sometimes ultrasonic oscillation if they are connected to a highly capacitive load. Use common-mode chokes and twisted-pair speaker cables instead.

Figure 27.17 — A common-mode RF choke wound on a toroid core is shown at top left. Several styles of ferrite cores for common-mode chokes are also shown.

radiated emission. The path is also open for i_{CM} to flow in the enclosure connection and add to the voltage that makes up V_G. Depending on the ground system impedance, some of i_{CM} can add to i_G, as well. This allows external noise and signals to get into the circuit's ground system and disrupt its operation.

Figure 27.16C illustrates the situation when the differential-mode signal is an input to the circuit. Noise and signals on the circuit ground system can still escape the enclosure. In addition, the common-mode current i_{CM} combines with i_G which modifies V_G and V_{IN}. This can easily cause a lot of problems if the circuit is a receiver front end or other sensitive function.

Figure 27.3D showed a similar situation with two wires inside a shield. This is common for data or control connections where there might be several data lines and a dedicated signal return or signal ground circuit that is separate from the overall shield. Treat the signal return circuit as an independent circuit and do not connect it to the enclosure. Most shielded data cables have separate signal ground and shield connections. Only the shield should connect to the enclosure.

Not connecting the shield at all breaks the path for the desired differential-mode current on the inside of the shield. This forces it to find another return path, often through ground systems or power wiring. The gap in the shield creates an antenna similar to a magnetic loop that not only radiates the differential-mode signal but allows the undesired common-mode current to combine with the differential-mode signals. The whole system acts as if it were unshielded.

The need to connect the shields of cables to a shielding enclosure is clear whether they are coaxial cables, shielded twisted-pair, or multiconductor data cables. If the shield connection penetrates the enclosure and is connected directly to the circuit's ground system, both radiated emissions and incoming RFI are the likely result. In addition, the unintended current path can affect the impedance of the connection to the cable as discussed in the material on common-mode chokes later in this section

and in the **Transmission Lines** chapter. It is possible to devise alternate connections, such as for transceiver microphone cables, but RF filtering or chokes and careful circuit ground system design and construction are required.

27.7.3 Common-Mode Chokes

Common-mode chokes on ferrite cores are the most effective answer to RFI from a common-mode signal. Differential-mode filters are *not* effective against common-mode signals. (AC-line filters usually only perform differential-mode filtering as described in the preceding section.) Common-mode chokes work differently, but equally well, with coaxial cable and paired conductors. (Additional material on common-mode chokes is found in sections 3.5 and 3.6 of Ott.)

The most common form of common-mode choke is multiple turns of cable wound on a ferrite toroid core as shown in **Figure 27.17**. The following explanation applies to chokes wound on rods as well as toroids, but avoid rod cores since they may couple to nearby circuits at HF. At HF, toroid cores are recommended — beads and clamp-on ferrite cores are usually adequate.

Most of the time, a common-mode signal on a coaxial cable or a shielded, multi-wire cable is a current flowing on the outside of the cable's shield. By wrapping the cable around a magnetic core the current creates a flux in the core, creating a high impedance in series with the outside of the shield.

(An impedance of a few hundred to several thousand ohms are required for an effective choke.) The impedance then blocks or reduces the common-mode current. Because equal-and-opposite fields are coupled to the core from each of the differential-mode currents, the common-mode choke has no effect on differential-mode signals inside the cable.

When the cable consists of two-wire, unshielded conductors such as zip cord or twisted-pair, the equal-and-opposite differential currents each create a magnetic flux in the core. The equal-and-opposite fluxes cancel each other and the differential-mode signal experiences zero net effect. To common-mode signals, however, the choke appears as a high impedance in series with the signal: the higher the impedance, the lower the common-mode current.

It is important to note that common-mode currents on a transmission line will result in radiation of a signal from the feed line. (See the sidebar for an explanation of balanced vs unbalanced transmission lines.) The radiated signal can then cause RFI in nearby circuits. This is most common when using coaxial cable as a feed line to a balanced load, such as the dipole in the sidebar. Reducing common-mode current with a common-mode choke at the antenna feed point and where the feed line enters the residence can help reduce RFI caused by signals radiated from the feed line's shield.

Common-mode noise is also picked up by feed lines. If it is allowed to flow into the

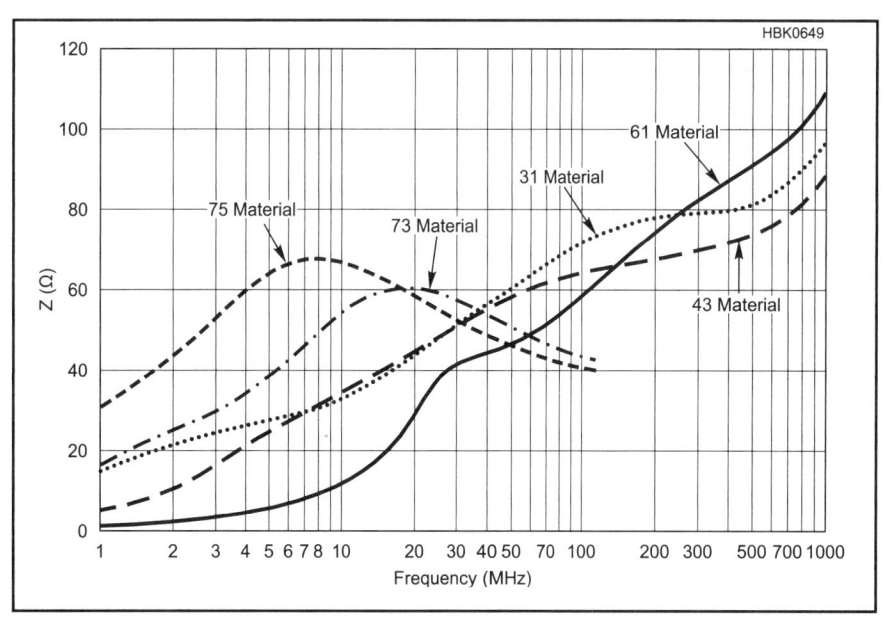

Figure 27.18 — Impedance vs. frequency plots for "101" size ferrite beads illustrate the effect of various ferrite materials across different frequency ranges. A 3.50 mm × 1.30 mm × 6.00 mm bead (Fair-Rite 301 size) was used for the above curve for material comparison, however all materials are not available in all shapes and sizes. Type 73 material is only available in smaller cores, type 31 is only available in larger cores, and type 75 is currently only available as a toroid core. [Graph courtesy of the Fair-Rite Corporation]

station, it can also be converted to differential-mode signals at connectors and by coupling to other cables and wiring in the station. Chokes can block this current and eliminate this source of received noise and unwanted signals which can contribute to the noise level considerably.

Common-mode chokes using ferrite cores are discussed at length in the **RF Techniques** and **Transmission Lines** chapters. They block common-mode RF current by adding a large value of resistive impedance in series with the common-mode circuit. The choke actually behaves as a parallel-self-resonant circuit that includes the winding inductance and stray capacitance along with the resistance of the core material at that frequency. (The electrical characteristics of ferrite at RF are discussed in the **RF Techniques** chapter.)

The self-resonance of a conductor passing once through most ferrite cores (considered to be one turn) used for suppression is in the range of 150 MHz, and this is where a core simply clamped around a cable will be effective. To obtain good suppression in the range of 1-50 MHz, we must wind multiple turns through the ferrite core to lower the resonant frequency. Common-mode chokes are typically wound on toroid cores with a 1-inch or greater inside diameter or a split-core clamp-on core.

Figure 27.18 is a combined graph of the impedance of single turns through a ferrite bead of different mixes. It gives an idea of the range of ferrites that are available. By using the right material and the right number of turns through the core, choke impedance can be optimized for resistance and for the frequency range desired. Resistive impedance is desired to avoid interacting with the conductor's reactance at the frequency of use. The right material to use is specified for "suppression" over the frequency range required. (Fair-Rite mixes #31, #43, #44, and #61 are of the most use to amateurs.) This means the core's impedance is primarily resistive in that range. Chokes wound on these cores have a very low Q (because they are dissipating energy instead of storing it) so the choke's bandwidth can be as much as an octave. Chokes can be designed to work over different frequency ranges – placing chokes optimized for different ranges in series works over the combined frequency range.

Type 31 material is a good all-purpose material for HF and low-VHF applications, especially at low HF frequencies. Type 43 is widely used for HF through VHF and UHF. The **Component Data and References** chapter includes a table of ferrite materials and characteristics. This discussion only touches on the basic characteristics of ferrite-core common-mode chokes as they apply to dealing with RFI.

Warning: Surplus Ferrite Cores

Don't use a core to make a common-mode choke if you don't know what type of material it is made of. Such cores may not be effective in the frequency range you are working with. This may lead to the erroneous conclusion that a common-mode choke doesn't work when a core with the correct material would have done the job.

Feed Line Radiation — The Difference Between Balanced and Unbalanced Transmission Lines

The physical differences between balanced and unbalanced feed lines are obvious. Balanced lines are parallel-type transmission lines, such as ladder line or twin lead. The two conductors that make up a balanced line run side-by-side, separated by an insulating material (plastic, air, whatever). Unbalanced lines, on the other hand, are coaxial-type feed lines. One of the conductors (the shield) completely surrounds the other (the center).

In an ideal world, both types of transmission lines would deliver RF power to the load (typically your antenna) without radiating any energy along the way. It is important to understand, however, that both types of transmission lines require a balanced condition in order to accomplish this feat. That is, the currents in each conductor must be equal in magnitude, but opposite in polarity.

The classic definition of a balanced transmission line tells us that both conductors must be symmetrical (same length and separation distance) relative to a common reference point, usually ground. It's fairly easy to imagine the equal and opposite currents flowing through this type of feeder. When such a condition occurs, the fields generated by the currents cancel each other-hence, no radiation. An imbalance occurs when one of the conductors carries more current than the other. This additional "imbalance current" causes the feed line to radiate.

Things are a bit different when we consider a coaxial cable. Instead of its being a symmetrical line, one of its conductors (usually the shield), is grounded. In addition, the currents flowing in the coax are confined to the outside portion of the center conductor and the inside portion of the shield.

When a balanced load, such as a resonant dipole antenna, is connected to unbalanced coax, the outside of the shield can act as an electrical third conductor (see **Figure 27.A**). This phantom third conductor can provide an alternate path for the imbalance current to flow. Whether the small amount of stray radiation that occurs is important or not is subject to debate. In fact, one of the purposes of a balun (a contraction of balanced to unbalanced) is to reduce or eliminate imbalance current flowing on the outside of the shield. See the **Transmission Lines** chapter of this book for more information on baluns.

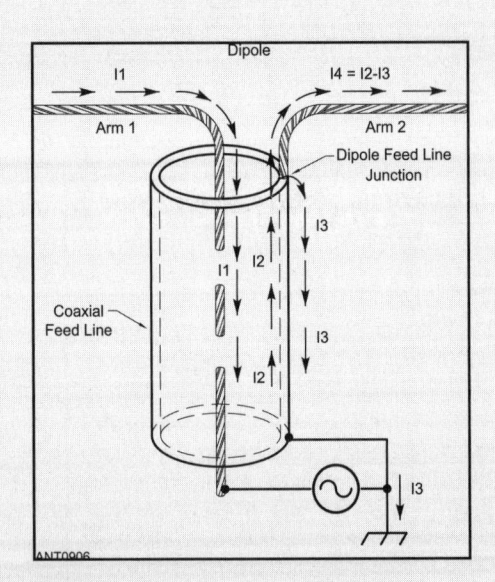

Fig 27.A — Various current paths are present at the feed point of a balanced dipole fed with unbalanced coaxial cable. The diameter of the coax is exaggerated to show the currents clearly.

27.8 Troubleshooting RFI

Troubleshooting an RFI problem is a multi-step process, and all steps are equally important. First you must determine the type(s) of noise source(s) that are involved. Next, diagnose the problem by locating the noise source and the means by which it creates the noise. The final step is to identify the path by which the noise or signals reach the victim device. Only then can you cure the problem by breaking the path from source to victim.

Each step in troubleshooting an RFI problem involves asking and answering several questions: Is the problem caused by harmonics, fundamental overload, conducted emissions, radiated emissions or a combination of all of these factors? Should it be fixed with a low-pass filter, high-pass filter, common-mode chokes or ac-line filter? How about shielding, isolation transformers, a different ground or antenna configuration? By the time you finish with these questions, the possibilities could number in the millions. You probably will not see your exact problem and cure listed in this book or any other. You must not only diagnose the problem but find a cure as well!

Now that you have learned some RFI fundamentals, you can work on specific technical solutions. A systematic approach will identify the problem and suggest a cure. Most RFI problems can be solved in this way by the application of standard techniques. The following sections suggest specific approaches for different types of common interference problems. This advice is based on the experience of the ARRL RFI Desk, but is not guaranteed to provide a solution to your particular problem. Armed with your RFI knowledge, a kit of filters and tools, your local TC and a determination to solve the problem, it is time to begin. You should also get a copy of the *ARRL RFI Book*. It's comprehensive and picks up where this chapter leaves off.

27.8.1 General RFI Troubleshooting Guidelines

Before diving into the problem, take a step back and consider some of these "pre-troubleshooting steps."

Is It Really EMI? — Before trying to solve a suspected case of EMI, verify that the symptoms actually result from external causes. A variety of equipment malfunctions or external noise can look like interference.

Is It Your Station? — "Your" EMI problem might be caused by another ham or a radio transmitter of another radio service, such as a local CB or police transmitter. If it appears that your station is involved, operate your station on each band, mode and power level that you use. Note all conditions that produce interference. If no transmissions produce the problem, your station *may* not be the cause. (Although some contributing factor may have been missing in the test.) Have your neighbor keep notes of when and how the interference appears: what time of day, what station, what other appliances were in use, what was the weather? You should do the same whenever you operate. If you can readily reproduce the problem with your station, you can start to troubleshoot the problem.

Take One Away — Can you remove the source or victim entirely? The best cure for an RFI problem is often removing the source of the noise. If the source is something broken, for example, the usual solution is to repair it. Power-line noise and an arcing electric fence usually fall into this category. If a switchmode power supply is radiating noise, replace it with a linear supply. Victim devices can sometimes be replaced with a more robust piece of equipment, as well.

Look Around — Aside from the brain, the eyes are a troubleshooter's best tool. Installation defects contribute to many RFI problems. Look for loose connections, shield breaks in a cable-TV installation or corroded contacts in a telephone installation. Have these fixed these first. Look for wiring connected to the victim equipment that might be long enough to be resonant on one or more amateur bands. If so, a common-mode choke may be an easy cure. Ideally you'll generally want place the choke as close to the victim device as practical. If this placement proves too difficult or additional suppression is required, chokes placed at the middle of the wiring may help break up resonances. These are just a few of the possible deficiencies in a home installation.

At Your Station — Make sure that your own station and consumer equipment are clean. This cuts the size of a possible interference problem from your station in half! Once this is done, you won't need to diagnose or troubleshoot your station later. Also, any cures successful at your house may work at your neighbor's as well. If you do have problems in your own home, continue through the troubleshooting steps and specific cures and take care of your own problem first.

Simplify the Problem — Don't tackle a complex system — such as a telephone system in which there are two lines running to 14 rooms — all at once. You could spend the rest of your life running in circles and never find the true cause of the problem.

There's a better way. In our hypothetical telephone system, first locate the telephone jack closest to the telephone service entrance. Disconnect the lines to more remote jacks and connect one RFI-resistant telephone at the remaining jack. (Old-style rotary-dial phones are often quite immune to RF.) If the interference remains, try cures until the problem is solved, then start adding lines and equipment back one at a time, fixing the problems as you go along. If you are lucky, you will solve all of the problems in one pass. If not, at least you can point to one piece of equipment as the source of the problem.

Multiple Causes — Many RFI problems have multiple causes. These are usually the ones that give new RFI troubleshooters the most trouble. For example, consider a TVI problem caused by the combination of harmonics from the transmitter due to an arc in the transmitting antenna, an overloaded TV preamplifier, fundamental overload generat-

---

Dummy Detectives

One particularly useful troubleshooting tool for determining where RFI is entering a victim device is called a "dummy" – a short test cable that can be inserted in a signal path. The dummy's cable shield is connected on each end of the cable but the center conductor is not connected. The dummy will allow common-mode current to flow on the shield, but will not pass a differential-mode signal. This technique was devised by Bill Whitlocak of Jensen Transformers.

Dummies are quite useful in identifying where RFI is being introduced in a signal path. If the interference goes away when the dummy is inserted, the RFI is being introduced upstream of the dummy. If the interference is common-mode, it will still be present when the dummy is inserted upstream of the victim equipment that is detecting it because the dummy's shield passes common-mode noise to the victim.

An F connector dummy is easily made with two F plugs installed on a short length of coax. A double-receptacle F "barrel" adaptor can be attached to one of the plugs to create an extension cable. At one or both of the plugs, the center conductor is snipped flush with the shield so that it does not make contact with the mating connector.

Dummies made with RCA and 1/8-in connectors (mono and stereo) are also useful for the same purpose in home entertainment systems and other consumer electronics. Use high-quality connectors, such as those made by Switchcraft and Neutrik, and use good shielded cable that fits the connector, such as RG-174 subminiature coax. Cut the center conductor of the coaxial cable so that it does not make contact with the connector pins.

ing harmonics in the TV tuner, induced and conducted RF on the ac-power connections, and a common-mode signal picked up on the shield of the TV's coaxial feed line. You would never find a cure for this multiple-cause problem by trying only one cure at a time.

In this case, the solution requires that all of the cures be present at the same time. When troubleshooting, if you try a cure, leave it in place even if it doesn't solve the problem. When you add a cure that finally solves the problem entirely, start removing the "temporary" attempts one at a time. If the interference returns, you know that there were multiple causes.

Take Notes — In the process of troubleshooting an RFI problem, it's easy to lose track of what remedies were applied, to what equipment, and in what order. Configurations of equipment can change rapidly when you're experimenting. To minimize the chances of going around in circles or getting confused, take lots of notes as you proceed. Sketches and drawings can be very useful. When you do find the cause of a problem and a cure for it, be sure to write all that down so you can refer to it in the future.

RFI Survival Kit — **Table 27.1** is a list of the material needed to troubleshoot and solve most RFI problems. Having all of these materials in one container, such as a small tackle or craft box, makes the troubleshooting process go a lot smoother.

27.8.2 Transmitters

We start with transmitters not because most interference comes from transmitters, but because your station transmitter is under your direct control. Many of the troubleshooting steps in other parts of this chapter assume that your transmitter is "clean" (free of unwanted RF output).

Start by looking for patterns in the interference. Problems that occur only on harmonics of a fundamental signal usually indicate the transmitter is the source of the interference. Harmonics can also be generated in nearby semiconductors, such as an unpowered VHF receiver left connected to an antenna, rectifiers in a rotator control box, or a corroded connection in a tower guy wire. Harmonics can also be generated in the front-end components of the TV or radio experiencing interference.

If HF transmitter spurs at VHF are causing interference, a low-pass filter at the transmitter output will usually cure the problem. If an amplifier is used, be sure it is adjusted properly and not mistuned. If a filter at the transmitter is insufficient either the amplifier or transmitter may need repair or something else may be creating the harmonics. Transmitting filters are generally designed for 50 Ω input and output impedances, so install any filters on the input side of an antenna tuner, if one is used. Install a low-pass filter as your first step in any in-terference problem that involves another radio service at VHF or higher frequencies.

Interference from non-harmonic spurious emissions is extremely rare in commercial radios. Any such problem indicates a malfunction that should be repaired.

27.8.3 Television Interference (TVI)

Digital TV has somewhat better immunity than the obsolete analog system but for both formats, clear reception requires a strong signal at the TV antenna-input connector so the receiver must be in what is known as a *strong-signal area*.

TVI to a TV receiver (or a video monitor) normally has one of the following causes:
• Spurious signals within the TV channel coming from your transmitter or station.
• The TV set may be overloaded by your transmitter's fundamental signal.

Table 27.1
RFI Survival Kit
Quantity Item
(2) 75-Ω high-pass filter
(2) Commercially available clamp-on ferrite cores: #31 and #43 material, 0.3" ID
(12) Assorted ferrite cores: #31 and #43 material, FT-140 and FT-240 size
(3) Telephone RFI filters
(2) Brute-force ac line filters
(6) 0.01-µF ceramic capacitors
(6) 0.001-µF ceramic capacitors

Miscellaneous:
• Hand tools, assorted screwdrivers, wire cutters, pliers
• Hookup wire
• Electrical tape
• Soldering iron and solder (use with caution!)
• Assorted lengths 75-Ω coaxial cable with connectors
• Spare F connectors, male, and crimping tool
• F-connector female-female "barrel"
• Clip leads
• Notebook and pencil
• Portable multimeter

"Keeping It Simple"

Filters and chokes are the number one weapons of choice for many RFI problems whether the device is the source or the victim. They are relatively inexpensive, easy to install, and do not require permanently modifying the device.

Common-mode choke — Making a common-mode choke is simple. Select the type of core and ferrite material for the frequency range of the interference. (Type 31 is a good HF/low-VHF material, type #43 from 5 MHz through VHF) Wrap several turns of the cable or wire pairs around the toroid. Six to 8 turns is a good start at 10-30 MHz and 10 to 15 turns from 1.8 to 7 MHz. (Ten to 15 turns is probably the practical limit for most cables.) Ferrite clamp-on split cores and beads that slide over the cable or wire are not as effective as toroid-core chokes at HF but are the right solution at VHF and higher frequencies. For a clamp-on core, the cable doesn't even need to be disconnected from its end. Use type 31 or type 43 material at VHF, type 61 at UHF. At 50 MHz, use two turns through type 31 or 43 cores.

"Brute-Force" ac-line filters — RF signals often enter and exit a device via an ac power connection. "Brute-force" ac-line filters are simple and easy to install. Most ac filters only provide differential-mode suppression as described in the text. It is essential to use a filter rated to handle the device's required current.

General installation guidelines for using chokes and filters

1. If you have a brute-force ac-line filter, put one on the device or power cord. If RFI persists, add a common-mode choke to the power cord at the device.
2. Simplify the problem by removing cables one at a time until you no longer detect RFI. Start with cables longer than 1/10th-wavelength at the highest frequency of concern. If the equipment can't operate without a particular cable, add common-mode chokes at the affected or source device.
3. Add a common-mode choke to the last cable removed and verify its effect on the RFI. Some cables may require several chokes in difficult cases.
4. Begin reconnecting cables one at a time. If RFI reappears, add a common-mode choke to that cable. Repeat for each cable.
5. Once the RFI goes away, remove the common-mode chokes you added one at a time. If the RFI does not return, you do not need to reinstall the choke. If the RFI returns after removing a choke, reinstall it. Keep only those chokes required to fix the problem.

- Signals within the TV channel from some source other than your station, such as electrical noise, an overloaded mast-mounted TV preamplifier or a transmitter in another service.

- The TV set might be defective or misadjusted, making it look like there is an interference problem.

- One or more connecting cables is loose or defective. Be sure cables are of good-quality and that connectors are installed properly, especially older crimp-type F connectors.

All of these problems are made potentially more severe because TV receiving equipment is hooked up to *two* antenna systems: (1) the incoming antenna or cable feed line and (2) the ac power line and interconnecting cables. These two antenna systems can couple significant levels of fundamental or harmonic energy into the TV set or video display! The *TVI Troubleshooting Flowchart* in **Figure 27.19** is a good starting point.

The problem could also be caused by direct pickup of the transmitted signal by an unshielded TV or device connected to the TV.

Certain types of television receivers and video monitors are reported to cause broadband RF interference *to* amateur signals — large-screen plasma display models were at one time reported to be the most frequent offender — and this may be difficult to cure due to the nature of the display technology. Fortunately, less-expensive, more power-efficient, and RF-quieter LCD technology has displaced plasma technology for current models.

The manufacturer of the TV or video equipment can sometimes help with an interference problem. The Consumer Electronics Association (CEA) can also help you contact equipment manufacturers. Contact them directly for assistance in locating help at **www.ce.org**.

COMMON SOURCES OF TVI

HF transmitters — A nearby HF transmitter is most likely to cause fundamental overload. This is usually indicated by interference to all channels, or at least all VHF channels. To cure fundamental overload from an HF transmitter to an antenna-connected TV, install a high-pass filter directly at the TV set's antenna input. (Do not use a high-pass filter on a cable-TV input because the HF range is used for data and other system signals.)

A strong HF signal can also result in a strong common-mode signal on the TV's feed line. A common-mode choke will block signals on the outside of the feed line shield, leaving the desired signals inside the feed line unaffected. **Figure 27.20** shows how a common-mode choke is constructed for a coaxial feed line. The same choke can be applied

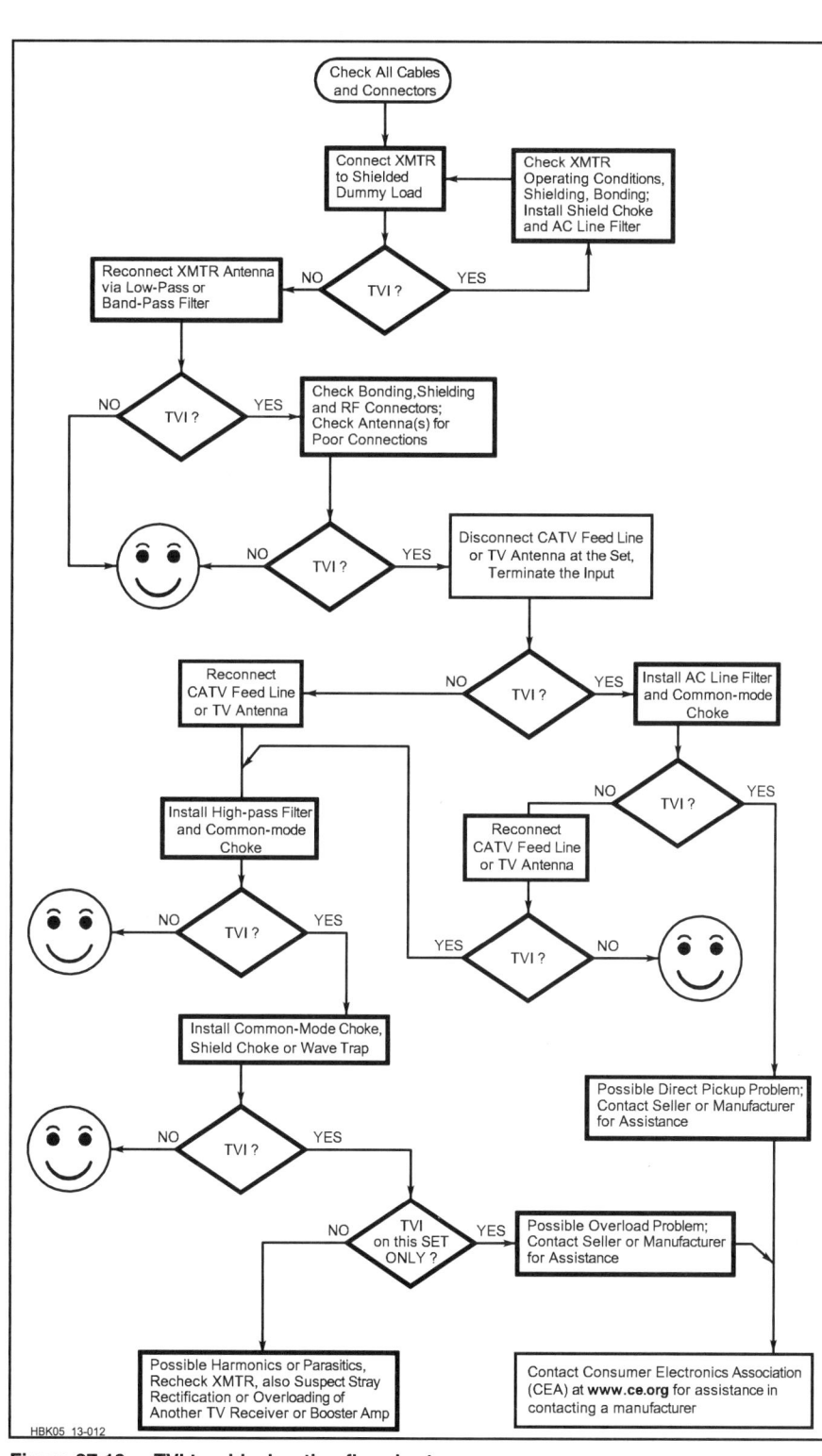

Figure 27.19 — TVI troubleshooting flowchart.

Figure 27.20 — To eliminate HF and VHF signals on the outside of a coaxial cable, use an 1- to 2-inch OD toroid core and wind as many turns of the cable on the core as practical.

to audio, control, and power cables, as well, to prevent RFI caused by common-mode ingress via these non-RF paths.

These filters and chokes can probably cure most cases of TVI! **Figure 27.21** shows a "bulletproof" installation for both over-the-air and cable TV receivers. If one of these methods doesn't cure the problem, the problem is likely direct pickup in which a signal is received by the TV set's circuitry without any conducting path being required. In that case, don't try to fix it yourself — it is a problem for the TV manufacturer.

High-pass filters *should not* be used in a cable TV feed line (Figure 27.21A) with two-way cable devices such as cable modems, set-top boxes, and newer two-way Cable-CARD-equipped TVs. The high-pass filter may prevent the device from communicating via the cable network's upstream signal path.

VHF Transmitters —Most TV tuners are not very selective and a strong VHF or UHF signal, including those from nearby FM and TV transmitters, can overload the tuner easily, particularly when receiving VHF or UHF broadcasts over the air and not via a cable or satellite system. In this case, a notch or stopband filter at the TV can help by attenuating the fundamental signal that overloads the TV tuner. Channel Plus (**www.solidsignal.com**), PAR Electronics (**www.parelectronics.com**), and Scannermaster (**www.scannermaster.com**) sell notch filters. A common-mode choke may also be necessary if the TV is responding to the common-mode fundamental signal present on the TV's feed line. Note that most TV broadcasts are now in the UHF spectrum, regardless of what channel number they use in their identification. You can find the actual channel used by a TV station at **transition.fcc.gov/dtv/markets** and **www.fcc.gov/media/engineering/dtvmaps** provides coverage maps based on Zip code.

If the VHF transmitter is generating a harmonic or other spurious emission causing RFI, a transmission line stub filter may be a good solution. The stub can be designed to remove a signal at the transmitter. If the transmitter's fundamental signal is overloading the receiver, a notch filter stub can also be applied at the receiver. See the **Transmission Lines** chapter for more information about these filters.

TV Preamplifiers — Preamplifiers are only needed in weak-signal areas and they often cause trouble, particularly when used unnecessarily in strong-signal areas. They are subject to the same overload problems as TVs and when located on the antenna mast it can be difficult to install the appropriate cures. You may need to install a high-pass or notch filter at the input of the preamplifier, as well as a common-mode choke on the input, output and power-supply wiring (if separate) to effect a complete cure. All filters, connections, and chokes must be weatherproofed. A common-mode choke will reduce RF current on the feed line's shield.

For a common-mode feed line choke, use two 1-inch long type 43 clamp-on ferrite cores if VHF signals are causing the interference and type 61 material for UHF. HF choke design is discussed in the section on Common-Mode Chokes.

Spurious Emissions — You are responsible for spurious emissions produced by your station. If your station is generating any interfering spurious signals, the problem must be cured there. Start by analyzing which TV channels are affected. A TV Channel Chart showing the relationship of the amateur allocations and their harmonics to over-the-air and cable channels is provided in this book's downloadable supplemental material. Each channel is 6 MHz wide. If the interference is only on channels that are multiples of your transmitting frequency, you probably have interference caused by harmonics of your transmitted signal. Harmonics from commercial transceivers, however, are quite rare. As mentioned earlier, significant harmonics from such equipment probably indicates a failure that needs to be repaired.

It is not certain that these harmonics are coming from your station, however. Harmonics can be generated by overloaded preamplifiers or tuner input circuits. Harmonics can also be generated like IMD products by nonlinear junctions near your station transmitter or very near the TV receiver antenna. (See the section on Intermodulation Distortion.) If your transmitter and station check "clean" — check to see if you have interference on a TV set in your own home — then you must look elsewhere for the source of the harmonics.

An inexpensive SDR receiver is a good way to see if spurious emissions of any sort — not necessarily just harmonics — are present. Several *QST* vendors sell complete SDR packages and SDR projects are available, as well. An online survey of SDR receivers, including portable models, is available on-

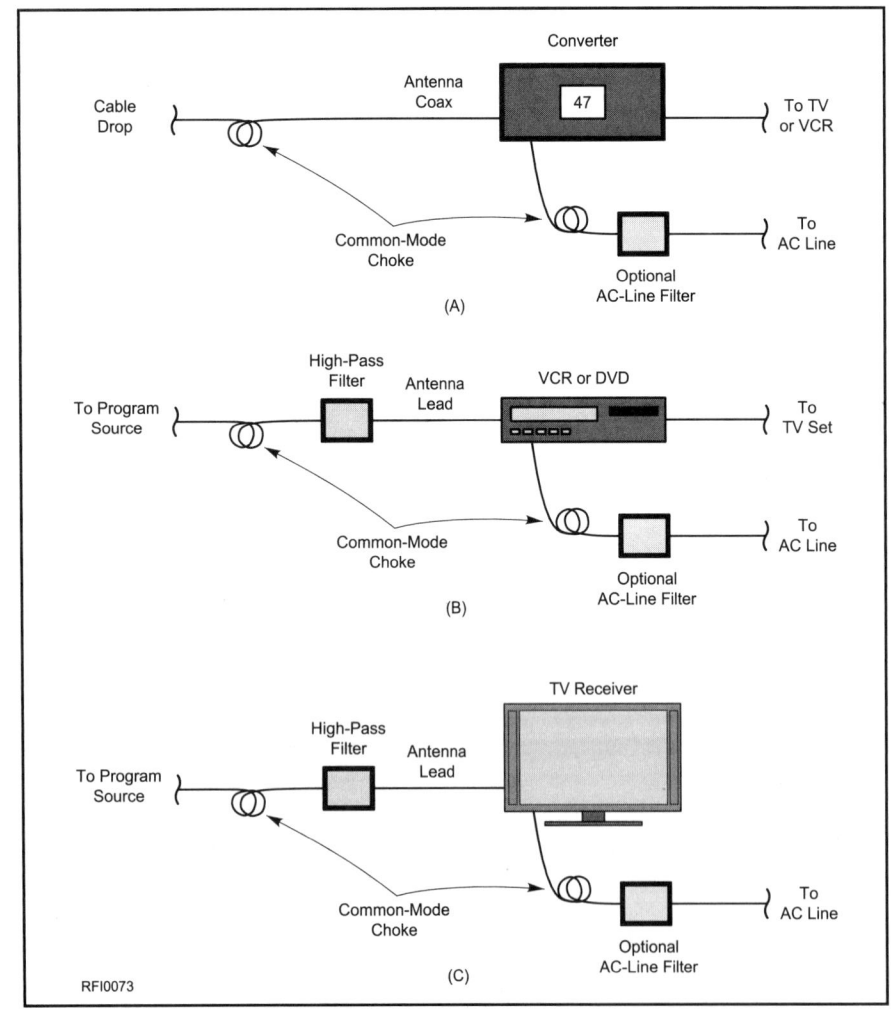

Figure 27.21 — Installing common-mode chokes and high-pass filters will cure most fundamental overload interference from HF sources. Apply common-mode chokes in the ac power cord before adding ac-line filters. This technique does not address direct pickup or spurious emission problems.

line at **www.rtl-sdr.com/roundup-software-defined-radios**.

Electrical Noise — Digital TV signals are fairly resistant to electrical noise, but in extreme cases can cause the picture to freeze or fail to be displayed as discussed in the following section on Digital TV Receivers.

On an AM receiver (including SSB or CW receivers), electrical noise usually sounds like a buzz, sometimes changing in intensity as the arc or spark sputters a bit. If you have a problem with electrical noise, refer to the section on Electrical Noise.

DIGITAL TV (DTV) RECEIVERS

Nearly all over-the-air TV broadcasters in the US, with the exception of low-power TV stations and translators, are using the DTV (digital TV) format. Digital TV signals can operate with much lower signal-to-noise ratios, but are still susceptible to interference.

Interference to digital TV signals from amateur signals — narrowband interference, for instance, a CW carrier — to a 6 MHz-wide digital TV signal generally has two effects. If the interfering signal is strong enough, it will cause degraded *modulation error ratio* (MER) and degraded *bit error rate* (BER) in the digital video signal. If the amplitude of the interference is sufficient, the digital receiver's *forward error correction* (FEC) circuitry will be unable to fix the broken bits, and the digital video signal will "crash." (See the **Digital Modes** chapter for more information on coding and error correction in digital protocols.)

TV viewers watching any of the multiple video streams that may be contained within the digital video signal won't see any problems in the picture (or hear anything wrong in the sound), until the so-called "crash point" is reached. At that point, the picture will begin to show intermittent "tiling" (the picture breaking up into small squares) or blocking (freezing) in the image. As the amplitude of the interfering signal increases perhaps another 0.5 dB to 1 dB, the crash point or "digital cliff" is reached, and the picture and sound are gone! As you can see, there is a tiny window between receiving a perfect picture and receiving no picture. The same effect is produced by signal fading and may be difficult to distinguish from RFI.

Interference to the digital signal does not make its presence known through visual or audible artifacts such as streaks, lines, or tearing in the picture, or garbled audio. This means that a viewer experiencing interference may not be able to identify its source, but troubleshooting interference may also become more difficult. Nevertheless, the more robust digital modulation is often less susceptible to interference from narrowband amateur signals. A clue to the source of the interference is that interference caused by an amateur signal will occur in sync with the amateur's transmissions while other types of interference will have no correlation.

The techniques for curing interference between amateur and digital TV signals are largely the same as they were for analog TV. Fundamental overload generally responds well to filters in the antenna or RF inputs. Interference caused by spurious emissions from the amateur station can be eliminated by filtering at the amateur transmitter. Common-mode problems in which RF signals are conducted into the television receiver's circuitry by external audio, video, and power cables are no more or less likely than for analog TV sets and can be addressed as described elsewhere in this chapter.

ANALOG TV RECEIVERS

Even though over-the-air TV broadcasting largely switched to a digital format in 2009, many analog TV receivers are still in use for cable TV, satellite TV, with converter boxes for digital broadcast signals, and for displaying video from DVDs and other video sources. Older VCR and DVD players may also include an analog TV tuner to receive analog TV signals.

Interference to video displays and monitors that do not receive RF signals from an antenna or RF modulator should be assumed to be common-mode interference or direct pickup. The same applies to interference to a TV set displaying video signals (not through the antenna input). Interference that is present only on the audio is probably a case of common-mode RFI. (See the Stereos and Home Entertainment Systems section of this chapter.)

27.8.4 Cable TV

Cable TV has generally benefited Amateur Radio with respect to TVI. The cable system delivers a strong, consistent signal to the TV receiver, reducing susceptibility to interference from amateur signals. It is also a shielded system so an external signal shouldn't be able to cause interference. Most cable companies are responsible about keeping signal leakage (*egress*) and *ingress* — the opposite of leakage — under control, but problems do happen. Cable companies are not responsible for direct pickup or common-mode interference problems, but are responsible for leakage, ingress, and any noise radiated by common-mode currents from their equipment.

Cable companies are able to take advantage of something known as frequency reuse. That is, all radio frequencies higher than 5 MHz are used to transmit TV signals. The latter is possible because the cables and components used to transport signals to and from paying subscribers comprise what is known as a closed network. In other words, a cable company can use frequencies inside of its cables that may be used for entirely different purposes in the over-the-air environment. As long as the shielding integrity of the cable network is maintained, the cable company's signals won't interfere with over-the-air services, and vice-versa.

The reality is that the shielding integrity of a cable network *is* sometimes compromised, perhaps because of a loose or damaged connector, a cracked cable shield, rodent damage, poorly shielded customer premises equipment (CPE) such as cable-ready TVs and

---

Common Mistake — It's the Cable System

The cable company is often incorrectly blamed for causing interference that is actually generated by consumer devices. Remember that all the individual circuit grounds in your home are bonded at the service entrance panel. The National Electrical Code also requires the cable TV ground to be bonded to this same ground system.

When you now consider that most RFI problems, especially at HF, involve conducted emissions, it's easy to see what can happen. Conducted emissions from a consumer device can propagate along ground conductors and wind up on the shield of the cable TV coax. The cable (and possibly other components of the cable TV system) can then radiate the noise.

Ron Hranac, NØIVN, also adds the following from an industry point of view:

"A key point that needs to be emphasized related to this topic is that in many cases wideband noise from consumer devices that is being coupled to and radiated from the cable TV network is often assumed to be leaking cable modem digital signals. The cable company channelizes its digital signals (downstream channel bandwidths are 6 MHz, and upstream channel bandwidths are typically either 3.2 MHz or 6.4 MHz). The cable company generally does not use upstream frequencies below about 15 MHz for cable modem data transmission, although there might be a narrowband data carrier from set-top boxes in the roughly 8 MHz to 12 MHz range. Cable modem upstream signals are generally found in the 20 MHz to 42 MHz range, sometimes as low as 15 MHz or so. The cable company does not transmit signals in the diplex filter cutoff region of about 42 MHz to 50 MHz, nor does it transmit signals below about the previously mentioned 8 MHz or so."

Conclusion: Don't automatically assume that the cable TV system is the cause of an RFI problem just because it is radiating the noise. — *Mike Gruber, W1MG, ARRL Test Engineer*

DVD and Blu-Ray players, and problems that may happen when someone tries to steal cable service! §76.605(a)(12) of the FCC Rules defines the maximum allowable signal leakage (*egress*) field strength at specified measurement distances, and §76.613 covers harmful interference. FCC Rules also mandate that cable operators "…shall provide for a program of regular monitoring for signal leakage by substantially covering the plant every three months," and leaks greater than 20 microvolts per meter (µV/m) at a 10 ft. measurement distance repaired in a reasonable period of time. As well, an annual "snapshot" of leakage performance must be characterized via a flyover measurement of the cable system, or a ground-based measurement of 75% of the network.

CABLE TV FREQUENCY USAGE

A typical modern North American cable network is designed to use frequencies in the 5 to 1002 MHz spectrum. Signals that travel from the cable company to the subscriber occupy frequencies from just above 50 MHz to as high as 1002 MHz range (this is the downstream or forward spectrum), and signals that travel from the subscriber to the cable company are carried in the 5 to as high as 42 MHz range, known as the upstream or return spectrum. The downstream is divided into 6 MHz-wide channel slots, which carry 64- or 256-QAM digitally modulated signals used for digital video, high-speed data, and telephone services. (Analog cable service has been phased out.) Upstream signals from cable modems and two-way set-top boxes are generally carried on specific frequencies chosen by the cable company. **Table 27.2** summarizes cable downstream channel allocations that overlap Amateur Radio bands. The complete North American channel plan is controlled by EIA standard 542-B. A summary of the channel structure for North America is maintained at **en.wikipedia.org/wiki/North_American_television_frequencies#cite_note-14**.

COMMON MECHANISMS FOR LEAKAGE AND INGRESS

As noted previously, cable TV leakage and ingress occur when the shielding integrity of the cable network is compromised. A large cable system that serves a major metropolitan area has literally millions of connectors, tens of thousands of miles of coaxial cable, thousands of amplifiers, hundreds of thousands of passives (splitters, directional couplers, and similar devices), and uncountable customer premises equipment connected to the cable network! Any of these may be a source of leakage and ingress.

DIGITAL SIGNAL LEAKAGE

The digitally modulated signals carried in a cable TV network use 64-QAM or 256-QAM, the latter more common. (See the **Modulation** chapter for more information on Digital TV modulation.) If a QAM signal were to leak from a cable TV network, it is possible for interference to an over-the-air service to occur, but very unlikely to be identified as from a digital TV signal. The reason for this is that a QAM signal is noise-like, and sounds like normal background noise or hiss on a typical amateur receiver. The QAM signal's digital channel power — its average power over the entire occupied bandwidth — is typically 6 to 10 dB lower than what an analog TV signal's visual carrier peak envelope power (PEP) would be on the same channel. As well, a QAM signal occupies most of the 6 MHz channel slot, and there are no carriers *per se* within that channel bandwidth. Note that over-the-air 8-VSB digital TV broadcast signals transmit a pilot carrier near the lower end of the digital "haystack," but the QAM format used by cable operators has no comparable pilot carrier.

What makes the likelihood of interference occurring (or not occurring) has in large part to do with the behavior of a receiver in the presence of broadband noise. While each downstream cable TV QAM signal occupies close to 6 MHz of RF bandwidth, the IF bandwidth of a typical amateur FM receiver might be approximately 20 kHz. Thus, the noise power in the receiver will be reduced by $10 \log_{10} (6,000,000/20,000) = 24.77$ dB because of the receiver's much narrower IF bandwidth compared to the QAM signal's occupied bandwidth. In addition, there is the 6 to 10 dB reduction of the digital signal's average signal PEP.

Field tests during 2009 confirmed this behavior, finding that a leaking QAM signal would not budge the S meter of a Yaesu FT-736R at low to moderate field strength leaks, even when the receiver's antenna — a resonant half-wave dipole — was located just 10 feet from a calibrated leak. In contrast, a CW carrier that produced a 20 µV/m leak resulted in an S meter reading of S9 +15 dB, definitely harmful interference! When the CW carrier was replaced by a QAM signal whose digital channel power was equal to the CW carrier's PEP and which produced the same leakage field strength (the latter integrated over the full 6 MHz channel bandwidth), the S-meter read <S1. When the leakage field strength was increased to 100 µV/m, the CW carrier pegged the S meter at S9 +60 dB, while the QAM signal was S3 in FM mode and between S1 and S2 in USB mode. It wasn't until the leaking QAM signal's field strength reached

Table 27.2
Amateur Radio Bands Relative to Cable TV Downstream Channels

Amateur Band	Over-The-Air Frequency Range	Cable Channel	Cable Frequency Range
6 meters	50-54 MHz	Below Ch. 2	50-54 MHz, sometimes used for narrowband telemetry carriers
2 meters	144-148 MHz	Ch. 18	144-150 MHz
1.25 meters	222-225 MHz	Ch. 24	222-228 MHz
70 cm	420-450 MHz	Ch. 57	420-426 MHz
		Ch. 58	426-432 MHz
		Ch. 59	432-438 MHz
		Ch. 60	438-444 MHz
		Ch. 61	444-450 MHz
33 cm	902-928 MHz	Ch. 142	900-906 MHz
		Ch. 143	906-912 MHz
		Ch. 144	912-918 MHz
		Ch. 145	918-924 MHz
		Ch. 146	924-930 MHz

Table 27.3
VHF Midband Cable Channels

Channel Number	Standard Video Carrier (STD) (MHz)	Harmonically Related Video Carrier (HRC) (MHz)	Incrementally Related Video Carrier (IRC) (MHz)	Audio Carrier (MHz)
98	109.25	108.0054	109.25	113.75
99	115.25	114.0057	115.25	119.75
14	121.25	120.006	121.25	125.75
15	127.25	126.0063	127.25	131.75
16	133.25	132.0066	133.25	137.75
17	139.25	138.0069	139.25	143.75
18	145.25	144.0072	145.25	149.75
19	151.25	150.0075	151.25	155.75
20	157.25	156.0078	157.25	161.75
21	163.25	162.0081	163.25	167.75
22	169.25	168.0084	169.25	173.75

several hundred μV/m that the "noise" (and it literally sounded like typical white noise) could be construed to be harmful interference.

One of the most common signs of possible leakage is interference to the 2 meter amateur band, especially in the vicinity of standard (STD) cable channel 18's visual carrier on 145.25 MHz. If you suspect cable leakage, listen for the telltale broadband noise from the digital video signal over the 144-150 MHz range, and check other STD, incrementally related carrier (IRC), and harmonically related carrier (HRC) visual carrier frequencies on nearby channels listed in **Table 27.3** using a wide range receiver or scanner. (Leakage of an analog TV signal on cable channel 18 sounds like buzzing at the carrier frequencies in the table on or near 145.25 MHz. Also listen for TV channel sound on the FM aural carriers 4.5 MHz above the visual carriers.)

LOCATING LEAKAGE SOURCES

When a cable company technician troubleshoots signal leakage, the process is similar to Amateur Radio fox hunting. The technician uses radio direction finding techniques that may include equipment such as handheld dipole or Yagi antennas, Doppler antenna arrays on vehicles, near-field probes, and commercially manufactured signal leakage detectors. Many leakage detectors incorporate what is known as "tagging" technology to differentiate a leaking cable signal from an over-the-air signal or electrical noise that may exist on or near the same frequency. Most leakage detection is done on a dedicated cable channel in the 108-138 MHz frequency range.

ELIMINATING LEAKAGE

A large percentage of leakage and ingress problems are not the result of a single shielding defect, although this does happen. For example, a squirrel might chew a hardline feeder cable, or a radial crack might develop in the shield as a consequence of environmental or mechanical damage. Most often, leakage and ingress are caused by several small shielding defects in an area: loose or corroded hardline connectors and splices, old copper braid subscriber drop cabling, improperly installed F connectors, subscriber-installed substandard "do-it-yourself" components, and the previously mentioned poorly shielded cable-ready TVs and other *customer premises equipment* (*CPE*).

Other leakage and ingress problems can be caused by improper shield connections at the cable TV set-top box. The return data signal in the low HF region (3.7-5.5 MHz) can be radiated in this way, as well. Common-mode chokes at the equipment with the poor shield connection can block the RF current.

After the cable technician locates the source(s) of the leakage, it is necessary to repair or replace the culprit components or cabling. In the case of poorly shielded TVs or DVD players, the cable technician cannot repair those devices, only recommend that they be fixed by a qualified service shop. Often the installation of a set-top box will take care of a cable-ready CPE problem because the subscriber drop cabling is no longer connected directly to the offending device.

It is important to note that interference from leakage that is received over the air cannot be eliminated at the receiver. It is an "in-band" signal just like the desired signal and can't be filtered out or suppressed with chokes. It must be eliminated at the source of the leakage.

Similarly, RFI from cable ingress — where a clean, transmitted signal gets into the cable system signals through similar defects to those that cause leakage — must also be eliminated at the point at which the transmitted signal enters the cable system.

In both cases, a little RFI detective work may be necessary. Refer to the various RFI troubleshooting sections of this chapter and radio direction finding techniques may come in handy, as well. Once the source of leakage or point of ingress is determined, like power-line noise, it becomes the job of the cable company to repair.

VERIFYING AN RFI SOURCE TO BE LEAKAGE

Spurious signals, birdies, harmonics, intermodulation, electrical noise, and even interference from Part 15 devices are sometimes mistaken for cable signal leakage. One of the most common is emissions from Part 15 devices that become coupled to the cable TV coax shield in some way. Non-leakage noise or spurious signals may radiate from the cable TV lines or an amplifier location, but only because the outer surface of the cable shield is carrying the coupled interference as a common-mode current.

A common non-leakage interference that may radiate from a cable network is broadband electrical interference or other noise in the MF and lower end of the HF spectrum. A common misconception is that since cable companies carry digital signals on frequencies that overlap portions of the over-the-air spectrum below 30 MHz, any "noise" that radiates from the cable plant must be leaking digital signals. This type of interference is almost always power-line electrical interference or other noise that is coupled to the cable network's shield as a common-mode signal.

Leakage of downstream digital signals sound like broadband noise as described above, over a range of frequencies given in the channels of Table 27.3. Upstream digital signals from cable modems, which have channel bandwidths of 1.6, 3.2 or 6.4 MHz, are typically transmitted in the roughly 20 to 40 MHz range, and are bursty in nature rather than continuous like downstream digital signals. Set-top box upstream telemetry carriers are narrowband frequency shift keying (FSK) or quadrature phase shift keying (QPSK) carriers usually in the approximately 8 to 11 MHz range.

If normal leakage troubleshooting techniques do not clearly identify the source of the interference, sometimes the cable company may temporarily shut off its network in the affected neighborhood. If the interference remains after the cable network is turned off, it is not leakage, and the cable company is not responsible for that type of interference. If the interference disappears when the cable network is turned off, then it most likely is leakage or something related to the cable network. Turning off even a small portion of the cable network is a last resort and may not be practical because of the service disruption to subscribers. It may be easier for the cable company to temporarily shut off a suspect cable channel briefly. Here, too, if the interference remains after the channel is turned off, the interference is not leakage.

HOW TO REPORT LEAKAGE

If you suspect cable signal leakage is causing interference to your amateur station, *never attempt your own repairs to any part of the cable network, even the cabling in your own home*! Document what you have observed. For instance, note the frequency or frequencies involved, the nature of the interference, any changes to the interference with time of day, how long it has been occurring, and so forth. If you have fox-hunting skills and equipment, you might note the probable source(s) of the interference or at least the direction from which it appears to be originating.

Next, contact the cable company. You will most likely reach the cable company's customer service department, but ask to speak with the local cable system's Plant Manager (may also be called Chief Engineer, Director of Engineering, Chief Tech, VP of Engineering, or similar), and explain to him or her that you are experiencing what you believe to be signal leakage-related interference. If you cannot reach this individual, ask that a service ticket be created, and a technician familiar with leakage and ingress issues be dispatched. Share the information you have gathered about the interference. And as with all RFI issues, remember diplomacy!

In the vast majority of cases when cable leakage interference to Amateur Radio occurs, it is able to be taken care of by working with local cable system personnel. Every now and then for whatever reason, the affected ham is unable to get the interference resolved locally. Contact the ARRL for help in these cases.

27.8.5 DVD and Video Players

A DVD or similar video player usually contains a television tuner. Older models may have an analog TV channel output. (Newer models typically have an HDMI digital video interface which is less susceptible to RFI.) It is also connected to an antenna or cable system and the ac line, so it is subject to all of the interference problems of a TV receiver. Start by proving that the video player is the susceptible device. Temporarily disconnect the device from the television or video monitor. If there is no interference to the TV, then the video player is the most likely culprit. (Cables between the video player and monitor can also be the means by which RF is getting into the monitor, so a cable dummy (see the sidebar) may be a useful way to determine if that is the case and which cable or cable(s) are the problem.)

Next, find out how the interfering signal is getting into the video player. Temporarily disconnect the antenna or cable feed line from the video player. If the interference goes away, then the antenna line is involved. In this case, you can probably fix the problem with a common-mode choke or high-pass filter.

Figure 27.21 shows a bulletproof video player installation. If you have tried all of the cures shown and still have a problem, the player is probably subject to direct pickup. In this case, you can replace it or contact the manufacturer through the CEA.

Older analog-type VCRs are quite susceptible to RFI from HF signals. The video baseband signal extends from 30 Hz to 3.5 MHz, with color information centered around 3.5 MHz and the FM sound subcarrier at 4.5 MHz. The entire video baseband is frequency modulated onto the tape at frequencies up to 10 MHz. Direct pickup of strong signals by VCRs is a common problem and may not be easily solved, short of replacing the VCR with a better-shielded model or a modern DVD player.

27.8.6 Non-Radio Devices

Interference to non-radio devices is not the fault of the transmitter. (A portion of the *FCC Interference Handbook*, 1990 Edition, is shown in **Figure 27.22**. Although the FCC no longer offers this *Handbook*, an electronic version is available in this book's downloadable supplemental information, from the ARRL at **www.arrl.org/fcc-rfi-information** or search the ARRL website for "cib interference handbook".) In essence, the FCC views non-radio devices that pick up nearby radio signals as improperly functioning; contact the manufacturer and return the equipment. The FCC does not require that non-radio devices include RFI protection and they don't offer legal protection to users of these devices that are susceptible to interference.

TELEPHONES

Landline or "wired" telephones present a very common non-TVI interference problem to Amateur Radio. As more people switch over to mobile telephone service instead of landline, this problem is gradually diminishing. Nevertheless, landline and cordless phones which are connected to the landline will continue to be with us for many years. Most cases of telephone interference to these phones can be cured by correcting any installation defects and installing telephone RFI filters where needed. The remainder of this section assumes the telephone is connected to landline service.

Telephones can improperly function as radio receivers. Semiconductor devices inside many telephones act like diodes. When such a telephone is connected to the telephone wiring (a large antenna) an AM radio receiver can be formed. When a nearby transmitter goes on the air, these telephones can be affected.

Troubleshooting techniques were discussed earlier in the chapter. The suggestion to simplify the problem applies especially to telephone interference. Disconnect all telephones except one, right at the service entrance if possible, and start troubleshooting the problem there.

If any single device or bad connection in the phone system detects RF and puts the detected signal back onto the phone line as audio, that audio cannot be removed with filters. Once the RF has been detected and turned into audio, it cannot be filtered out because the interference is at the same frequency as the desired audio signal. To effect a cure, you must locate the detection point and correct the problem there.

Defective telephone company lightning arrestors can act like diodes, rectifying any nearby RF energy. Telephone-line amplifiers or other electronic equipment may also be at fault. Do not attempt to diagnose or repair any telephone company wiring or devices on the "telco" side of your service box or that were installed by the phone company. Request a service call from your phone company.

Inspect the telephone system installation. Years of exposure in damp basements, walls or crawl spaces may have caused deterioration. Be suspicious of anything that is corroded or discolored. In many cases, homeowners have installed their own telephone wiring, often using substandard wiring. If you find sections of telephone wiring made from nonstandard cable, replace it with standard twisted-pair telephone or CAT5 cable. If you

---

PART II

INTERFERENCE TO OTHER EQUIPMENT

CHAPTER 6

TELEPHONES, ELECTRONIC ORGANS, AM/FM RADIOS, STEREO AND HI-FI EQUIPMENT

Telephones, stereos, computers, electronic organs and home intercom devices can receive interference from nearby radio transmitters. When this happens, the device improperly functions as a radio receiver. Proper shielding or filtering can eliminate such interference. The device receiving interference should be modified in your home while it is being affected by interference. This will enable the service technician to determine where the interfering signal is entering your device.

The device's response will vary according to the interference source. If, for example, your equipment is picking up the signal of a nearby two-way radio transmitter, you likely will hear the radio operator's voice. Electrical interference can cause sizzling, popping or humming sounds.

Figure 27.22 — Part of page 18 from the FCC *Interference Handbook* (1990 edition) explains the facts and places responsibility for interference to non-radio equipment.

do use telephone cable, be sure it is high-quality twisted-pair to minimize differential-mode pickup of RF signals.

Next, evaluate each of the telephone instruments. If you find a susceptible telephone, install a telephone RFI filter on that telephone, such as those sold by K-Y Filters. (**www.ky-filters.com**) or use DSL filters that keep the DSL data signals out of the telephones. If the home uses a DSL broadband data service, be sure that the filters do not affect DSL performance by testing online data rates with and without a filter installed at the telephone instrument.

If you determine that you have interference only when you operate on one particular ham band, the telephone wiring system either has an "RF hot spot" at that point when excited on that band or some cable in the system could be resonant and thus especially responsive on that band. Install common-mode chokes on the wiring to add a high impedance in series with the "antenna." A telephone RFI filter may also be needed. (See the section on DSL Equipment for filtering suggestions.)

Telephone Accessories — Answering machines and fax machines (two more telephone-related instruments that are slowly disappearing) are also prone to interference problems. All of the troubleshooting techniques and cures that apply to telephones also apply to these telephone devices. In addition, many of these devices connect to the ac mains. Try a common-mode choke and/or ac-line filter on the power cord (which may be an ac cord set, a small transformer or power supply).

Cordless Telephones — A cordless telephone is an unlicensed *radio* device that is manufactured and used under Part 15 of the FCC regulations. The FCC does not intend Part 15 devices to be protected from interference. These devices usually have receivers with very wide front-end filters, which make them very susceptible to interference.

A likely path for interference to cordless phones is as common-mode current on the base unit's connecting cables that will respond to common-mode chokes. In addition, a telephone filter on the base unit and an ac line filter may help. The best source of help is the manufacturer but they may point out that the Part 15 device is not protected from interference.

Newer cordless phone systems operating at 900 MHz and higher frequencies are often less susceptible to interference than older models are less susceptible to interference.

AUDIO EQUIPMENT

Consumer and commercial audio equipment such as stereos, home entertainment systems, intercoms and public-address systems can also pick up and detect strong nearby transmitters. The FCC considers these non-radio devices and does not protect them from licensed radio transmitters that may interfere with their operation. The RFI can be caused by one of several things: pickup on speaker leads or interconnecting cables, pickup by the ac mains wiring or direct pickup. If the interference involves wiring connected to the affected device, common-mode chokes are the most likely solution.

Use the standard troubleshooting techniques discussed earlier in this chapter to isolate problems. In a multi-component home entertainment system (as in **Figure 27.23**), for example, you must determine what combination of components is involved with the problem. First, disconnect all auxiliary components to determine if there is a problem with the main receiver/amplifier. Long speaker or interconnect cables are prime suspects.

Stereos and Home Entertainment Systems — If the problem remains with the main amplifier isolated, determine if the interference level is affected by the volume control. If so, the interference is getting into the circuit *before* the volume control, usually through accessory wiring. If the volume control has no effect on the level of the interfering sound, the interference is getting in *after* the control, usually through speaker wires.

Speaker wires are often effective antennas on HF and sometimes into VHF and above. The speaker terminals are often connected directly to the output amplifier transistors. Modern amplifier designs use a negative feedback loop to improve fidelity. This loop can conduct the detected RF signal back to the high-gain stages of the amplifier. The combination of all of these factors often makes the speaker cables the dominant receiving antenna for RFI.

There is a simple test that will help determine if the interfering signal is being coupled into the amplifier by the speaker leads. Temporarily disconnect the speaker leads from the amplifier, and plug in a test set of headphones with short leads. If there is no interference with the headphones, filtering the speaker leads will likely cure the problem.

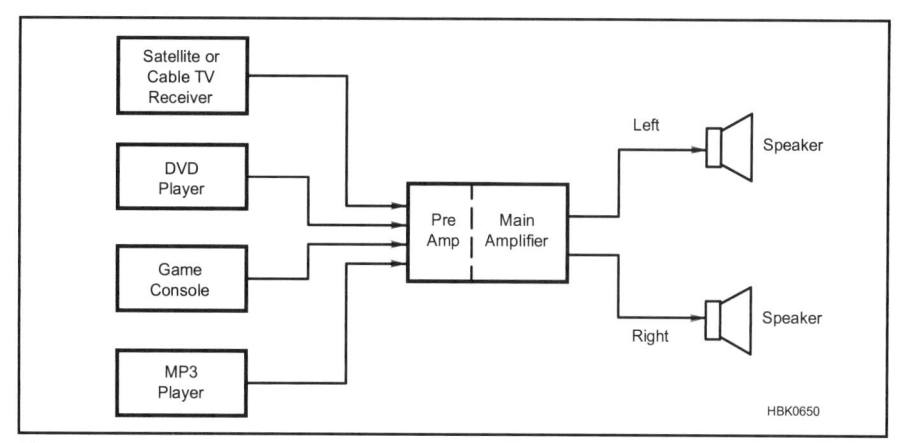

Figure 27.23 — A typical modern home-entertainment system.

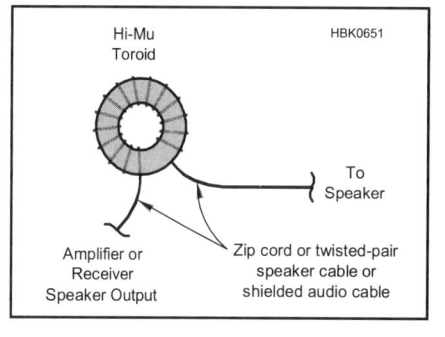

Figure 27.24 — Making a speaker-lead common-mode choke. Use ferrite material appropriate for the frequency of the RF interference.

Start by applying common-mode chokes. **Figure 27.24** shows how to wrap speaker wires around an large (2-inch O.D. or larger) ferrite core to cure speaker-lead RFI. Type 31 material is preferred at HF. (See the section on Common-Mode Chokes in this chapter.)

In some cases, the speaker wires may be picking up RF as a differential-mode signal. To reduce differential-mode pickup, replace the zip cord speaker wire with twisted-pair wire. (#16 AWG will work for most systems with higher-power systems requiring #12 AWG.)

Powered Speakers — A powered speaker is one that has its own built-in power amplifier. Powered subwoofers are common in home entertainment systems and small powered speakers are often used with computer and gaming systems. If a speaker runs on batteries and/or an external power supply, or is plugged into mains power, it is a powered loudspeaker. Powered loudspeakers are notoriously susceptibility to common-mode interference from internally misconnected cable shields and poor shielding. Apply suitable common-mode chokes to all wiring, including power wiring. If the RFI persists, try an RF filter

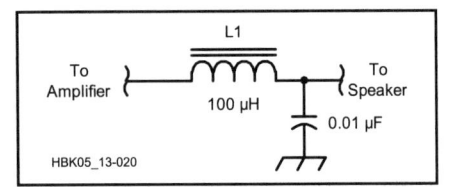

Figure 27.25 — A low-pass LC filter.

at the input to the speaker, such as the LC low-pass filter in **Figure 27.25**. Unshielded speakers may not be curable, however.

Intercoms and Security Systems — RFI to these systems is nearly always caused by common-mode current on interconnect wiring. Common-mode chokes are the most likely cure, but you may also need to contact the manufacturer to see if they have any additional, specific information. Twisted-pair wiring (CAT5 network cable contains four such pairs) should be used, including for audio output wiring. Wiring can often be complex, so any work on these systems should be done by a qualified sound contractor.

Public-Address Systems — Common-mode current is also the culprit here. Powered speakers are increasingly used and can be treated as described above. Work to remove interference should be done by the installing contractor and may require coordination between the amateur and contractor to characterize the interference and provide test assistance while the work is being done.

COMPUTERS AND OTHER UNLICENSED RF SOURCES

Computers and microprocessor-based devices such as video games or audio players can be sources or victims of interference. These devices contain oscillators that can and do radiate RF energy. In addition, the internal functions of a computer generate different frequencies, based on the various data signals. All of these signals are digital — with fast rise and fall times that are rich in harmonics.

Computing devices are covered under Part 15 of the FCC regulations as unintentional emitters. As for any other unintentional emitter, the FCC has set absolute radiation limits for these devices. As previously discussed in this chapter, FCC regulations state that the operator or owner of Part 15 devices must take whatever steps are necessary to reduce or eliminate any interference they cause to a licensed radio service. This means that if your neighbor's video game interferes with your radio, the neighbor is responsible for correcting the problem. (Of course, your neighbor may appreciate your help in locating a solution!)

The FCC has set up two tiers of limits for computing devices. Class A is for computers used in a commercial environment. FCC Class B requirements are more stringent —

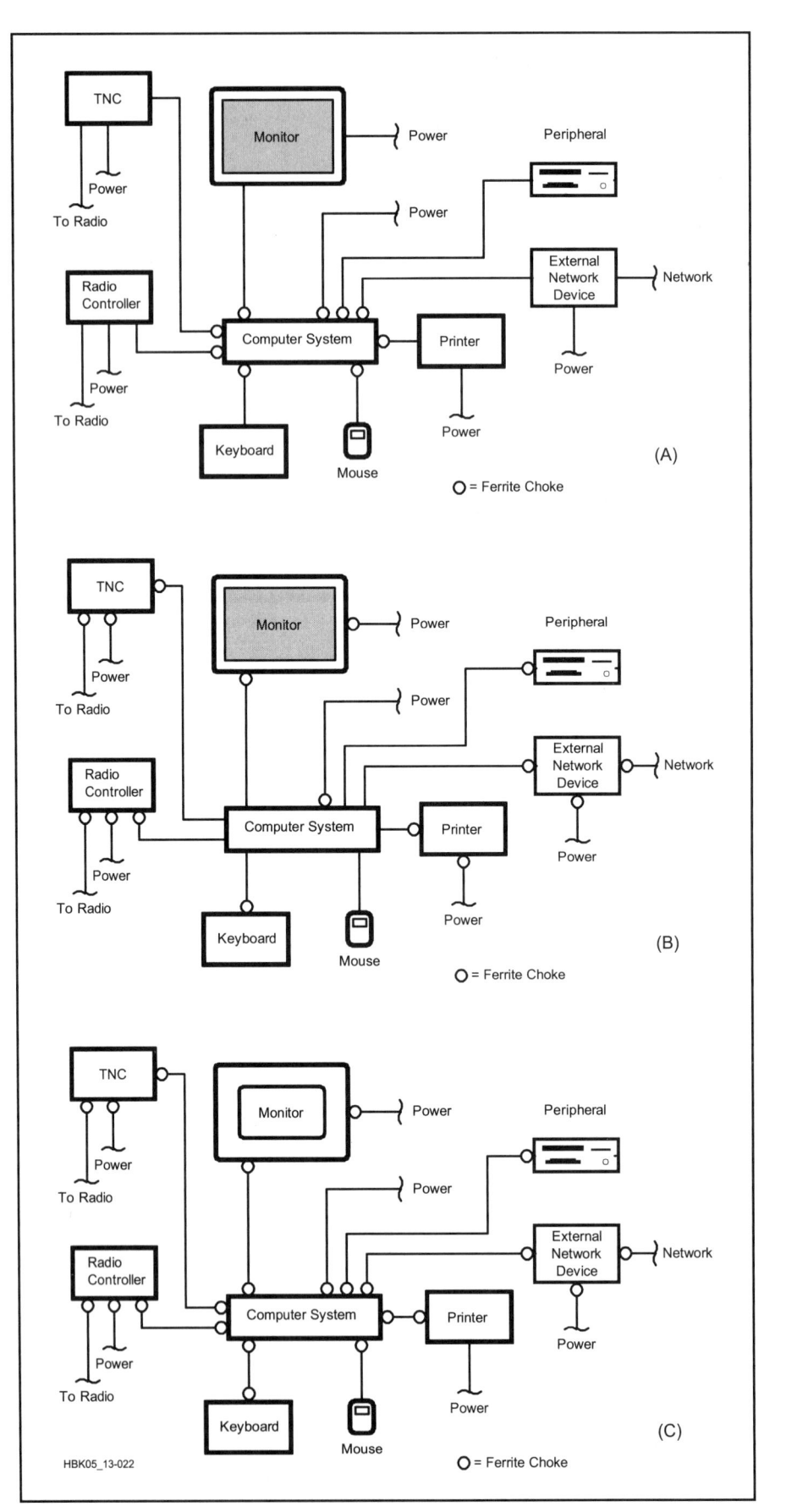

Figure 27.26 — Where to locate ferrite chokes in a computer system. At A, the computer is noisy, but the peripherals are quiet. At B, the computer is quiet, but external devices are noisy. At C, both the computer and externals are noisy.

27.44 Chapter 27

for computers used in residential environments. If you buy a computer or peripheral, be sure that it is Class B certified or it will probably generate interference to your amateur station or home-electronics equipment.

If you find that your computer system is interfering with your radio (not uncommon in this digital-radio age), start by simplifying the problem. Temporarily remove power from as many peripheral devices as possible and disconnect their cables from the back of the computer. (It is necessary to physically remove the power cable from the device, since many devices remain in a low-power state when turned off from the front panel or by a software command.) If possible, use just the computer, keyboard and monitor. This test may identify specific peripherals as the source of the interference.

It can be difficult to determine whether peripheral connecting cables are shielded. If possible, use shielded cables for all peripherals. Replace any unshielded cables with shielded ones; this often significantly reduces RF noise from computer systems. The second line of defense is the common-mode choke. The choke should be installed as close to the computer and/or peripheral device as practical. **Figure 27.26** shows the location of common-mode chokes in a complete computer system where both the computer and peripherals are noisy. USB-power devices can also create noise from internal power supplies and are discussed in K9YC's *National Contest Journal* paper listed in the References section.

A multi-turn common-mode choke wound for the HF bands is often ineffective at VHF. When VHF antennas are located close to these devices (or if a more distant beam is pointed at them), it may also be necessary to add one or two 2-turn chokes to suppress noise on 6 meters and multiple, single-turn, clamp-on cores for 2 meter noise. The cores for the higher frequencies should always be placed closest to the noise source, and when two pieces of digital equipment are connected, each should be considered a potential source, so VHF cores may be needed on both ends.

Switchmode power supplies in computers are often sources of interference. A common-mode choke and/or ac-line filter may cure this problem. In extreme cases of computer interference you may need to improve the shielding of the computer. (Refer to the *ARRL RFI Book* for more information about this.) Don't forget that some peripherals (such as modems) are connected to the phone line, so you may need to treat them like telephones.

GROUND-FAULT AND ARC-FAULT CIRCUIT INTERRUPTORS (GFCI AND AFCI)

GFCIs are occasionally reported to "trip" (open the circuit) when a strong RF signal, such as an amateur's HF transmission, is present. GFCI circuit breakers operate by sensing unbalanced currents in the hot and neutral conductors of an ac circuit. In the absence of RF interference, such an imbalance indicates the presence of a fault somewhere in the circuit, creating a shock hazard. The breaker then trips (opens) to remove the shock hazard.

An Arc Fault Circuit Interrupter (AFCI) circuit breaker is similar in that it monitors current to watch for a fault condition. Instead of current imbalances, the AFCI detects patterns of current that indicate an arc — one of the leading causes of home fires. The AFCI is not supposed to trip because of "normal" arcs that occur when a switch is opened or a plug is removed.

Under current codes, GFCI protection is required for all basement outlets, outdoor outlets, and for outlets in kitchens and bathrooms. AFCI protection is now required for all circuits that supply bedrooms and other areas of a home as well. Code requirements can vary so be sure to check with your local building inspector for those that apply in a specific case.

RF interference to GFCI breakers is caused by RF current or voltage upsetting normal operation of the imbalance detection circuit, resulting in the false detection of a fault. Similarly, RF current or voltage could upset the arc detection circuitry of an AFCI breaker. Some early GFCI breakers were susceptible to RFI, but as the technology has improved, fewer and fewer such reports have been received. While it is possible to add filtering or RF suppression to the breaker wiring, a simpler and less expensive solution is to replace the GFCI breaker with a new unit less susceptible to RF.

The ARRL Lab has received favorable reports on the following GFCI products:

• Leviton (**www.leviton.com**) GFCI outlets which are available in both 15 and 20 A versions for 120 V ac circuits as well as cord sets and user-attachable plugs and receptacles.

• Bryant (**www.bryant-electric.com**) ground fault receptacles which feature published 0.5 V immunity from 150 kHz to 230 MHz.

• Cooper (**www.cooperindustries.com**) GFCI products that are labeled "UL 943 compliant" on the package.

A web page on the ARRL website is maintained on GFCI/AFCI technology (**www.arrl.org/gfci-and-afci-devices**). Reports have not been received on AFCI products as of early 2013. Although there have been numerous reported immunity problems with AFCI products, they are now greatly reduced. Manufacturers seem to have largely fixed these issues. See **www.arrl.org/afci-devices** for more information.

WALL TRANSFORMER SWITCHING SUPPLIES

While small, low-current linear power supplies known as "wall warts" have been widely used for many years, it is now becoming common for these devices to contain switchmode or "switcher" supplies. Because they must be manufactured very inexpensively, these supplies often have little or no RF filtering at either the ac input or dc output, frequently creating significant RFI to nearby amateurs.

The least expensive course of action may be to simply replace the switchmode supply with a linear model. If the system in which the supply is used is still under warranty, the distributor or manufacturer may be able to replace it. Otherwise, a third-party linear replacement may be available with the same voltage rating and current output equal to or higher than the original supply. Adapters may be available to convert output connector styles where necessary or new connectors installed. Older linear-style supplies can be re-used if you are willing to splice them in to replace the switchmode model.

If replacing the supply with a linear model is not an option, you will have to apply RF filters to the supply. These supplies are rarely serviceable, so filters much be installed externally. Noise is usually radiated from the output cable so winding the cable onto a ferrite core creates a common-mode RF choke as described in this chapter's Elements of RFI Control section. Since the wall-wart style supply plugs directly into a wall-mounted receptacle, a short ac extension cord or power strip cord can be made into a common-mode choke, as well.

27.9 Automotive RFI

Automobiles have evolved from a limited number of primitive electrical components to high technology, multi-computer systems on-wheels. Every new technology deployed can potentially interfere with amateur equipment.

Successful mobile operation depends on a multitude of factors such as choosing the right vehicle, following installation guidelines, troubleshooting and deploying the appropriate RFI fixes as needed.

A number of these factors will be covered in this section. Additionally, newly emerging electrical and hybrid-electric vehicles will be discussed, which pose unique challenges to amateur equipment installations and operation.

27.9.1 Before Purchasing a Vehicle

When shopping for a new vehicle intended for a mobile amateur installation, begin with research. A wealth of information is available on the Internet, and specifically at **www.arrl.org/automotive**, where the ARRL has compiled years of data from automotive manufacturers and other hams. Email reflectors and websites may provide information from hams willing to share their experiences concerning mobile communications in their own vehicles that may be the very make and model you were considering.

Armed with research, your next stop is your dealer. The manufacturer of each vehicle is the expert on how that vehicle will perform. The dealer should have good communication with the manufacturer and should be able to answer your questions. Ask about service bulletins and installation guidelines. You can also ask your dealer about fleet models of their vehicles. Some manufacturers offer special modifications for vehicles intended for sale to police, taxicabs and other users who will be installing radios (usually operating at VHF and UHF) in their cars.

When shopping for a vehicle, it is useful to take along some portable (preferably battery operated) receivers or scanners and have a friend tune through your intended operating frequencies while you drive the vehicle. This will help identify any radiated noise issues associated with that model vehicle, which can be more difficult to resolve than conducted noise. If you intend to make a permanent transceiver installation, give some consideration to how you will mount the transceiver and route the power and/or antenna cables. While looking for ways to route the wiring, keep in mind that some newer cars have the battery located in the trunk or under the rear seat, and that may make power wire routing easier.

Test the car before you buy it. A dealer expects you to take the car for a test ride; a cooperative dealer may let you test it for radio operation, too. A fair amount of checking can easily be performed without digging too deeply into the car. Check the vehicle for noise with a portable receiver on VHF, where your handheld transceiver will do the job nicely. On HF, you can usually locate noise with a portable short-wave receiver, or operate your HF transceiver with a portable antenna and cigarette-lighter plug. With the engine running, tune across the bands of interest. You may hear some noise, or a few birdies, but if the birdies don't fall on your favorite frequency, this is an encouraging sign! Check with the vehicle completely off, with the key in the ignition, and with the vehicle running — electronic subsystems operate in different ways with the vehicle running or not running.

To test the vehicle for susceptibility to your transmitted signal, you must transmit. It is important to note that without a full and complete installation, you will not be able to fully assess the effects of full-power transmissions on a vehicle. Any testing done with temporary equipment installations cannot be considered an absolute guarantee because an installed transmitter connected directly to the vehicle's power source may cause the vehicle to act differently.

To perform transmit tests, bring your radio and a separate battery (if permitted by dealer) so you can transmit at full power while in motion without having to run cables to the vehicle battery. Use a magnet-mount antenna (several *QST* advertisers sell mounts suitable for HF) for temporary testing. (Use the magnet-mount carefully; it is possible to scratch paint if any particles of dirt get on the bottom of the magnets.) Transmit on each band you will use to see if the RF has any effect on the vehicle. Lack of response to your transmissions is a good sign, but does not mean the vehicle is immune to RF as a permanent installation will result in different (likely stronger) field strengths and distributions in and around the vehicle and a permanent antenna more effectively coupled to the vehicle.

On both transmit and receive, you may want to experiment with the placement of the antenna. Antenna placement plays an important role in operation, and you may be able to find an optimal location for the antenna that predicts good performance with a permanent installation.

27.9.2 Transceiver Installation Guidelines

While most amateurs are familiar with the process of installing a transceiver, there are preferred practices that will help minimize potential problems. These include support from the automotive dealer, typical "best practices" installations, and consideration of special situations.

The first step is to ensure that your installation complies with both the vehicle manufacturer's and radio transceiver manufacturer's installation guidelines. Links to domestic automotive manufacturer installation guidelines are found at **www.arrl.org/automotive**. Automotive manufacturers that import vehicles for sale here do not publish installation guidelines because their vehicles are not typically used in police, fire and taxicab applications within the US.

The installation guidelines of different manufacturers vary as to how to install a radio transceiver's power leads. Most manufacturers recommend that the positive and negative leads from the radio be run directly to the battery. This minimizes the potential for the interaction between the radio's negative lead currents and vehicle electronics. If the manufacturer recommends that both wires be connected to the battery, they will also require that both wires be fused. This is necessary because, in the unlikely event that the connection between the battery and the engine block were to fail, excessive current could be drawn on the radio's negative lead when the vehicle starter is engaged.

Some vehicles provide a "ground block" near the battery for a negative cable to be connected. On these vehicles, run the negative power lead, un-fused, to the "ground block." When this technique is recommended by the manufacturer, the interaction between the power return currents and vehicle electronics has been evaluated by the manufacturer. In all cases, the most important rule to remember is this: If you want the manufacturer to support your installation, do it exactly the way the installation guidelines tell you to do it!

If no installation guidelines are available for your vehicle, the practices outlined below will improve compatibility between in-vehicle transceivers and vehicle electronics:

1) Transceivers
 • Transceivers should be mounted in a location that does not interfere with vehicle operator controls and visibility, provides transceiver ventilation, and be securely mounted.
 • Ensure all equipment and accessories are removed from the deployment path of the airbag and safety harness systems.

2) Power Leads
 • The power leads should be twisted together from the back of the rig all the way to the battery. This minimizes the area formed by the power leads, reducing susceptibility to transients and RFI.
 • Do not use the vehicle chassis as a power return.

- The power leads should be routed along the body structure, away from vehicle wiring harnesses and electronics.
- Any wires connected to the battery should be fused at the battery using fuses appropriate for the required current.
- Use pass-through grommets when routing wiring between passenger and engine compartments.
- Route and secure all under hood wiring away from mechanical hazards.

3) Coaxial Feed Lines
- The coaxial feed line should have at least 95% braid coverage. The cable shield should be connected to every coaxial connector for the entire circumference (no "pigtails").
- Keep antenna feed lines as short as practical and avoid routing the cables parallel to vehicle wiring.

4) Antennas
- Antenna(s) should be mounted as far from the engine and the vehicle electronics as practical. Typical locations would be the rear deck lid or roof. Metal tape can be used to provide an antenna ground plane on non-metallic body panels.
- Care should be used in mounting antennas with magnetic bases, since magnets may affect the accuracy or operation of the compass in vehicles, if equipped.
- Since the small magnet surface results in low coupling to the vehicle at HF, it is likely that the feed line shield will carry substantial RF currents. A large (2-inch OD or larger toroid) common-mode choke at the antenna will help reduce this current, but will also reduce any radiation produced by that current.
- Adjust the antenna for a low SWR.

27.9.3 Diagnosing Automotive RFI

Most VHF/UHF radio installations should result in no problems to either the vehicle systems or the transceiver, while HF installations are more likely to experience problems. In those situations where issues do occur, the vast majority are interference to the receiver from vehicle on-board sources of energy that are creating emissions within the frequency bands used by the receiver. Interference to one of the on-board electronic systems can be trivial or it can cause major problems with an engine control system.

The dealer should be the first point of contact when a problem surfaces, because the dealer should have access to information and factory help that may solve your problem. The manufacturer may have already found a fix for your problem and may be able to save your mechanic a lot of time (saving you money in the process). If the process works properly, the dealer/customer-service network can be helpful. In the event the dealer is unable to solve your problem, the next section includes general troubleshooting techniques you can perform independently.

GENERAL TROUBLESHOOTING TECHNIQUES

An important aspect is to use the source-path-victim model presented earlier in this chapter. The path from the source to the receiver may be via radiation or conduction. If the path is radiation, the electric field strength (in V/m) received is reduced as a function of the distance from the source to the receiver. In most cases, susceptible vehicle electronics is in the near-field region of the radiating source, where the electric and magnetic fields can behave in complex ways. In general, however, the strength of radiated signals falls off with distance.

The best part of all this is that with a general-coverage receiver or spectrum analyzer, a fuse puller and a shop manual, the vehicle component needing attention may be identified using a few basic techniques. The only equipment needed could be as simple as:
- A mobile rig, scanner or handheld transceiver, or
- Any other receiver with good stability and an accurate readout, and
- An oscilloscope for viewing interference waveforms

BROADBAND NOISE

Automotive broadband noise sources include:
- Electric motors such as those that operate fans, windows, sunroof, AM/FM antenna deployment, fuel pumps, etc.
- Ignition spark

If you suspect electric motor noise is the cause of the problem, obtain a portable AM or SSB receiver to check for this condition. Switch on the receiver and then activate the electric motors one at a time. When a noisy motor is switched on, the background noise increases. It may be necessary to rotate the radio, since portable AM radios use a directional ferrite rod antenna.

To check whether fuel pumps, cooling fans, and other vehicle-controlled motors are the source of noise, pull the appropriate fuse and see whether the noise disappears.

A note concerning fuel pumps: virtually every vehicle made since the 1980s has an electric fuel pump, powered by long wires. It may be located inside the fuel tank. Don't overlook this motor as a source of interference just because it may not be visible. Electric fuel-pump noise often exhibits a characteristic time pattern. When the vehicle ignition switch is first turned on, without engaging the starter, the fuel pump will run for a few seconds, and then shut off when the fuel system is pressurized. At idle, the noise will generally follow the pattern of being present for a few seconds before stopping, although in some vehicles the fuel pump will run almost continuously if the engine is running.

NARROWBAND NOISE

Automotive narrowband noise sources include:
- Microprocessor based engine control systems
- Instrument panel
- RADAR obstacle detection
- Remote keyless entry
- Key fob recognition systems
- Tire pressure monitoring systems
- Global positioning systems
- Pulse width modulating motor speed controls
- Fuel injectors
- Specialized electric traction systems found in newer hybrid/electric vehicles

Start by moving the antenna to different locations. Antenna placement is often key to resolving narrowband RFI problems. However, if antenna location is not the solution, consider pulling fuses. Tune in and stabilize the noise, then find the vehicle fuse panels and pull one fuse at a time until the noise disappears. If more than one module is fed by one fuse, locate each module and unplug it separately. Some modules may have a "keep-alive" memory that is not disabled by pulling the fuse. These modules may need to be unplugged to determine whether they are the noise source. Consult the shop manual for fuse location, module location, and any information concerning special procedures for disconnecting power.

A listening test may verify alternator noise, but if an oscilloscope is available, monitor the power line feeding the affected radio. Alternator whine appears as full-wave rectified ac ripple and rectifier switching transients superimposed on the power system's dc power voltage (see **Figure 27.27**).

Alternators rely on the low impedance of the battery for filtering. Check the wiring from the alternator output to the battery for corroded contacts and loose connectors when alternator noise is a problem.

Receivers may allow conducted harness noise to enter the RF, IF or audio sections (usually through the power leads), and interfere with desired signals. Check whether the

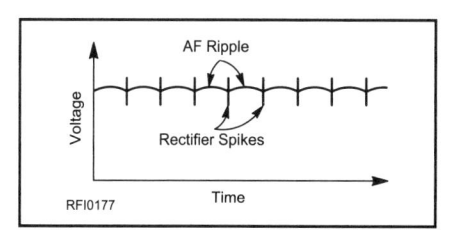

Figure 27.27 — Alternator whine consists of full-wave rectified ac, along with pulses from rectifier switching, superimposed on the vehicle's dc power voltage.

interference is still present with the receiver powered from a battery or power supply instead of from the vehicle. If the interference is no longer present when the receiver is operating from a battery or external supply, the interference is conducted via the radio power lead. Power line filters installed at the radio may resolve this problem.

27.9.4 Eliminating Automotive RFI

The next section includes various techniques to resolve the more common RFI problems. As a caveat, performing your own RFI work, in or out of warranty, you assume the same risks as you do when you perform any other type of automotive repair. Most state laws (and common sense) say that those who work on cars should be qualified to do so. In most cases, this means that work should be done either by a licensed dealer or automotive repair facility.

CONDUCTED INTERFERENCE

To reduce common-mode current, impedance can be inserted in series with the wiring in the form of common-mode chokes. (See this chapter's section on Common-Mode Chokes.) Wire bundles may also be wound around large toroids for the same effect.

Mechanical considerations are important in mobile installations. A motor vehicle is subject to a lot of vibration. If a choke is installed on a wire, this vibration may cause the choke to flex the wire, which may ultimately fail. It is critical that any additional shielding and/or chokes placed on wiring have been installed by qualified personnel who have considered these factors. These must be properly secured, and sometimes cable extenders are required to implement this fix.

RFI TO ON-BOARD CONTROL SYSTEMS

RFI to a vehicle's on-board control and electronic modules should be treated with common-mode chokes at the connection to the module. Some success has been reported by using braid or metal foil to cover a wire bundle as a shield and connecting the shield to the vehicle chassis near the affected module. Vehicle electronic units should not be modified except by trained service personnel according to the manufacturer's recommendations. The manufacturer may also have specific information available in the form of service bulletins.

FILTERS FOR DC MOTORS

If the motor is a conventional brush- or commutator-type dc motor, the following cures shown in **Figure 27.28** are those generally used. As always, the mechanic should consult with the vehicle manufacturer. To diagnose motor noise, obtain an AM or SSB receiver to check the frequency or band of interest. Switch on the receiver, and then activate the electric motors one at a time. When a noisy motor is switched on, the background noise increases as well.

The pulses of current drawn by a brush-commutator motor generate broadband RFI that is similar to ignition noise. However, the receiver audio sounds more like bacon frying rather than popping. With an oscilloscope displaying receiver audio, the noise appears as a series of pulses with random space between the pulses. Such broadband noise generally has a more pronounced effect on AM receivers than on FM. Unfortunately, the pulses may affect FM receivers by increasing the "background noise level" and will reduce perceived receiver sensitivity because of the degraded signal-to-noise ratio.

ALTERNATOR AND GENERATOR NOISE

As mentioned previously, brush-type motors employ sliding contacts which can generate noise. The resulting spark is primarily responsible for the "hash" noise associated with these devices. Hash noise appears as overlapping pulses on an oscilloscope connected to the receiver audio output. An alternator also has brushes, but they do not interrupt current. They ride on slip rings and supply a modest current, typically 4 A to the field winding. Hence, the hash noise produced by alternators is relatively minimal.

Generators use a relay regulator to control field current and thus output voltage. The voltage regulator's continuous sparking creates broadband noise pulses that do not overlap in time. They are rarely found in modern automobiles.

Alternator or generator noise may be conducted through the vehicle wiring to the power input of mobile receivers and transmitters and may then be heard in the audio output. If alternator or generator noise is suspected and an oscilloscope is not available, temporarily remove the alternator belt as a test. (This may not be possible in vehicles with a serpentine belt.)

IGNITION NOISE

Ignition noise is created by fast-rise-time pulses of coil current discharging across air gaps (distributor and spark plug). The theoretical models (zero rise time) of such pulses are called impulse functions in the time domain. When viewed in the frequency domain, the yield is a constant spectral energy level starting nearly at 0 Hz and theoretically extending up in frequency to infinity. In practice, real ignition pulses have a finite rise time, so the spectral-energy envelope decreases above some frequency.

It turns out that noise generated by ignition sparks and fuel injector activation manifest themselves as a regular, periodic "ticking" in the receiver audio output, which varies with engine RPM. If an oscilloscope were connected to the audio output, a series of distinct, separate pulses would appear. At higher speeds it sounds somewhat musical, like alternator whine, but with a harsher note (more harmonic content).

A distinguishing feature of ignition noise is that it increases in amplitude under acceleration. This results from the increase in the required firing voltage with higher cylinder pressure. (Noise at higher frequencies may also be reproduced better by the audio circuits.) Since ignition noise is usually radiated noise, it should disappear when the antenna element is disconnected from the antenna mount. The radiation may be from either the secondary parts of the system or it may couple from the secondary to the primary of the coil and be conducted for some distance along the primary wiring to the ignition system, then radiated from the primary wiring.

Two main methods are employed to sup-

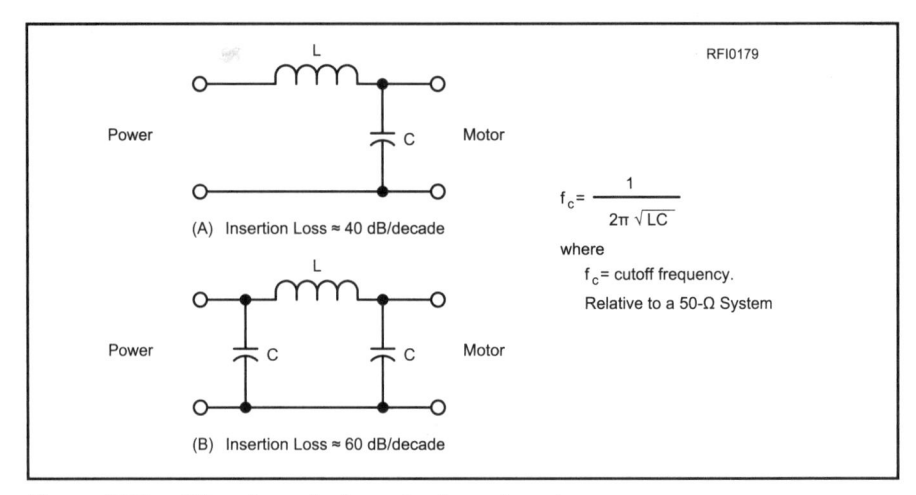

Figure 27.28 — Filters for reducing noise from dc motors

$$f_c = \frac{1}{2\pi\sqrt{LC}}$$

where
f_c = cutoff frequency.
Relative to a 50-Ω System

(A) Insertion Loss ≈ 40 dB/decade
(B) Insertion Loss ≈ 60 dB/decade

press this noise — one involves adding an inductance, and the other involves adding a resistance — both in the secondary (high voltage) wiring. This is shown in **Figure 27.29**. The addition of these elements does not have a measurable effect on the engine operation, because the time constants involved in the combustion process are much longer than those associated with the suppression components. (Note that modifying your vehicle's ignition system may be considered as tampering with your vehicle's emission control system and may affect your warranty coverage — work with your dealer or limit your efforts to changing spark plug wires or possibly shielding them.)

The resistance method suppresses RFI by dissipating energy that would have been radiated and/or conducted. Even though the amount of energy dissipated is small, it is still enough to cause interference to sensitive amateur installations. The other method uses inductance and even though the energy is not dissipated, suppression occurs because the inductor will store the pulse energy for a short time. It then releases it into the ignition burn event, which is a low impedance path, reducing the RFI.

For traditional "Kettering" inductive discharge ignition systems, a value of about 5 kΩ impedance (either real and/or reactive) in the spark plug circuit provides effective suppression and, with this value, there is no detectable engine operation degradation. (Capacitor discharge systems, in comparison, are required to have very low impedance on the order of tens of ohms in order to not reduce spark energy, so they are not tolerant of series impedance). Most spark plug resistances are designed to operate with several kV across the plug gap, so a low-voltage ohmmeter may not give proper resistance measurement results.

The term "resistor wire" is somewhat misleading. High-voltage ignition wires usually contain both resistance and inductance. The resistance is usually built into suppressor spark plugs and wires, while there is some inductance and resistance in wires, rotors and connectors. The elements can be either distributed or lumped, depending on the brand, and each technique has its own merit. A side benefit of resistance in the spark plug is reduced electrode wear.

COIL-ON-PLUG IGNITION NOISE

Many newer spark-ignition systems incorporate a "coil on plug" (COP) or "coil near plug" (CNP) approach. There are advantages to this from an engine operation standpoint, and this approach may actually reduce some of the traditional sources of ignition system RFI. This is because of the very short secondary wires that are employed (or perhaps there are no wires — the coil is directly attached to the spark plug). This reduces the likelihood of coupling from the secondary circuit to other wires or vehicle/engine conductive structures.

There will always be some amount of energy from the spark event that will be conducted along the lowest impedance path. It may mean that the energy that would have been in the secondary circuit will be coupled back on the primary wiring harness attached to the coils. This means that the problem may go from a radiated to a conducted phenomenon.

The fix for this in some cases may actually be easier or harder than one might think. Two approaches that have been used with success are ferrite cores and bypass capacitors.

Ferrite cores are recommended as the first choice, since they require no electrical modification to the vehicle. Ferrite clamp-on split cores are added to the 12-V primary harness attached to the coils. Depending on the frequency of the noise and selection of the ferrite material, there can be significant improvement (as much as 10 dB). Key to optimizing the amount of suppression is to determine where the noise "peaks" and selecting the correct ferrite material for that frequency range (see this chapter's section Using Ferrite for RFI Suppression).

The second method is to add a bypass capacitor between the primary wire of the 12-V coil and ground in the harness near the coil assemblies (there may be 2, 3 or 4 coils). This must be done carefully because it could affect the functionality of the ignition system and — perhaps most importantly — may void the vehicle warranty. This "bypass" capacitor performs the same function that bypass capacitors in any other application perform — separating the noise from the intended signal/power.

27.9.5 Electric and Hybrid-Electric Vehicles

Electric vehicles (EV) and hybrid-electric vehicles (HEV) are quickly becoming a practical means of transportation. EV/HEVs are advanced vehicles that pose unique challenges for amateur equipment. While EV/HEVs provide improved emissions and fuel economy, EV/HEVs utilize switched high voltage and high current to control propulsion. The switching techniques used generate RFI within much of our frequency bands — a cause for concern, particularly for HF operation.

This section is designed to enlighten vehicle owners to the challenges and to make suggestions when installing mobile amateur

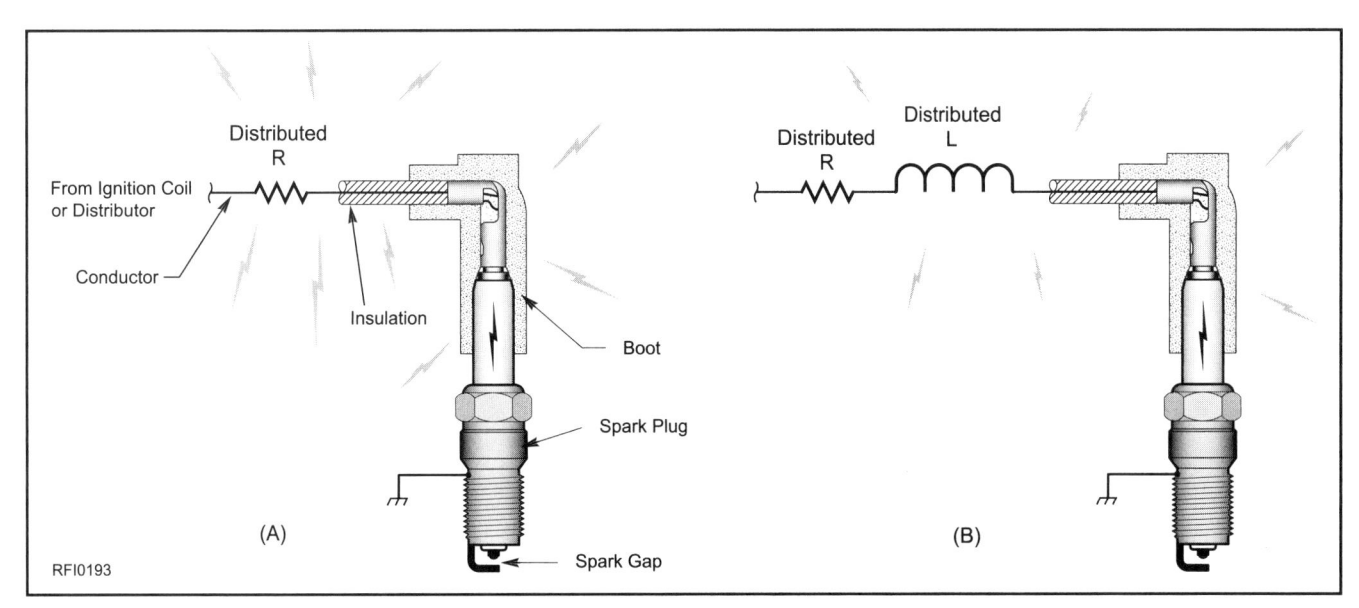

Figure 27.29 — Ignition noise suppression methods.

equipments in an EV/HEV.

EV AND HEV ARCHITECTURE

Most EVs and HEVs have similar electrical traction system (ETS) architectures consisting of a high voltage battery supplying energy to an inverter which controls an electric motor within a transmission connected to the drive wheels. The main difference between the two is that an HEV includes an internal combustion engine to aid in propulsion and a pure EV is strictly electrically powered.

The heart of the ETS is a device called an inverter. It simply converts dc voltage from the high voltage battery (typical voltage range from 42 to 350 V dc) to an ac waveform supplying the electric motor. This dc-to-ac conversion is performed by a matrix of six transistor switches. The switches chop the dc voltage into systematically varying pulses called pulse-width-modulation (PWM) to form an adjustable frequency and RMS voltage suitable to power electric motor.

In most cases, the ac voltage from the inverter is a three-phase waveform similar to industrial applications because three-phase motors can be smaller, more efficient, and provide greater torque than single-phase motors.

IMPORTANT — Bright orange cables connect the battery pack to the inverter and the inverter to the drive motor, transferring voltage and current to and from the inverter. Because of the non-sinusoidal waveforms being transferred, these cables are shielded and terminated at each end. Under no condition should these cables be disconnected or modified, because the high voltage system depends on a delicate balance of sensors and safety mechanisms. Possible malfunction and damage to the ETS may occur if modified.

EV AND HEV RFI CONCERNS

The inverter uses PWM to convert dc battery voltage to an ac waveform. The phase-to-phase terminal voltage appears in **Figure 27.30** as rectangular blocks with positive and negative amplitude equal to the battery voltage. For example, a 300 V dc battery pack will provide 600 V peak-to-peak at the motor terminals. In Figure 27.30, the same terminal voltage signal is sent through a low pass filter to show how PWM forms a sinusoidal waveform. Each pulse is essentially a square wave. Harmonics from these pulses fall within most of our amateur HF bands, affecting radio performance. Because EV/HEV systems are evolving rapidly, check the ARRL's Automotive RFI web page (**www.arrl.org/automotive**) for more information.

EV AND HEV RFI REMEDIES

Troubleshooting techniques described earlier apply in diagnosing RFI from EV/HEV systems. Limited RFI remedies are available associated to components within the ETS. Work with your dealer when you suspect the ETS as the RFI source. Do not attempt to modify or repair your ETS; the dealer's service center is most qualified to inspect and repair your EV/HEV electrical traction system.

During installation, mobile equipment power cables and antenna coaxial cables should be routed as far as possible from the bright orange cables. Common-mode chokes can decrease noise on 12-V dc power cables. Additionally, antenna placement plays a critical role in mobile equipment performance. Areas such as the top of a roof or trunk sometimes provide additional shielding.

27.9.6 Automotive RFI Summary

Most radio installations should result in no problems to either the vehicle systems or any issues with the transceiver. However, manufacturer, make and models differ, thus introducing challenges during amateur equipment installations.

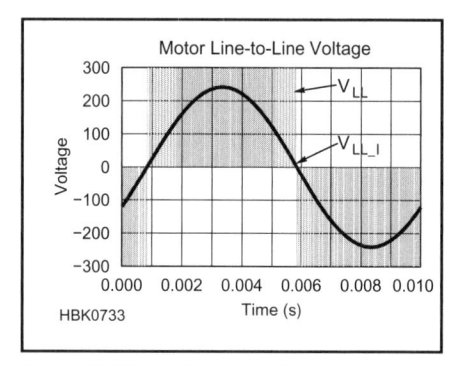

Figure 27.30 — Phase-to-phase motor terminal voltage.

Begin by researching your vehicle of interest and visiting the dealer. Insist on transmitting and receiving your favorite frequencies as you test drive. Request information pertaining to the manufacturer's transceiver installation guidelines. If manufacturer information is not available, follow the guidelines described earlier.

After installation, RFI problems may appear. Report you problem to the dealer, because they have access to manufacturer service bulletins which may describe a repair solution. Additional troubleshooting and remedies are also described previously to assist in successful communication.

Limited RFI remedies are available associated to components within the ETS. Work with your dealer when you suspect the ETS is the RFI source. Do not attempt to modify or repair your ETS; the dealer's service center is most qualified to inspect and repair your EV/HEV electrical traction system.

Lastly, the latest version of the *ARRL RFI Book* contains additional information on RFI in automobiles. More details are given about noise sources, troubleshooting techniques, a troubleshooting flow chart, additional filtering techniques, and information on EV/HEVs.

27.10 RFI Projects

Note: Additional RFI projects are included in the downloadable supplemental information accompanying this book.

27.10.1 Project: RF Sniffer

Every home is full of electrical equipment capable of emitting electromagnetic radiation to interfere with radio amateurs trying to listen to signals on the bands. This project detects the radiation that causes problems to the amateur, and the noise can be heard. This device will allow you to demonstrate the "noise" with which we have to contend.

CONSTRUCTION

The circuit (**Figure 27.31**) uses a telephone pick-up coil as a detector, the output of which is fed into a LM741 IC preamplifier, followed by a LM386 IC power amplifier. See **Table 27.4** for the complete component list.

The project is built on a perforated board (**Figure 27.32**), with the component leads pushed through the holes and joined with hook-up wire underneath. There is a wire running around the perimeter of the board to form an earth bus.

Build from the loudspeaker backwards to R8, apply power and touch the wiper of R8. If everything is OK you should hear a loud buzz from the speaker. Too much gain may cause a feedback howl, in which case you will need to adjust R8 to reduce the gain. Complete the rest of the wiring and test with a finger on the input, which should produce a click and a buzz. The pick-up coil comes with a lead and 3.5 mm jack, so you will need a suitable socket.

RELATIVE NOISES

Place a high-impedance meter set to a low-ac-voltage range across the speaker leads to

Table 27.4
Components List

Resistors	Value
R1	1 kΩ
R2, R6	100 Ω
R3, R4	47 kΩ
R5	100 kΩ
R7	10 Ω
R8	10 kΩ, with switch
Capacitors	*Value*
C1, C6	4.7 µF, 16 V electrolytic
C2, C5	0.01 µF
C3, C4	22 µF, 16 V electrolytic
C7	0.047 µF
C8	10 µF, 16 V electrolytic
C9, C11	330 µF, 16 V electrolytic
C10	0.1 µF
Semiconductors	
U1	LM741
U2	LM386
Additional Items	
LS1	Small 8-Ω loudspeaker
Perforated board	
9 V battery and clip	
3.5 mm mono-jack socket	
Case	
Telephone pick-up coil	

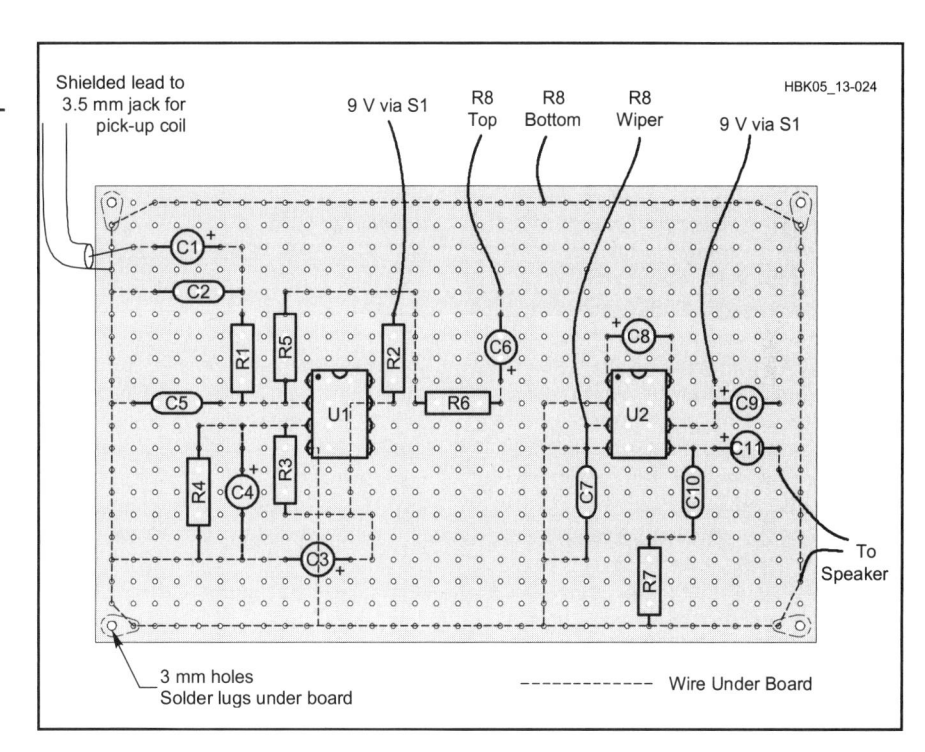

Figure 27.32 — The project is built on perforated board with point-to-point wiring underneath.

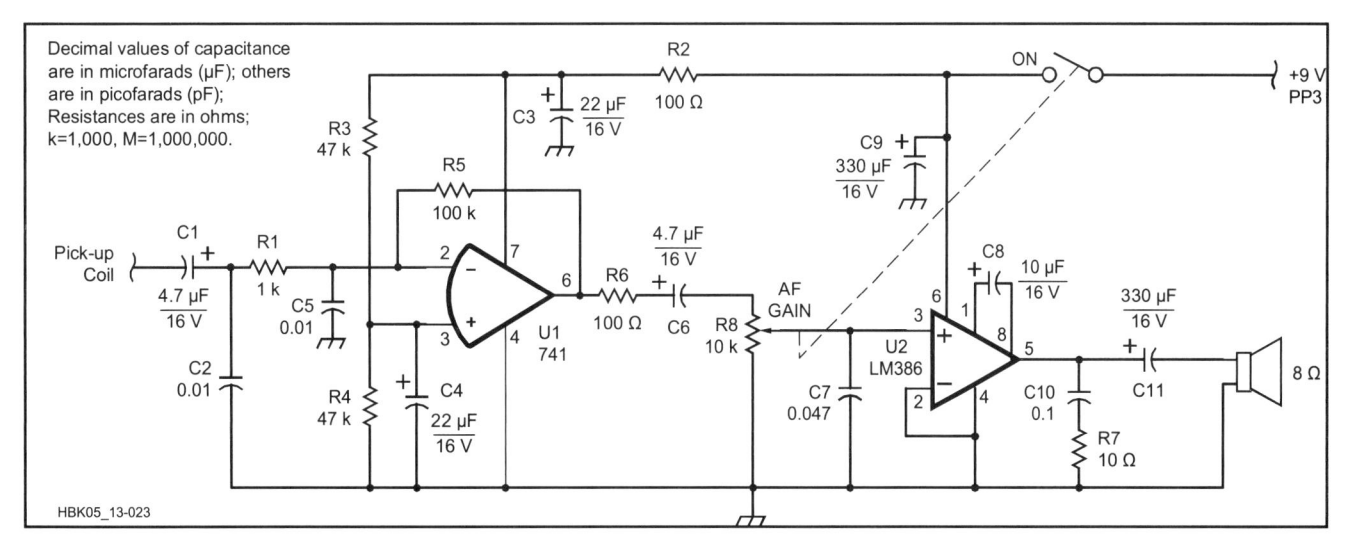

Figure 27.31 — The detector works by receiving stray radiation on a telephone pick-up coil and amplifying it to loudspeaker level.

give a comparative readout between different items of equipment in the home. Sample readings are shown in **Table 27.5**.

Table 27.5
Readings (pick-up coil near household items)

29-MHz oscilloscope	0.56 V	Old TV	1.2 V
Old computer CRT monitor	0.86 V	New TV	0.4 V
Old computer with plastic case	1.53 V	Plastic-cased hairdryer	4.6 V
New computer CRT monitor	0.45 V	Vacuum cleaner	3.6 V
New tower PC with metal case	0.15 V	Drill	4.9 V

27.11 RFI Glossary

Balanced circuit — A circuit whose two conductors have equal impedance to a common reference, such as a reference plane or circuit common.

Bond — (noun) A low-impedance, mechanically robust, electrical connection.

Common-mode — In a group of conductors, such as multi-conductor cable, voltage or current that is present with the same amplitude, phase and polarity on all conductors in a group, such as multi-conductor cable. AC current flowing on the outside of a coaxial cable shield is also considered to be common-mode current..

Conducted RFI — RFI received via a conducting path.

Coupled RFI — RFI received via inductive or capacitive coupling between conductors.

Differential mode — A signal that that is exists and is transmitted as a voltage *between* two conductors of a cable. At any instant, signal current on one conductor is equal to but of the opposite polarity to the current on the other conductor. Ordinary connections between equipment in systems are differential mode signals.

Disturbance — The improper operation of a device as a result of interference.

Electric field — The field present between two or more conductive objects as a result of potential difference (voltage) between those objects.

Electromagnetic field — The combination of a magnetic field and electric field in which the fields are directly related to each other, are at right angles to each other, and move through space as radio waves in a direction that is mutually perpendicular to both fields. An electrical conductor designed to produce electromagnetic fields when carrying an RF current is called an antenna.

Equipment ground — The connection of all exposed parts of electrical equipment to earth, or to a body that serves in place of earth.

Fundamental overload — 1. (Receiver Performance) Interference to a receiver caused by a signal at its input whose amplitude exceeds the maximum signal-handling capabilities of one or more receiver stages. 2. (RF interference) — Any disruption to the function of any RFI victim caused by the fundamental component of a transmitted signal or intended in-band output of a transmitter.

Ground — 1. A low impedance electrical connection to earth, or to a body that serves in place of earth. 2. A common signal connection in an electrical circuit.

Immunity — The ability of a device to function properly in the presence of unwanted electromagnetic energy. (After Ott, section 1.3)

Intentional radiator — A device that uses radio waves to transmit information by antenna action. A radio transmitter, with its associated antenna, is an intentional radiator.

Interference — 1. Disruption of a device's normal function as a result of an electromagnetic field, voltage, or current. 2. Disruption by a signal or noise of a receiver's ability to acquire and process a desired signal.

Magnetic field — The field produced by a permanent magnet or current flow through a conductor.

Path — The route by which electromagnetic energy is transferred from a transmitter to a receiver or from a source to a victim.

Radiated RFI — RFI received through radiation.

Shielding — A conductive barrier or enclosure interposed between two regions of space with the intent of preventing a field in one region from reaching the other region.

Source — A device that produces an electromagnetic, electric, or magnetic field, voltage, or current. If RFI is the result, the source is an *RFI source*.

Spurious emission — An emission outside the bandwidth needed for transmission of the mode being employed, the level of which may be reduced without reducing the quality of information being transmitted. Spurious emissions are most commonly the products of distortion (harmonics, intermodulation), of circuit instability (oscillation, including RF feedback), or of digital transmission with excessively fast rise times (including key clicks). Phase noise, such as that produced by a frequency synthesizer is also a spurious emission.

Susceptibility — The capability of a device to respond to unwanted electromagnetic energy. (After Ott, section 1.3)

System ground — A bond between one current-carrying conductor of the power system and earth.

Unintentional radiator — A device that produces RF as part of its normal operation but does not intentionally radiate it.

Victim — A device that receives interference from a *source*.

27.12 References and Bibliography

AES48-2005: AES standard on interconnections — Grounding and EMC practices — Shields of connectors in audio equipment containing active circuitry

"Identifying Power-Line Noise," ARRL, **www.youtube.com/watch?v=mD4GHcKMepU&feature=youtu.be**

Radio Frequency Interference web page, **www.arrl.org/radio-frequency-interference-rfi**

J. Brown, K9YC, "Power, Grounding, Bonding, and Audio," 2014, **k9yc.com/publish.htm**.

J. Brown, K9YC, "Building Contest Scores by Killing Receive Noise, Parts 1 and 2," National Contest Journal, May/June and July/Aug 2016, **k9yc.com/KillingReceiveNoise.pdf**.

J. Brown, K9YC, "RFI, Ferrites, and Common Mode Chokes For Hams," 2010, **k9yc.com/publish.htm**.

J. Brown, K9YC, "RF Interference in Audio Systems," 2008 Fall Convention of the Audio Engineering Society, **k9yc.com/AES-RFI-SF08.pdf**.

J. Brown, K9YC, "New Understandings of the Use of Ferrites in the Prevention and Suppression of RF Interference to Audio Systems," 119th AES Convention in New York, October 2005, **k9yc.com/AESPaperFerritesASGWeb.pdf**

C. Counselman, W1HIS, "Common Mode Chokes, **www.yccc.org/Articles/W1HIS/CommonModeChokesW1HIS2006Apr06.pdf**.

M. Foerster, WØIH, "Hunting Down RF Noises," *QST*, Feb 2015, pp. 45-46, **www.arrl.org/files/file/RFI/FOESTER.PDF**

M. Gruber, ed, *The ARRL RFI Book*, Third Edition, ARRL, 2010

M. Loftness, *AC Power Interference*, Third Edition, Revised, distributed by the ARRL

N. Muncy, "Noise Susceptibility in Analog and Digital Signal Processing Systems," presented at the 97th AES Convention of the Audio Engineering Society in San Francisco, CA, Nov. 1994.

H. Ott, *Electromagnetic Compatibility Engineering*, John Wiley and Sons, 2009

C. Paul, *Introduction to Electromagnetic Compatibility*, Wiley-Interscience, 1992

T. Thompson, WØIVJ, "Locating RF Interference at HF," *QST*, Nov 2014, p 33. **www.arrl.org/files/file/RFI/Thompson%20Noise.pdf**

Underwriter Labs Standard UL943, "Ground-Fault Circuit-Interrupters," **ulstandardsinfonet.ul.com/scopes/scopes.asp?fn=0943.html**

Contents

28.1 Electrical Safety
    28.1.1 Station Concerns
    28.1.2. Do-It-Yourself Wiring
    28.1.3 National Electrical Code (NEC)
    28.1.4 Station Power
    28.1.5 Connecting and Disconnecting Power
    28.1.6 Ground-Fault and Arc-Fault Circuit Interrupters
    28.1.7 Low-Voltage Wiring
    28.1.8 Grounding and Bonding
    28.1.9 Ground Conductors
    28.1.10 Antennas
    28.1.11 Lightning Transient Protection
    28.1.12 Other Hazards in the Station
    28.1.13 Electrical Safety References

28.2 Antenna and Tower Safety
    28.2.1 Legal Considerations
    28.2.2 Antenna Mounting Structures
    28.2.3 Tower Construction and Erection
    28.2.4 Antenna Installation
    28.2.5 Weatherproofing Cable and Connectors
    28.2.6 Climbing Safety
    28.2.7 Antenna and Tower Safety References

28.3 RF Safety
    28.3.1 How EMF Affects Mammalian Tissue
    28.3.2 Researching Biological Effects of EMF Exposure
    28.3.3 Safe Exposure Levels
    28.3.4 Cardiac Pacemakers and RF Safety
    28.3.5 Low-Frequency Fields
    28.3.6 Determining RF Power Density
    28.3.7 Further RF Exposure Suggestions

**Chapter 28 —
Downloadable Supplemental Content**

Supplemental Files
- *Electric Current Abroad* — U.S. Dept of Commerce
- "Shop Safety" by Don Daso, K4ZA
- "RF Safety at Field Day" by Greg Lapin, N9GL
- "Field Day Towers — Doing It Right" by Don Daso, K4ZA and Ward Silver, NØAX

Chapter 28

Safety

This chapter focuses on how to avoid three types of potential hazards. The first section, updated from material originally written by Jim Lux, W6RMK, and updated by Ward Silver, NØAX, details electrical safety, grounding, bonding, and related issues in the station. The following section on antenna and tower safety was written by Steve Morris, K7LXC, and updated by Don Daso, K4ZA both professional tower climbers and antenna installers with many years of experience. Finally, the ARRL RF Safety Committee explains good amateur practices, standards and FCC regulations as they apply to RF exposure.

Safety First — Always

We need to learn as much as possible about what could go wrong so we can avoid factors that might result in accidents. Amateur Radio activities are not inherently hazardous, but like many things in modern life, it pays to be informed. Stated another way, while we long to be creative and innovative, there is still the need to act responsibly. Safety begins with our attitude. Make it a habit to plan work carefully. Don't be the one to say, "I didn't think it could happen to me."

Having a good attitude about safety is not enough, however. We must be knowledgeable about common safety guidelines and follow them faithfully. Safety guidelines cannot possibly cover all situations, but if we approach each task with a measure of common sense, we should be able to work safely.

Involve your family in Amateur Radio. Having other people close by is always beneficial in the event that you need immediate assistance. Take the valuable step of showing family members how to turn off the electrical power to your equipment safely. Additionally, cardiopulmonary resuscitation (CPR) training can save lives in the event of electrical shock. Classes are offered in most communities. Take the time to plan with your family members exactly what action should be taken in the event of an emergency, such as electrical shock, equipment fire or power outage. Practice your plan!

28.1 Electrical Safety

The standard power available from commercial mains in the United States for residential service is 120/240-V ac. The "primary" voltages that feed transformers in our neighborhoods may range from 1300 to more than 10,000 V. Generally, the responsibility for maintaining the power distribution system belongs to a utility company, electric cooperative or city. The "ownership" of conductors usually transfers from the electric utility supplier to the homeowner where the power connects to the meter or weather head. If you are unsure of where the division of responsibility falls in your community, a call to your electrical utility will provide the answer. **Figure 28.1** shows the typical division of responsibility between the utility company and the homeowner. This section is concerned more with wiring practices in the shack, as opposed to within the equipment in the shack.

There are two facets to success with electrical power: safety and performance. Since we are not professionals, we need to pursue safety first and consult professionals for alternative solutions if performance is unacceptable. The ARRL's Volunteer Consulting Engineers program involves professional engineers who may be able to provide advice or direction on difficult problems.

28.1.1 Station Concerns

There never seem to be enough power outlets in your shack. A good solution for small scale power distribution is a switched power strip with multiple outlets. The strip should be listed by a nationally recognized testing laboratory (NRTL) such as Underwriters Lab, UL, and should incorporate a circuit breaker. See the sidebars "What Does UL Listing Mean?" and "How Safe are Outlet Strips?" for warnings about poor quality products. It is poor practice to "daisy-chain" several power strips

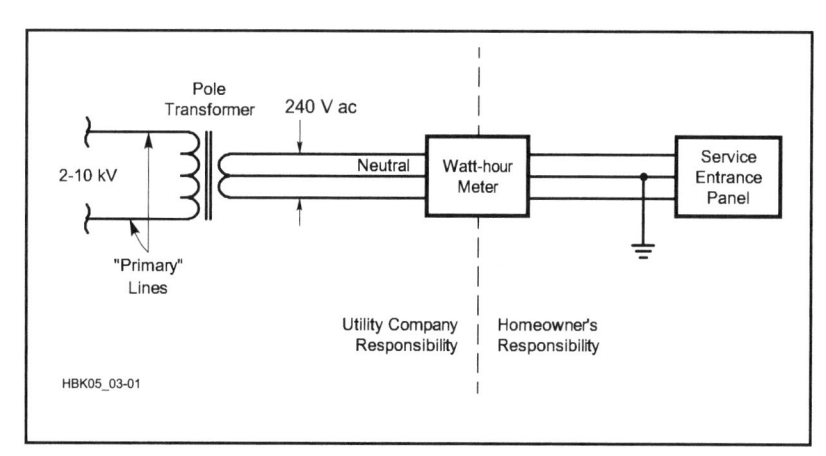

Figure 28.1 — Typical division of responsibility for maintenance of electrical power conductors and equipment. The meter is supplied by the utility company.

Safety   28.1

What Does UL Listing Mean?

UL is one of several nationally recognized testing laboratories (NRTLs), and probably the most well known. Listing *does not* mean what most consumers expect it to mean! More often than not the listing *does not* relate to the performance of the listed product. The listing simply indicates that a sample of the device meets certain manufacturers' construction criteria. Similar devices from the same or different manufacturers may differ significantly in overall construction and performance even though all are investigated and listed against the same UL product category. There is also a difference between a listed device and a listed component.

Many local laws and regulations, as well as the National Electrical Code, require that equipment and components used in electrical installations be listed by a NRTL. Some jurisdictions (Los Angeles County) require that any electrical equipment sold to consumers be listed.

The consumer must also be aware of the fine distinctions in advertising between a device or component that is advertised as "listed" or "designed to meet" or "meets." The latter two may not actually have been tested, or if tested, may have been tested by the manufacturer, and not an independent body.

It's also important to know that in some cases UL (and other standards organizations) only publish a standardized test procedure, but don't necessarily list or test the devices. Many standards also define varying levels of compliance, so knowing that your device meets some part of the standard may not be enough to know whether it meets *your* particular needs.

Grounding and Bonding for the Radio Amateur

There is so much information about ac safety, lightning protection, and dealing with RF in the station that it can be difficult to understand it all. While this chapter is a helpful summary, it is still just a summary. To help hams setting up a station for the first time or trying to improve and existing station, the ARRL has published *Grounding and Bonding for the Radio Amateur*. Along with its website (**www.arrl.org/grounding-and-bonding-for-the-radio-amateur**) the book collects information about these important practices into one reference.

How Safe Are Outlet Strips?

The switch in outlet strips is generally *not* rated for repetitive *load break* duty. Early failure and fire hazard may result from using these devices to switch heavy loads on and off. Misapplications are common (another bit of bad technique that has evolved from the use of personal computers), and manufacturers are all too willing to accommodate the market with marginal products. A lockable disconnect switch or circuit breaker is a better and safer station master switch.

Older power strips not complying with current standards can also be a safety hazard. MOVs in these older strips that are subjected to repeated transients can fail and cause a fire hazard, especially in outlet strips with plastic enclosures. Power strips made after 2009 that comply with UL standards are safe to use.

(by building owners), so long as the electrical codes are met. Before making changes to your wiring, it would be wise to determine what rules apply and what agency has the authority to enforce them. This is called the *authority having jurisdiction* (AHJ) and it varies from location to location. Also see the following section on the National Electrical Code.

Generally, the building owner must obtain an electrical permit before beginning changes or additions to permanent wiring. Some jobs may require drawings of planned work. Often the permit fee pays for an inspector to review the work. Considering the risk of injury or fire if critical mistakes are left uncorrected, a permit and inspection are well worth the effort. *Don't take chances* — seek assistance from the building officials or an experienced electrician if you have *any* questions or doubts about proper wiring techniques.

Ordinary 120-V circuits are the most common source of fatal electrical accidents. Line voltage wiring must use an approved cable, be properly installed in conduit and junction boxes, within a chassis with a cover or lid, or other means described in the electrical code. Remember that high-current, low-voltage power sources, such as car batteries and high-current power supplies, can be just as dangerous as high-voltage sources, from melting metal, sparks and short circuits.

Never work on electrical wiring with the conductors energized! Switch off the circuit breaker or remove the fuse and take positive steps to ensure that others do not restore the power while you are working, such as using a circuit-breaker lockout. (**Figure 28.2** illustrates one way to ensure that power will be off until you want it turned on.) Check the circuit with an ac voltmeter to be sure that it is "dead" *each time you begin work*.

Before restoring power, check the wiring with an ohmmeter: From the installed out-

Figure 28.2 — If the switch box feeding power to your shack is equipped with a lock-out hole, use it. With a lock through the hole on the box, the power cannot be accidentally turned back on. [Photo courtesy of American ED-CO]

let, there should be good continuity between the neutral conductor (white wire, "silver" screw) and the grounding conductor (green or bare wire, green screw). An ohmmeter should indicate a closed circuit between the conductors. (In the power line, high voltage world, line workers apply a shorting jumper before starting work so if the power does get reapplied, the safety jumper takes the hit.)

With all other loads removed from the circuit (by turning off or unplugging them), an ohmmeter should indicate an *open* circuit between the hot wire and either of the other two conductors. There should be no continu-

---

and may actually be a code violation. If you need more outlets than are available on a strip, have additional wall outlets installed.

Whether you add new outlets or use power strips, be sure not to overload the circuit. National and local codes set permissible branch capacities according to a rather complex process. Here's a safe rule of thumb: consider adding a new circuit if the total load is more than 80% of the circuit breaker or fuse rating. (This assumes that the fuse or breaker is correct. If you have any doubts, have an electrician check it.)

28.1.2. Do-It-Yourself Wiring

Amateurs sometimes "rewire" parts of their homes to accommodate their hobby. Most local codes *do* allow for modification of wiring

ity between the hot conductor (black wire, "brass" screw) and the grounding conductor or the neutral conductor.

Commercially available plug-in testers are a convenient way to test regular three-wire receptacles, but can't distinguish between the neutral and ground being reversed.

It is wise to have an up-to-date reference guide to wiring practices. These guides may be available from home improvement stores and electrical supply houses. As of early 2017, one widely available book is the *Black & Decker Complete Guide to Wiring, 6th edition*. The book is inexpensive and includes many step-by-step instructions for basic and intermediate wiring projects.

28.1.3 National Electrical Code (NEC)

Fortunately, much has been learned about how to harness electrical energy safely. This collective experience has been codified into the *National Electrical Code*, or *NEC*, simply known as "the code." The code details safety requirements for many kinds of electrical installations. Compliance with the NEC provides an installation that is *essentially* free from hazard, but not necessarily efficient, convenient or adequate for good service (paraphrased from NEC Article 90-1a and b). While the NEC is national in nature and sees wide application, it is not universal.

Local building authorities set the codes for their area of jurisdiction. They often incorporate the NEC in some form, while considering local issues. For example, Washington State specifically exempts telephone, telegraph, radio and television wires and equipment from conformance to electrical codes, rules and regulations. However, some local jurisdictions (city, county and so on) do impose a higher level of installation criteria, including some of the requirements exempted by the state.

Code interpretation is a complex subject, and untrained individuals should steer clear of the NEC itself. The NEC is not written to be understood by do-it-yourselfers, and one typically has to look in several places to find *all* the requirements. (For instance, Articles 810, 250, *and* 100 all contain things applicable to typical Amateur Radio installations.) The *NEC Handbook* is a version of the code with additional drawings and discussion. It explains the requirements of the code and how to satisfy those requirements. Written for electricians, even the *NEC Handbook* may be difficult for the non-electrician to understand completely. You may wish to contact local sources of information about code compliance and acceptable practices such as local building officials or inspectors, electrical engineers, and practicing electricians. The NEC and the *NEC Handbook* are available from local libraries.

The Internet has a lot of information about electrical safety, the electrical code, and wiring practices, but you need to be careful to make sure the information you are using is current and not out of date. The ARRL Volunteer Consulting Engineer (VCE) program can help you find a professional who understands the amateur radio world, as well as the regulatory environment. There are also a variety of websites with useful information (such as www.mikeholt.com), but you need to be aware that advice may be specific to a particular installation or jurisdiction and not applicable for yours. With that understanding, let's look at a few NEC requirements for radio installations.

HOMEBREW AND "THE CODE"

In many cases, there are now legal requirements that electrical equipment have been listed by an NRTL, such as Underwriter Laboratories. This raises an issue for hams and homebrew gear, since it's unlikely you would take your latest project down to a test lab and pay them to evaluate it for safety.

For equipment that is not permanently installed, there's not much of an issue with homebrew, as far as the code goes, because the code doesn't deal with what's inside the equipment. For a lot of low voltage equipment, the code rules are fairly easy to meet, as well, as long as the equipment is supplied by a listed power source of the appropriate type.

The problem arises with permanent installations, where the scope of the code and local regulations is ever increasing. Such things as solar panel installations, standby generators, personal computers and home LANs all have received increased attention in local codes.

28.1.4 Station Power

Amateur Radio stations generally require a 120-V ac power source, which is then converted to the proper ac or dc levels required for the station equipment. In residential systems voltages from 110 V through 125 V are treated equivalently, as are those from 220 V through 250 V. Amateurs setting up a station in a light industrial or office environment may encounter 208 V line voltage. Most power supplies operate over these ranges, but it's a good idea to measure the voltage range at your station. (The measured voltage usually varies by hour, day, season and location.) Power supply application and use are covered in the **Power Sources** chapter.

Modern solid state rigs often operate from dc power, provided by a suitable dc power supply, perhaps including battery backups. Sometimes, the dc power supply is part of the rig (as in a 50-V power supply for a solid-state linear). Other times, your shack might have a 12-V (13.8 V) bus that supplies many devices.

About the National Electrical Code

Exactly how does the National Electrical Code become a requirement? How is it enforced?

Cities and other political subdivisions have the responsibility to act for the public safety and welfare. To address safety and fire hazards in buildings, regulations are adopted by local laws and ordinances usually including some form of permit and accompanying inspections. Because the technology for the development of general construction, mechanical and electrical codes is beyond most city building departments, model codes are incorporated by reference. There are several general building code models used in the US: Uniform, BOCA and Southern Building Codes are those most commonly adopted. For electrical issues, the National Electrical Code is in effect in virtually every community. City building officials will serve as "the authority having jurisdiction" (AHJ) and interpret the provisions of the Code as they apply it to specific cases.

Building codes differ from planning or zoning regulations: Building codes are directed only at safety, fire and health issues. Zoning regulations often are aimed at preservation of property values and aesthetics.

The NEC is part of a series of reference codes published by the National Fire Protection Association, a non-profit organization. Published codes are regularly kept up-to-date and are developed by a series of technical committees whose makeup represents a wide consensus of opinion. The NEC is updated every three years. It's important to know which version of the code your local jurisdiction uses, since it's not unusual to have the city require compliance to an older version of the code. Fortunately, the NEC is usually backward compatible: that is, if you're compliant to the 2008 code, you're probably also compliant to the 1999 code.

Do I have to update my electrical wiring as code requirements are updated or changed?

Generally, no. Codes are typically applied for new construction and for renovating existing structures. Room additions, for example, might not directly trigger upgrades in the existing service panel unless the panel was determined to be inadequate. However, the wiring of the new addition would be expected to meet current codes. Prudent homeowners, however, may want to add safety features for their own value. Many homeowners, for example, have added GFCI protection to bathroom and outdoor convenience outlets.

Safety 28.3

> **International Power Standards**
>
> The power grid of the United States and Canada uses a frequency of 60 Hz and the voltage at ac power outlets is 120 V. This is also the case in other North American countries. If you travel, though, you'll encounter 220 V and 50 Hz with quite an array of plugs and sockets and color codes. If you are planning on taking amateur radio equipment with you on a vacation or DXpedition, you'll need to be prepared with the proper adapters and/or transformers to operate your equipment.
>
> A table of international voltage and frequencies is provided with the downloadable supplemental content, along with a figure showing the most common plug and socket configurations.

Just because it's low voltage doesn't mean that there aren't aspects of the system that raise safety concerns. A 15-A, 12-V power supply can start a fire as easily as a 15-A, 120-V branch circuit.

28.1.5 Connecting and Disconnecting Power

Something that is sometimes overlooked is that you need to have a way to safely disconnect all power to everything in the shack. This includes not only the ac power, but also battery banks, solar panels, and uninterruptible power supplies (UPS). Most hams won't have the luxury of a dedicated room with a dedicated power feed and the "big red switch" on the wall, so you'll have several switches and cords that would need to be disconnected.

The realities of today's shacks, with computers, multiple wall transformers ("wall-warts"), network interfaces and the radio equipment itself makes this tricky to do. One convenient means is a switched outlet strip, as used for computer equipment, if you have a limited number of devices. If you need more switched outlets, you can control multiple low-voltage controlled switched outlets from a common source. Or you can build or buy a portable power distribution box similar to those used on construction sites or stage sets; they are basically a portable subpanel with individual circuit breakers (or GFCIs, discussed later) for each receptacle, and fed by a suitable cord or extension cord. No matter what scheme you use, however, it's important that it be labeled so that someone else will know what to do to turn off the power.

AC LINE POWER

If your station is located in a room with electrical outlets, you're in luck. If your station is located in the basement, an attic or other area without a convenient 120-V source, you may need to have a new line run to your operating position.

Stations with high-power amplifiers should have a 240-V ac power source in addition to the 120-V supply. Some amplifiers may be powered from 120 V, but they require current levels that may exceed the limits of standard house wiring. To avoid overloading the circuit and to reduce household light dimming or blinking when the amplifier is in use, and for the best possible voltage regulation in the equipment, it is advisable to install a separate 240 or 120-V line with an appropriate current rating if you use an amplifier.

The usual circuits feeding household outlets are rated at 15 or 20 A., This may or may not be enough current to power your station. To determine how much current your station requires, check the VA (volt-amp) ratings for each piece of gear. (See the **Electrical Fundamentals** chapter for a discussion of VA.) Usually, the manufacturer will specify the required current at 120 V; if the power consumption is rated in watts, divide that rating by 120 V to get amperes. Modern switching power supplies draw more current as the line voltage drops, so if your line voltage is markedly lower than 120 V, you need to take that into account.

Note that the code requires you to use the "nameplate" current, even if you've measured the actual current, and it's less. If the total current required is near 80% of the circuit's rating (12 A on a 15-A circuit or 16 A on a 20-A circuit), you need to install another circuit. Keep in mind that other rooms may be powered from the same branch of the electrical system, so the power consumption of any equipment connected to other outlets on the branch must be taken into account. If you would like to measure just how much power your equipment consumes, the inexpensive Kill-A-Watt meters by P3 International (**www.p3international.com**) measure volts, amps, VA and power factor.

If you decide to install a separate 120-V line or a 240-V line, consult the local requirements as discussed earlier. In some areas, a licensed electrician must perform this work. Others may require a special building permit. Even if you are allowed to do the work yourself, it might need inspection by a licensed electrician. Go through the system and get the necessary permits and inspections! Faulty wiring can destroy your possessions and take away your loved ones. Many fire insurance policies are void if there is unapproved wiring in the structure.

If you decide to do the job yourself, work closely with local building officials. Most home-improvement centers sell books to guide do-it-yourself wiring projects. If you have any doubts about doing the work yourself, get a licensed electrician to do the installation.

THREE-WIRE 120-V POWER CORDS

Most metal-cased electrical tools and appliances are equipped with three-conductor power cords. Two of the conductors carry

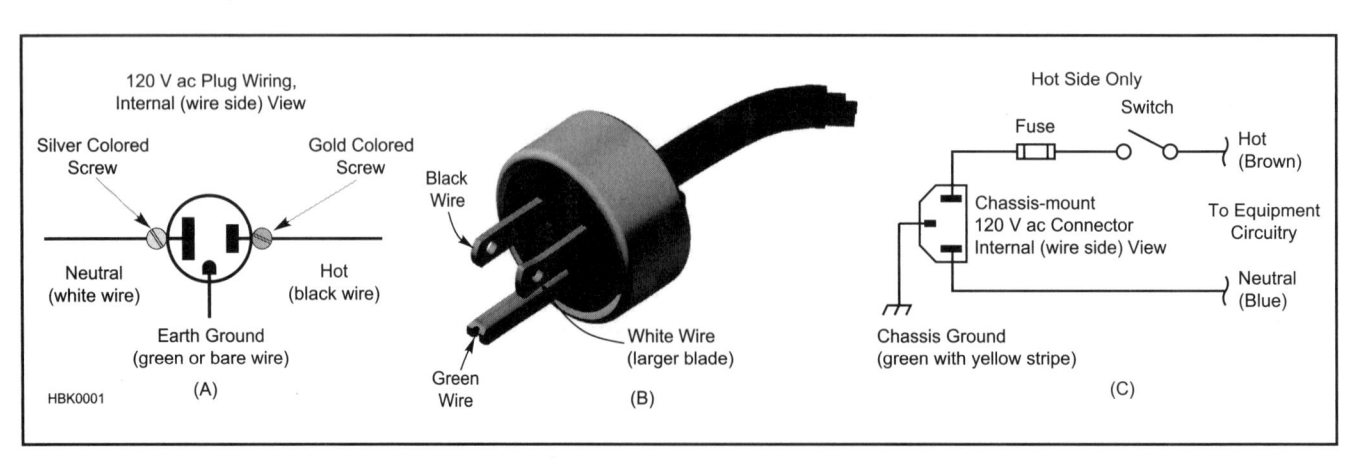

Figure 28.3 — 120 V ac plug wiring as viewed from the wire side (A) and viewed from the blade side (B). Wiring for an IEC type chassis connector is shown at C.

power to the device, while the third conductor is connected to the case, enclosure, or frame. **Figure 28.3** shows two commonly used connectors. (See the **Component Data and References** chapter for a more comprehensive drawing of ac plugs and receptacles.)

When both plug and receptacle are properly wired, the three-contact polarized plug bonds the equipment to the system ground. If an internal short from line to case occurs, the "ground" pin carries the fault current and hopefully has a low enough impedance to trip the branch circuit breaker or blow the fuse in the device. A second reason for grounding the case is to reduce the possibility of shock for a user simultaneously connected to ground and the device. In modern practice, however, shock prevention is often done with GFCI circuit breakers as described below. These devices trip at a much lower level and are more reliable. Most commercially manufactured test equipment and ac-operated amateur equipment is supplied with three-wire cords.

It's a good idea to check for continuity from case to ground pin, particularly on used equipment, where the ground connection might have been broken or modified by the previous owner. If there is no continuity, have the equipment repaired before use.

Use such equipment only with properly installed three-wire outlets. If your house does not have such outlets, either consult a local electrician to learn about safe alternatives or have a professional review information you might obtain from online or other sources.

Equipment with plastic cases is considered "double insulated" and fed with a two-wire cord. Such equipment is safe because both conductors are insulated from the user by two layers. Nonetheless, there is still a hazard if, say, a double insulated drill were used to drill an improperly grounded case of a transmitter that was still plugged in. Remember, all insulation is prey to age, damage and wear that may erode its initial protection.

TRANSFER SWITCHES AND GENERATORS

More hams are adding standby generators and using alternate power sources such as solar panels or wind turbines, not as standalone systems like at Field Day, but interconnected with their home electrical system. These present some potential safety problems, such as preventing the local generator from "back-feeding" the utility's system during a power failure, and the fact that a solar panel puts out power whenever there is light falling on it.

For generators, the recommended approach is to use a *transfer switch*, which is a multi-pole switch that connects a selection of the house's circuits to the generator, rather than the utility power. The NEC and local regulations should be consulted for transfer switch selection and connection. The required wiring practices for permanently installed (stationary) generators are different from those for portable generators. Some issues that need to be considered are whether the neutral should be switched (many transfer switches do not switch the neutral, only the hot wire), and how the generator chassis is bonded to the building's grounding/bonding system. Most proper transfer switches are of the ON-OFF-ON configuration, with a mechanical interlock that prevents directly switching from one source to the other in a single operation.

The most dangerous thing to do with a generator is to use a so-called "suicide cord" with a male plug at each end: one end plugged into the generator's output receptacle and the other plugged into a convenient receptacle in the home. This is frequently illegal and at any rate should be avoided because of the inherent danger of having exposed, live contacts and the ease of overloading the circuit being fed.

Back-feeding your home's power panel should *never* be done unless the main breakers are in the OFF position or preferably removed. If your home's circuit-breaker panel does not have main breakers that can disconnect the external power line, *do not* use this technique to connect your generator to the home's wiring. Your generator is likely to be damaged when power is restored, and back-feeding also endangers power utility workers. Connect appliances to the generator directly with extension cords.

28.1.6 Ground-Fault and Arc-Fault Circuit Interrupters

GFCIs are devices that can be used with common 120 V household circuits to reduce the chance of electrocution when the path of current flow leaves the branch circuit (say, through a person's body to another branch or ground). An AFCI is similar in that it monitors current to watch for a fault condition. Instead of current imbalances, the AFCI detects patterns of current that indicate an arc — one of the leading causes of home fires. The AFCI is not supposed to

---

Table 28.1
Traditional Divisions Among the Classes of Circuits

Class	Power	Notes
Class 1		
Power Limited	<30V, <1000VA	Transformer protected per Article 450. If not transformer, other overcurrent and fault protection requirements apply
Remote Control and Signaling	<600V	No limit on VA Transformers protected as defined in Article 450
Class 2	Power supply <100VA Voltage <30V	
Class 3	Power supply <100VA Voltage <100V	

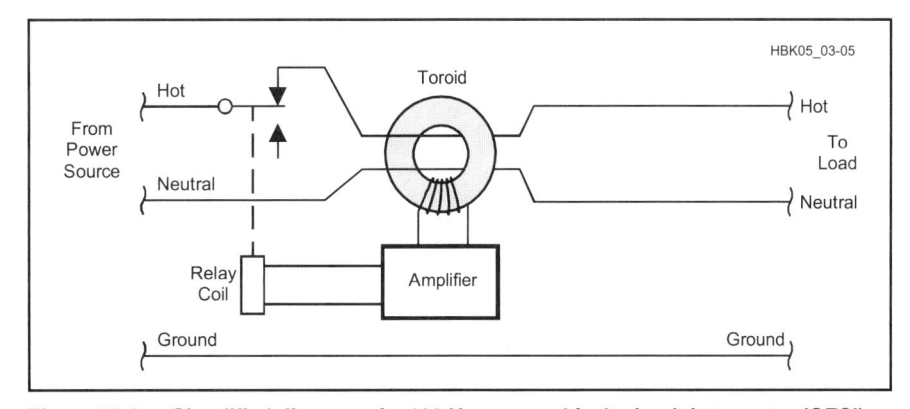

Figure 28.4 — Simplified diagram of a 120-V ac ground fault circuit interrupter (GFCI). When a stray current flows from the load (or outlet) side to ground, the current through the toroid becomes unbalanced allowing detection, amplification and relay actuation to immediately cut off power to the load (and to the stray path!) GFCI units require a manual reset after tripping. GFCIs are required in wet locations (near kitchen sinks, in garages, in outdoor circuits and for construction work.) They are available as portable units or combined with over-current circuit breakers for installation in entrance panels.

trip because of "normal" arcs that occur when a switch is opened or a plug is removed.

The NEC requires GFCI outlets in all wet or potentially wet locations, such as bathrooms, kitchens, and any outdoor outlet with ground-level access, garages and unfinished basements. AFCI protection is required for all circuits that supply bedrooms. Any area with bare concrete floors or concrete masonry walls should be GFCI equipped. GFCIs are available as portable units, duplex outlets and as individual circuit breakers. Some early units may have been sensitive to RF radiation but this problem appears to have been solved. Ham radio shacks in potentially wet areas (basements, out buildings) should be GFCI equipped. **Figure 28.4** is a simplified diagram of a GFCI.

Older equipment with capacitors in the 0.01 µF to 0.1 µF range connected between line inputs and chassis as an EMI filter (or that has been modified with bypass capacitors) will often cause a GFCI to trip, because of the leakage current through the capacitor. The must-trip current is 5 mA, but many GFCIs trip at lower levels. At 60 Hz, a 0.01 µF capacitor has an impedance of about 265 kΩ, so there could be a leakage current of about 0.5 mA from the 120 V line. If you had several pieces of equipment with such capacitors, the leakage current will trip the GFCI.

Some early GFCI breakers were susceptible to RFI but as the technology has improved, fewer and fewer such reports have been received. While it is possible to add filtering or RF suppression to the breaker wiring, a simpler and less expensive solution is to simply replace the GFCI breaker with a new unit less susceptible to RF. Reports have not yet been received on AFCI products. For more information on RFI and GFCI/AFCI devices, check the ARRL web page **www.arrl.org/gfci-devices**.

28.1.7 Low-Voltage Wiring

Many ham shacks use low-voltage control wiring for rotators or antenna relays. The electrical code isn't consistent in what it calls low voltage, but a guideline is "less than 50 V." Article 725 of the code contains most of the rules for low voltage/low power remote control and signaling, which is what hams are typically doing. These circuits are divided into three classes, with Class 1 being further subdivided, as shown in **Table 28.1**. There used to be code rules defining the classes in terms of power and voltage, but these days, the code is written so that the class of the circuit is defined by the power source, which has to be listed and labeled with the class. That is, if you have something powered by a wall transformer that is listed and labeled as Class 2, the circuit is Class 2.

A typical example of a Class 1 Power Limited circuit that you might find in your home is 12 V low-voltage garden lighting or halogen lightning systems. A lot of amateur homebrew gear probably is also in this class, although because it's not made with "listed" components, it technically doesn't qualify. The other Class 1 would apply to a circuit using an isolation transformer of some sort.

Class 2 is very common: doorbells, network wiring, thermostats, and so on are almost all Class 2. To be Class 2, the circuit must be powered from a listed power supply that's marked as being Class 2 with a capacity less than 100 VA. For many applications that hams encounter, this will be the familiar "wall wart" power supply. If you have a bunch of equipment that runs from dc power, and you build a dc power distribution panel with regulators to supply them from a storage battery or a big dc power supply, you're most likely not Class 2 anymore, but logically Class 1. Since your homebrew panel isn't likely to be listed, you're really not even Class 1, but something that isn't covered by the code.

A common example of a Class 3 circuit that is greater than 30 V is the 70 V audio distribution systems used in paging systems and the like. Class 3 wiring must be done with appropriately rated cable.

WIRING PRACTICES

Low voltage cables must be separated from power circuits. Class 2 and 3 cannot be run with Class 1 low voltage cables. They can't share a cable tray or the same conduit. A more subtle point is that the 2005 code added a restriction [Article 725.56(F)] that audio cables (speakers, microphone, etc.) cannot be run in the same conduit with other Class 2 and Class 3 circuits (like network wiring).

Low voltage and remote control wiring should not be neglected from your transient suppression system. This includes putting appropriate protective devices where wiring enters and leaves a building, and consideration of the current paths to minimize loops which can pick up the field from transients (or RF from your antenna).

28.1.8 Grounding and Bonding

As hams we are concerned with at least four kinds of connections called "ground," even if they really aren't in the sense of connection to the Earth. These are easily confused because we call each of them "ground."

1) Electrical safety ground (equipment ground or earth connection)
2) Lightning and transient dissipation ground
3) RF voltage and current management ("RF ground")
4) Common reference potential (chassis ground or circuit common)

This section of the chapter is primarily concerned with connections for electrical or safety grounding and lightning and transient dissipation. The remaining types are covered elsewhere in chapters on circuit- and antenna-building and in station construction.

Several commercial and military standards can be used as guidebooks for grounding and bonding:

National Electrical Code (NEC) — This is the primary standard for residential and commercial electrical work in the United States. NEC Article 250 deals with grounding and bonding. NEC Article 810 deals with antenna installation. (See the previous section on the NEC.)

MIL-HDBK-419A — *Grounding, Bonding, and Shielding for Electronic Equipments and Facilities (Vol 1 and 2)* — This military standard applies to communication facilities and equipment installations at any frequency. It provides many useful drawings and guidelines covering ground connections and how equipment should be bonded together. It is a public-domain document and may be downloaded without charge at **www.uscg.mil/petaluma/TPF/ET_SMS/Mil-STDs/MILHDBK419.pdf**.

R56 Standards and Guidelines for Communications Sites — Motorola is a large vendor of communications systems, mostly for VHF/UHF/microwave applications. This standard applies primarily to equipment and facilities used at those frequencies. It is not a public domain document but may be downloaded without charge from numerous sources.

IEEE Std 1100-2005 (also known as the "Emerald Book," see the Reference listing, section 28.1.13) provides detailed information from a theoretical and practical standpoint for grounding and powering electrical

---

Grounding or Bonding?

You may notice the term "bonding" is replacing "grounding" in many instances. A primary safety concern is for whatever carries fault currents to be mechanically rugged and reasonably conductive. It's also important that the fault-carrying conductor be connected to a ground rod, but that's a different consideration. Bonding is the term to use when contact between pieces of equipment or between conductors is the primary concern. Grounding is the term to use when referring to an earth connection for electrical safety or lightning protection.

equipment, including lightning protection and RF EMI/EMC concerns. It's expensive to buy, but is available through libraries.

BONDING

The definition of bonding is "to connect equipment together electrically in order to minimize the potential (voltage) difference between them." A good bonding connection must have very low impedance and approximately equal voltage everywhere along it at the frequency of interest. As amateurs know, electrical length and impedance of any type of conductor — wire, strap, braid, or sheet — varies with frequency. In addition, the amount of current flowing through the conductor can create significant voltage differences along the conductor. Because of these concerns, it is important to consider the purposes of bonding when making a bonding connection.

In general, for amateurs constructing a station, even a temporary one, it is a good practice to make bonding conductors as short as practical and as heavy as is needed to satisfy all bonding requirements. By doing so, the bonding connection will serve its purpose for all three of the primary bonding needs in your station: ac safety, lightning protection, and RF management.

ELECTRICAL SAFETY GROUND

Power-line ground is required by building codes to ensure the safety of life and property surrounding electrical systems. The NEC requires that all grounds be bonded together; this is a very important safety feature as well as an NEC requirement.

The usual term one sees for the "third prong" or "green-wire ground" is the *electrical safety ground* or *equipment ground*. The purpose of the third, non-load current carrying wire is to provide a path to ensure that the overcurrent protection will trip in the event of a line-to-case short circuit in a piece of equipment. This could either be the fuse or circuit breaker back at the main panel, or the fuse inside the equipment itself.

There is a secondary purpose — shock reduction: The electrical safety ground provides a common reference potential for all parts of the ac system. The conductive case of equipment is required to be connected to the bonded grounding system, which is also connected to earth ground at the service entrance, so someone who is connected to "earth" (for example, standing in bare feet on a conductive floor) that touches the case won't get shocked.

An effective safety ground system is necessary for every amateur station. If you have equipment at the base of the tower, generally, you need to provide a separate bonding conductor to connect the chassis and cases at the tower to the bonding system in the shack. **Figure 28.5A** shows an overall grounding system, emphasizing the requirement to bond all ground connections together, regardless of their purpose.

Equipment-to-equipment bonding can be done directly with wire (#6 to #14 AWG), strap (20 gauge), or through a bonding bus

Using Braid Instead of Strap

The standard for grounding in the communication industry is solid strap or heavy wire. Both can be used indoors or outdoors. Flat-weave, tinned grounding braid can be used if the equipment is subject to vibration or needs to be moved around. Any type of braid should never be used if it will be exposed to moisture or corrosive chemicals. Corrosion on the surface of the small wires used to make up the braid reduces its effectiveness by raising the surface resistance, where the RF currents flow. Poor contact between the individual wires can also result in noise and mixing products. Unless it is mechanically necessary, use solid strap or wire.

It is not recommended to reuse braid removed from coaxial cable. Once removed from its protective jacket, the braid wires immediately begin to loosen and oxidize or corrode. This reduces the braid's effectiveness at RF quite a bit, making it a poor choice for long-term grounding conductors.

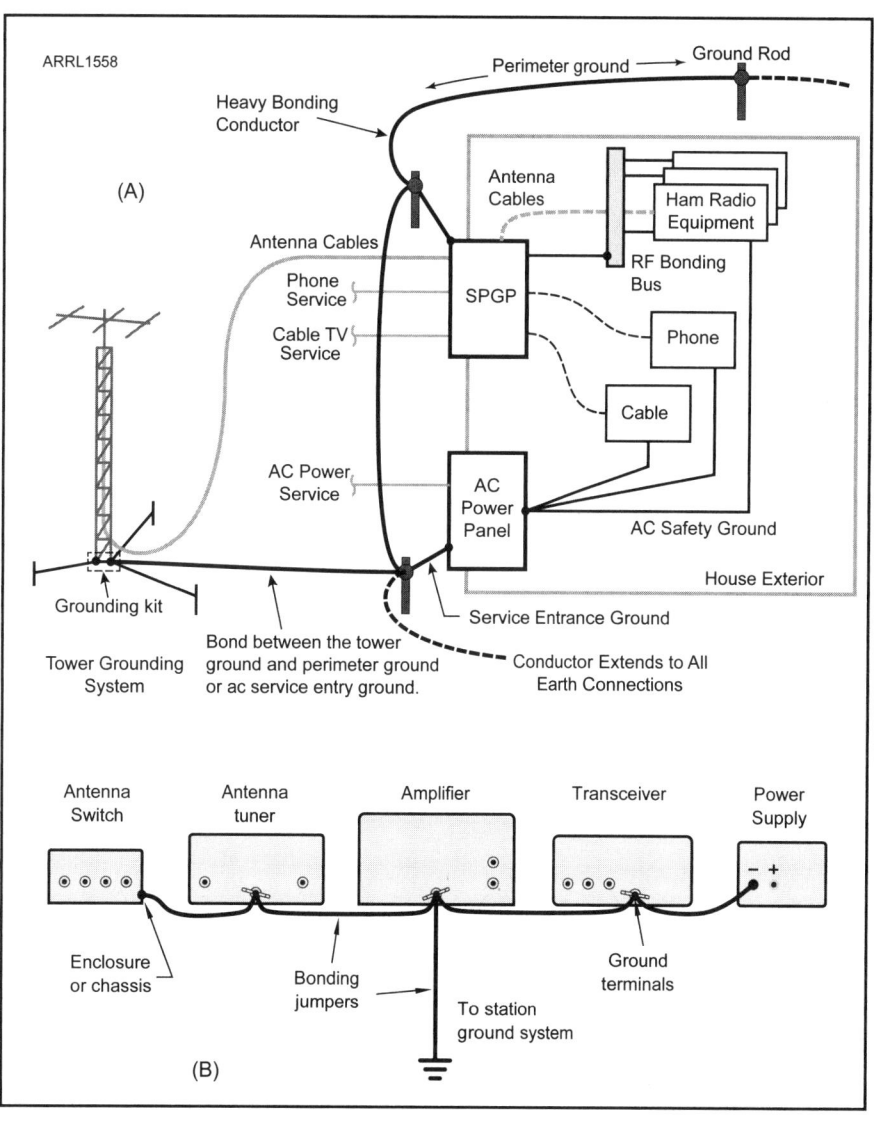

Figure 28.5 — A grounding system that includes ac safety, lightning protection, and RF management. All ground electrodes must be bonded together and to the residence's ac service entry ground rod. If a protected ac branch circuit is included, the protector should be mounted on the SPGP (single-point ground panel). Direct equipment-to-equipment bonding (B) can be done with heavy wire or strap or to an RF bonding bus. See the chapter on Assembling a Station for more information on making these connections.

or single-point ground panel (SPGP). The equipment ground or "third-wire" connection in a residence's branch circuit must be made with the same size wire as the hot and neutral conductors. Connections directly to a ground electrode, such as a ground rod, are made with heavy wire (#6 AWG minimum) or 20 gauge strap. Clamps and terminals should be rated or listed for grounding use, particularly for earth connections that are exposed to the weather or buried.

At ac power frequencies of 50 or 60 Hz, the wavelength is miles long so the electrical length of the connection is insignificant. Reactance created by the bonding conductor (about 1 nH per foot for a straight wire) is likewise negligible. The most important characteristics of the bonding connection is resistance and mechanical strength. Unfortunately, an effective bonding conductor at 60 Hz may present very high impedance at RF because of the inductance, or worse yet, wind up being an excellent antenna that picks up the signals radiated by your antenna.

RF MANAGEMENT AND CHASSIS GROUND

"RF ground" is an obsolete term that from days gone by when most operation was at low frequencies and a wire from the chassis or antenna tuner in the shack to a ground rod had low RF impedance. The RF voltage difference between the chassis and "Earth ground" was small. And even if there were small potential differences, the surrounding equipment of those days was relatively insensitive to them.

Today, we have a lot of circuits that are sensitive to interfering signals at millivolt levels, such as audio signals to and from sound cards. As a result, we can no longer ignore the RF voltage differences and shouldn't be using the equipment enclosures or shielding conductors as part of the RF circuit.

Instead, we design our stations to manage the RF picked up on cables, connecting wires, and enclosures so that it does not cause problems. The first step is to create a common reference potential, called the *ground plane* or *reference plane*. Equipment connected to the ground plane is maintained at a common potential. This minimizes RF current that would flow between pieces of equipment. (See the **RF Interference** and **Assembling a Station** chapters for more information.) The ground plane can be an actual sheet of metal or a low-inductance conductor to which all of the equipment can be connected, often called an RF bonding bus. The ground plane is then bonded to the station ground system.

It is sometimes suggested that RF grounds should be isolated from the ac safety and lightning protection ground system — that is not correct! All grounds, including safety, RF, lightning protection and commercial communications, must be bonded together in order to protect life and property. The electrical code requires that antenna grounds be bonded to the rest of the grounding system, although that connection can have an RF choke. Remember that the focus of the electrical code bonding requirement is safety in the event of a short to a power distribution line or other transient.

For decades, amateurs have been advised to bond all equipment cabinets to an RF ground located near the station. Given today's operating frequencies and equipment sensitivity, this practice is inadequate. Even a few meters of wire can have an impedance of hundreds of ohms (1 µH/meter = 88 Ω/meter at 14 MHz). So a better approach is to connect the chassis together in a well-organized fashion to ensure that the chassis-to-chassis connections minimize RF voltage differences as in Figure 28.5B. An RF bonding bus can be used, as well. (See the **RF Interference** and **Assembling a Station** chapters for more information.)

LIGHTNING DISSIPATION GROUND

Lightning dissipation ground is concerned with conducting currents to the surrounding earth. There are distinct similarities between lightning dissipation ground systems and a good ground system for a vertical antenna. Lightning strokes produce electrical energy from a few kHz to more than 10 MHz so the length of the connection is important as well as its resistance. The difference is that an antenna ground plane may handle perhaps a few tens of amps, while the lightning ground needs to handle a peak current of tens of kiloamperes.

A typical lightning stroke is a pulse with a rise time of a few microseconds, a peak current of 20 to 30 kA, and a fall time of 50 µs. The average current is not all that high (a few hundred amps), so the conductor size needed to carry the current without melting is surprisingly small.

However, large conductors (usually specified as #6 AWG minimum by building codes) are used in lightning grounds for other reasons: to reduce inductance, to handle the mechanical forces from the magnetic fields, and for ruggedness to prevent inadvertent breakage. A large diameter wire, or even better, a wide flat strap, has lower inductance. The voltage along a wire is proportional to the change in current and the inductance:

$$|V| = L \frac{\Delta i}{\Delta t}$$

where

$\Delta i / \Delta t$ = rate of change in current, about 20kA/2µs for lightning, or 10^9 A/s, and
L = the inductance.

Consider a connection box on a tower that contains some circuitry terminating a control cable from the shack, appropriately protected internally with overvoltage protection. If the connection from the box to ground is high inductance, the lightning transient will raise the box potential (relative to the wiring coming from the shack), possibly beyond the point where the transient suppression in the box can handle it. Lowering the inductance of the connection to ground reduces the potential.

The other reason for large conductors on lightning grounds is to withstand the very high mechanical forces from the high currents. This is also the reason behind the recommendation that lightning conductors be run directly, with minimal bends and large radii for bends that are needed, and certainly no loops. A wire with 20,000 A has a powerful magnetic field surrounding it, and if current is flowing in multiple wires that are close to each other, the forces pushing the wires together or apart can actually break the conductors or deform them permanently.

The force between two conductors carrying 20,000 A, spaced a centimeter apart, is 8000 Newtons/meter of length (over 500 pounds/foot). Such forces can easily break cable strands or rip up brackets and screws. This problem is aggravated if there are loops in the wire, since the interaction of the current and its magnetic field tends to make the loop get larger, to the point where the wire will actually fail from the tension stresses.

EARTH GROUND

Earth ground usually takes one of several forms, all identified in the NEC and NFPA 780. The preferred earth ground, both as required in the NEC, and verified with years of testing in the field, is a *concrete encased grounding electrode* (CEGR), also known as a *Ufer ground*, after Herb Ufer, who invented it as a way to provide grounding for military installations in dry areas where ground rods are ineffective. The CEGR can take many forms, but the essential aspect is that a suitable conductor at least 20 feet long is encased in concrete which is buried in the ground. The conductor can be a copper wire (#8 AWG at least 20 feet long) or the reinforcing bars (rebar) in the concrete, often the foundation footing for the building. The connection to the rebar is either with a stub of the rebar protruding through the concrete's top surface or the copper wire extending through the concrete. There are other variations of the CEGR described in the NEC and in the electrical literature, but they're all functionally the same: a long conductor embedded in a big piece of concrete.

The electrode works because the concrete has a huge contact area with the surrounding soil, providing very low impedance and, what's also important, a low current density, so that localized heating doesn't occur. Concrete tends to absorb water, so it is also less susceptible to problems with the soil drying out around a traditional ground rod.

The techniques required for welding rebar and making the necessary connection to the CEGR are somewhat specialized. If you are not familiar with those skills, hire a professional to do the job correctly. Similarly, unless you have documented evidence that the necessary rebar connection or embedded wire are present in a concrete footing or slab, do not attempt to use it as a CEGR.

Ground rods are a traditional approach to making a suitable ground connection and are appropriate as supplemental grounds, say at the base of a tower, or as part of an overall grounding system. The best ground rods to use are those available from an electrical supply house. The code requires that at least 8 feet of the rod be in contact with the soil, so if the rod sticks out of the ground, it must be longer than 8 feet (10 feet is standard). The rod doesn't have to be vertical, and can be driven at an angle if there is a rock or hard layer, or even buried laying sideways in a suitable trench, although this is a compromise installation. Suitable rods are generally 10 feet long and made from steel with a heavy copper plating. (Stainless steel and galvanized rods are also available and may be required by soil conditions in your area. Check with a local electrician or electrical inspector.) Do not depend on shorter, thinly plated rods sold by some home electronics suppliers, as they can quickly rust and soon become worthless.

If multiple ground rods are installed, many references specify a minimum spacing of the rod's length. If the rods are not spaced by at least half the length of the rod, the effectiveness is compromised. IEEE Std 142 and IEEE Std 1100 (see the Reference listing) and other references have tables to give effective ground resistances for various configurations of multiple rods.

Once the ground rods are installed, they must be connected with either an exothermic weld (such as CadWeld) or with a listed pressure clamp. The exothermic weld is preferred, because it doesn't require annual inspection like a clamp does. Some installers use brazing to attach the wiring to the ground rods. Although this is not permitted for a primary ground, it is acceptable for secondary or redundant grounds. Soft solder (tin-lead, as used in plumbing or electrical work) should never be used for grounding conductors because it gets brittle with temperature cycling and can melt if a current surge (as from a lightning strike) heats the conductor. Soft solder is specifically prohibited in the code.

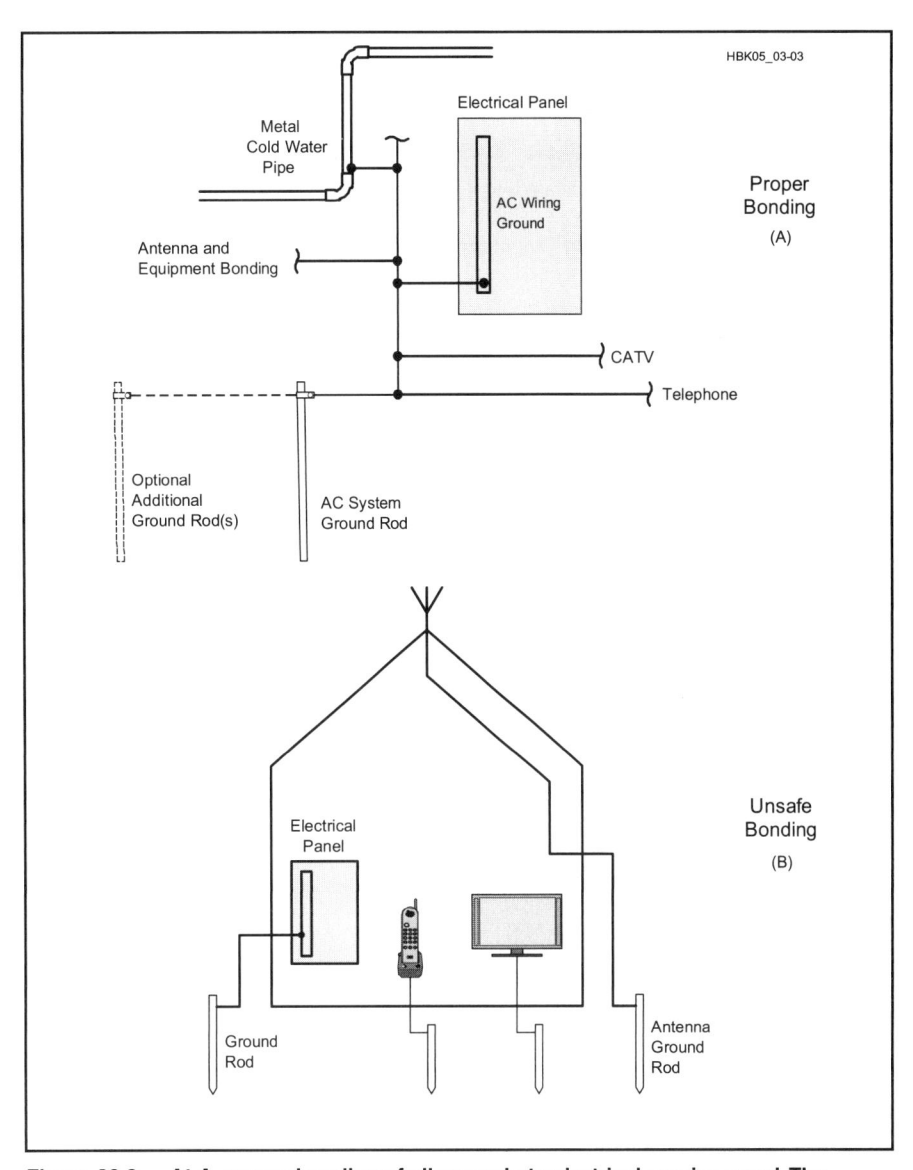

Figure 28.6 — At A, proper bonding of all grounds to electrical service panel. The installation shown at B is unsafe — the separate grounds are not bonded. This could result in a serious accident or electrical fire.

Building cold water supply systems were used as station grounds in years past, but this is no longer recommended or even permitted in some jurisdictions, because of increased used of plastic plumbing both inside and outside houses and concerns about stray currents causing pipe corrosion.. If you do use the cold water line, perhaps because it is an existing grounding electrode, it must be bonded to the electrical system ground, typically at the service entrance panel.

28.1.9 Ground Conductors

Building codes and wiring standards are quite specific as to the types of conductors that can be used for bonding the various parts of the system together. Grounding conductors may be made from copper, aluminum, copper-clad steel, bronze or similar corrosion-resistant materials. Note that the sizes of the conductors required are based largely on mechanical strength considerations (to insure that the wire isn't broken accidentally) rather than electrical resistance. Insulation is not required.

There is a "unified" grounding electrode requirement — it is necessary to bond *all* grounds to the electric service entrance ground. All utilities, antennas and any separate grounding rods used must be bonded together. **Figure 28.6** shows correct (A) and incorrect (B) ways to bond ground rods. **Figure 28.7** demonstrates the importance of correctly bonding ground rods. (Note: The NEC requirements do not address effective

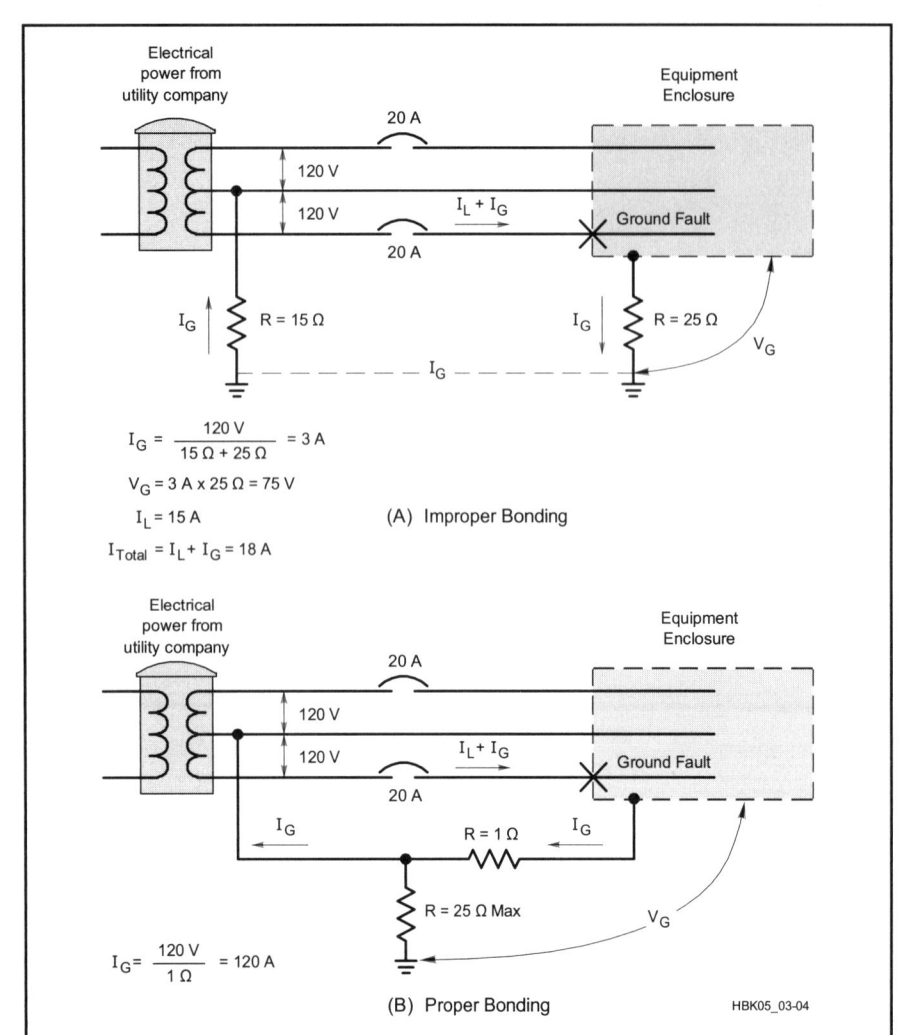

Figure 28.7 — These drawings show the importance of properly bonded ground rods. In the system shown in A, the 20-A breaker will not trip. In the system in B, the 20-A circuit breaker trips instantly. There is an equipment internal short to ground — the ground rod is properly bonded back to the power system ground. Of course, the main protection should be in a circuit ground wire in the equipment power cord itself!

Coax Shields as a Grounding Conductor

The importance of significant current-carrying capability in a grounding conductor is determined by your local circumstances. If lightning is a problem or contact with power-carrying conductors due to wind or ice is a possibility, the ability of the coax shield to carry a lot of current is important and a separate grounding conductor is a good idea. In areas where hazards are reduced, a smaller conductor may suffice. Contact a licensed electrician if you aren't sure about what is prudent for your area.

RF bonding. See the **RF Interference** and **Assembling a Station** chapters of this book for information about RF practices. Keep in mind that RFI is not an acceptable reason to violate the NEC.) For additional information on good grounding practices, the *NEC Handbook* and IEEE "Emerald Book" (IEEE STD 1100-2005) are good references. Both are available through libraries. Home wiring guides are also available at home improvement stores.

Additionally, the NEC covers safety inside the station. All grounding conductors inside the building must be at least 4 inches away from conductors of any lighting or signaling circuit except when they are separated from other conductors by conduit or insulator. Other code requirements include enclosing transmitters in metal cabinets that are bonded to the grounding system. Of course, conductive handles and knobs must be grounded as well.

28.1.10 Antennas

Article 810 of the NEC includes several requirements for wire antennas and feed lines that you should keep in mind when designing your antenna system. The "protective grounding conductor" (main conductor running to the ground rod) must be as large as the antenna lead-in, but not smaller than #10 AWG. The grounding conductor (used to bond equipment chassis together) must be at least #14 AWG.

The single most important thing to consider for safety is to address the potential for contact between the antenna system and power lines. As the code says, "One of the leading causes of electric shock and electrocution, according to statistical reports, is the accidental contact of radio, television, and amateur radio transmitting and receiving antennas and equipment with light or power conductors." (See Article 810.13, Fine Print Note.) The requirements in the code for wire sizes, bonding requirements, and installation practices are mostly aimed at preventing tragedy, by avoiding the contact in the first place, and by mitigating the effects of a contact if it occurs.

Article 820 of the NEC applies to Cable TV installations, which almost always use coaxial cable, and which require wiring practices different from Article 810 (for instance, the coax shield can serve as the grounding conductor). Your inspector may look to Article 820 for guidance on a safe installation of coax, since there are many more satellite TV and cable TV installations than Amateur Radio. Ultimately, it is the inspector's call as to whether your installation is safe.

Article 830 applies to Network Powered Communication Systems, and as amateurs do things like install 802.11 wireless LAN equipment at the top of their tower, they'll have to pay attention to the requirements in this Article. The NEC requirements discussed in these sections are not adequate for lightning protection and high-voltage transient events. See the section "Lightning/Transient Protection" later in this chapter for more information.

ANTENNA CONDUCTORS

Transmitting antennas should use hard-drawn copper wire: #14 AWG for unsupported spans less than 150 feet, and #10 AWG for longer spans. Copper-clad steel, bronze or other high-strength conductors must be #14 AWG for spans less than 150 feet and #12 AWG for longer spans. Open-wire transmission line conductors must be at least as large as those specified for antennas. Stealth antennas made with light-gauge wire are not code-compliant.

LEAD-INS

There are several NEC requirements for antenna lead-in conductors (transmission lines are lead-in conductors). For transmitting stations, their size must be equal to or greater than that of the antenna. Lead-ins attached to buildings must be firmly mounted at least 3 inches clear of the surface of the building on nonabsorbent insulators. Lead-in conductors must enter through rigid, noncombustible, nonabsorbent insulating tubes or bushings, through an opening provided for the purpose that provides a clearance of at least two inches; or through a drilled windowpane. All lead-in conductors to transmitting equipment must be arranged so that accidental contact is difficult. As with stealth antennas, installations with feed lines smaller than RG-58 are likely not code compliant depending on how your local inspector interprets the code.

ANTENNA DISCHARGE UNITS (LIGHTNING ARRESTORS)

All antenna systems are required to have a means of draining static charges from the antenna system. A listed antenna discharge unit (lightning arrestor) must be installed on each lead-in conductor that is not protected by a permanently and effectively grounded metallic shield, unless the antenna itself is permanently and effectively grounded, such as for a shunt-fed vertical. Note that the usual transient protectors are *not* listed antenna discharge units. (The code exception for shielded lead-ins does *not* apply to coax, but to shields such as thin-wall conduit. Coaxial braid is neither "adequate" nor "effectively grounded" for lightning protection purposes.) An acceptable alternative to lightning arrestor installation is a switch (capable of withstanding many kilovolts) that connects the lead-in to ground when the transmitter is not in use. A garden-variety knife switch for household appliances is not adequately rated for this job.

ANTENNA BONDING (GROUNDING) CONDUCTORS

In general the code requires that the conductors used to bond the antenna system to ground be at least as big as the antenna conductors, but also at least #10 AWG in size. Note that the antenna grounding conductor rules are different from those for the regular electrical safety bonding, or lightning dissipation grounds, or even for CATV or telephone system grounds.

MOTORIZED CRANK-UP ANTENNA TOWERS

If you are using a motorized crank-up tower, the code has some requirements, particularly if there is a remote control. In general,

---

Manufacturers of Lightning Protection Equipment

For current vendor contact information, use your favorite Internet search tool.
- Alpha Delta Communications: Coax lightning arrestors, coax switches with surge protectors.
- The Wireman: copper wire up to #4 AWG, 2-inch flat copper strap, 8-ft copper clad ground rods and 1 × ¼-inch buss bar.
- ERICO International Corporation: CadWeld bonding system and lightning protection equipment.
- Harger Lightning & Grounding: lightning protection components.
- Industrial Communication Engineers, Ltd (ICE): Coax lightning arrestors.
- KF7P Metalwerks: Entrance panels, lightning arrestors, surge protectors, grounding and bonding hardware, and so on.
- PolyPhaser Corporation: Many lightning protection products for feed lines, towers, equipment, and so on.
- Zero Surge Inc: Power line surge protector.

---

there has to be a way to positively disconnect power to the motor that is within sight of the motorized device, so that someone working on it can be sure that it won't start moving unexpectedly. From a safety standpoint, as well, you should be able to see or monitor the antenna from the remote control point.

28.1.11 Lightning/Transient Protection

Nearly everyone recognizes the need to protect themselves from lightning. From miles away, the sight and sound of lightning boldly illustrates its destructive potential. Many people don't realize that destructive transients from lightning and other events can reach electronic equipment from many sources, such as outside antennas, power, telephone and cable TV installations. Many hams don't realize that the standard protection scheme of several decades, a ground rod and simple "lightning arrestor," is *not* adequate.

Lightning and transient high-voltage protection follows a familiar communications scenario: identify the unwanted signal, isolate it and dissipate it. The difference here is that the unwanted signal is many megavolts at possibly 200,000 A. What can we do?

Effective lightning protection system design is a complex topic. There are a variety of system tradeoffs which must be made and which determine the type and amount of protection needed. A amateur station in a home is a very different proposition from an air traffic control tower which must be available 24 hours a day, 7 days a week. Hams can easily follow some general guidelines that will protect their stations against high-voltage events that are induced by nearby lightning strikes or that arrive via utility lines. Let's talk about where to find professionals first, and then consider construction guidelines.

PROFESSIONAL HELP

Start with your local government. Find out what building codes apply in your area and have someone explain the regulations about antenna installation and safety. For more help, look in your telephone yellow pages for professional engineers, lightning protection suppliers and contractors.

Companies that sell lightning-protection products may offer considerable help to apply their products to specific installations. One such source is PolyPhaser Corporation. Look under "References" later in this chapter for a partial list of PolyPhaser's publications.

CONSTRUCTION GUIDELINES
Bonding Conductors

Copper strip (or *flashing*) comes in a number of sizes. The *minimum* recommended grounding conductor for lightning protection is 1.5 inches wide and 0.051 inch thick or #6 AWG stranded wire. Do not use braided strap outside or in wet areas because the individual strands oxidize over time, greatly reducing the effectiveness of braid as an ac conductor. Bear in mind that copper strap has about the same inductance as a wire of the same length. While strap may be easier to install and provides a lower RF loss (if it's part of a vertical antenna grounding system, for instance), it doesn't provide significant improvement over round wire for power line frequencies (the NEC's concern) or lightning (where inductance dominates the effects).

Use bare copper for buried ground wires. (There are some exceptions; seek an expert's advice if your soil is corrosive.) Exposed runs above ground that are subject to physical damage may require additional protection (a conduit) to meet code requirements. Wire size depends on the application, but never use anything smaller than #6 AWG for bonding conductors. The NEC specifies conductors using wire gauge, and doesn't describe the use of flashing. Local lightning-protection experts or building inspectors can recommend sizes for each application.

Tower and Antennas

Because a tower is usually the highest metal object on the property, it is the most likely strike target. Proper tower grounding is essential to lightning protection. The goal is

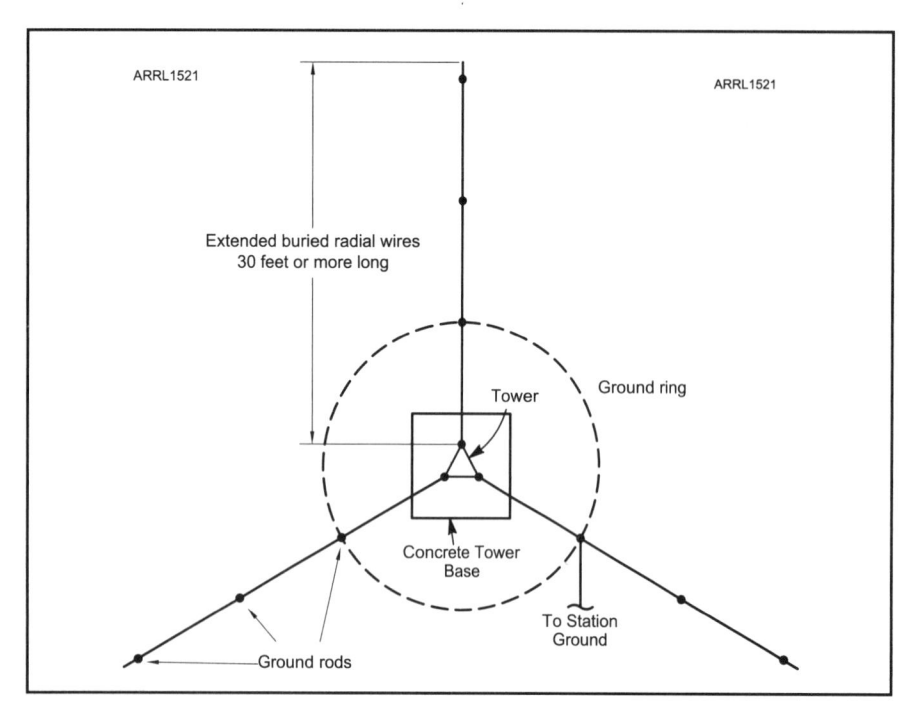

Figure 28.8 — Schematic of a properly grounded tower. A bonding conductor connects each tower leg to a ground rod and a buried (1 foot deep) bare, tinned copper ring (dashed line), which is also connected to the station ground and then to the ac safety ground. Make the ring diameter large enough that ground rods aligned with the tower legs will be approximately 6 feet apart. Buried radial wires extending beyond the ring are recommended but optional. All connectors should be compatible with the tower and conductor materials to prevent corrosion. See text for conductor sizes and details of lightning and voltage transient protection.

Voltage Rise On Wires With Fast Transients

A rule of thumb is that a single wire has an inductance of about 1 µH per meter of length. The voltage across an inductor V = L $\Delta i/\Delta t$. ($\Delta i/\Delta t$ is the change in current per unit of time.) A lightning stroke has a rise time of about 1-2 µs, so the current might go from zero to 10 kA in a microsecond or two, a $\Delta i/\Delta t$ of over 1 kA/µs (10^9 A/s). An inductance as low as 1 µH would create a voltage of 1000 volts from this current transient.

---

to establish short multiple paths to the Earth so that the strike energy is divided and dissipated.

Connect each tower leg and each fan of metal guy wires to a separate ground rod. Space the rods at least 6 feet apart. Bond the leg ground rods together with #6 AWG or larger copper bonding conductor (form a ring around the tower base, see **Figure 28.8**). Connect a continuous bonding conductor between the tower ring ground and the entrance panel. Make all connections with fittings approved for grounding applications. *Do not use solder for these connections.* Solder will be destroyed in the heat of a lightning strike.

Because galvanized steel (which has a zinc coating) reacts with copper when combined with moisture, use stainless steel hardware between the galvanized metal and the copper grounding materials. Rohn and other manufacturers now offer ground clamps designing for connecting galvanized tower legs to copper ground conductors.

To prevent strike energy from entering a shack via the feed line, ground the feed line *outside* the home. Ground the coax shield *to the tower* at the antenna and the base to keep the tower and line at the same potential. Several companies offer grounding blocks that make this job easy.

All grounding media at the home must be bonded together. This includes lightning-protection conductors, electrical service, telephone, antenna system grounds and underground metal pipes. Any ground rods used for lightning protection or entrance-panel grounding should be spaced at least 6 feet from each other and the electrical service or other utility grounds and then bonded to the ac system ground as required by the NEC.

A Single-Point Ground Panel (SPGP)

The basic concept with transient protection is to make sure that all the radio and other equipment is tied together and "moves together" in the presence of a transient voltage. It's not so important that the shack be at "ground" potential, but, rather, that everything is at the *same* potential. For fast rise-time transients such as the individual strokes that make up a lightning strike, even a short wire has enough inductance that the voltage drop along the wire is significant, so whether you are on the ground floor, or the 10th floor of a building, your shack is "far" from Earth potential.

The easiest way to ensure that everything is at the same potential is to tie all the signal ground connections to a common reference.

In large facilities, this reference would be provided by a grid of large diameter cables under the floor, or by wide copper bars, or even a solid metal floor. A more practical approach for smaller facilities such as a ham shack is to have a *single-point ground panel* (SPGP). The SPGP may be a separate metal panel or it can be enclosed in an electrical box. See the reference articles by Block for a complete discussion of the SPGP. The articles are available online through the ARRL's Radio Technology Topics website (**www.arrl.org/radio-technology-topics**) under Safety and in the ARRL book *Grounding and Bonding for the Radio Amateur*.

The SPGP should be mounted outside the building. The easiest way to do this is to install a large metal enclosure or a metal panel as a bulkhead and grounding block. The panel should be connected to the lightning dissipation ground with a short wide conductor (for minimum impedance), and, like all grounds, bonded to the electrical system's ground. Mount all protective devices, switches, and relay disconnects on the outside facing wall. The enclosure or panel should be installed in a way that if lightning currents cause a component to fail, the molten metal and flaming debris do not start a fire.

Every conductor that enters the structure, including antenna system control lines, telephone, and CATV cables, should have its own surge suppressor on an entrance panel. Suppressors are available from a number of manufacturers, including Industrial Communication Engineers (ICE) and PolyPhaser, as well as the usual electrical equipment suppliers such as Square-D.

We want to control the flow of the energy in a strike and eliminate any possible paths for surges to enter the building. Route feed lines, rotator control cables, and so on at least six feet away from other nearby grounded metal objects. Keep incoming, unprotected cables well away from cables on the protected side of any lightning arrestors, as well.

Lightning Arrestors

Feed line lightning arrestors are available for both coax cable and balanced line. Most of the balanced line arrestors use a simple spark gap arrangement, but a balanced line *impulse* suppressor is available from ICE.

DC blocking arrestors for coaxial cable have a fixed frequency range. They present a high-impedance to lightning (less than 1 MHz) while offering a low impedance to RF.

DC continuity arrestors (gas tubes and spark gaps) can be used over a wider frequency range than those that block dc. Where the coax carries supply voltages to remote devices (such as a mast-mounted preamp or remote coax switch), dc-continuous arrestors *must* be used.

28.1.12 Other Hazards in the Station

UPS AND ALTERNATE ENERGY SOURCES

Many hams have alternate energy sources for their equipment, or an uninterruptible power supply (UPS), so that they can keep operating during a utility power outage. This brings some additional safety concerns, because it means that the "turning off the breaker" approach to make sure that power is disconnected might not work.

In commercial installations, fire regulations or electrical codes often require that the emergency power off (EPO) system (the big red button next to the door) also disconnect the batteries of the UPS system, or at least, disable the ac output. This is so that firefighters who may be chopping holes with conductive tools or spraying conductive water don't face the risk of electrocution. (According to NEC, Articles 645-10 and 645-11, UPSs above 750 VA installed within information technology rooms must be provided with a means to disconnect power to all UPS supply and output circuits. This disconnecting means shall also disconnect the battery from its load. The code further requires that the control for these disconnecting means shall be grouped and identified and shall be readily accessible at the principal exit doors.)

A similar problem exists with solar panel installations. Just because the breaker is turned off doesn't mean that dangerous voltages don't exist on the solar panel. As long as light is falling on them, there is voltage present. With no load, even a relatively dim light falling on part of the panels might present a shock or equipment damage hazard. Modern grid-tie solar systems with no batteries often have the panels wired in series, so several hundred volts is not unusual.

Recent revisions of the NEC have addressed many of the aspects of photovoltaic (PV) installations that present problems with disconnects, bonding, and grounding. Consulting your local authorities is always wise, and there are several organizations such as the Southwest Technology Development Institute at New Mexico State University that have prepared useful information (see the references at the end of this section). In general, PV systems at 12 or 24 V aren't covered by the NEC.

ENERGIZED CIRCUITS

Working with energized circuits can be very hazardous since, without measuring devices, we can't tell which circuits are live. The first thing we should ask ourselves when faced with troubleshooting, aligning or other "live" procedures is, "Is there a way to reduce the hazard of electrical shock?" Here are some ways of doing just that.

1) If at all possible, troubleshoot with an ohmmeter. With a reliable schematic diagram and careful consideration of how various circuit conditions may reflect resistance readings, it will often be unnecessary to do live testing.

2) Keep a fair distance from energized circuits. What is considered "good practice" in terms of distance? The NEC specifies minimum working space around electric equipment depending on the voltage level. The principle here is that a person doing live work needs adequate space so they are not forced to be dangerously close to energized equipment.

3) If you need to measure the voltage of a circuit, install the voltmeter with the power safely off, back up, and only then energize the circuit. Remove the power before disconnecting the meter.

4) If you are building equipment that has hinged or easily removable covers that could expose someone to an energized circuit, install interlock switches that safely remove power in the event that the enclosure is opened with the power still on. Interlock switches are generally not used if tools are required to open the enclosure.

5) Never assume that a circuit is at zero potential even if the power is switched off and the power cable disconnected. Capacitors can retain a charge for a considerable period of time and may even partially recharge after being discharged. Bleeder resistors should be installed, but don't assume they have discharged the voltage. Instead, after power is removed and disconnected use a "shorting stick" to ground all exposed conductors

---

Electrical Shock Hazards and Effects

What happens when someone receives an electrical shock?

Electrocutions (fatal electric shocks) usually are caused by the heart ceasing to beat in its normal rhythm. This condition, called ventricular fibrillation, causes the heart muscles to quiver and stop working in a coordinated pattern, in turn preventing the heart from pumping blood.

The current flow that results in ventricular fibrillation varies between individuals but may be in the range of 100 mA to 500 mA. At higher current levels the heart may have less tendency to fibrillate but serious damage would be expected. Studies have shown 60-Hz alternating current to be more hazardous than dc currents. Emphasis is placed on application of cardiopulmonary resuscitation (CPR), as this technique can provide mechanical flow of some blood until paramedics can "restart" the heart's normal beating pattern. Defibrillators actually apply a carefully controlled waveform to "shock" the heart back into a normal heartbeat. It doesn't always work but it's the best procedure available.

What are the most important factors associated with severe shocks?

You may have heard that the current that flows through the body is the most important factor, and this is generally true. The path that current takes through the body affects the outcome to a large degree. While simple application of Ohm's Law tells us that the higher the voltage applied with a fixed resistance, the greater the current that will flow. Most electrical shocks involve skin contact. Skin, with its layer of dead cells and often fatty tissues, is a fair insulator. Nonetheless, as voltage increases the skin will reach a point where it breaks down. Then the lowered resistance of deeper tissues allows a greater current to flow. This is why electrical codes refer to the term "high voltage" as a voltage above 600 V.

How little voltage can be lethal?

This depends entirely on the resistance of the two contact points in the circuit, the internal resistance of the body, and the path the current travels through the body. Historically, reports of fatal shocks suggest that as little as 24 V *could* be fatal under extremely adverse conditions. To add some perspective, one standard used to prevent serious electrical shock in hospital operating rooms limits leakage flow from electronic instruments to only 50 µA due to the use of electrical devices and related conductors inside the patient's body.

and terminals to ensure that voltage is not present. If you will be working with charged capacitors that store more than a few joules of energy, you should consider using a "discharging stick" with a high wattage, low value resistor in series to ground that limits the discharge current to around 5-10 A. A dead short across a large charged capacitor can damage the capacitor because of internal thermal and magnetic stress. Avoid using screwdrivers, as this brings the holder too close to the circuit and could ruin the screwdriver's blade. For maximum protection against accidentally energizing equipment, install a shorting lead between high-voltage circuits and ground while you are working on the equipment.

6) Shorting a series string of capacitors does not ensure that the capacitors are discharged. Consider two 400 µF capacitors in series, one charged to +300 V and the other to −300 V with the midpoint at ground. The net voltage across the series string is zero, yet each has significant (and lethal) energy stored in it. The proper practice is to discharge each capacitor in turn, putting a shorting jumper on it after discharge, and then moving to the next one.

7) If you must hold a probe to take a measurement, always keep one hand in your pocket. As mentioned in the sidebar on high-voltage hazards, the worst path current could take through your body is from hand to hand since the flow would pass through the chest cavity.

8) Make sure someone is in the room with you and that they know how to remove the power safely. If they grab you with the power still on they will be shocked as well.

9) Test equipment probes and their leads must be in very good condition and rated for the conditions they will encounter.

10) Be wary of the hazards of "floating" (ungrounded) test equipment. A number of options are available to avoid this hazard.

11) Ground-fault circuit interrupters can offer additional protection for stray currents that flow through the ground on 120-V circuits. Know their limitations. They cannot offer protection for the plate supply voltages in linear amplifiers, for example.

12) Older radio equipment containing ac/dc power supplies have their own hazards. If you are working on these live, use an isolation transformer, as the chassis may be connected directly to the hot or neutral power conductor.

13) Be aware of electrolytic capacitors that might fail if used outside their intended applications.

14) Replace fuses only with those having proper ratings. The rating is not just the current, but also takes into account the speed with which it opens, and whether it is rated for dc or ac. DC fuses are typically rated at lower voltages than those for ac, because the current in ac circuits goes through zero once every half cycle, giving an arc time to quench. Switches and fuses rated for 120 V ac duty are typically not appropriate for high-current dc applications (such as a main battery or solar panel disconnect).

28.1.13 Electrical Safety References

ARRL Technical Information Service Web page on electrical safety in the Technology area of the ARRL website.
Black & Decker Complete Guide to Wiring, 6th Edition, Cold Spring Press, 2014.
Block, R.W., "Lightning Protection for the Amateur Radio Station," Parts 1-3 (Jun, Jul and Aug 2002 *QST*).
Block. R.W., "The "Grounds" for Lightning and EMP Portection," Polyphaser Corporation, 1993.
Federal Information Processing Standards (FIPS) publication 94: *Guideline on Electrical Power for ADP Installations*. FIPS are available from the National Technical Information Service.
IAEI: *Soares' Book on Grounding*, available from International Association of Electrical Inspectors (IAEI).
"IEEE Std 1100 - 2005 IEEE Recommended Practice for Powering and Grounding Electronic Equipment," *IEEE Std 1100-2005 (Revision of IEEE Std 1100-1999)*, pp 0_1-589, 2006. "This document presents recommended design, installation, and maintenance practices for electrical power and grounding (including both safety and noise control) and protection of electronic loads such as industrial controllers, computers, and other information technology equipment (ITE) used in commercial and industrial applications."
National Electrical Code Handbook 2017, NFPA 70, National Fire Protection Association, Quincy, MA (**www.nfpa.org**), also available through libraries.
Silver, W., *Grounding and Bonding For the Radio Amateur*, ARRL, 2017.
Solar energy websites — **www.nmsu.edu/~tdi/PV=NEC_HTML/pv-nec/pv-nec.html** and **www.solarabcs.org**
Standard for the Installation of Lightning Protection Systems, NFPA 780, National Fire Protection Association, Quincy, MA (**www.nfpa.org**).
See the Protection Group's list of white papers contained in the Knowledge Base **www.protectiongroup**.com.

28.2 Antenna and Tower Safety

By definition, all of the topics in this book are about radio telecommunications. For those communications, receive and transmit antennas are required and those antennas need to be up in the air to work effectively. While antenna design and construction are covered elsewhere, this section covers many of the topics associated with installing antennas, along with related safety issues.

A substantially more detailed treatment of techniques used to erect towers and antennas is available in these references:
The ARRL Antenna Book
Up the Tower: The Complete Guide to Tower Construction by Steve Morris, K7LXC
Antenna Towers for Radio Amateurs by Don Daso, K4ZA, published by the ARRL.

28.2.1 Legal Considerations

Some antenna support structures fall under local building regulations as well as neighborhood restrictions. Many housing developments have Homeowner's Associations (HOAs) as well as Covenants, Conditions and Restrictions (CC&Rs) that may have a direct bearing on whether a tower or similar structure can be erected at all. This is a broad topic with many pitfalls. Detailed background on these topics is provided in *Antenna Zoning for the Radio Amateur* by Fred Hopengarten, K1VR, an attorney with extensive experience in towers and zoning. You may also want to contact one of the ARRL Field Organization's Volunteer Counsels.

Even without neighborhood issues, a building permit is likely to be required. With the proliferation of cellular and other commercial wireless devices and their attendant RF sites, many local governments now require that the structures meet local building codes. Again, K1VR's book is extremely helpful in sorting all this out. Building permit applications may also require Professional Engineer (PE) calculations and stamp (certification). The ARRL Field Organization's Volunteer Consulting Engineer program may be useful with the engineering side of your project.

28.2.2 Antenna Mounting Structures

TREES AND POLES

The original antenna supports were trees: if you've got them, use them. They're free and unregulated, so it couldn't be easier. Single-trunked varieties such as fir and pine trees are easier to use than the multi-trunked varieties. Multi-trunked trees are not impossible to use — they just require a lot more work. For dipoles or other types of wire antennas, plan for the tree to support an end of the wire; trying to install an inverted V or similar configuration is almost impossible due to all of the intervening branches.

Install a screw-eye with a pulley at the desired height, trim away enough limbs to create a "window" for the antenna through the branches and then attach a rope halyard to the antenna insulator. Here's a useful tip: Make the *halyard* a continuous loop as shown in **Figure 28.9**. Since it's almost always the antenna wire that breaks, a continuous halyard makes it easy to reattach the wire and insulator. With just a single halyard, if the antenna breaks, the tree will have to be climbed to reach the pulley, then reinstall and attach the line. If you're unable to climb the support tree, contact a local tree service. Professional tree climbers are often willing to help out for a small fee.

Another way to get wires into trees is with some sort of launcher. Using a bow-and-arrow is a traditional method of shooting a fishing line over a tree to pull up a bigger line. There are now commercial products available that are easier to use and reach higher in the tree. For example, wrist-rocket slingshots and compressed-air launchers can reach heights of more than 200 feet!

Wooden utility poles offer a tree-related alternative but are not cheap, require special installation with a pole-setting truck, and there is no commercial antenna mounting hardware available for them. That makes them a poor choice for most installations.

TOWERS

The two most important parameters to consider when planning a tower installation are the maximum local *wind speed* and the proposed antenna *wind load*. Check with your local building department to find out what the maximum wind speed is for your area. Another source is a list of maximum wind speeds for all counties in the US from the TIA-222, *Structural Standard for Antenna Supporting Structures and Antennas*. This is an expensive professional publication so it's not for everyone, but the list is posted on the Champion Radio Products website under "Tech Notes." Tower capacities are generally specified in square feet of antenna load and antenna wind load specifications are provided by the antenna manufacturer.

Before beginning, learn and follow K7LXC's Prime Directive of tower construction — "DO what the manufacturer says." (And DON'T do what the manufacturer doesn't say to do.) Professional engineers have analyzed and calculated the proper spec-

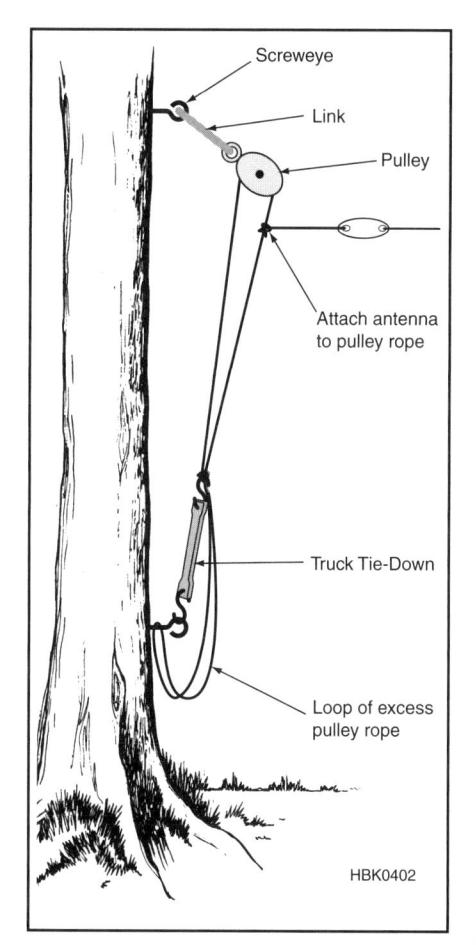

Fig 28.9 — Loop and halyard method of supporting wire antennas in trees. Should the antenna break, the continuous loop of rope allows antenna repair or replacement without climbing the tree.

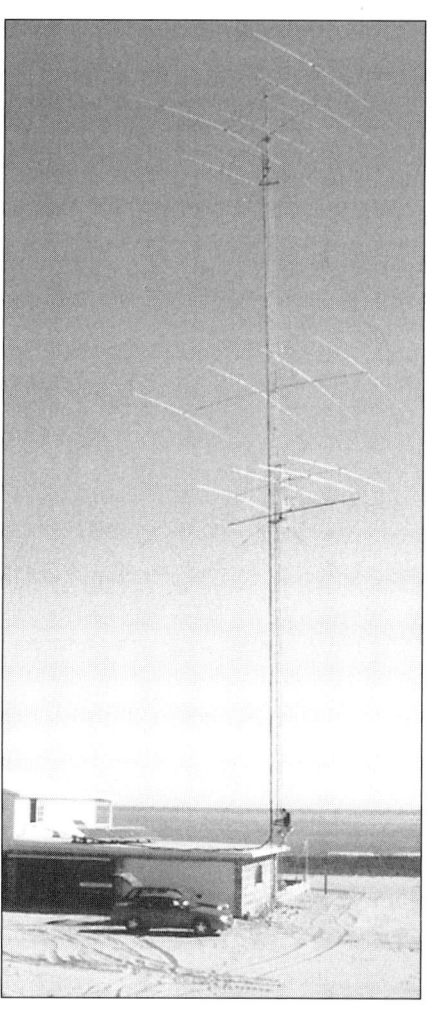

Figure 28.10 — A guyed tower with a good-sized load of antennas at XE2DV-W7ZR in Baja California, is shown at the left. At the right, the Trylon Titan self-supporting tower of W7WVF and N7YYG in Bandon, Oregon. [Steve Morris, K7LXC, photos]

Safety 28.15

ifications and conditions for tower structures and their environment. Taking any shortcuts or making different decisions will result in a less reliable installation.

Towers come in the two varieties shown in **Figure 28.10** — guyed and self-supporting. Guyed towers require a bigger footprint because the guys have to be anchored away from the tower — typically 80% of the tower height. Self-supporting towers need bigger bases to counteract the overturning moment and are more expensive than a guyed tower because there is more steel in them (the cost of a tower is largely determined by the cost of the steel).

The most popular guyed towers are the Rohn 25G and 45G. The 25G is a light-duty tower and the 45G is capable of carrying fairly big loads. The online Rohn catalog (see the References) has most of the information you'll need to plan an installation and is considered a "bible" of information for tower construction.

Self-supporting towers are made by several manufacturers and allow building a tower up to 100 feet or higher with a small footprint. Rohn, Trylon and AN Wireless are popular vendors. Another type of self-supporting tower is the *crank-up*, shown in **Figure 28.11**. Using a system of cables, pulleys and winches, crank-up towers can extend from 20 feet to over 100 feet high. These are moderately complex devices. Because they consist of a variety of moving parts, crank-up towers require more maintenance than guyed or other self-supporting designs. The largest manufacturer of crank-up towers is US Towers.

Figure 28.12 — The roof-mounted tower holding the AA2OW antenna system. [AA2OW photo]

Another simple and effective way to get an antenna up in the air is with a *roof-mounted tower*, seen in **Figure 28.12**. These are four-legged aluminum structures of heights from four to more than 20 feet. While they are designed to be lag-screwed directly into the roof trusses, it is often preferable to through-bolt them into a long 2×4 or 2×6 that acts a backing plate, straddling three to four roof trusses. In any case, if it is not clear how best to install the tower on the structure, have a roofing professional or engineer provide advice. Working on a roof-mounted tower also requires extra caution because of climbing on a roof while also working on a tower. Many of these lightweight, aluminum towers cannot be climbed, so you must use a ladder to access the antenna. Again, extreme caution is required.

28.2.3 Tower Construction and Erection
THE BASE

Once all the necessary materials and the required approvals have been gathered, tower installation can begin. Let's assume you and your friends are going to install it. The first

Figure 28.11 — The bottom of N6TV's crank-up tower is shown at left. The motor drive mechanism is on the left and a fishing net on the right catches and coils the feed lines and control cables as the tower is lowered. On the right, K6KR's fully loaded crank-up extended to its maximum height of 90 feet. [Steve Morris, K7LXC, photos]

Principles of Working Safely

The following safety tenets are adapted to amateur antenna system and tower work from selected items of the Chevron Tenets of Operation. These are founded on three fundamental principles: Do it safely or not at all; There's always time to do it right; and If it's worth doing, do it better.

1. Never load or operate structures or equipment outside the design limits. Be careful with tools, ropes, pulleys, and other equipment that can cause injury or damage if they fail due to overload. Use the right stuff!

2. Always move to a safe, controlled condition and seek assistance when a situation is not understood. This is particularly important when working on towers and antennas. If something doesn't look right or isn't going according to plan, return to a safe state and figure out what to do.

3. Always operate with the safety mechanisms engaged. If a safety mechanism prevents you from doing something, either the task is unsafe or you may not be using the right equipment.

4. Always follow safe work practices and procedures. Make a plan before you start and don't do something you know is unsafe.

5. Act to stop unsafe practices. The team's safety depends on every team member. Do not hesitate to stop work if you see it is unsafe. Don't be afraid to speak up or ask for help! Regroup and do it right.

6. Clarify and understand procedures before proceeding. This is particularly important when working with a crew. Be sure everyone understands the procedure and how to communicate.

7. Involve people with expertise and firsthand knowledge in decisions and planning. Ask for advice and guidance from experienced hams when planning a task with which you are unfamiliar.

---

job is to construct the base. A base for a guyed tower can be hand-dug as can the guy anchors. For a self-supporting tower, renting an excavator of some sort will make it much easier to move the several cubic yards of dirt.

Next, some sort of rebar cage will be needed for the concrete. Guyed towers only require rudimentary rebar while a self-supporting tower will need a bigger, heavier and more elaborate cage. Consult the manufacturer's specifications for the exact materials and dimensions.

Typical tower concrete specs call for 3000 psi (minimum) compressive strength concrete and 28 days for a full cure. A local pre-mix concrete company can deliver it. Pouring the concrete is easiest if the concrete truck can back up to the hole. If that's not possible, a truck- or trailer-mounted line pump can pump it up to 400 feet at minimal expense if using a wheelbarrow is not possible or practical. Packaged concrete from the hardware store mixed manually may also be used. Quikrete Mix #1101 is rated at 2500 psi after seven days and 4000 psi after 28 days.

TOOLS

Once the base and anchors are finished and the concrete has cured, the tower can be constructed. There are several tools that will make the job easier. If the tower is a guyed tower, it can be erected either with a crane or a *gin-pole*. The gin-pole, shown in **Figure 28.13**, is a pipe that attaches to the leg of the tower and has a pulley at the top for the haul rope. Use the gin-pole to pull up one section at a time (see below).

Another useful tool for rigging and hoisting is the *carabiner*. Shown in **Figure 28.14** (A and B), carabiners are oval steel or aluminum snap-links popularized by rock and mountain climbers. They have spring-loaded gates and can be used for many tower tasks. For instance, there should be one at the end of the haul rope for easy and quick attachment to rotators, parts and tool buckets — virtually anything that needs to be raised or lowered. It can even act as a "third hand" on the tower.

Along with the carabiner, the *nylon loop sling* in Figure 28.14C can be wrapped around large or irregularly shaped objects such as antennas, masts or rotators and attached to ropes with carabiners. For a complex job, a professional will often climb with eight to ten slings and use every one!

A pulley or two will also make the job easier. At a minimum, one is needed for the haul rope at the top of the tower. A *snatch block* is also useful; this is a pulley whose top opens up to "snatch" (attach it to) the rope at any point. **Figure 28.15** shows two snatch-block pulleys used for tower work.

ROPES

Speaking of ropes, use a decent haul rope. Rope that is one-half inch diameter or larger affords a good grip for lifting and pulling. There are several choices of rope material. The best choice is a synthetic material such as nylon or Dacron. A typical twisted rope is fine for most applications. A synthetic rope with a braid over the twisted core is known as *braid-on-braid* or *kernmantle*. While it's more expensive than twisted ropes, the outer braid provides better abrasion resistance. The least expensive type of rope is polypropylene. It's a stiff rope that doesn't take a knot as well as other types but is reasonably durable and cheap. **Table 28.2** shows the safe working load ratings for common types of rope.

When doing tower work, being able to tie knots is required. Of all the knots, the *bowline* is the one to know for tower work. The old "rabbit comes up through the hole, around the tree and back down the hole" is the most familiar method of tying a bowline. Most amateurs are knot-challenged so it's a great advantage to know at least this one.

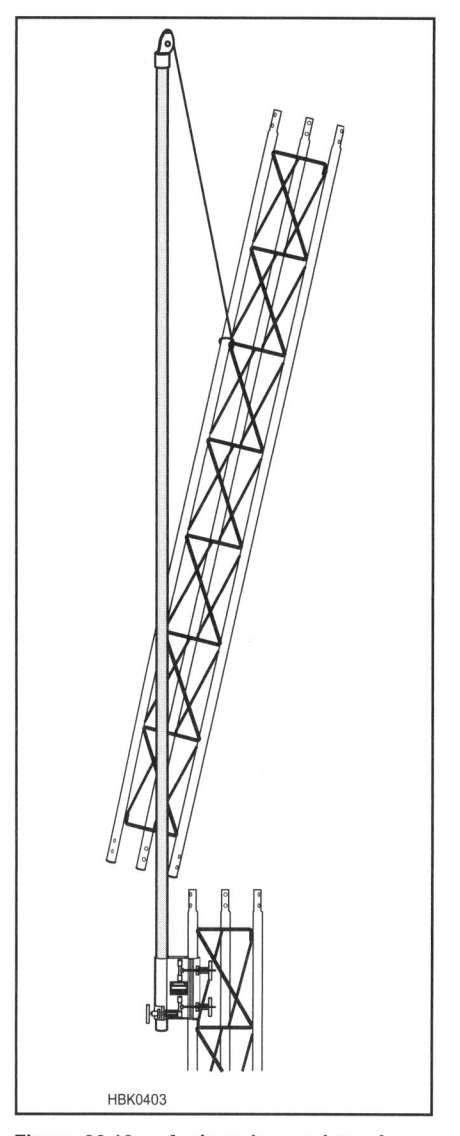

Figure 28.13 — A gin-pole consists of a leg clamp fixture, a section of aluminum mast and a pulley. It is used to lift the tower section high enough to be safely lowered into place and attached. (Based on Rohn EF2545.)

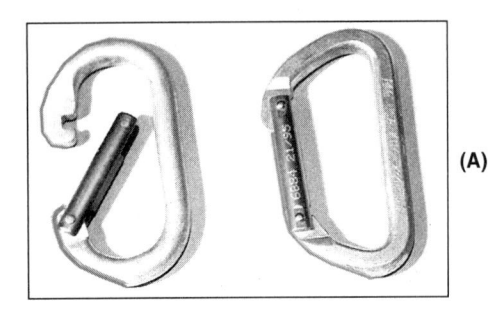

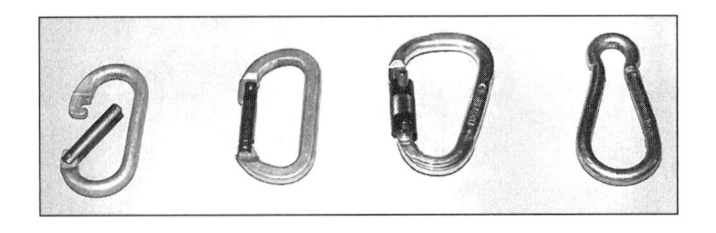

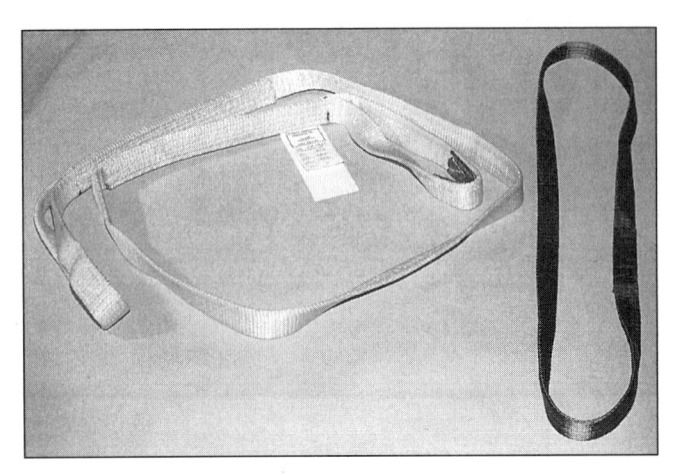

Figure 28.14 — (A) Oval mountain climbing type carabiners are ideal for tower workloads and attachments. The gates are spring loaded — the open gate is shown for illustration. (B) An open aluminum oval carabiner; a closed oval carabiner; an aluminum locking carabiner; a steel snaplink. (C) A heavy duty nylon sling on the left for big jobs and a lighter-duty loop sling on the right for everything else. [Steve Morris, K7LXC, photos]

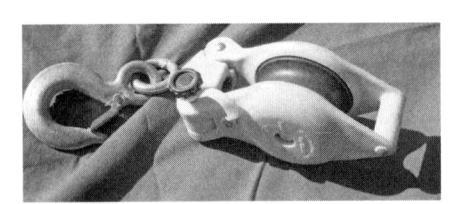

Figure 28.15 — Snatch blocks can be opened to place a rope directly on the sheave without having to thread it through the housing. A lightweight plastic block is shown at left, and two metal housing blocks at right.

Table 28.2
Rope Sizes and Safe Working Load Ratings in Pounds

3 Strand Twisted Line

Diameter	Manila	Nylon	Dacron	Polypropylene
¼	120	180	180	210
⅜	215	405	405	455
½	420	700	700	710
⅝	700	1140	1100	1050

Double-Braided Line

Diameter	Nylon	Dacron
¼	420	350
⅜	960	750
½	1630	1400
⅝	2800	2400

INSTALLING TOWER SECTIONS

The easiest way to erect a tower is to use a crane. It's fast and safe but more expensive than doing it in sections by hand. To erect a tower by sections, a gin-pole is needed (see Figure 28.13). It consists of two pieces — a clamp or some device to attach it to the tower leg and a pole with a pulley at the top. The pole is typically longer than the work piece being hoisted, allowing it to be held above the tower top while being attached or manipulated.

With the gin-pole mounted on the tower, the haul rope runs up from the ground, through the gin-pole mast and pulley at the top of the gin-pole, and back down the tower. The haul rope has a knot (preferably a bowline) on the end for attaching things to be hauled up or down. A carabiner hooked into the bight of the knot can be attached to objects quickly so that you don't have to untie and re-tie the bowline with every use.

It's a good idea to pass the haul rope through a snatch-block at the bottom of the tower, changing the direction of the rope from vertical to horizontal. This allows the ground crew an easier view up the tower and keeps them back, away from the tower base, in case the climbers accidentally drop something.

GUYS

For guyed towers, an important construction parameter is guy wire material and *guy tension*. Do *not* use rope or any other material not rated for use as guy cable as permanent tower guys. Guyed towers for amateurs typically use either 3/16-inch or 1/4-inch *EHS* (extra high strength) steel guy cable. The only other acceptable guy material is Phillystran — a lightweight cable made of Kevlar fibers. Phillystran is available with breaking strength similar to EHS cable. The advantage of Phillystran is that it is non-conducting and does not create unwanted electrical interaction with antennas on the tower. It is an excellent choice for towers supporting multiple Yagi and wire antennas and does not have to be broken up into short lengths with insulators.

EHS wire is very stiff — to cut it, use a hand-grinder with thin cutting blades or a circular saw with a metal-cutting aggregate blade. Wear safety glasses and gloves when cutting since there will be lots of sparks of burning steel being thrown off. Phillystran can be cut with a utility knife or a hot knife for cutting plastic.

If the guys are too loose, the result will be wind-induced shock loading. Guys that are too tight exert extra compressive load on the tower legs, reducing the overall capacity and reliability of the tower. The proper tension of EHS or Phillystran guys is 10% of the material's *ultimate breaking strength*. For 3/16-inch EHS the ultimate breaking strength is 4900 pounds and for 1/4-inch it's 6000 pounds so the respective guy tension should be 490 pounds and 600 pounds. The easiest to use, most accurate, and least expensive way to measure guy tension is by using a Loos tension gauge, developed for sailboat rigging. It is available at some marine supply stores or from Champion Radio Products.

Guy wires used to be terminated in a loop with cable clamps but those have been largely replaced by pre-formed Big Grips, shown in **Figure 28.16**. These simply twist onto the guy wire and are very secure. They grip the guy cable by squeezing the cable as tension is applied. Be sure to use the right type of Big Grips for the thickness and material of the guy cable.

28.2.4 Antenna Installation

Once the tower is up, it's time to install the antennas. VHF/UHF whips and wire antennas are pretty straightforward, but installing an HF Yagi is a more challenging situation. With a self-supporting tower, there are no guy wires to contend with — generally, the antenna can just be hauled up the tower face. Sometimes it is simply that easy!

In most cases, short of hiring a crane, the easiest way to get a Yagi up and down a tower is to use the *tram* method. A single tramline is suspended from the tower to the ground and the load is suspended under the tramline. Another technique is the *trolley* method in which two lines are suspended from the tower to the ground and the antenna rides on top of the lines like a trolley car on tracks. Problems with the trolley technique include trying to get the lines to have the same tension, balancing the antenna so that it won't fall off of the lines, and the added friction of pulling the antenna up two lines. The tram method has none of these problems. **Figure 28.17** illustrates the tram method of raising antennas.

Tram and trolley lines are typically attached to the mast above the top of the tower. In the case of a big load, the lines may exert enough force to bend the mast. If in doubt, *back-guy* the mast with another line in the opposite direction for added support.

MASTS

A mast is a pipe that sticks out of the top of the tower and connects the rotator to the antenna. For small antenna loads and moderate wind speeds, any pipe will work. But as wind speed and wind load increase, more force will be exerted on the mast.

There are two materials used for masts — *pipe* and *tubing*. Pipe can be water pipe or conduit (EMT). Pipe is a heavy material with not much strength since its job is just to carry water or wires. Pipe is acceptable as mast material for small loads only. Another problem is that 1.5-in. pipe (pipe is measured by its inside diameter or ID) is only 1.9-in. OD. Since most antenna boom-to-mast hardware is designed for a 2-in. mast, the less-than-perfect fit may lead to slippage.

For any larger load use carbon-alloy steel tubing rated for high strength. A moderate antenna installation in an 80 MPH wind might exert 40,000 to 50,000 pounds per square inch (psi) on the mast. Pipe has a yield strength of about 35,000 psi, so you can see that pipe is not adequately rated for this type of use. Chrome-moly steel tubing is available with yield strengths from 40,000 psi up to 115,000 psi but it is expensive. **Table 28.3** shows the

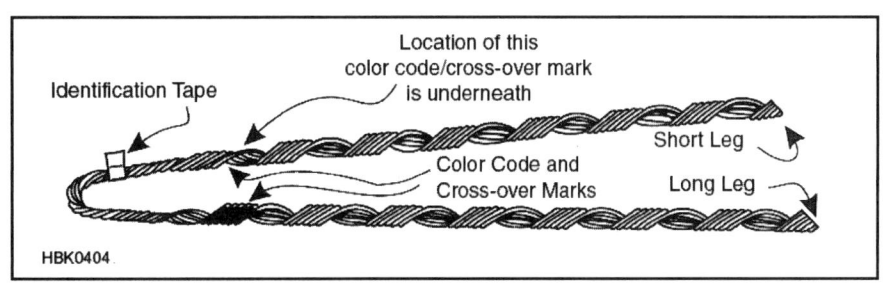

Figure 28.16 — A PreFormed Line Products Big Grip for guy wires.

Table 28.3
Yield Strengths of Mast Materials

Material	Specification	Yield Strength (lb/in.^{2})
Drawn aluminum tube	6063-T5	15,000
	6063-T832	35,000
	6061-T6	35,000
	6063-T835	40,000
	2024-T3	42,000
Aluminum pipe	6063-T6	25,000
	6061-T6	35,000
Extruded alum. tube	7075-T6	70,000
Aluminum sheet and plate	3003-H14	17,000
	5052-H32	22,000
	6061-T6	35,000
Structural steel	A36	33,000
Carbon steel, cold drawn	1016	50,000
	1022	58,000
	1027	70,000
	1041	87,000
	1144	90,000
Alloy steel	2330 cold drawn	119,000
	4130 cold worked	75,000
	4340 1550 °F quench 1000 °F temper	162,000
Stainless steel	AISI 405 cold worked	70,000
	AISI 440C heat-treated	275,000

(From *Physical Design of Yagi Antennas* by David B. Leeson, W6NL)

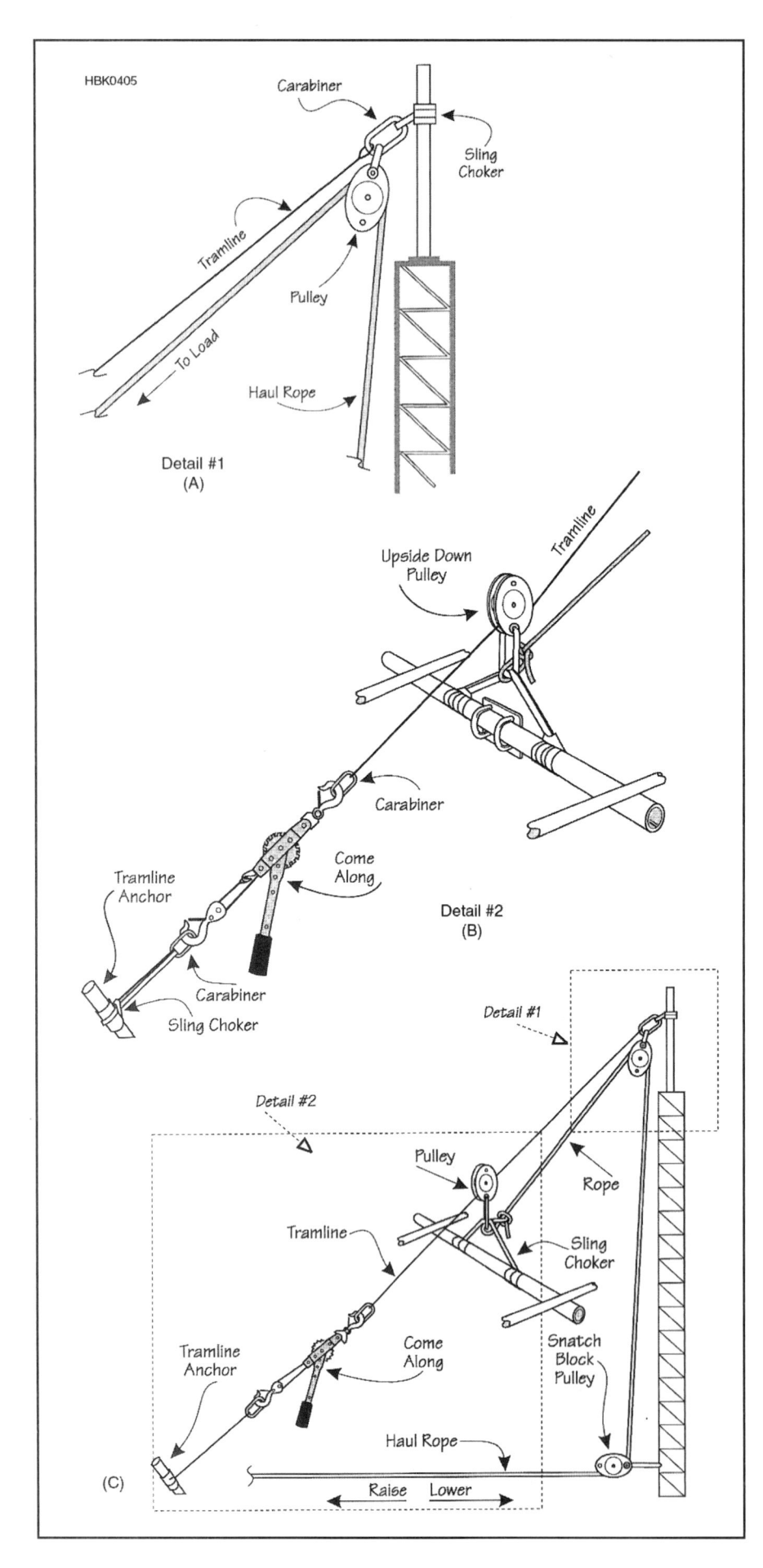

ratings of several materials used as masts for amateur radio antennas.

Calculating the required mast strength can be done by using a software program such as the *Mast, Antenna and Rotator Calculator (MARC)* software. (See the References.) The software requires as inputs the local wind speed, antenna wind load, and placement on the mast. The software then calculates the mast bending moment and will recommend a suitable mast material.

28.2.5 Weatherproofing Cable and Connectors

The biggest mistake amateurs make with coaxial cable is improper weatherproofing. (Coax selection is covered in the chapter on **Transmission Lines**.) **Figure 28.18** shows how to do it properly. First, use high-quality electrical tape, such as 3M Scotch 33+ or Scotch 88 (same as 33+ but 1.5 mil thicker). Avoid inexpensive utility tape. Before weatherproofing, tighten the connector (use pliers carefully to seat threaded connectors — hand-tight isn't good enough).

When you're done making a tape wrap, sever the tape with a knife or tear it very carefully — *do not* stretch the tape until it breaks. This invariably leads to "flagging" in which the end of the tape loosens and blows around in the wind. Let the tape relax before applying the next layer.

Begin by applying two wraps of electrical tape around the joint. Next put a layer of butyl rubber *vapor wrap* over the joint. (3M Butyl Mastic Tape 2212 is one such material. Butyl rubber tape is usually available in the electrical section of hardware and home improvement stores.) Finally, add two more layers of regular tape over the vapor wrap, creating a professional-quality joint that will never leak. Finally, if the coax is vertical, be sure to wrap the final layer so that the tape is going *up* the cable as shown in Figure 28.18. In that way, the layers will act like roofing shingles, shedding water off the connection. Wrapping it top to bottom will guide water between the layers of tape.

An alternative method suggested by K4ZA begins with a wrap of "military grade" Teflon tape — a thread wrapping tape thicker than what you'll find at your local hardware store. (McMaster-Carr #6802K44) Over that,

Figure 28.17 — At A, rigging the top of the tower for tramming antennas. Note the use of a sling and carabiner. (B) Rigging the anchor of the tramline. A come-along is used to tension the tramline. (C) The tram system for getting antennas up and down. Run the antenna part way up the tramline for testing before installation. It just takes a couple of minutes to run an antenna up or down once the tramline is rigged.

install a layer of Scotch 130C (liner-less rubber sealing tape), using a 50% wrap (half the tape width is overlapped). Cover that with a layer of either Scotch 33+ or Scotch 88. Taken apart, 20-year-old joints have revealed connectors with like new appearance.

28.2.6 Climbing Safety

Tower climbing is a potentially dangerous activity, so you'll need to use the proper safety equipment and techniques. OSHA, the Federal Occupational Safety and Health Administration, publishes rules for workplace safety. Although amateurs are not bound by those rules, you'll be much better off by following them. What equipment and techniques you use are up to you. As long as you've got the right safety equipment and follow the basic safety rules you won't have any problems.

SAFETY AWARENESS AND PREPARATION

One of the most important aspects of safety is having the knowledge and awareness to do a job safely and efficiently. You must have the mental ability to climb and work at altitude while constantly rethinking all connections, techniques and safety factors. Safely climbing and working on towers is 90% mental. Mental preparedness is something that must be learned. This is an occasion where there is no substitute for experience. The biggest obstacle for anyone is making the mental adjustment. Properly installed towers are inherently safe and accidents are relatively rare.

You should also check your safety equipment every time before you use it. Inspect it for any nicks or cuts to your belt and safety strap. Professional tower workers are required to check their safety equipment every day and you should check yours before each use.

One of the most important lessons for tower climbing is that you have four points of attachment and security — two hands and two feet. When climbing, move only one point at a time. That leaves you with three points of contact and a wide margin of safety if you ever need it. This is in addition to having your fall-arrest lanyard (see below) connected at all times.

Another recommended technique is to always do everything the same way every time. That is, always wear your positioning lanyard on the same D-ring and always connect it in the same way. Always look at your belt D-ring while clipping in with your safety strap. This way you'll always confirm that you're securely belted in. Always look!

PERSONAL SAFETY EQUIPMENT

The most important pieces of safety equipment are the *personal fall arrest system* (PFAS) you wear and the accompanying lanyards that attach to it (**Figure 28.19**). The PFAS has leg loops and suspenders to help spread the fall forces over more of your body and has the ability to hold you in a natural position with your arms and legs hanging below you where you're able to breathe normally.

Two or more lanyards are used. One is the positioning lanyard (**Figure 28.20**). That is, it holds you in working position and attaches to the D-rings at your waist. They can be adjustable or fixed and are made from different materials such as nylon rope, steel chain or special synthetic materials. An adjustable positioning lanyard will adjust to almost

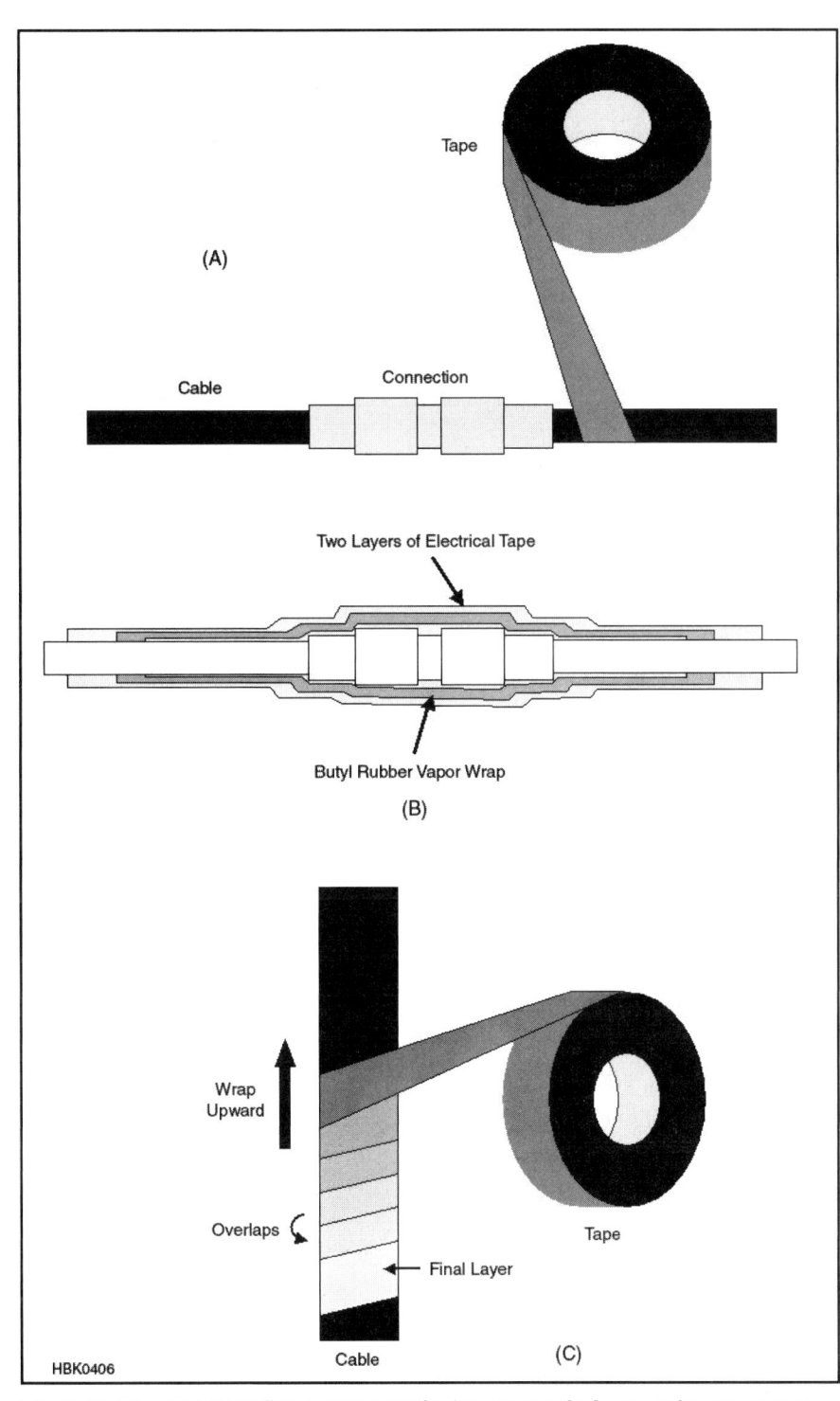

Figure 28.18 — Waterproofing a connector in three steps. At A, cover the connectors with a layer of good-quality electrical tape. B shows a layer of butyl rubber vapor wrap between the two layers of electrical tape. C shows how to wrap tape on a vertical cable so that the tape sheds water away from the connection. (Drawing (C) reprinted courtesy of *Circuitbuilding for Dummies*, Wiley Press)

Figure 28.19 —The well-dressed tower climber with a climbing or "gorilla" hook (A). Note the waist D-rings at (B) for attaching the positioning lanyard as well as the suspenders and leg loops. The climber also has working boots, gloves, safety glasses, and hardhat. [Don Daso, K4ZA, photos]

any situation whereas a fixed-length one is typically either too long or too short. A rope lanyard is the least expensive.

Leather safety equipment was outlawed some years ago by OSHA so don't use it. This includes the old-fashioned safety belt that utility pole linemen used for years but offers no fall arrest capability. If you drop down while wearing a safety belt, your body weight can cause it to rise up from your waist to your ribcage where it will immobilize your diaphragm and suffocate you. On the other hand, you can use a safety belt for positioning when it's worn over an FAH. Just don't depend on it to catch you in case of a fall.

The other lanyard is the fall arrest lanyard, shown in **Figure 28.21**, which attaches to a D-ring between your shoulder blades. The other end attaches to the tower above the work position and catches you in case of a fall. The simplest is a 6 foot rope lanyard which is inexpensive but doesn't offer any shock absorption. There are also shock absorbing varieties that typically have bar-tacked stitches that pull apart under force to decelerate you. *DO NOT* cut corners on buying or using safety equipment; you bet your life on it every time you use it!

Figure 28.20 —Left-to-right, a collection of locking clips, a belt-type positioning lanyard, a fall-arrest lanyard, and a versatile adjustable lanyard. [Don Daso, K4ZA, photos]

Figure 28.21 — The fall-arrest lanyard is above the climber so that the climber can climb up to it. The fall-arrest and positioning lanyards are then "leapfrogged" so that the climber remains attached to the tower 100 percent of the time. [Steve Morris, K7LXC, photo]

OSHA rules and good common sense say you should be attached to the tower 100% of the time. You can do this several ways. One is to attach the fall arrest lanyard above you and climb up to it. Use your positioning lanyard to hold you while you detach it and move it up again. Repeat as necessary. Another option is to use a pair of fall arrest lanyards, attaching one then the other as you climb the tower. This typically means using one with your left hand then the second with your right hand. The attachment point on the tower should be capable of sustaining a 3000-pound load.

Boots should be leather with a steel or fiberglass shank. Diagonal bracing on Rohn 25G is only 5/16 inch rod — spending all day standing on that small step will take a toll on your feet. The stiff shank will support your weight and protect your feet; tennis shoes will not. Leather boots are mandatory on towers like Rohn BX that have sharp X-cross braces. Your feet are always on a slant and that is hard on feet.

A hard hat and safety goggles is highly recommended. Just make sure they are ANSI or OSHA approved and that you and your crew wear them. As you'll be looking up and down a lot, a chin strap is essential to keep the hard hat from falling off.

If you do a lot of tower work, your hands will take a beating. Gloves are essential — keep several spare pair for ground crew members who show up without them. Cotton gloves are fine for gardening but not for tower work; they don't provide enough friction for climbing or working with a haul rope. Leather gloves are the only kind to use; either full leather or leather-palmed are fine. The softer the gloves the more useful they'll be. Stiff leather construction gloves are fine for the ground crew but pigskin and other soft leathers are better for the climber because you can thread a nut or do just about any other delicate job with these gloves on. K4ZA recommends what are called "framer's gloves," which are leather gloves with the thumb and two index finger-tips removed. This provides heavy-duty protection for the palm and backs of the hands, but allows fine finger-tip control for delicate work.

SAFETY TIPS

1) Don't climb with anything in your hands; attach it to your safety belt if you must climb with it or have your ground crew send it up to you in a bucket.

2) Don't put any hardware in your mouth; it can easily be swallowed.

3) Remove any rings and/or neck chains; they can get hooked on things. Long hair should be secured.

4) Be on the lookout for bees, wasps, hornets, and their nests. If you do run into a stinging insect, use Adolph's Meat Tenderizer on the sting — it contains the enzyme papain which neutralizes the venom. Have a small jar in your tool kit.

5) Don't climb when tired; that's when most accidents occur.

6) Don't try to lift anything by yourself; one person on a tower has very little leverage or strength. Let the ground crew use their strength; save yours for when you really need it.

7) If a procedure doesn't work, assess the situation and re-rig, if necessary, before trying again.

GROUND CREW SAFETY

The climber on the tower is the boss. Before tower work starts, have a safety meeting with the ground crew. This "tailgate" meeting is important to get everyone on the same page, work-wise, detailing the work to be done and how to do it. This also the time and place to introduce the ground crew to gear or hardware they may be unfamiliar with such as a capstan winch, carabiners, rock climbing gear, special tools, and so on.

Explain what is going to be done and how to do it as well as introducing them to any piece of hardware with which they may not be familiar (for example, carabiners, slings or come-along winches).

As part of the ground crew, there are a few rules to follow:

1) The climber on the tower is in charge.

2) Don't do anything unless directed by the climber in charge on the tower. This includes handling ropes, tidying up, moving hardware, and so on.

3) If not using radios to communicate, when talking to the climber on the tower, look up and talk directly to him or her in a loud voice. The ambient noise level is higher up on the tower because of traffic, wind and nearby equipment.

4) Communicate with the climber on the tower. Let him or her know when you're ready or if you're standing by or if there is a delay. Advise the climber when lunch is ready!

28.2.7 Antenna and Tower Safety References

AN Wireless — **www.anwireless.com**
ARRL Volunteer Counsel program — **www.arrl.org/volunteer-counsel-program**
ARRL Volunteer Consulting Engineer program — **www.arrl.org/volunteer-consulting-engineer-program**
D. Brede, W3AS, "The Care and Feeding of an Amateur's Favorite Antenna Support — the Tree," *QST*, Sep 1989, pp 26-28, 40.
Champion Radio Products — **www.championradio.com**
D. Daso, K4ZA, *Antenna Towers for Radio Amateurs* (ARRL, 2010)
D. Daso, K4ZA, "Workshop Chronicles" (column), *National Contest Journal*
F. Hopengarten, K1VR, *Antenna Zoning for the Radio Amateur* (ARRL, 2002)
Knot-tying website — **www.animatedknots.com**
Loos tension gauge — **www.championradio.com/rigging.html**
MARC software — **www.championradio.com/misc.html**
S. Morris, K7LXC, *Up the Tower: The Complete Guide to Tower Construction* (Champion Radio Products, 2009)
Rohn Tower — **www.rohnnet.com**
H.W. Silver, NØAX, ed., *The ARRL Antenna Book*, 23rd ed. (ARRL, 2012)
Trylon — **www.trylon.com**
US Towers — **www.ustower.com**

28.3 RF Safety

Amateur Radio is basically a safe activity. In recent years, however, there has been considerable discussion and concern about the possible hazards of electromagnetic fields (EMF), including both RF energy and power frequency (50-60 Hz) EMF. FCC regulations set limits on the maximum permissible exposure (MPE) allowed from the operation of radio transmitters. Following these regulations, along with the use of good RF practices, will make your station as safe as possible. This section, written by the ARRL RF Safety Committee (see sidebar), deals with the topic of electromagnetic safety.

28.3.1 How EMF Affects Mammalian Tissue

All life on Earth has adapted to live in an environment of weak, natural, low frequency electromagnetic fields, in addition to the Earth's static geomagnetic field. Natural low-frequency EM fields come from two main sources: the sun and thunderstorm activity. During the past 100 years, man-made fields at much higher intensities and with different spectral distributions have altered our EM background. Researchers continue to look at the effects of RF exposure over a wide range of frequencies and levels.

Both RF and power frequency fields are classified as *nonionizing radiation* because the frequency is too low for there to be enough photon energy to ionize atoms. *Ionizing radiation*, such as X-rays, gamma rays and some ultraviolet radiation, has enough energy to knock electrons loose from atoms. When this happens, positive and negative *ions* are formed. Still, at sufficiently high power densities, non-ionizing EMF poses certain health hazards.

It has been known since the early days of radio that RF energy can cause injuries by heating body tissue. Anyone who has ever touched an improperly grounded radio chassis or energized antenna and received an *RF burn* will agree that this type of injury can be quite painful. Excessive RF heating of the male reproductive organs can cause sterility by damaging sperm. Other health problems also can result from RF heating. These heat related health hazards are called *thermal effects*. A microwave oven is an application that puts thermal effects to practical use.

There also have been observations of changes in physiological function in the presence of RF energy levels that are too low to cause heating. These functions generally return to normal when the field is removed. Although research is ongoing, no harmful health consequences have been linked to these changes.

In addition to the ongoing research, much else has been done to address this issue. For example, FCC regulations set limits on exposure from radio transmitters. The Institute of Electrical and Electronics Engineers, the American National Standards Institute and the National Council for Radiation Protection and Measurement, among others, have recommended voluntary guidelines to limit human exposure to RF energy. The ARRL maintains an RF Safety Committee, consist-

The ARRL RF Safety Committee

Imagine you wake up one day and the newspaper headlines are screaming that scientists have discovered radio waves cause cancer. How would you react? How would your neighbor react? You may not have to imagine very hard because the news has been inundated with this type of story regularly over the past couple of decades. Clearly our society has not been decimated by epidemics of diseases since the vast increase in cellular telephone use. Some people deal with this discrepancy by ignoring all scientific reports. Others adopt a pessimistic attitude that technology is going to kill us all eventually, while still others treat every such story as "the truth" and militantly try to stop the transmission of RF energy. The reality is that while all scientific study is complex, the study of electromagnetic biological effects is even more so. Few newspaper reporters are capable of understanding the nuances of a scientific study and are even less able to properly report its results to the lay public. As a result many newspaper stories mislead the public into thinking that a scientific study has found something about which they need to be warned.

The ARRL has dealt with this dilemma by creating the RF Safety Committee, a group of experts in the facets of medical, scientific and engineering investigation needed to fully critique and understand the results of studies on electromagnetic biological effects. Experts in Dosimetry, Public Health, Epidemiology, Statistical Methods, General Medicine and specific diseases are well suited to reading and understanding published scientific reports and critiquing their validity.

It is not uncommon to examine how an experiment was performed only to realize that errors were made in the design of the experiment or the interpretation of its results. It takes a group of reviewers with a wide range of expertise to consider the implications of all aspects of the study to recognize the value of the results.

The field of biological effects of electromagnetic energy constitutes a complex combination of scientific disciplines. Many scientific studies in this field do not generate reliable results because they are not based on input from experts in the many fields that affect the interactions between electromagnetic energy and biological organisms. Even well designed scientific studies are subject to misinterpretation when the results are presented to a public that does not understand or appreciate the complex interactions that occur between the physical world and biological organisms and how these affect public health.

Since the 1960s there have been thousands of scientific studies that were intended to discover if electromagnetic energy had an adverse affect on biological tissue. A large number of these studies, designed and performed by biologists, did not accurately expose the subjects to known levels of electromagnetic energy. A field of expertise in RF engineering, called dosimetry, was developed to accurately determine the exact field strengths of both electrical and magnetic fields to which subjects were exposed. It has been imperative that an expert in electromagnetic dosimetry be involved in study design, though even today this requirement is often ignored. The RF Safety committee contains expertise in dosimetry that often discovers experimental errors in published results due to misstatements of the amount of exposure that subjects experienced.

Epidemiological studies have the potential to recognize disease trends in populations. However, they can also develop misleading results. Epidemiology looks for health trends among people with similar types of exposures as compared to a similar group of people that does not have the same type of exposure. (This type of study has become difficult to perform with cellular telephones because it is hard to find people who do not use them). The great diversity of the population makes it difficult to know that there is not some other exposure that affects the study group. The RF Safety committee contains expertise in epidemiology to make sense of claims based on epidemiological evidence, and the review of the methods and results can reveal a lesser impact of the study than the author or the press had implied.

Some experimental studies correctly demonstrate biological changes due to exposure to electromagnetic fields. A change in a biological tissue that occurs because of the presence of some form of energy may be an interesting finding, but it does not imply that this change will lead to a public health problem. (An obvious example is contraction of the eye pupil in the presence of bright light, a form of electromagnetic energy). The RF Safety Committee contains expertise in Public Health that helps to determine if there may be a correlation between a laboratory finding and any potential concern for the health of people in our society.

The ARRL RF Safety Committee serves as a resource to the ARRL Board of Directors, providing advice that helps them formulate ARRL policy related to RF safety. The RFSC interacts with the ARRL HQ staff to ensure that RF safety is appropriately addressed in ARRL publications and on the ARRL website. The Amateur Radio community corresponds with the RFSC for help with RF safety-related questions and problems. RFSC members monitor and analyze relevant published research. Its members participate in standards coordinating committees and other expert committees related to RF safety. The RFSC is responsible for writing the RF safety text that is included in ARRL publications. The accuracy of RF safety-related issues in articles submitted to *QST* and *QEX* are confirmed by committee members. The RFSC also participates in developing the RF safety questions for FCC amateur question pools and works with the FCC in developing its environmental regulations. Radio amateurs with questions related to RF safety can contact the RFSC via its liaison, Ed Hare, W1RFI, **w1rfi@arrl.org**. The RFSC maintains a webpage at **www.arrl.org/arrl-rf-safety-committee**.

ing of concerned scientists and medical doctors, who volunteer to serve the radio amateur community to monitor scientific research and to recommend safe practices.

THERMAL EFFECTS OF RF ENERGY

Body tissues that are subjected to *very high* levels of RF energy may suffer serious heat damage. These effects depend on the frequency of the energy, the power density of the RF field that strikes the body and factors such as the polarization of the wave and the grounding of the body.

At frequencies near the body's natural resonances RF energy is absorbed more efficiently. In adults, the primary resonance frequency is usually about 35 MHz if the person is grounded, and about 70 MHz if insulated from the ground. Various body parts are resonant at different frequencies. Body size thus determines the frequency at which most RF energy is absorbed. As the frequency is moved farther from resonance, RF energy absorption becomes less efficient. *Specific absorption rate (SAR)* is a measure that takes variables such as resonance into account to describe the rate at which RF energy is absorbed in tissue, typically measured in watts per kilogram of tissue (W/kg).

Maximum permissible exposure (MPE) limits define the maximum electric and magnetic field strengths, and the plane-wave equivalent power densities associated with these fields, that a person may be exposed to without harmful effect, and are based on whole-body SAR safety levels. The safe exposure limits vary with frequency as the efficiency of absorption changes. The MPE limits Safety factors are included to insure that the MPE field strength will never result in an unsafe SAR.

Thermal effects of RF energy are usually not a major concern for most radio amateurs because the power levels normally used tend to be low and the intermittent nature of most amateur transmissions decreases total exposure. Amateurs spend more time listening than transmitting and many amateur transmissions such as CW and SSB use low-duty-cycle modes. With FM or RTTY, though, the RF is present continuously at its maximum level during each transmission. It is rare for radio amateurs to be subjected to RF fields strong enough to produce thermal effects, unless they are close to an energized antenna or unshielded power amplifier. Specific suggestions for avoiding excessive exposure are offered later in this chapter.

ATHERMAL EFFECTS OF EMF

Biological effects resulting from exposure to power levels of RF energy that do not generate measurable heat are called *athermal effects*. A number of athermal effects of EMF exposure on biological tissue have been seen in the laboratory. However, to date all athermal effects that have been discovered have had the same features: They are transitory, or go away when the EMF exposure is removed, and they have not been associated with any negative health effects.

28.3.2 Researching Biological Effects of EMF Exposure

The statistical basis of scientific research that confuses many non-scientists is the inability of science to state unequivocally that EMF is safe. Effects are studied by scientists using statistical inference where the "null hypothesis" assumes there is no effect and then tries to disprove this assumption by proving an "alternative hypothesis" that there is an effect. The alternative hypothesis can never be entirely disproved because a scientist cannot examine every possible case, so scientists only end up with a *probability* that the alternative hypothesis is *not* true. Thus, to be entirely truthful, a scientist can never say that something was proven; with respect to low-level EMF exposure, no scientist can guarantee that it is absolutely safe. At best, science can only state that there is a very low probability that it is unsafe. While scientists accept this truism, many members of the general public who are suspicious of EMF and its effects on humans see this as a reason to continue to be afraid.

There are two types of scientific study that are used to learn about the effects of EMF exposure on mammalian biology: laboratory and epidemiological.

LABORATORY STUDY

Scientists conduct laboratory research using animals to learn about biological mechanisms by which EMF may affect mammals. The main advantage of laboratory studies on the biological effects of EMF is that the exposures can be controlled very accurately.

Some major disadvantages of laboratory study also exist. EMF exposure may not affect the species of animals used in the investigations the same way that humans may respond. A common example of this misdirection occurred with eye research. Rabbits had been used for many years to determine that exposure of the eyes to high levels of EMF could cause cataracts. The extrapolation of these results to humans led to the fear that use of radio would harm one's vision. However, the rabbit's eye is on the surface of its skull while the human eye is buried deep within the bony orbit in the skull. Thus, the human eye receives much less exposure from EMF and is less likely to be damaged by the same exposures that had been used in the laboratory experiments on rabbits.

Some biological processes that affect tissue can take many years to occur and laboratory experiments on animals tend to be of shorter duration, in part because the life spans of most animals are much shorter than that of humans. For instance, a typical laboratory rat can be studied at most for two years, during which it progresses from youth to old age with all of the attendant physiological changes that come from normal aging. A disease process that takes multiple exposures over many years to occur is unlikely to be seen in a laboratory study with small animals.

EPIDEMIOLOGICAL RESEARCH

Epidemiologists look at the health patterns of large groups of people using statistical methods. In contrast to laboratory research, epidemiological research has very poor control of its subjects' exposures to EMF but it has the advantages of being able to analyze the effects of a lifetime of exposure and of being able to average out variations among large populations of subjects. By their basic design, epidemiological studies do not demonstrate cause and effect, nor do they postulate mechanisms of disease. Instead, epidemiologists look for associations between an environmental factor and an observed pattern of illness. Apparent associations are often seen in small preliminary studies that later are shown to have been incorrect. At best, such results are used to motivate more detailed epidemiological studies and laboratory studies that narrow down the search for cause-and-effect.

Some preliminary studies have suggested a weak association between exposure to EMF at home or at work and various malignant conditions including leukemia and brain cancer. A larger number of equally well-designed and performed studies, however, have found no association. Risk ratios as high as 2 have been observed in some studies. This means that the number of observed cases of disease in the test group is up to 2 times the "expected" number in the population. Epidemiologists generally regard a risk ratio of 4 or greater to be indicative of a strong association between the cause and effect under study. For example, men who smoke one pack of cigarettes per day increase their risk for lung cancer tenfold compared to nonsmokers and two packs per day increases the risk to more than 25 times the nonsmokers' risk.

Epidemiological research by itself is rarely conclusive, however. Epidemiology only identifies health patterns in groups — it does not ordinarily determine their cause. There are often confounding factors. Most of us are exposed to many different environmental hazards that may affect our health in various ways. Moreover, not all studies of persons likely to be exposed to high levels of EMF have yielded the same results (see sidebar on preliminary epidemiological studies).

Preliminary Epidemiology

Just about every week you can pick up the newspaper and see a screaming banner headline such as: "Scientists Discover Link Between Radio Waves and Disease." So why are you still operating your ham radio? You've experienced the inconsistency in epidemiological study of diseases. This is something that every radio amateur should understand in order to know how to interpret the real meaning of the science behind the headlines and to help assuage the fears that these stories elicit in others.

Just knowing that someone who uses a radio gets a disease, such as cancer, doesn't tell us anything about the cause-and-effect of that disease. People came down with cancer, and most other diseases, long before radio existed. What epidemiologists try to identify is a group of people who all have a common exposure to something and all suffer from a particular disease in higher proportion than would be expected if they were not exposed. This technique has been highly effective in helping health officials notice excesses of disease due to things such as poisoning of water supplies by local industry and even massive exposures such as smoking. However, epidemiology rarely proves that an exposure causes a disease; rather it provides the evidence that leads to further study.

While the strength of epidemiology is that it helps scientists notice anomalies in entire populations, its weakness is that it is non-specific. An initial epidemiological study examines only two things: suspected exposures and rates of diseases. These studies are relatively simple and inexpensive to perform and may point to an apparent association that then bears further study. For instance, in one study of the causes of death of a selection of Amateur Radio operators, an excess of leukemia was suggested. The percentage of ham radio operators who died of leukemia in that study was higher than expected based on the percentage of the rest of the population that died of leukemia. By itself, this has little meaning and should not be a cause for concern, since the study did not consider anything else about the sample population except that they had ham licenses. Many other questions arise: Were the study subjects exposed to any unusual chemicals? Did any of the study subjects have a family history of leukemia? Did the licensed amateurs even operate radios, what kind and how often? To an epidemiologist, this result might provide enough impetus to raise the funds to gather more specific information about each subject and perform a more complete study that strengthens the apparent associations. However, a slight excess of disease in a preliminary study rarely leads to further study. Commonly, an epidemiologist does not consider a preliminary study to be worth pursuing unless the ratio of excess disease, also called the risk ratio, is 4:1 or greater. Unfortunately, most news reporters are not epidemiologists and do not understand this distinction. Rather, a slight excess of disease in a preliminary study can lead to banner headlines that raise fear in the society, causing unreasonable resistance to things like cell phones and ham radios.

Headlines that blow the results of preliminary epidemiological studies out of proportion are rarely followed by retractions that are as visible if the study is followed up by one that is more complete and shows no association with disease. In the case of the aforementioned epidemiological study of hams' licensing and death records, overblown publicity about the results has led to the urban legend that ham radio operators are likely to come down with leukemia. Not only is this an unfounded conclusion due to the preliminary nature of the original study, but a similar study was recently performed by the National Cancer Institute using a far larger number of subjects and no significant excess of any disease was found. Hams should be able to recognize when sensationalistic headlines are based on inconclusive science and should be prepared to explain to their families, friends and neighbors just how inconclusive such results are.

28.3.3 Safe Exposure Levels

How much EMF energy is safe? Scientists and regulators have devoted a great deal of effort to deciding upon safe RF-exposure limits. This is a very complex problem, involving difficult public health and economic considerations. The recommended safe levels have been revised downward several times over the years — and not all scientific bodies agree on this question even today. The latest Institute of Electrical and Electronics Engineers (IEEE) C95.1 standard for recommended radio frequency exposure limits was published in 2006, updating one that had previously been published in 1991 and adopted by the American National Standards Institute (ANSI) in 1992. In the new standard changes were made to better reflect the current research, especially related to the safety of cellular telephones. At some frequencies the new standard determined that higher levels of exposure than previously thought are safe (see sidebar, "Where Do RF Safety Standards Come From?").

The IEEE C95.1 standard recommends frequency-dependent and time-dependent maximum permissible exposure levels. Unlike earlier versions of the standard, the 1991 and 2006 standards set different RF exposure limits in *controlled environments* (where energy levels can be accurately determined and everyone on the premises is aware of the presence of EM fields) and in *uncontrolled environments* (where energy levels are not known or where people may not be aware of the presence of EM fields). FCC regulations adopted these concepts to include controlled/occupational and uncontrolled/general population exposure limits.

The graph in **Figure 28.22** depicts the 1991 IEEE standard (which is still used as the basis of FCC regulation). It is necessarily a complex graph, because the standards differ not only for controlled and uncontrolled environments but also for electric (E) fields and magnetic (H) fields. Basically, the lowest E-field exposure limits occur at frequencies between 30 and 300 MHz. The lowest H-field exposure levels occur at 100-300 MHz. The ANSI standard sets the maximum E-field limits between 30 and 300 MHz at a power density of 1 mW/cm^2 (61.4 V/m) in controlled environments — but at one-fifth that level (0.2 mW/cm^2 or 27.5 V/m) in uncontrolled environments. The H-field limit drops to 1 mW/cm^2 (0.163 A/m) at 100-300 MHz in controlled environments and 0.2 mW/cm^2 (0.0728 A/m) in uncontrolled environments. Higher power densities are permitted at frequencies below 30 MHz (below 100 MHz for H fields) and above 300 MHz, based on the concept that the body will not be resonant at those frequencies and will therefore absorb less energy.

In general, the ANSI/IEEE standard requires averaging the power level over time periods ranging from 6 to 30 minutes for power-density calculations, depending on the frequency and other variables. The ANSI/IEEE exposure limits for uncontrolled environments are lower than those for controlled environments, but to compensate for that the standard allows exposure levels in those environments to be averaged over much longer time periods (generally 30 minutes). This long averaging time means that an intermittent RF source (such as an Amateur Radio transmitter) will result in a much lower exposure than a continuous-duty station, with all other parameter being equal. Time averaging is based on the concept that the human body can withstand a greater rate of body heating (and thus, a higher level of RF energy) for a short time.

Another national body in the United States, the National Council for Radiation Protection and Measurement (NCRP), also has adopted recommended exposure guidelines. NCRP urges a limit of 0.2 mW/cm^2 for nonoccupational exposure in the 30- 300 MHz range. The NCRP guideline differs from IEEE in that it takes into account the effects of modu-

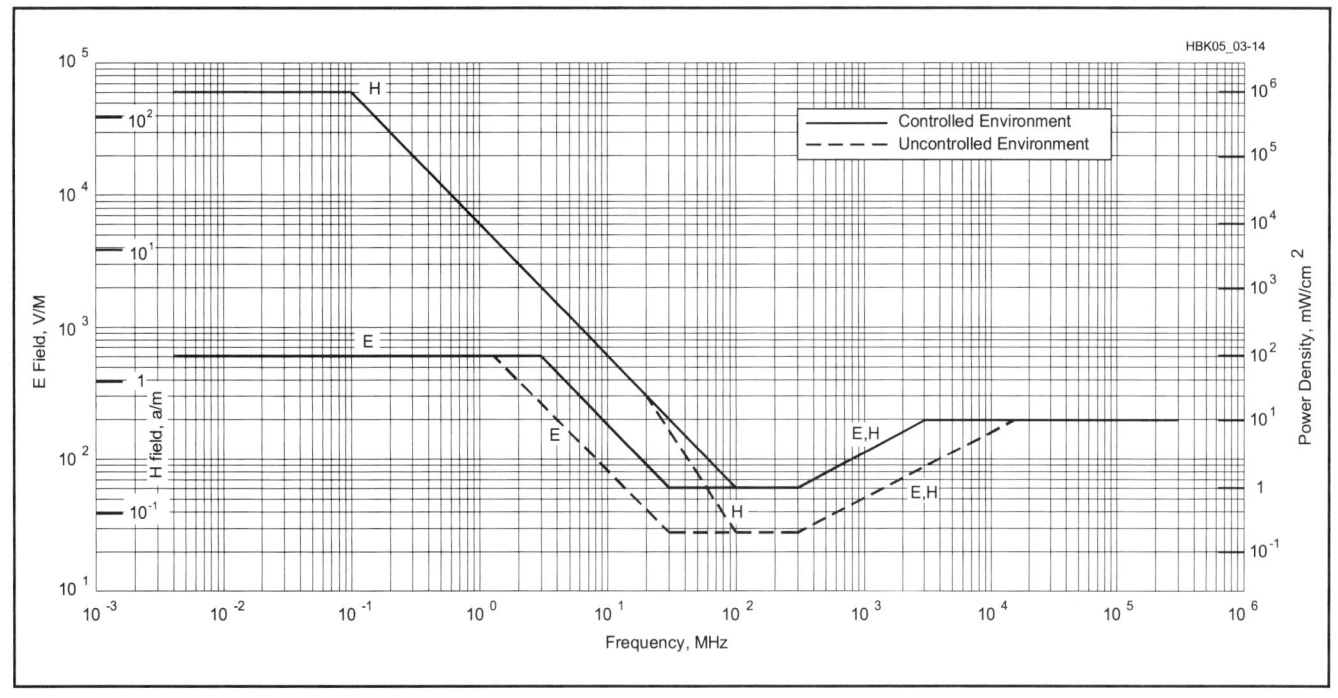

Figure 28.22 — 1991 RF protection guidelines for body exposure of humans. It is known officially as the "IEEE Standard for Safety Levels with Respect to Human Exposure to Radio Frequency Electromagnetic Fields, 3 kHz to 300 GHz."

Where Do RF Safety Standards Come From?

So much of the way we deal with RF Safety is based on "Safety Standards." The FCC environmental exposure regulations that every ham must follow are largely restatements of the conclusions reached by some of the major safety standards. How are these standards developed and why should we trust them?

The preeminent RF safety standard in the world was developed by the Institute of Electrical and Electronics Engineers (IEEE). The most recent edition is entitled *C95.1 -2005: IEEE Standard for Safety Levels with Respect to Human Exposure to Radio Frequency Electromagnetic Fields, 3 kHz to 300 GHz*. The IEEE C95.1 Standard has a long history. The first C95.1 RF safety standard was released in 1966, was less than 2 pages long and listed no references. It essentially said that for frequencies between 10 MHz and 100 GHz people should not be exposed to a power density greater than 10 mW/cm^2. The C95.1 standard was revised in 1974, 1982, 1991 and 2005. The latest (2005) edition of the standard was published in 2006, is 250 pages long and has 1143 references to the scientific literature. Most of the editions of the IEEE C95.1 standard were adopted by the American National Standards Institute (ANSI) a year or two after they were published by IEEE. The 2005 edition was adopted by ANSI in 2006.

The committee at IEEE that developed the latest revision to C95.1 is called International Committee on Electromagnetic Safety Technical Committee 95 Subcommittee 4 and had a large base of participants. The subcommittee was co-chaired by C-K Chou, Ph.D., of Motorola Laboratories, and John D'Andrea, PhD, of the U.S. Naval Health Research Center. The committee had 132 members, 42% of whom were from 23 countries outside the United States. The members of the committee represented academia (27%), government (34%), industry (17%), consultants (20%) and the general public (2%).

Early editions of C95.1 were based on the concept that heat generated in the body should be limited to prevent damage to tissue. Over time the standard evolved to protect against *all known adverse biological effects* regardless of the amount of heat generated. The 2005 revision was based on the principles that the standard should protect human health yet still be practical to implement, its conclusions should be based solely on scientific evidence and wherever scientifically defensible it should be harmonized with other international RF safety standards. It based its conclusions on 50 years of scientific study. From over 2500 studies on EMF performed during that time, 1300 were selected for their relevance to the health effects of RF exposure. The science in these studies was evaluated for its quality and methodology and 1143 studies were referenced in producing the latest standard.

Other major standards bodies have published similar standards. The National Council for Radiation Protection and Measurement (NCRP) published its safety standard entitled, *Report No. 86: Biological Effects and Exposure Criteria for Radiofrequency Electromagnetic Fields* in 1986. The International Commission on Non-Ionizing Radiation Protection (ICNIRP) published its safety standard entitled *Guidelines for Limiting Exposure to Time-Varying Electric, Magnetic, and Electromagnetic Fields (Up to 300 GHz)* in 1998.

FCC RF Exposure Regulations

FCC regulations control the amount of RF exposure that can result from your station's operation (§§97.13, 97.503, 1.1307 (b)(c)(d), 1.1310, 2.1091 and 2.1093). The regulations set limits on the maximum permissible exposure (MPE) allowed from operation of transmitters in all radio services. They also require that certain types of stations be evaluated to determine if they are in compliance with the MPEs specified in the rules. The FCC has also required that questions on RF environmental safety practices be added to Technician and General license examinations.

THE RULES
Maximum Permissible Exposure (MPE)

All radio stations regulated by the FCC must comply with the requirements for MPEs, even QRP stations running only a few watts or less. The MPEs vary with frequency, as shown in **Table A**. MPE limits are specified in maximum electric and magnetic fields for frequencies below 30 MHz, in power density for frequencies above 300 MHz and all three ways for frequencies from 30 to 300 MHz. For compliance purposes, all of these limits must be considered *separately*. If any one is exceeded, the station is not in compliance. In effect, this means that both electric and magnetic field must be determined below 300 MHz but at higher frequencies determining either the electric or magnetic field is normally sufficient.

The regulations control human exposure to RF fields, not the strength of RF fields in any space. There is no limit to how strong a field can be as long as no one is being exposed to it, although FCC regulations require that amateurs use the minimum necessary power at all times (§97.311 [a]).

Table A
(From §1.1310) Limits for Maximum Permissible Exposure (MPE)

(A) Limits for Occupational/Controlled Exposure

Frequency Range (MHz)	Electric Field Strength (V/m)	Magnetic Field Strength (A/m)	Power Density (mW/cm^2)	Averaging Time (minutes)
0.3-3.0	614	1.63	(100)*	6
3.0-30	1842/f	4.89/f	(900/f^2)*	6
30-300	61.4	0.163	1.0	6
300-1500	—	—	f/300	6
1500-100,000	—	—	5	6

f = frequency in MHz
* = Plane-wave equivalent power density (see Notes 1 and 2).

(B) Limits for General Population/Uncontrolled Exposure

Frequency Range (MHz)	Electric Field Strength (V/m)	Magnetic Field Strength (A/m)	Power Density (mW/cm^2)	Averaging Time (minutes)
0.3-1.34	614	1.63	(100)*	30
1.34-30	824/f	2.19/f	(180/f^2)*	30
30-300	27.5	0.073	0.2	30
300-1500	—	—	f/1500	30
1500-100,000	—	—	1.0	30

f = frequency in MHz
* = Plane-wave equivalent power density (see Notes 1 and 2).

Note 1: This means the equivalent far-field strength that would have the E or H-field component calculated or measured. It does not apply well in the near field of an antenna. The equivalent far-field power density can be found in the near or far field regions from the relationships: $P_d = |E_{total}|^2 / 3770$ mW/cm^2 or from $P_d = |H_{total}|^2 \times 37.7$ mW/cm^2.

Note 2: $|E_{total}|^2 = |E_x|^2 + |E_y|^2 + |E_z|^2$, and $|H_{total}|^2 = |H_x|^2 + |H_y|^2 + |H_z|^2$

Environments

The FCC has defined two tiers of exposure limits — *occupational/controlled limits* and *general population/uncontrolled limits*. Occupational/controlled limits apply when people are exposed as a condition of their employment and when they are aware of that exposure and can take steps to minimize it, if appropriate. General population/uncontrolled limits apply to exposure of the general public or people who are not normally aware of the exposure or cannot exercise control over it. The limits for general population/uncontrolled exposure are more stringent than the limits for occupational/controlled exposure. Specific definitions of the exposure categories can be found in Section 1.1310 of the FCC rules.

Although occupational/controlled limits are usually applicable in a workplace environment, the FCC has determined that they generally apply to amateur operators and members of their immediate households. In most cases, occupational/lation on an RF carrier.

The FCC MPE regulations are based on a combination of the 1992 ANSI/IEEE standard and 1986 NCRP recommendations. The MPE limits under the regulations are slightly different than the ANSI/IEEE limits and do not reflect all the assumptions and exclusions of the ANSI/IEEE standard.

28.3.4 Cardiac Pacemakers and RF Safety

It is a widely held belief that cardiac pacemakers may be adversely affected in their function by exposure to electromagnetic fields. Amateurs with pacemakers may ask whether their operating might endanger themselves or visitors to their shacks who have a pacemaker. Because of this, and similar concerns regarding other sources of EM fields, pacemaker manufacturers apply design methods that for the most part shield the pacemaker circuitry from even relatively high EM field strengths.

It is recommended that any amateur who has a pacemaker, or is being considered for one, discuss this matter with his or her physician. The physician will probably put the amateur into contact with the technical representative of the pacemaker manufacturer. These representatives are generally excellent resources, and may have data from laboratory or "in the field" studies with specific model pacemakers.

One study examined the function of a modern (dual chamber) pacemaker in and around an Amateur Radio station. The pacemaker generator has circuits that receive and process electrical signals produced by the heart, and also generate electrical signals that stimulate (pace) the heart. In one series of experiments, the pacemaker was connected to a heart simulator. The system was placed on top of the cabinet of a 1-kW HF linear amplifier during SSB and CW operation. In another test, the system was placed in close proximity to several 1 to 5-W 2-meter hand-held transceivers. The test pacemaker was connected to the heart simulator in a third test, and then placed on the ground 9 meters below and 5 meters in front of a three-element Yagi HF antenna. No interference with pacemaker function was

controlled limits can be applied to your home and property to which you can control physical access. The general population/uncontrolled limits are intended for areas that are accessible by the general public, such as your neighbors' properties.

The MPE levels are based on average exposure. An averaging time of 6 minutes is used for occupational/controlled exposure; an averaging period of 30 minutes is used for general population/uncontrolled exposure.

Station Evaluations

The FCC requires that certain amateur stations be evaluated for compliance with the MPEs. Although an amateur can have someone else do the evaluation, it is not difficult for hams to evaluate their own stations. The ARRL book *RF Exposure and You* contains extensive information about the regulations and a large chapter of tables that show compliance distances for specific antennas and power levels. Generally, hams will use these tables to evaluate their stations. Some of these tables have been included in the FCC's information — *OET Bulletin 65* and its *Supplement B* (available for downloading at the FCC's RF Safety website). If hams choose, however, they can do more extensive calculations, use a computer to model their antenna and exposure, or make actual measurements.

Categorical Exemptions

Some types of amateur stations do not need to be evaluated, but these stations must still comply with the MPE limits. The station licensee remains responsible for ensuring that the station meets these requirements.

The FCC has exempted these stations from the evaluation requirement because their output power, operating mode and frequency are such that they are presumed to be in compliance with the rules.

Stations using power equal to or less than the levels in **Table B** do not have to be evaluated on a routine basis. For the 100-W HF ham station, for example, an evaluation would be required only on 12 and 10 meters.

Hand-held radios and vehicle-mounted mobile radios that operate using a push-to-talk (PTT) button are also categorically exempt from performing the routine evaluation.

Repeater stations that use less than 500 W ERP or those with antennas not mounted on buildings; if the antenna is at least 10 meters off the ground, also do not need to be evaluated.

Correcting Problems

Most hams are already in compliance with the MPE requirements. Some amateurs, especially those using indoor antennas or high-power, high-duty-cycle modes such as a RTTY bulletin station and specialized stations for moon bounce operations and the like may need to make adjustments to their station or operation to be in compliance.

The FCC permits amateurs considerable flexibility in complying with these regulations. As an example, hams can adjust their operating frequency, mode or power to comply with the MPE limits. They can also adjust their operating habits or control the direction their antenna is pointing.

More Information

This discussion offers only an overview of this topic; additional information can be found in *RF Exposure and You* and on the ARRL website at **www.arrl.org/rf-exposure**. The ARRL website has links to the FCC website, with OET Bulletin 65 and Supplement B and links to software that hams can use to evaluate their stations.

Table B
Power Thresholds for Routine Evaluation of Amateur Radio Stations

Wavelength Band	Evaluation Required if Power* (watts) Exceeds:
MF	
160 m	500
HF	
80 m	500
75 m	500
40 m	500
30 m	425
20 m	225
17 m	125
15 m	100
12 m	75
10 m	50
VHF (all bands)	50
UHF	
70 cm	70
33 cm	150
23 cm	200
13 cm	250
SHF (all bands)	250
EHF (all bands)	250
Repeater stations (all bands)	Non-building-mounted antennas: height above ground level to lowest point of antenna < 10 m *and* power > 500 W ERP
	Building-mounted antennas: power > 500 W ERP

*Transmitter power = Peak-envelope power input to antenna. For repeater stations only, power exclusion based on ERP (effective radiated power).

---

observed in these experiments.

Although the possibility of interference cannot be entirely ruled out by these few observations, these tests represent more severe exposure to EM fields than would ordinarily be encountered by an amateur — with an average amount of common sense. Of course prudence dictates that amateurs with pacemakers, who use handheld VHF transceivers, keep the antenna as far as possible from the site of the implanted pacemaker generator. They also should use the lowest transmitter output required for adequate communication. For high power HF transmission, the antenna should be as far as possible from the operating position, and all equipment should be properly grounded.

28.3.5 Low-Frequency Fields

There has been considerable laboratory research about the biological effects of power line EMF. For example, some separate studies have indicated that even fairly low levels of EMF exposure might alter the human body's circadian rhythms, affect the manner in which T lymphocytes function in the immune system and alter the nature of the electrical and chemical signals communicated through the cell membrane and between cells, among other things. Although these studies are intriguing, they do not demonstrate any effect of these low-level fields on the overall organism.

Much of this research has focused on low-frequency magnetic fields, or on RF fields that are keyed, pulsed or modulated at a low audio frequency (often below 100 Hz). Several studies suggested that humans and animals could adapt to the presence of a steady RF carrier more readily than to an intermittent, keyed or modulated energy source.

The results of studies in this area, plus speculations concerning the effect of various types of modulation, were and have remained somewhat controversial. None of the research to date has demonstrated that low-level EMF causes adverse health effects.

Given the fact that there is a great deal of ongoing research to examine the health consequences of exposure to EMF, the American Physical Society (a national group of highly respected scientists) issued a statement in May 1995 based on its review of available data pertaining to the possible connections of cancer to 60-Hz EMF exposure. Their report is exhaustive and should be reviewed by anyone with a serious interest in the field. Among its general conclusions are the following:

1. The scientific literature and the reports of reviews by other panels show no consistent, significant link between cancer and power line fields.

2. No plausible biophysical mechanisms for the systematic initiation or promotion of cancer by these extremely weak 60-Hz fields have been identified.

3. While it is impossible to prove that no deleterious health effects occur from exposure to any environmental factor, it is necessary to demonstrate a consistent, significant, and causal relationship before one can conclude that such effects do occur.

In a report dated October 31, 1996, a committee of the National Research Council of the National Academy of Sciences has concluded that no clear, convincing evidence exists to show that residential exposures to electric and magnetic fields (EMF) are a threat to human health.

A National Cancer Institute epidemiological study of residential exposure to magnetic fields and acute lymphoblastic leukemia in children was published in the *New England Journal of Medicine* in July 1997. The exhaustive, seven-year study concludes that if there is any link at all, it is far too weak to be of concern.

In 1998, the US National Institute on Environmental Health Sciences organized a working group of experts to summarize the research on power-line EMF. The committee used the classification rules of the International Agency for Research on Cancer (IARC) and performed a meta-analysis to combine all past results as if they had been performed in a single study. The NIEHS working group concluded that the research did not show this type of exposure to be a carcinogen but could not rule out the possibility either. Therefore, they defined power-line EMF to be a Class 2b carcinogen under the IARC classification. The definition, as stated by the IARC is: "Group 2B: The agent is possibly carcinogenic to humans. There is limited pidemiological evidence plus limited or inadequate animal evidence." Other IARC Class 2b carcinogens include automobile exhaust, chloroform, coffee, ceramic and glass fibers, gasoline and pickled vegetables.

Readers may want to follow this topic as further studies are reported. Amateurs should be aware that exposure to RF and ELF (60 Hz) electromagnetic fields at all power levels and frequencies has not been fully studied under all circumstances. "Prudent avoidance" of any avoidable EMF is always a good idea. Prudent avoidance doesn't mean that amateurs should be fearful of using their equipment. Most amateur operations are well within the MPE limits. If any risk does exist, it will almost surely fall well down on the list of causes that may be harmful to your health (on the other end of the list from your automobile). It does mean, however, that hams should be aware of the potential for exposure from their stations, and take whatever reasonable steps they can take to minimize their own exposure and the exposure of those around them.

Although the FCC doesn't regulate 60-Hz fields, some recent concern about EMF has focused on 60 Hz. Amateur Radio equipment can be a significant source of 60 Hz fields, although there are many other sources of this kind of energy in the typical home. Magnetic fields can be measured relatively accurately with inexpensive 60-Hz meters that are made by several manufacturers.

Table 28.4 shows typical magnetic field intensities of Amateur Radio equipment and various household items.

Table 28.4
Typical 60-Hz Magnetic Fields Near Amateur Radio Equipment and AC-Powered Household Appliances
Values are in milligauss.

Item	Field	Distance
Electric blanket	30-90	Surface
Microwave oven	10-100	Surface
	1-10	12 in.
IBM personal computer	5-10	Atop monitor
	0-1	15 in. from screen
Electric drill	500-2000	At handle
Hair dryer	200-2000	At handle
HF transceiver	10-100	Atop cabinet
	1-5	15 in. from front
1-kW RF amplifier	80-1000	Atop cabinet
	1-25	15 in. from front

(Source: measurements made by members of the ARRL RF Safety Committee)

Table 28.5
Typical RF Field Strengths Near Amateur Radio Antennas
A sampling of values as measured by the Federal Communications Commission and Environmental Protection Agency, 1990

Antenna Type	Freq (MHz)	Power (W)	E Field (V/m)	Location
Dipole in attic	14.15	100	7-100	In home
Discone in attic	146.5	250	10-27	In home
Half sloper	21.5	1000	50	1 m from base
Dipole at 7-13 ft	7.14	120	8-150	1-2 m from earth
Vertical	3.8	800	180	0.5 m from base
5-element Yagi at 60 ft	21.2	1000	10-20	In shack
			14	12 m from base
3-element Yagi at 25 ft	28.5	425	8-12	12 m from base
Inverted V at 22-46 ft	7.23	1400	5-27	Below antenna
Vertical on roof	14.11	140	6-9	In house
			35-100	At antenna tuner
Whip on auto roof	146.5	100	22-75	2 m antenna
			15-30	In vehicle
			90	Rear seat
5-element Yagi at 20 ft	50.1	500	37-50	10 m antenna

28.3.6 Determining RF Power Density

Unfortunately, determining the power density of the RF fields generated by an amateur station is not as simple as measuring low-frequency magnetic fields. Although sophisticated instruments can be used to measure RF power densities quite accurately, they are costly and require frequent recalibration. Most amateurs don't have access to such equipment, and the inexpensive field-strength meters that we do have are not suitable for measuring RF power density.

Table 28.5 shows a sampling of measurements made at Amateur Radio stations by the Federal Communications Commission and the Environmental Protection Agency in 1990. As this table indicates, a good antenna well removed from inhabited areas poses no hazard under any of the ANSI/IEEE guidelines. However, the FCC/EPA survey also indicates that amateurs must be careful about using indoor or attic-mounted antennas, mobile antennas, low directional arrays or any other antenna that is close to inhabited areas, especially when moderate to high power is used.

Ideally, before using any antenna that is in close proximity to an inhabited area, you should measure the RF power density. If that is not feasible, the next best option is make the installation as safe as possible by observing the safety suggestions listed in **Table 28.6**.

It also is possible, of course, to calculate the probable power density near an antenna using simple equations. Such calculations have many pitfalls. For one, most of the situations where the power density would be high enough to be of concern are in the near field. In the near field, ground interactions and other variables produce power densities that cannot be determined by simple arithmetic. In the far field, conditions become easier to predict with simple calculations. (See the February 2013 *QST* article "Q and the Energy Stored Around Antennas" by Kai Siwiak, KE4PT and the **Antennas** chapter of this book for more information about stored energy density near antennas.)

The boundary between the near field and the far field depends on the wavelength of the transmitted signal and the physical size and configuration of the antenna. The boundary between the near field and the far field of an antenna can be as much as several wavelengths from the antenna.

Computer antenna-modeling programs are another approach you can use. *MININEC* or other codes derived from *NEC* (Numerical Electromagnetics Code) are suitable for estimating RF magnetic and electric fields around amateur antenna systems.

These models have limitations. Ground interactions must be considered in estimating near-field power densities, and the "correct ground" must be modeled. Computer modeling is generally not sophisticated enough to predict "hot spots" in the near field — places where the field intensity may be far higher than would be expected, due to reflections from nearby objects. In addition, "nearby objects" often change or vary with weather or the season, therefore the model so laboriously crafted may not be representative of the actual situation, by the time it is running on the computer.

Intensely elevated but localized fields often can be detected by professional measuring instruments. These "hot spots" are often found near wiring in the shack, and metal objects such as antenna masts or equipment cabinets. But even with the best instrumentation, these measurements also may be misleading in the near field. One need not make precise measurements or model the exact antenna system, however, to develop some idea of the relative fields around an antenna. Computer modeling using close approximations of the geometry and power input of the antenna will generally suffice. Those who are familiar with *MININEC* can estimate their power densities by computer modeling, and those who have access to professional power-density meters can make useful measurements.

While our primary concern is ordinarily the intensity of the signal radiated by an antenna, we also should remember that there are other potential energy sources to be considered. You also can be exposed to excessive RF fields directly from a power amplifier if it is operated without proper shielding. Transmission lines also may radiate a significant amount of energy under some conditions. Poor microwave waveguide joints or improperly assembled connectors are another source of incidental exposure.

28.3.7 Further RF Exposure Suggestions

Potential exposure situations should be taken seriously. Based on the FCC/EPA measurements and other data, the "RF awareness" guidelines of Table 28.6 were developed by the ARRL RF Safety Committee. A longer version of these guidelines, along with a complete list of references, appeared in a *QST* article by Ivan Shulman, MD, WC2S ("Is Amateur Radio Hazardous to Our Health?" *QST*, Oct 1989, pp 31-34).

In addition, the ARRL has published a book, *RF Exposure and You* that helps hams comply with the FCC's RF-exposure regulations. The ARRL also maintains an RF-exposure news page on its website. See **www.arrl.org/rf-exposure**. This site contains reprints of selected *QST* articles on RF exposure and links to the FCC and other useful sites.

SUMMARY

The ideas presented in this chapter are intended to reinforce the concept that ham radio, like many other activities in modern life, does have certain risks. But by understanding the hazards and how to deal effectively with them, the risk can be minimized. Common-sense measures can go a long way to help us prevent accidents. Traditionally, amateurs are inventors, and experimenting is a major part of our nature. But reckless chance-taking is never wise, especially when our health and well-being is involved. A healthy attitude toward doing things the right way will help us meet our goals and expectations.

Table 28.6
RF Awareness Guidelines

These guidelines were developed by the ARRL RF Safety Committee, based on the FCC/EPA measurements of Table 28.4 and other data.

- Although antennas on towers (well away from people) pose no exposure problem, make certain that the RF radiation is confined to the antennas' radiating elements themselves. Provide a single, good station ground (earth), and eliminate radiation from transmission lines. Use good coaxial cable or other feed line properly. Avoid serious imbalance in your antenna system and feed line. For high-powered installations, avoid end-fed antennas that come directly into the transmitter area near the operator.
- No person should ever be near any transmitting antenna while it is in use. This is especially true for mobile or ground-mounted vertical antennas. Avoid transmitting with more than 25 W in a VHF mobile installation unless it is possible to first measure the RF fields inside the vehicle. At the 1-kW level, both HF and VHF directional antennas should be at least 35 ft above inhabited areas. Avoid using indoor and attic-mounted antennas if at all possible. If open-wire feeders are used, ensure that it is not possible for people (or animals) to come into accidental contact with the feed line.
- Don't operate high-power amplifiers with the covers removed, especially at VHF/UHF.
- In the UHF/SHF region, never look into the open end of an activated length of waveguide or microwave feed-horn antenna or point it toward anyone. (If you do, you may be exposing your eyes to more than the maximum permissible exposure level of RF radiation.) Never point a high-gain, narrow-bandwidth antenna (a paraboloid, for instance) toward people. Use caution in aiming an EME (moonbounce) array toward the horizon; EME arrays may deliver an effective radiated power of 250,000 W or more.
- With hand-held transceivers, keep the antenna away from your head and use the lowest power possible to maintain communications. Use a separate microphone and hold the rig as far away from you as possible. This will reduce your exposure to the RF energy.
- Don't work on antennas that have RF power applied.
- Don't stand or sit close to a power supply or linear amplifier when the ac power is turned on. Stay at least 24 inches away from power transformers, electrical fans and other sources of high-level 60-Hz magnetic fields.

Escape with the TM-281A

On or off the road, Kenwood's TM-281A is a mobile radio you can always count on.

As tough as nails, this MIL-STD-compliant transceiver delivers powerful performance, excellent audio clarity, and a host of advanced features. It offers superb operating ease day or night thanks to the large backlit LCD and illuminated keys. So the next time you take off, take the TM-281A.

KENWOOD

Customer Support: (310) 639-4200
Fax: (310) 537-8235

Scan with your phone to download TM-281A brochure.

www.kenwood.com/usa

ISO9001 Registered
JVCKENWOOD Corporation

ADS#23219

APRS® / D-STAR®

TH-D74A 144/220/430 MHz Tribander

The TH-D74A for the ultimate in APRS and D-STAR performance. KENWOOD has already garnered an enviable reputation with the TH-D72A handheld APRS amateur radio transceiver. And now it has raised the bar even further with the TH-D74A, adding support for D-STAR, the digital voice & data protocol developed by the JARL, and enabling simultaneous APRS and D-STAR operation.

- ▼ APRS compliance using packet communication to exchange real-time GPS position information and messages
- ▼ Compliant with digital/voice mode D-STAR digital amateur radio networks
- ▼ Built-in high performance GPS unit with Auto Clock Setting
- ▼ Wide-band and multi-mode reception
- ▼ 1.74" (240 x 180 pixel) Transflective color TFT display
- ▼ IF Filtering for improved SSB/CW/AM reception
- ▼ High performance DSP-based audio processing & voice recording
- ▼ Compliant with Bluetooth, microSD & Micro-USB standards
- ▼ External Decode function (PC Decode 12kHz IF Output, BW:15 kHz)
- ▼ Free software for Memory and Frequency Control Program
- ▼ Data Import / Export (Digital Repeater List, Call sign, Memory Channel)
- ▼ Four TX Power selections (5/2/0.5/0.05 W)
- ▼ Dust and Water resistant IP54/55 standards

APRS (The Automatic Packet Reporting System) is a registered American trademark of WB4APR (Mr. Bob Bruninga). D-Star is a digital radio protocol developed by JARL (Japan Amateur Radio League).

KENWOOD

Customer Support/Distribution Customer Support:
(310) 639-4200 Fax: (310) 537-8235

www.kenwood.com/usa

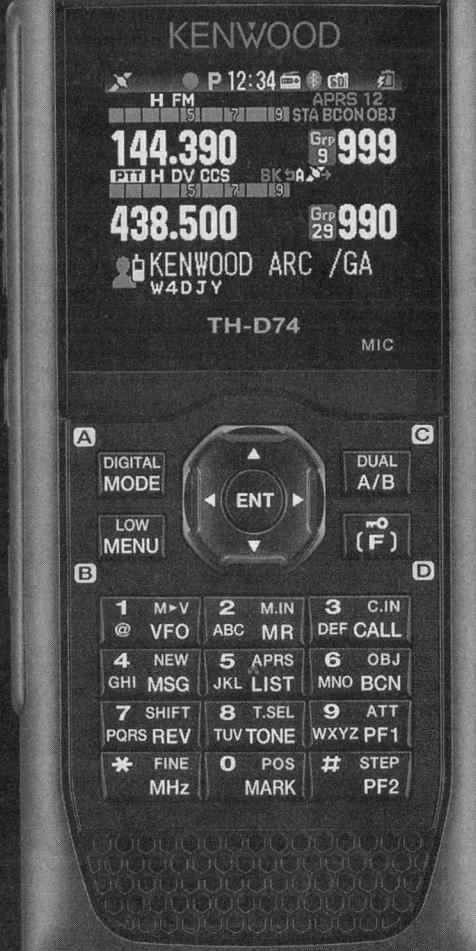

ADS#23319

KENWOOD

3rd IMDR **110** dB*
RMDR **122** dB*
BDR **150** dB*

Performance Exceeding Expectations.

The most happy and sublime encounters happen in the worst circumstances and under the harshest conditions.

There are enthusiasts who know this all too well because of their love of HF radio.

Results born of certainty and not circumstance. Delivered through impeccable performance. This is our offering to you.

"The Kenwood TS-890S has the highest RMDR of any radio I have ever measured."
— *Rob Sherwood - NC0B - December 2018*

HF/50MHz TRANSCEIVER
TS-890S
NEW

Top-class receiving performance
3 kinds of dynamic range make for top-class performance.

- Third order intermodulation Dynamic Range (3rd IMDR) 110dB*
- Reciprocal Mixing Dynamic Range (RMDR) 122dB*
- Blocking Dynamic Range (BDR) 150dB*

*Values are measured examples. (2kHz spacing:14.1 MHz, CW, BW 500 Hz, Pre Amp OFF)

- Full Down Conversion RX
- High Carrier to Noise Ratio 1st LO
- H-mode mixer

4 kinds of built-in roofing filters
500Hz / 2.7kHz / 6kHz / 15kHz (270Hz Option)

7 inch Color TFT Display
- Roofing frequency sampling band scope
- Band scope auto-scroll mode
- Multi-information display including filter scope

Clean and tough 100W output
Built-in high-speed automatic antenna tuner
32-bit floating-point DSP for RX / TX and Bandscope

*: 2 kHz spacing measurement standard - Receiver frequency 14.2 MHz, MODE CW, BW 500 Hz, PRE AMP OFF

Customer Support: (310) 639-4200

www.kenwood.com/usa

ADS#23419

Advertisers Index

Advertising Department Staff

Janet Rocco, W1JLR, *Advertising Sales Manager*
Lisa Tardette, KB1MOI, *Account Executive*
Diane Szlachetka, KB1OKV, *Advertising Graphic Design*

800-243-7768

Direct Line: 860-594-0207 ▪ Fax: 860-594-4285 ▪ e-mail: ads@arrl.org ▪ Web: www.arrl.org/ads

Advanced Specialties
— www.advancedspecialties.net A-8

Ameritron
— www.ameritron.com A-4

ARRL
— www.arrl.org A-6

Command Productions
— www.LicenseTraining.com A-8

DX Engineering
— www.DXEngineering.com A-11

Haggerty Radio Company
— www.WA1FFL.com A-8

Ham Radio Outlet
— www.hamradio.co A-7

Icom America Inc.
— www.icomamerica.com A-10

Kenwood USA Corporation
— www.kenwoodusa.com .... A-i, A-ii, A-iii

MFJ Enterprises
— www.mfjenterprises.com A-2, A-3, A-5

Mosely Electronics
— www.mosley-electronics.com A-6

Palstar
— www.palstar.com A-9

Yaesu USA
— www.yaesu.com .... Cover 2, Cover 3

If your company provides products or services of interest to our readers,
please contact the ARRL Advertising Department today for information on building your business.

MFJ

Dealer/Catalog/Manuals
Visit: http://www.mfjenterprises.com
or call toll-free 800-647-1800

- 1 Year *No Matter What*™ warranty • 30 day money back guarantee (less s/h) on orders direct from MFJ

MFJ ENTERPRISES, INC.
300 Industrial Pk Rd, Starkville, MS 39759
PH: (662) 323-5869 **Tech:** (662) 323-0549
FAX: (662)323-6551 8-4:30 CST, Mon.-Fri. *Add shipping.*
Prices and specifications subject to change. (c) 2015 MFJ Enterprises, Inc.

VISA / DISCOVER / PayPal / f

MFJ-259C Analyzer, $299⁹⁵
World's best selling antenna analyzer covers 530 KHz to 230 MHz, LCD, SWR and impedance or SWR bargraph, analog meters, signal generator, freq counter.

MFJ-269C Analyzer, $399⁹⁵
Upgraded MFJ-269C has all features of MFJ-259C plus 415-470 MHz, 12-bit A/D converter, characteristic impedance 0-600 Ohms, coax calculator, parallel equivalent R/X.

MFJ-226 VNA Analyzer, $359⁹⁵
1-230 MHz. Plots *SWR, Impedance, Resistance, Reactance, Phase Angle, Complex Return Loss, Smith Chart.* Open-Short-Load calibration. Memories download to PC via USB.

MFJ-949E Tuner $199⁹⁵
More hams use MFJ-949E tuners than all others in the world! Large 3" cross-needle SWR/Wattmeter, 8 position antenna switch, dummy load, Match any antenna 1.8-30 MHz.

MFJ-969 Tuner $244⁹⁵
World's only 6-160 Meters 300 Watt *AirCore*™ Roller Inductor antenna tuner gives you absolute minimum SWR. 3" cross-needle meter, true peak reading meter, dummy load, 8 pos. antenna switch.

MFJ-962D Tuner $339⁹⁵
Compact roller inductor antenna tuner handles popular Ameritron AL-811H/811 amps. *AirCore*™ inductor, 3" Cross-Needle meter, 6-position antenna switch, 800W SSB PEP output.

MFJ-989D Tuner $439⁹⁵
Legal-limit antenna tuner has *Air-Core*™ inductor, 500pF air variable capacitors, fast-tune crank, high voltage balun, 3" meter, dummy load, ant. switch.

MFJ-929 AutoTuner $229⁹⁵
Compact 200 Watt *IntelliTuner*™ tunes any unbalanced antenna *ultra-fast!* 20,000 Virtual Memories, Antenna Switch, Efficient L-network, Matches 6-1600 Ohms from 1.8-30 MHz.

MFJ-993B AutoTuner $269⁹⁵
Select 300 Watts (6-1600 Ohms) or 150 Watts (6-3200 Ohms) with the *world's only* dual power automatic tuner. 1.8-30 MHz, 4:1 current balun, LED lighted cross meter, backlit LCD, more!

MFJ-998 AutoTuner $699⁹⁵
Full 1500 Watts SSB/CW. Digital and analog SWR/Wattmeter, 12-1600 Ohms from 1.8-30 MHz, built-in antenna switch, auto amp bypass.

MFJ-1778 G5RV $59⁹⁵
Efficient, *all band* G5RV antenna is only 102' long, has 32.5' ladder line matching section ending in an SO-239 for feedline. Operate 80-10 Meters with tuner. 1500 Watts.

MFJ-16XX HF Sticks $17⁹⁵
Rugged, sleek 6-40M mobile *HamTenna*™ antennas, **$17.95** each band. 250 Watts, 7' extended, collapse to about 4 feet for storage. Quickly screws into any 3/8-24 female mount for quick band changing. **60-75M, $27.95.**

MFJ-1836H Cobweb $279⁹⁵
For restricted spaces: 6-bands: 20/17/15/12/10/6 Meters. Sky gray fiberglass spreaders and nearly invisible wire elements (flat 9x9x½ sq.ft., 8 lbs) blends in and stands tough against nasty weather.

MFJ-1786 Hi-Q Loop $474⁹⁵
10-30 MHz Super Hi-Q loop, remote control. 36" dia. all welded construction, butterfly tuning capacitor. ABS plastic housing. **MFJ-1788, $529.95.** 7-22 MHz.

MFJ-260C Dry Load $44⁹⁵
300W VHF/HF Dry Dummy Load handles full load for 30 seconds. Derating curve to 5 minutes. SWR below 1.1:1 to 30 MHz. 1.5:1 from 30-650 MHz. **MFJ-264, $79.95.** 1.5kW load.

MFJ-1702C Ant Switch $44⁹⁵
2-position antenna switch has center ground, auto grounding of unused position, 2.5 kW PEP and works to over 500 MHz. Lightning surge protection. SO-239 Connectors. **MFJ-1704, $99.95.** 4 positions.

MFJ-915 RFI Isolator $34⁹⁵
Prevents unwanted RF from traveling on your coax shield into your expensive transceiver. Prevents stray RF that cause painful RF "bites" and erratic operation. Heavy duty weather protected PVC is 2Wx5H inches. 1.5 kW. 1.8-30 MHz.

MFJ-918 4:1 Balun $34⁹⁵
High-permeability ferrite beads on high-quality RG-303 *Teflon*(R) coax. True 1:1 current balun/center insulator. 2" diameter by 6" long. 14 gauge stranded copper wire. Handles 1.5 kW 1.8-30 MHz.

MFJ-270 Surge Protect $21⁹⁵
Safeguard your expensive equipment. Shunts to 5000 Amps of peak impulse current harmlessly to ground. SWR less than 1.1:1, less than 0.1 dB loss. Use to 1000 MHz, 400W PEP.

MFJ-392B Headphones $34⁹⁵
Perfect for Ham Radio and shortwave listening -- SSB, FM, AM, data and CW. Super lightweight (8 oz.) padded headband and ear cushioned design. Each earphone has own volume control. 3.5mm/1/4" plugs, 9' cord.

MFJ-4230MV 30A PS $94⁹⁵
World's most compact 30A switching power supply. V/A meter. 4-16 Volts, adjustable. 5Wx2½H x6D inches, 3 pounds! Selectable input voltage 120/240 VAC.

MFJ-4035MV 30A PS $159⁹⁵
19.2 lb. transformer delivers 35A maximum, 30A continuous. 1-14 VDC out, 110 VAC in. Highly regulated, 1% load regulation. 1 mV Ripple. 5-way binding posts, quick connects.

MFJ-4245MV 45A PS $159⁹⁵
Switching power supply. 45A surge/40A continuous. 9-15 VDC out. 85-260 VAC in. Low ripple, highly regulated. 5-way posts, cig lighter, quick connects. 5 lbs., 7½Wx4¾Hx9D".

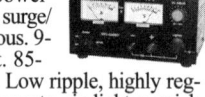

MFJ-4275MV 75A PS $274⁹⁵
Switching power supply. 75A max/70A cont. Great for ALS-500M solid state amp. Adjustable 4-16 VDC. Input 110/220 VAC. Battery charger. 10.5 lbs.

Antenna Window Feedthrough Panels
Bring your antenna cables into your hamshack without drilling holes through walls! Place in window sill, close window. *Real* western cedar 3/4" thick wood naturally resistant to rot, decay and insects, weather edge foam tape included. *Teflon*(R) SO-239s for HF/VHF/UHF antennas, *ceramic* feed-thrus for balanced line/random wire, ground post. Stainless steel in/out plates. **MFJ-4602, $74⁹⁵**

MFJ-868B Giant Meter $159⁹⁵
Largest HF+6M SWR/Wattmeter in the world has 6.5" diagonal scale. 20/200/2000W ranges.

MFJ-1026 Noise Cancel $219⁹⁵
Wipe out interference! 60 dB null. SSB/CW/AM/FM. BCB to lower VHF. RF sense T/R switch.

MFJ-4416C BattBoost $189⁹⁵
Keep mobile rig operational. Boosts low battery voltage. Up to 25 Amps. 7¾Wx4Hx2⅛".

MFJ-148BRC Clock $64⁹⁵
Two atomic 24/12 hour clocks -- *single time base*. UTC time, 10-minute ID timer. 1.5 inch LCD.

MFJ-281 Speaker $13⁹⁵
Get speech fidelity you never knew existed! 3" speaker, 8W, 8 Ohms impedance, 6' cord, 3.5 mm mono.

MFJ-461 CodeReader $99⁹⁵
Decodes and displays Morse code on two-line high-contrast LCD. Just hold close to receiver.

MFJ-557 CodeOsc/Key $44⁹⁵
Practice sending Morse code. Telegraph key, code oscillator, speaker on heavy non-skid steel base. Volume/tone controls. Use 9V battery.

MFJ-564 IambicPaddles $99⁹⁵
Deluxe Iambic paddles. Tension/contact spacing adjustments, steel bearings, precision frame, non-skid feet. Chrome or Black.

MFJ-108B 24/12 Clock $24⁹⁵
Read both UTC and local time *simultaneously*. BIG 5/8 inch digits! Solid brushed aluminum frame. 4¼Wx2Hx1D".

MFJ-1724B Mobile $29⁹⁵
World's Best Selling 2Meter 440 MHz magnet mount antenna has 3.5" magnet, 19" stainless steel whip, handles 300 Watts, 15 feet coax.

MFJ-1728B Mobile $29⁹⁵
5/8 wave 2M mobile antenna gives maximum possible gain of any single element antenna. 1/4 Wave 6M. 300W, magnet mount, 12' coax, 53" whip.

MFJ-1729 Mobile $44⁹⁵
Ham radio's *most powerful* magnet mount dual band 2M/440 mobile. Get whopping GAIN. 300 Watts, 27.5" stainless steel whip, 12' coax.

www.mfjenterprises.com

MFJ Components for Homebrew Projects

Air Variable Capacitors

Figure	Part No. #	Price	Cap. pF	VRMS	Gap	Plates	Dimensions
A	282-2005	$23.85	16-208	1000	.032"	50	1.4Wx1Hx3D in.
A	282-8700	$14.95	10-26	1500	.080"	18	1.4Wx1Hx2.8D in.
B	282-2010	$17.25	2-10	640	.016"	2	1.4Wx1Hx1.7D in.
B	282-2012	$16.02	5-51	1000	.032"	13	1.4Wx1Hx1D in.
B	282-2150	$18.90	6-154	640	.016"	20	1.4Wx1Hx1.3D in.
C	282-2006	$18.51	12-313	640	.016"	40	1.4Wx1Hx1.3D in.
D*	282-5050-1	$19.62	5-67	1200	.045"	15	1.2Wx1.3Hx1.3D in.
D*	282-5160	$17.97	6-180	350	.010"	15	1.2Wx1.3Hx1.3D in.

* Items D are broadcast style variables and are used in MFJ Analyzers and Transceivers. A 8:1 Vernier drive is built into the capacitor.

High Voltage Air Variable Capacitors

Figure	Part No. #	Price	Cap. pF	VRMS	Gap	Plates	Dimensions
A	282-2007-1	$30.94	10-125	3.5 kV	.120"	27	2.5Wx3.6Hx6D"
A	282-2018-1	$35.68	10-250	1.5 kV	.045"	37	2.5Wx3.6Hx6D"
A	282-2008-1	$53.68	10-250	3 kV	.120"	53	2.5wx3.6hx10.8d"
B	282-2009-1	$61.64	75-500	2.5 kV	.075"	75	2.5wx2.6hx6D"
C*	282-2015	$53.52	40-300	3.5 kV	.120"	79	2.5wx2.6hx10.8d"
D*	282-2020	$70.56	40-493	1.5 kV	.045"	35	3.5Wx4.5Hx6D"
D*	282-2028	$100.08	50-996	1.5 kV	.045"	72	3.5Wx4.5Hx9.6D"
E*	282-2016	$69.95	12-67	1.5 kV	.045"	56	2.5Wx3.5hx6D"
E*	282-2017	$89.95	18-136	1.5 kV	.045"	112	2.5wx3.5hx10.8d"
D*	282-2026	$100.08	50-916	1.5 kV	.045"	72	insulated rotor sections

Item C is a differential capacitor, as used in the MFJ-986 antenna tuner. Items D are dual-gang capacitors, capacitance specified is total capacitance. Items E are butterfly tuning capacitors. Used in MFJ loop tuners, have no rotating contacts, super low losses.

Amplifier high-voltage Variable Caps

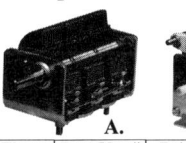

Figure	Part No. #	Price	Cap. pF	VRMS	Gap	Plates	Dimensions
A	282-2113	$26.19	20-823	800 V	.017"	23 x 3	1.8Wx1.8Hx3.3D"
B	282-2112-1	$36.52	20-250	2.5 kV	.075"	37	2.8Wx2.6Hx5D"
B	282-2572-1	$46.18	20-405	1.5 kV	.045"	37	2.8Wx2.6Hx4D"
B	282-2573-1	$57.34	25-800	1.1 kV	.030"	53	2.8Wx2.6Hx4.5D"
C	282-2570	$51.68	20-171	3.5 kV	.120"	37	2.8Wx2.6Hx7D"
D	282-3700	$39.95	15-176 7-23	2.5 kV	.075"	31	2.8Wx2.6Hx6D"

Used in Ameritron high power linear amplifiers. Items B have delrin insulated shaft. Item D has two capacitance sections.

Shaft coupler for rollers, caps, switches
725-3105-1, $0.95.
3/4 Diameter by 1 1/4" length, Nickel plated brass Shaft Coupler for 1/4 inch diameter shaft has two 10-32 hex socket set screws.

MFJ Knobs, Pointers and Ball Drives

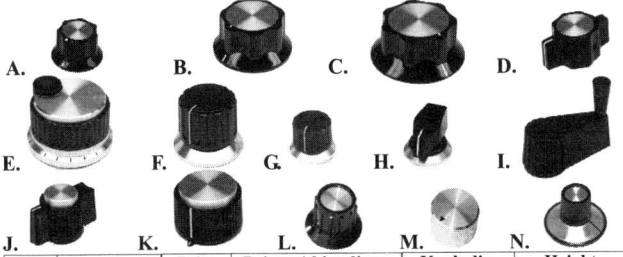

Fig.	Part No. #	Price	Pointer/skirt diam.	Knob dia.	Height
A	760-0035	$1.25	1 inch	11/16 inch	9/16 inches
B	760-0125	$2.80	1 1/2 inches	1 1/4 inches	3/4 inches
C	760-2281-1	$4.95	2 inches	1 5/8 inches	7/8 inches
D	760-0550	$3.00	1 1/2 inches	1 inch	3/4 inches
E	760-0275B	$9.95	2 1/8 inches	1 7/8 inches	1 3/8 inches
F	760-0277	$3.25	1 7/8 inches	1 1/16 inches	1 inch
G	760-0278	$1.95	7/8 inches	3/4 inches	11/16 inches
H	760-0276	$1.95	7/8 inches	13/16 inches	5/8 inches
I	760-2409	$4.95	1 3/4 inches	1 1/4 inches	1 1/4 inches
J	760-0176	$2.95	1 1/4 inches	11/16 inches	1/2 inches
K	760-0177A	$1.78	1 1/8 inches	1 1/4 inches	7/8 inches
L	760-0033	$1.25	13/16 inches	7/8 inches	5/8 inches
M	760-1233	$1.25	1 inch	1 inch	5/8 inches
N	760-1720	$1.95	1 1/4 inches	9/32 inches	3/4 inches

MFJ Knobs are made of the highest quality heat and impact-resistant phenolic resin. Shaft holes fit 1/4" round shaft. Knobs have metal inserts. Supplied with set screws.

Edge-wound AirRoller Inductor 404-1032, $140.00.
Silver Plated! Edge-Wound
Flat wire, edge-wound, *high power* air roller inductor. Silver plated Cu coil, silver plated contact discs/shaft. Heavy duty 1/4" thick fiberglass. 16 uH, 31 turns, 2 1/2" diameter, 1/4" round by 3" shaft length. 2 3/4Wx3 1/8Hx8D".

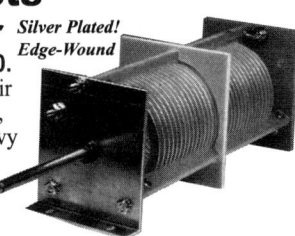

MFJ AirCore™ Roller Inductors

Exclusive *heavy duty* AirCore™ roller Inductors are cores that can't burn up! Ultra high-Q, lowest loss, highest efficiency, highest power handling of any inductor in ham radio. *Self-Resonance Killer*™ keeps po-tentially damaging self-resonances away from your operating position. Large, self-cleaning wiping contact gives excellent low-resistance operation without contact arcing or burning. Solid 1/4" brass shaft, self-align bearings for smooth rotation. 12 gauge tin-plated copper, silver plated wheel/shaft. Fiberglass frame.

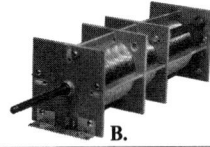

Figure	Part No. #	Price	L. uH	Turns	Coil Dia.	shaft size	Dimensions
A	404-1052	$59.00	33	43	2"	3 1/2"	3Wx3Hx7 1/2D"
B	404-1056	$62.65	44	57	2"	3"	3Wx3Hx9 1/4D"
C*	404-1060	$53.60	22	31	2"	2 1/2"	3Wx4 1/2Hx7 1/2D"

*C item has 1/4" round phenolic tuning shaft, has no "self-resonance-killer". A and B have 1/4" round brass tuning shaft.

MFJ Air-Wound Coils

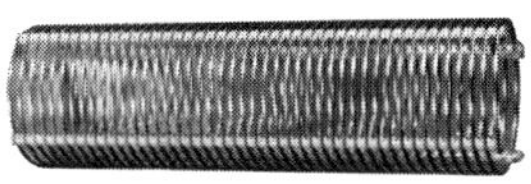

MFJ *air-wound* coils constructed with a solid rigid round acrylic rod and embedded tin-plated solid copper wires. Super strong and superbly crafted. MFJ winds them so they stay wound. Select MFJ *air-wound* coils for mobile and portable antennas, antenna tuners, amplifiers and other radio projects.

Part No.	Price	Inductance	Coil length	Coil Diameter	Turns per Inch	Wire size (AWG)
404-0811	$22.95	70 uH	9 1/2 in.	1 3/4 in.	10	14
404-0600	$37.95	44 uH	12 in.	2 in.	6	10
404-0669	**$37.95**	**79 uH**	**12 in.**	**2 in.**	**8**	**12**
404-0700	$37.95	77 uH	12 in.	2 in.	8	10
404-0008	**$22.95**	**159 uH**	**10 in.**	**2 1/2 in.**	**10**	**16**
404-0024	$37.95	35 uH	11 in.	3 in.	4	10
404-0009	**$22.95**	**230 uH**	**10.5 in.**	**3 in.**	**10**	**16**
404-2289	$39.95	45 uH	12 in.	2 in.	7	14
755-4001-1	$3.00	 Designed to clip on air-wound coil for wire size up to AWG 12. 1/4" wide silver plated contact has set screw to secure. Contact socket for banana plug.				

MFJ high power RF rotary switches

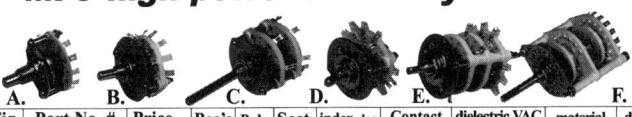

Fig.	Part No. #	Price	Pos's	Pole	Sect.	index deg	Contact	dielectric VAC	material	dia.
A	500-2026	$24.48	12	1	1	30	3 Amps	1500	glass epoxy	1.44"
B	500-2038	$62.68	6	1	1	30	9 Amps	1500	ceramic	1.88"
C	500-2027	$74.32	6	2	2	60	9 Amps	1500	ceramic	1.88"
D*	500-2811	$57.60	6	2	1	30	9 Amps	1500	ceramic	1.88"
E*	500-2135	$102.40	6	4	3	30	9 Amps	1500	ceramic	1.88"
F*	500-3557-1B	$195.58	6	4	2	20	17 Amps	3000	ceramic	2.81"
B	500-2017	$77.95	6	2	1	30	9 Amps	2000	ceramic	1.88"

MFJ high-voltage switches have 3/8-32 bushing and 1/4 inch round shaft. *D, E, and F are switches that are specially designed for amplifier band switching.

Vernier Reduction Ball Drive
729-0142-1, $11.92
6:1 Tuning Ratio. Used in Ameritron amplifiers and tuners. Dial plate mounting flange. Two pre-tap pointer mounting holes, mates with 1/4" shaft, has pre-tap set screw holes. 1/4" shaft, 3 1/4"Length.

Knob Pointers
726-0227R, $1.55
Red, 1 1/4" Length, matches two inch tuning knobs.

726-0230R, $1.25
Red 1-inch length, matches 1 1/2" tuning knob. **Both** pointers are made to fit 729-0142, 6:1 reduction drive.

Turn Counter Set
MFJ-TC11, $14.95
Includes counter module, 2 gears and mounting bracket. Driving gear fits 1/4" round shaft. Counter ratio is 3:1. Reset button, 3-digits, counts up to 999 turns.

MFJ ENTERPRISES, INC. 300 Industrial Pk Rd, Starkville, MS 39759 **PH:** (662) 323-5869 **Tech Help:** (662) 323-0549
FAX:(662)323-6551 8-4:30 CST, Mon.-Fri. **Add** shipping. *Prices and specifications subject to change.* (c) 2014 MFJ Enterprises, Inc.

Power Supply Transformers

These transformers are for building power supplies and amplifiers. 406-3800 is designed for linear power supplies, that is capable of delivering current up to 30 Amps at 13.6 VDC. 406-1109-2C is designed for a single 3-500Z tube, 1000 Watts HF Amplifier. Has buck/boost winding. Can be used as a replacement transformer for Heathkit SB-1000, AL-80A.

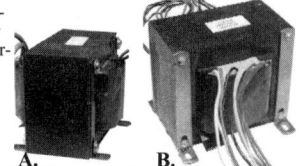

Fig.	Part No. #	Price	Pri. Voltage	SEC Voltg	Current	Dimensions	Weight
A	406-3800	$34.95	120V	18V	30A	4Wx4Lx3¾H"	11 lbs.
B	406-1109-2C	$180.00	90-140, 205-250 w/buck boost winding	1. 1047Vac 2. 22 Vac CT 3. 5.2Vac CT	.1 Adc 1.5 Adc 15 Aac	6Wx6Lx5¼H"	26 lbs.

Amplifier Power & Filament Transformers

Specially designed for our most popular HF amplifiers. Has unique buck-boost winding to adapt to low or high line voltage conditions.
Use of electrical silicone steel lamination makes these transformers highly efficient, resulting in low loss and producing less heat. Well constructed for low noise and coated with varnish. 110/220 VAC. Usable for 50 or 60 Hz.

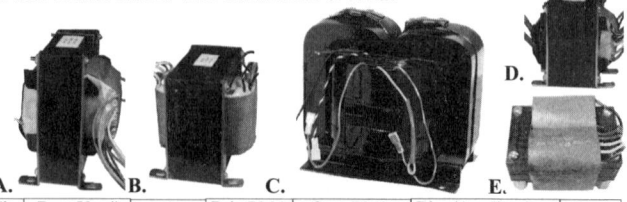

Fig.	Part No. #	Price	Pri. (Volt)	Sec. (Volt)	Dim./Applications	Weight
A	406-1532	$105.50	110/220 w/ buck-boost	1500VAC@.5A 12VAC@1A 6.5VAC@16A	5Wx4¼Hx6¼D 811A 4-tube amplifier	17 lbs.
B	406-1572	$142.60	110/220 w/ buck-boost	900V@.5A 12V CT@1A	6Wx5¼Hx5¼D 572B,4-tube amp	23 lbs.
B	406-1248-1	$247.00	110/220 w/ buck-boost	868VAC@.5A 22VCT@1.5A 12.8V@5A	6Wx7½Hx5¼D 3CX800A7 2-tube amp	33 lbs.
C	406-1418-1D Hypersil(R)	$403.00	110/220 V	2570 Vac@.8A	8Wx7Hx7D 3CX1500A7 3CX1200A7/Z7 2x3-500G amps	32 lbs.
D	406-1419-1J	$74.00	110/220 V	5.6V@30A 14V@2A	2½Wx3Hx3¾D 3-500Z filament	5 lbs.
D	406-1419-2J	$74.00	110/220 V	7.7V@21A 14V@2A	2½Wx3Hx3¾D 3CX1200A7 Filam	5 lbs.
D	406-1419-3J	$74.00	110/220 V	5.6V@15A 14V@2A	2½Wx3Hx3¾D 3CX1500A7 Filam	5 lbs.
E	406-1620	$49.00	120 V	50V@2A, 32V@1A	4Wx2¾Hx3D	4 lbs.

Non-Inductive Resistors ... Ideal for Dummy Loads

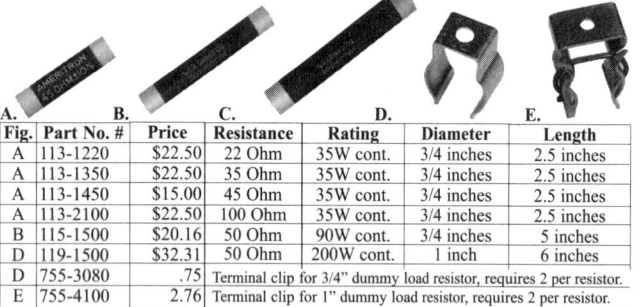

Fig.	Part No. #	Price	Resistance	Rating	Diameter	Length
A	113-1220	$22.50	22 Ohm	35W cont.	3/4 inches	2.5 inches
A	113-1350	$22.50	35 Ohm	35W cont.	3/4 inches	2.5 inches
A	113-1450	$15.00	45 Ohm	35W cont.	3/4 inches	2.5 inches
A	113-2100	$22.50	100 Ohm	35W cont.	3/4 inches	2.5 inches
B	115-1500	$20.16	50 Ohm	90W cont.	3/4 inches	5 inches
B	119-1500	$32.31	50 Ohm	200W cont.	1 inch	6 inches
D	755-3080	.75	Terminal clip for 3/4" dummy load resistor, requires 2 per resistor.			
E	755-4100	2.76	Terminal clip for 1" dummy load resistor, requires 2 per resistor.			

Insulating Spacers

These spacers are used to properly isolate your dummy load resistor from the chassis. Withstands high power/frequencies.

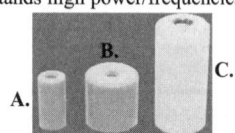

A. 719C-0500C, $0.50. Ceramic spacer, 1/4"OD, 1/2" long, 6-32 threaded both ends.
B. 719C-0500C-2, $2.50. Same as A except 1/2" OD.
C. 718D-1000, $1.71. Delrin spacer, 1/2" dia. by 1" long, 8-32 threaded holes on both ends.

Cooling Fans, Blowers

High output box fans and blowers are ideal for cooling amplifiers.

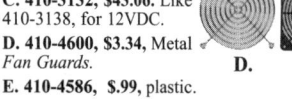

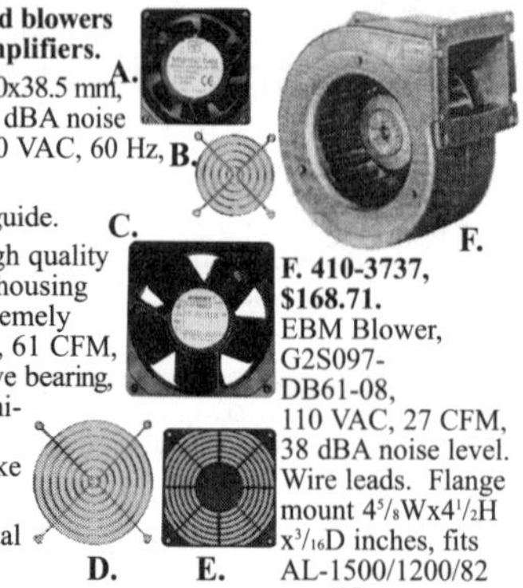

A. 410-3583, $18.85. 80x80x38.5 mm, 1800 RPM, 28 CFM, 30 dBA noise level, sleeve bearing, 120 VAC, 60 Hz, w/ 14" wire lead.
B. 410-4584, $.90. Fan guide.
C. 410-3138, $43.06, high quality box fan by EBM, metal housing with metal impeller, extremely quiet 120x120x38.5 mm, 61 CFM, 28 dBA noise level, sleeve bearing, 120 VAC, 60 Hz, wire terminals. Fits AL-80A/B.
C. 410-3132, $43.06. Like 410-3138, for 12VDC.
D. 410-4600, $3.34, Metal Fan Guards.
E. 410-4586, $.99, plastic.
F. 410-3737, $168.71. EBM Blower, G2S097-DB61-08, 110 VAC, 27 CFM, 38 dBA noise level. Wire leads. Flange mount 4⅝Wx4½H x³⁄₁₆D inches, fits AL-1500/1200/82 amplifiers.

Ameritron sells Eimac(R) Tubes

Ameritron sells *Eimac*(R) tubes for amateur radio, broadcast and industrial uses. *Call for a quote!*
A. 3CX800A7
B. 3CX1200D7
C. 3CX1500A7

811A, 572B, 3-500Zs ...

Don't just buy any untested tube that can damage your amp. Buy Ameritron *fully tested and warranteed* tubes. *Match* pairs are also available.
A. 380-0811A, $24.95, 811A tube.
B. 380-0572B, $79.95, 572B tube
C. 380-0500GT, $219.95, Taylor 3-500ZG tube

Tube Sockets

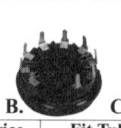

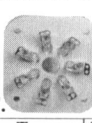

Fig.	Part No. #	Price	Fit Tube Type	#pin	Manufacturer PN/Description
A	50-0080-5	$32.20	3-500Z, 3CX1200A7	5	custom made glass epoxy socket
B	625-8199	$2.49	6LQ6 or equivalent	9	PCB mount pins
C	625-8731-1	$35.00	3CX1500A7/8877	7	Ceramic
D	625-8800	$29.95	3CX800A7	11	EF Johnson 124-0311-100
E	625-8811	$3.20	811A, 572B or equiv.	4	4-pin ceramic

Tube Plate Caps & Heatsinks

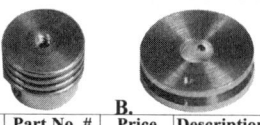

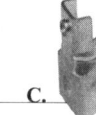

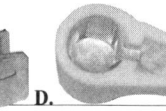

Fig.	Part No. #	Price	Description
A	750-1800	$5.95	Plate cap for 3-500Ztubes. Finned aluminum heat sink with set screw. ¾" dia. by ⁹⁄₁₆" thick.
B	750-0323	$8.98	Plate cap for 3-500Z tubes. Finned aluminum heat sink with set screw. 1¼" dia. by ⁵⁄₁₆" thick.
C	755-3626	$8.28	Plate clip for 3CX1500A7/8877 tube.
D	755-6811	$2.50	Ceramic plate cap for 811A, 572B

Tube Glass Chimneys

A. 391-1500, $25.62
Chimney for 3CX1500A7/8877 tube
B. 391-3500, $35.47
Chimney for 3CX1200A7 and 3-500Z tubes.

Amplifier Plates and Filament Chokes

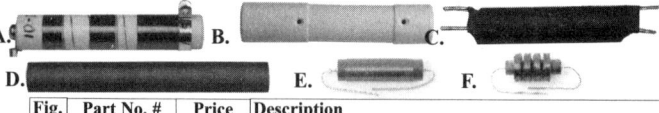

Fig.	Part No. #	Price	Description
A	10-15197	$24.95	Complete plate choke covers 1.8-30 MHz, includes WARC bands, 225 uH, handles 1.5A, 4 kV. Wound on 1"dia. x 5⅝" long glazed ceramic form. Used in Ameritron amps.
B	719F-7380C	$7.95	Glazed ceramic plate choke form. 1" dia. by 5" long. Both ends tap for 1/4"-20 screw.
C	10-15115-1	$19.95	Complete broadband filament choke. Use for 3-500Z, 3CX800A7, 3CX1200A7 and 3CX1500A7 tubes. Handles 30A, covers 1.8-30 MHz. 12 gauge enamel wire, bifilar wound on .5" dia. by 4" long ferrite rod.
D	412-0109	$9.00	Filament choke ferrite rod. 5" dia. by 4" long. Used in 10-15115-1.
E	401-4090-1	$9.60	RF Choke, 90 uH, 1A, ferrite core, 3/8Dx1½L"
F	401-6250-1	$11.95	RF Choke, 2.5 mH, 300 mA, phenolic core, 1/2Dx1L"

Feedthru Insulators

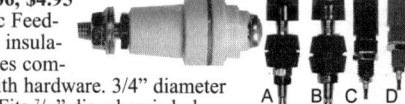

606-1006, $4.95
Ceramic Feed-through insulator comes complete with hardware. 3/4" diameter x1¼". Fits ⁷⁄₁₆" dia. chassis hole.

HT Adapter Cables

Release the strain on your HT antenna connector with these adapter cables. SMA or BNC. Flexible, mini coax, 3 feet.
A. MFJ-5612S, $16.95. SMA Male to SO-239 adapter cable.
B. MFJ-5612SF, $16.95. Female SMA to SO-239
C. MFJ-5612B, $16.95. BNC Male to SO-239 adapter.

A. 606-0014, $2.95. 5-way binding post, black, 30 Amp, insulated.
B. 606-0013, $2.95. 5-way binding post, red, 30A insulated
C. 606-0004, $1.95. 5-way binding post, black, 15 Amp.
D. 606-0003, $1.95. 5-way binding post, red, 15Amp.

AMERITRON(R)

116 Willow Road, Starkville, MS 39759 **TECH** (662) 323-8211 • **FAX** (662) 323-6551
8 a.m. - 4:30 p.m. CST Monday - Friday *Prices and specifications subject to change without notice.*© 2019 Ameritron.

Power Supply Electrolytic Caps

High capacitance, computer grade aluminum can electrolytic capacitors. Long life, low ESR and can handle high ripple currents. Themal-Pak extended cathode foil construction assures cool operation. Great choice for high-capacitor amplfiier, power supply and energy storage application. **10-32 screw terminals**.

Part No. #	Price	Value (uF)	WVDC	Ripple (I)	Size (DxL) inches
270-6270-7	$13.53	270 uF	450V	1.5A	1³/₈x2¹/₈
270-6380-7	$21.60	470 uF	450V	2.4A	1³/₈x3¹/₈
270-8270-2	$33.50	27000 uF	75V	9.0A	2x4⁵/₈

Can-type electrolytic capacitors ideal for amplifiers and power supply applications. **Snap-in PCB terminals**.

Part No. #	Price	Cap uF	WVDC	D x L (in.)
270-6220-7B	$5.44	220	400 V	1³/₁₆x1⁵/₈
270-7100-5A	$9.95	1000	250 V	1³/₈x2

RF Ceramic Doorknob Capacitors

P/N: 290-0500-7, $22.25.
P/N: 290-0170-7, $22.95.
P/N 290-0500-7 is 500 pF, 20%, 7.5 kV. P/N: 290-0170-7 is 170 pF, 20%, 7.5 kV. Both are HT50, RF Ceramic Doorknob Capacitors manufactured by High Energy. These RF transmitting capacitor are ideal for use in RF amplifiers. Threaded 6-32 ends for easy connection. ³/₄" diameter x .625" long.

High-Voltage Vacuum Relays

These vacuum relays are ideal for amplifier QSK switches. Contacts are capable of carrying 10 Amps and break down voltage is 5 kV.

A. 408-8100, $19.95. Kilovac S05FJA238, DPST-NO, contact form, 2A, 5kV rating between contacts, current is 10A DC or 5A RF, 12 VDC coil voltage and 500 Ohm coil resistance.
B. 408-8500, $14.95. Wabash 1017-20-1, DPST, one pole normally open, one pole normally closed. 12 VDC coil voltage.

Power Relays

Special relays designed for amplifier TR switching, in-rush current protection and other high current applications.

Fig.	Part No. #	Price	Coil Volts	Contacts/Rating	Description
A	408-6140	$20.34	12 VDC	3PDT -- 10A	PCB terminals, 80B/600/500 T/R
A	408-6148	$15.30	12 VAC	5PDT -- 10A	Solder lugs, In-Rush, 80B/600
A	408-6240	$18.24	240 VDC	SPST -- 10A	PCB terminals, amplifier in-rush
A	408-6145	$15.54	120 VDC	SPDT -- 10A	PCB terminals, amplifier in-rush
A	408-6077	$15.99	120 VAC	SPDT -- 10A	Solder lugs, stub mount, general purposes P&B KA5AG
B	408-1255	$19.95	12 VDC	DPDT -- 10 A	P&B KUP-11D55-12
B	408-4700	$17.64	120 VAC	SPST -- 15A	Chassis mount, QC terminals, in-rush
C	408-7110	$15.75	12 VDC	DPDT -- 20A	QC Terminals, dust cover, flange mount, Sigma 45R2C112-12 VDC
C	408-6230	$12.95	24 VDC	3 PDT -- 10A	Midtex relays 157-33C200, silver contacts, .187" quick connect terminals

Slug Core Tuning Tool

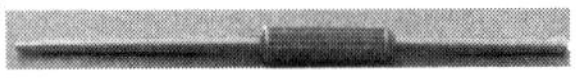

965-6204, $3.00. Plastic tuning stick for adjusting slug cores. Has .1 inch hex end, 7¹/₄" long. Fits all Ameritron tube amplifier input coils.

Precision Mechanical Turns Counter

MFJ-TC12, $69.95. This Precision designed mechanical deluxe turns counter is for use with roller inductors, vacuum capacitors, air variable capacitors, etc.
Precision 5-digit counter is enclosed in a dust-free plastic casing. Counts to 9999.9 turns. Counter is coupled to a 1/4" shaft at right angles with bevel gears.
1/8 inch thick aluminum mounting plate is coated with texture powder paint.
Has #4 counter sink mounting holes. Mount in 1x3" cutout hole. Unit is 2¹/₄Wx3¹/₂H in. Assembly includes 1/4 inch shaft coupler and a 1³/₄" fast-turned crank knob.

Pre-wound 200 Watts and 1.5kW Baluns

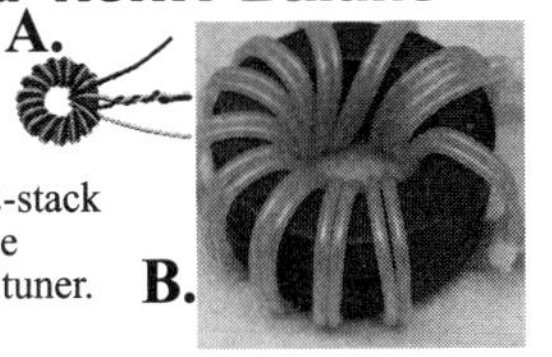

A. 10-10002B, $9.95. Bifiliar wound balun, 1" diameter, ferrite toroid core, 200 Watts, 1.8-30 MHz. Used in 200/300 Watts antenna tuners.
B. 10-10989D, $29.95. Bifiliar wound balun, 2-stack 2¹/₂" ferrite toroid cores wound with high-voltage wire. 1.5 kW, 1.8-30 MHz. Used in MFJ-989D tuner.

Precision Cross-Needle Meters

Unique, two-meters-in-one Cross-Needle design makes these meters ideal for use in amps and SWR/Wattmeters. Rugged construction with removeable clear plastic cover. Plug-in 12 VDC meter lamp, front panel "zero" adjustment. *NEW!* **"L" models have super bright LED backlight!!!!** Raised window for recessed front panel mounting. Solder lug terminals for meter movement, lamp. Linear moving coil movement.

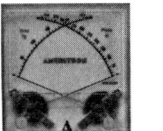

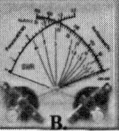

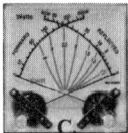

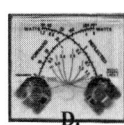

Figure	Part No. #	Price	Sens./Resist./Size	Scale Description
A	400-3580L LED Light	$26.80	1mA/120 Ohm 2.8Wx2.8Hx1.4D"	10-250 mA grid current & 0-750 mA plate current
B	400-3581L LED Light	$26.80	1mA/120 Ohm 2.8Wx2.8Hx1.4D"	0-2.0 KW Fwd power, 0-500W ref power, 0-35 ALC/ HV, SWR
C	400-3084A 400-3084L LED Light	$21.60 $26.80	200uA/750 Ohm 2.8Wx2.8Hx1.4D"	0-300W fwd power, 0-60W ref power, SWR. "L"model is LED backlit.
D	400-3083A 400-3083Y LED Light	$17.82 $19.10	200uA/750 Ohm 2.1Wx1.8x1.4D"	0-300 fwd power, 0-60 ref power, SWR curves "Y" model is LED backlit.

LED/Incandescent Bulb Replacements

Figure	Part #	Price	Description
A	355-2299	$1.80	Incandescent replacement bulb for small and large Cross-Needle Meters, (2.1"W or 2.8"W)
B	355-3200	$3.99	LED light replacement for large (2.8"W) Cross-Needle Meter
C	355-3201	$3.99	LED light replacement for small (2.1"W) XMeter

Miniature DC Panel Meters

Quality, compact and inexpensive panel meters. Clear, removeable cover, raised window for recessed mounting. Solder lug terminals, moving coil movement. 100 uA movement, 750 Ohm resistance. Size is 1.6Wx1.6Hx1D inches.

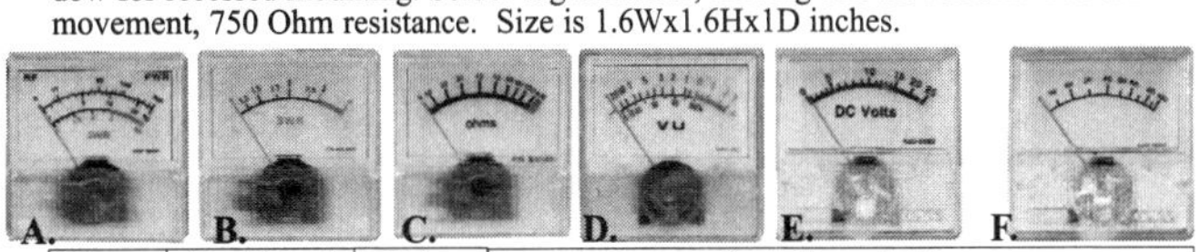

Figure	Part No. #	Price	Scale Description
A	400-0014A	$9.39	0-300 Pwr, 0-30 Pwr, SWR, red/black dual color scale, used in tuners and wattmeters
B	400-0035	$7.92	SWR, red/black scale used in analyzers
C	400-0047	$7.92	0-400 Ohm resistance, red/black scale used in analyzers
D	400-0027	$7.92	-20+3dB, 0-100% VU modulation scale, red/black dual color for line audio monitor
E	400-0090	$7.92	0-25 DC Volts, red/black scale for DC volt monitors
F	400-0026A	$7.92	0-100 general purpose scale

Precision DC Panel Meters

Rugged construction with removeable clear plastic cover. Built-in 12 VDC lamp, front panel "zero" adjustment. Raised window for recessed front panel mounting. Solder lug terminals for meter movement/lamp. Linear moving coil movement. 2.7Wx2.7Hx1.4D"

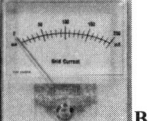

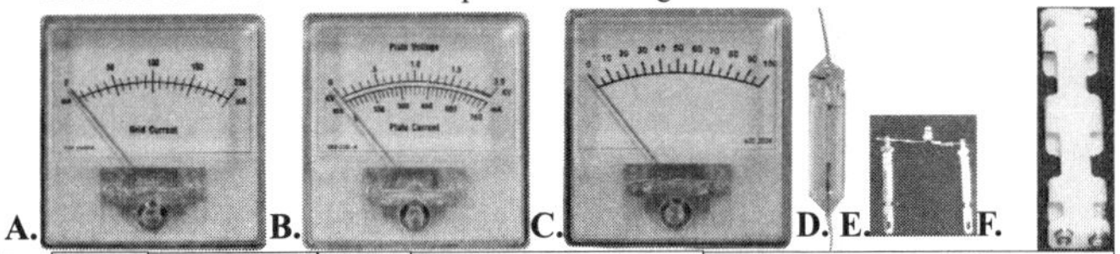

Figure	Part No. #	Price	Sensitivity/Resistance	Scale Description
A	400-2600AL	$21.92	1mA/120 Ohm	0-200 mA Grid Current Meter for AL-811/H amp. LED lamp.
B	400-2601AL	$21.92	1mA/120 Ohm	0-2.0 kV plate V, 0-700 mA plate I for AL-811/H. LED lamp.
C	400-2026	$16.92	1mA/120 Ohm	0-100 general purpose scale
D	355-0320	$1.80		Replacement bulb for 400-2XXX meters, above.
E	355-0320L	$3.99		Replacement LED for 2XXX meters. Set for 15 VDC
F	730-2342	$2.50		Replacement battery holder for MFJ-259/B. Holds four AA batteries. Requires two per analyzer. $2.50 each holder.

Ferrite and Iron Powder Toroidal Cores

Get RFI out of television, telephone and other electronic devices. Use for baluns, chokes, RF coils, transformers, filters, more.

Part No. #	Price	Size: ODxIDxTH inches	Description
420-6102	.33	.375x.187x.125	#61 Ferrite
420-6103	.72	.500x.281x.188	#61 Ferrite
420-6114	$1.08	1.00x.610x.320	#61 Ferrite
420-7510	$2.80	1.00x.610x.320	#75 Ferrite
420-6138	$10.23	2.40x1.40x.500	#61 Ferrite
421-02037	.40	.375x.205x.128	T-37-2 Iron Powder Mix 2
421-02050	.80	.5x.303x.90	T-50-2 Iron Powder Mix 2
421-02068	.98	.69x.370x.190	T-68-2 Iron Powder Mix 2
421-02094	$1.08	.942x.560x.312	T-94-2 Iron Powder Mix 2
421-02106	$1.36	1.00x.57x.437	T-106-2 Iron Powder Mix 2
421-02157	$3.32	1.57x.950x.570	T-157-2 Iron Powder Mix 2
421-02200	$6.96	2x1.25x.530	T-200-2 Iron Powder Mix 2
420-7800	$1.86	1.00x.50x.410	Iron Powder Mix 2

MFJ ENTERPRISES, INC. 300 Industrial Pk Rd, Starkville, MS 39759 **PH:** (662) 323-5869 **Tech Help:** (662) 323-0549 **FAX:**(662)323-6551 8-4:30 CST, Mon.-Fri. *Add shipping.* Prices and specifications subject to change. (c) 2014 MFJ Enterprises, Inc.

80 Years of Antenna Know-How

The ARRL Antenna Book for Radio Communications is a single resource covering antenna theory, design and construction, and practical treatments and projects. This book contains everything you need to understand how radio signals propagate, how antennas work, and how to construct your own antenna system. Use **The Antenna Book** to build hundreds of antenna designs: long-wires, verticals, loops, beams, and more.

Captured in this 24th edition of **The Antenna Book** is persistent pioneering development by radio amateurs, for radio amateurs. You'll find new and time-tested antenna projects for radio communications across nearly any frequency, mode, and circumstance you can think of.

New and Updated Content

- New coverage of small transmitting loops
- New and expanded coverage of microwave antennas
- Many new MF, HF, and 6 meter antenna design articles
- Instructions to acquire HFTA terrain profiles online
- An overview of VHF/UHF rover antenna systems
- New chapter on VHF/UHF Antenna systems
- Rotator ratings, installation, and maintenance
- Updated transmitting choke design and selection
- Updated ground system analysis and detailed set of ground conductivity maps
- Updated propagation and solar activity information, and new sunspot data definitions
- New material on MF band propagation
- Log-periodic BOLPA antenna design
- Updated coverage of antenna modeling software
- K1EA transmission-line method for switching stacked antennas
- Powerboat antenna system grounding
- Updated treatment of wire antenna construction materials
- Expanded material on grounding and bonding
- Updated antenna analyzer techniques
- Antenna tuner troubleshooting
- Updated content for low-band receive antennas

The ARRL Antenna Book for Radio Communications
Softcover Edition
Only $49.95

ARRL The national association for AMATEUR RADIO®
www.arrl.org/shop

HB 2020

MOSLEY ANTENNAS

Mosley

AIRCRAFT GRADE ALUMINUM ELEMENTS & BOOMS and STAINLESS STEEL HARDWARE

STRONG!
Snow, ice or rain are no match for Mosley Quality!

...built to last!

..."a better Antenna!"

Call 800-325-4016
REQUEST A CATALOG
www.mosley-electronics.com
or
www.mosleyelectronics.com

A-6   Advertising

Grounding and Bonding
for the Radio Amateur

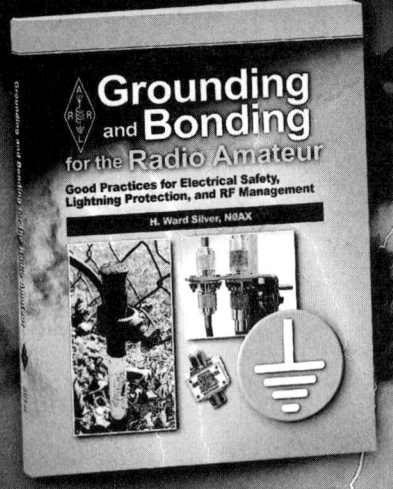

Good Practices for Electrical Safety, Lightning Protection, and RF Management

H. Ward Silver, NØAX

Proper Station Grounding is Important!

Build Your Ham Radio Station with Effective Grounding and Bonding Techniques:

- **AC safety:** protects against shock hazards from ac-powered equipment by providing a safe path for current when a fault in wiring or insulation occurs.

- **Lightning protection:** keeps all equipment at the same voltage during transients from lighting and dissipate the lightning's charge in the Earth, routing it away from equipment.

- **RF management:** prevents unwanted RF currents and voltages from disrupting the normal functions of equipment.

ARRL Item No. 0659
ARRL Member Price!
Only **$22.95** (retail $25.95)

ARRL The national association for AMATEUR RADIO®
www.arrl.org/shop

HB 2020

Ham Radio Outlet

WWW.HAMRADIO.COM

NOBODY BEATS AN HRO DEAL!

FTDX5000MP Limited | *200W HF + 6M Xcvr*
- Internal Power Supply • Two Totally Independent Receivers • Super Sharp "Roofing" Filters • High Performance Yaesu Custom-designed 32-bit Floating Point DSP • True Analog Meter Precision

FTDX3000 | *100W HF + 6M Transceiver*
- 100 Watt HF/6 Meters • Large and wide color LCD display • High Speed Spectrum Scope built-in • 32 bit high speed DSP /Down Conversion 1st IF

FT-991A | *HF/VHF/UHF All Mode Transceiver*
Real-time Spectrum Scope with Automatic Scope Control • Multi-color waterfall display • State of the art 32-bit Digital Signal Processing System • 3kHz Roofing Filter for enhanced performance • 3.5 Inch Full Color TFT USB Capable • Internal Automatic Antenna Tuner • High Accuracy TCXO

FTDX101D | *HF + 6M Transceiver*
- Narrow Band SDR & Direct Sampling SDR • Crystal Roofing Filters Phenomenal Multi-Signal Receiving Characteristics • Unparalleled - 70dB Maximum Attenuation VC-Tune • 15 Separate (HAM 10 + GEN 5) Powerful Band Pass Filters • New Generation Scope Displays 3-Dimensional Spectrum Stream

FT-891 | *HF+50 MHz All Mode Mobile Transceiver*
Rugged Construction in an Ultra Compact Body • Stable 100 Watt Output with Efficient Dual Internal Fans • 32-Bit IF DSP Provides Effective and Optimized QRM Rejection • Large Dot Matrix LCD Display with Quick Spectrum Scope • USB Port Allows Connection to a PC with a Single Cable • CAT Control, PTT/RTTY Control

FREE YSK-857

FT-857D | *Ultra Compact HF/VHF/UHF*
- 100w HF/6M, 50W 2M, 20W UHF • DSP included • 32 color display • 200 mems • Detachable front panel (YSK-857 required)

FT-2980R | *Heavy-Duty 80W 2M FM Transceiver*
- Massive heatsink guarantees 80 watts of solid RF power • Loud 3 watts of audio output for noisy environments • Large 6 digit backlit LCD display for excellent visibility • 200 memory channels for serious users

FTM-100DR | *C4FM FDMA/FM 144/430 MHz Xcvr*
- Power Packed System Fusion Transceiver • High Audio Output Power • Rugged Powerful Transmitter • Integrated 66ch High Sensitivity GPS • 1200/9600 APRS Data Communications

FTM-400XD | *2M/440 Mobile*
- Color display-green, blue, orange, purple, gray • GPS/APRS • Packet 1200/9600 bd ready • Spectrum scope • Bluetooth • MicroSD slot • 500 memory per band

FT-70DR *C4FM/FM 144/430MHz Xcvr*
- System Fusion Compatible • Large Front Speaker delivers 700 mW of Loud Audio Output • Automatic Mode Select detects C4FM or Fm Analog and Switches Accordingly • Huge 1,105 Channel Memory Capacity • External DC Jack for DC Supply and Battery Charging

FT-2DR *C4FM/FM 144/430 MHz Xcvr*
- Analog/C4FM Dual Monitor (V+V/U+U/V+U) System Fusion compatible • 1200/9600 APRS Data Communications • Integrated 66ch High Sensitivity GPS • Wide Band Receiver • Snapshot Picture Taking Capability With Optional MH-85A11U

FT-65R | *144/430 MHz Transceiver*
Compact Commercial Grade Rugged Design • Large Front Speaker Delivers 1W of Powerful Clear Audio • 5 Watts of Reliable RF Power Within a compact Body • 3.5-Hour Rapid Charger Included • Large White LED Flashlight, Alarm and Quick Home Channel Access

FT-60R | *2M/440 5W HT*
- Wide receiver coverage • AM air band receive • 1000 memory channels w/alpha labels • Huge LCD display • Rugged die-cast, water resistant case • NOAA severe weather alert with alert scan

---

5 Ways to Shop!
- RETAIL LOCATIONS – Store hours 10:00AM - 5:30PM - Closed Sunday
- PHONE – Toll-free phone hours 9:30AM - 5:30PM
- ONLINE – WWW.HAMRADIO.COM
- FAX – All store locations
- MAIL – All store locations

YAESU *The radio*

ANAHEIM, CA (800) 854-6046	OAKLAND, CA (877) 892-1745	PORTLAND, OR (800) 765-4267	PHOENIX, AZ (800) 559-7388	MILWAUKEE, WI (800) 558-0411	WOODBRIDGE, VA (800) 444-4799	PLANO, TX (877) 455-8750
BURBANK, CA (877) 892-1748	SAN DIEGO, CA (877) 520-9303	DENVER, CO (800) 444-9476	ATLANTA, GA (800) 444-7927	NEW CASTLE, DE (800) 644-4476	SALEM, NH (800) 444-0047	ONLINE STORE WWW.HAMRADIO.COM

Contact HRO for promotion details. Toll-free including Hawaii, Alaska and Canada. All HRO 800-lines can assist you. If the first line you call is busy, you may call another. Prices, specifications and descriptions subject to change without notice.

ADVANCED SPECIALTIES INC.

New Jersey's Communications Store

• OPEK • COMET • MALDOL • MFJ •
• UNIDEN • ANLI • YAESU • WHISTLER •

YAESU *The radio*
Authorized Dealer

FT-2980R
80W 2M Mobile

Yaesu FTM-7250DR
Digital
Dual Band

Uniden Bearcat SDS100
Police Scanner

VX-6R
Tri Band
Submersible
HT

FT-857D
HF, 6M, 2M, 70 CM

Yaesu FT3DR
System
Fusion
Digital
Dual Band
Radio

Orders/Quotes: (201)-VHF-2067
Closed Sunday & Monday – 114 Essex Street ■ Lodi, NJ 07644

Big Online Catalog at: **www.advancedspecialties.net**

AMATEUR RADIO – SCANNERS – BOOKS – ANTENNAS – MOUNTS
FILTERS – ACCESSORIES AND MORE!

You have your Ham License.
Now move up to the *highest class* FCC Commercial License!

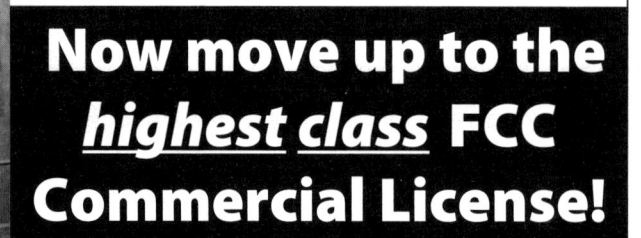

Get your "FCC Radiotelephone License" with our proven Home-Study Course!

- No costly school or classes to attend.
- Learn at home. Low cost!
- No previous experience needed!
- GUARANTEED PASS! You get your FCC License or money refunded!

The ULTIMATE LICENSE

Your "ticket" to 1,000's of high paying jobs in Radio, TV, Communications, Avionics, Radar, Maritime and more... even start your own business!

visit: **www.LicenseTraining.com**
or call for FREE Information Kit: **(800) 932-4268**

COMMAND FCC LICENSE TRAINING
Industrial Center, 480 Gate Five Rd., POB 3000, Sausalito, CA 94966-3000

Our 40th Year

ARRL E-Store
For more technical publications visit...
www.arrl.org/shop
Shop Now

AD9951-Based Direct-Digital VFO

Driver Amp Kits For Tube Rigs Now Available.

Complete Kits for Sale On-Line

See www.WA1FFL.com for Ordering and Technical Information.

- High SFDR. 0.5-30 MHz Coverage
- CAL, RIT, Transmit Offset
- Flash EEPROM Memory Storage
- Surface-Mount Components Pre-Soldered
- Display and Shaft Encoder Included.

New! Rotary-Switched Overtone Software for Tube Rigs

HAGERTY Radio Company
www.WA1FFL.com

PALSTAR LA-1K
1000W HF AMPLIFIER

Only Palstar incorporates an all-band diplexer in the Low Pass Filter circuit preventing 3rd Harmonic energy from reflecting back in to the LDMOS devices. This allows cooler operation with less distortion

SSB Power:	Power levels up to 1000W
CW Mode:	1000 Watts CW ICAS
FM/RTTY:	500 watts
AM:	275 watts
Frequency Range:	1.8 to 54 MHz - ALL MARS
LOCKOUT:	26 - 28 mHz
Display:	Color TFT touch screen
Output:	3 x RF SO-239 or Type N
ALC:	Exciter power control
Gain:	13dB + or -1dB (nominal)
RF Sensing:	Auto Band Switching without Band Data Cable from transceiver
RF Output:	Vacuum RELAY T/R Switching
Power supply:	Internal Medical grade
AC Power:	100-125VAC 15A/200-250VAC 10A
DC supply:	50VDC @42A
Power Devices:	2 x 5600H 600W LDMOS
Auto-Protect:	SWR/Short Circuit/Over Temp
Cooling:	Variable Speed Fans (3 speed)
Intermod:	Low IMD Distortion >-35dB
Pure signal:	Sample@+10dBm (Rear Panel@1kW output)

RF SENSING

The LA-1K is a conservatively engineered RF Sensing Dual HF LDMOS 1000 Watt Amplifier. While the LA-1K will work with a wide variety of tuners and transceivers, Palstar custom-designed the LA-1K to work as the perfect match for our very popular HF-AUTO autotuner.

Available at your local AMATEUR RADIO dealer or directly from PALSTAR, Inc.:

1-800-773-7931   www.palstar.com

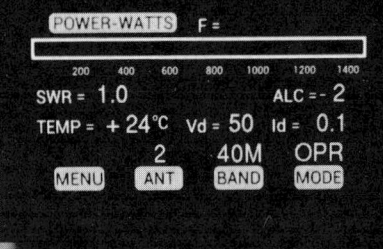

PALSTAR INCORPORATED | 9676 N. LOONEY RD, PIQUA, OH 45356 | TEL: 800-773-7931 | www.palstar.com | paul@palstar.com

Contest From Home or Remotely

Stay Connected With Icom's SDR Technology.

IC-9700: VHF / UHF SDR Transceiver

- RF Direct Sampling on 2m / 70cm
- 100W on 2M / 75W on 70CM / 10W on 23cm
- Dual Independent Receivers Capable of Full Duplex and Dual Receive
- Dedicated Amateur Satellite Operation
- Ethernet port with RS-BA1 Internal Server

IC-7300: HF / 6M SDR Transceiver

- 100 Watt Output Power*
- Entry level HF SDR/High-End Features

*40W on AM

IC-7610: The Perfect Trifecta
Round-Out Your Contesting Station Today

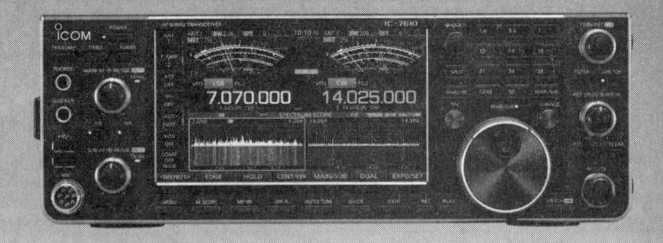

- 100 Watt Output Power*
- Dual Independent Receiver
- Ethernet port with RS-BA1 internal server

*40W on AM

For the love of ham radio.

©2019 Icom America Inc. The Icom logo is a registered trademark of Icom Inc. All other trademark remain the property of their respective owners. All specifications are subject to change without notice or obligation. 31323

ICOM

Get the best out of your radio with...
...a bhi DSP noise cancelling product!

bhi

ParaPro EQ20 Audio DSP Range with parametric equalisation

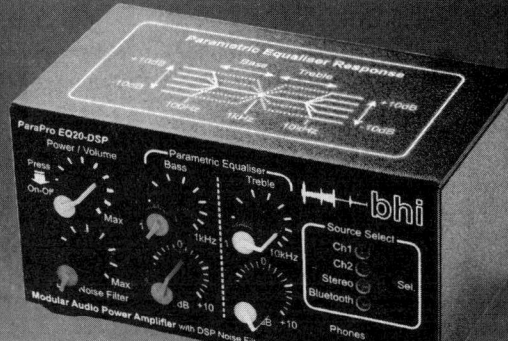

- 20W audio and parametric equalisation on all units
- Powerful high-performance audio processing system
- Precise audio adjustment to compensate for hearing loss
- DSP noise cancelling and Bluetooth versions
- Simple control of all DSP functions
- Two separate mono inputs or one stereo input
- Use with passive speakers or headphones
- Fine-tune the audio to maximise your enjoyment
- Four models EQ20, EQ20B, EQ20-DSP, EQ20B-DSP

Boost your receive audio to suit your ears!

High-performance audio processing...
...with world-class DSP noise cancelling...
...for a great listening experience

Dual In-Line

Fully featured flexible dual channel DSP noise cancelling unit - 8 Filter levels 9 to 40dB - 3.5mm mono or stereo inputs - Line level input/output - 7 watts mono speaker output - Headphone socket - Suitable for all types of radio incl' SDR - Easy to use controls for quick and easy operation - Enjoy clear intelligble "noise-free" speech from your radio - Replacement for bhi NEIM1031 In-Line

Compact In-Line

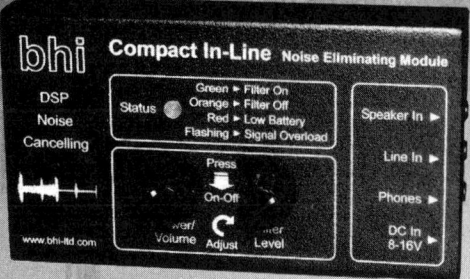

Easy to use in-line DSP noise cancelling unit with simple "real-time" control of audio and functions

- Powerful high-performance audio processor
- Unique DSP noise cancelling technology - Remove noise and interference - Hear weak signals clearly
- Rotary encoders perform all functions
- Easy to use with "real time" adjustment
- Use with headphones or a loudspeaker
- 3.5mm line level and speaker level inputs

DSPKR

10W DSP noise cancelling speaker
- Simple control
- 8 filter levels
- Volume control
- Input overload LED
- Headphone socket
- Supplied with user manual and fused DC power lead

DESKTOP

10W Amplified DSP noise cancelling base station speaker
- Easy to use "real-time" control of all functions
- 8 filter levels 9 to 40dB
- Suitable for all radios incl' SDR, Elecraft and FlexRadio products
- Headphone socket
- Speaker level and line level input sockets

DX ENGINEERING
DXEngineering.com - 1-800-777-0703   www.bhi-ltd.com

EA&O

VISA PayPal MasterCard

Index

Editor's Note: Except for commonly used phrases and abbreviations, topics are indexed by their noun names. Many topics are also cross-indexed.

The letters "ff" after a page number indicate coverage of the indexed topic on succeeding pages.

A separate Project Index and Author Index follow the main index.

A

A index: 19.13
Abbreviations list: 22.62ff
Absorption: 19.2
   Atmospheric: 19.25
   D-layer: 19.13
   MF: 19.3
Absorption Glass Mat, battery (AGM): 7.45
Absorption wavemeter: 25.11
AC circuit models: 5.14ff
AC component: 25.1, 25.9
AC ground: 4.33
AC measurements: 25.9
   Average: 25.9
   Frequency response: 25.10
   Oscilloscope: 25.10
   Peak, peak-to-peak: 25.9
   RMS: 25.9
   RMS, true-RMS: 25.9ff
AC power: 7.2ff
AC-DC power conversion: 7.4
   Comparison of rectifier circuits: 7.7
   Filter, capacitive and inductive: 7.5
   Full-wave bridge and center-tap rectifier: 7.6
   Half-wave rectifier: 7.5
   Ripple: 7.4
AC-line filter: 27.14, 27.31
Accuracy (measurement): 25.2
Active filter: 4.50, 10.11
   Design examples: 10.14
Adaptive compression: 15.4
Adaptive filter: 10.22
Adcock antenna: 21.65
Adjacent channel rejection: 25.34
Adjacent-channel power (ACP): 11.27
Admittance (Y): 3.20
Advanced Circuits (PCB vendor): 23.28
Advanced Design System (ADS): 6.10
AFSK: 15.6
AGC (*see* Automatic gain control)
Airmail: 15.27
ALC (*see* Automatic Level Control)
Aliasing: 8.19
   Digital oscilloscope: 25.14
Alignment tools: 23.7, 23.25
Alphabet size: 15.15
Alternating current (ac): 2.3, 3.1
   Average values: 3.7
   Frequency: 3.2
   Fundamental: 3.2
   Harmonic: 3.2
   Instantaneous values: 3.5

   Non-sinusoidal measurements: 3.6
   Peak and peak-to-peak values: 3.6
   Peak envelope power (PEP): 3.8
   Peak power: 3.8
   Period: 3.2
   Periodic waveform: 3.2
   Phase: 3.3
   Root-mean-square (RMS): 3.6
   Waveform measurements: 3.5
   Waveforms: 3.1
Alternator whine: 27.47
Aluminum
   Alloy types and specifications: 22.41
   Tubing sizes: 21.31
AM (*see* Amplitude modulation)
Amateur Radio
   American Radio Relay League (ARRL): 1.1
   Call sign: 1.7
   Contesting: 1.13
   Direction finding: 1.18
   DXing: 1.13
   Getting on the air: 1.10
   In the classroom: 1.20
   License: 1.5
   Log (on-air activity): 1.9
   Mobile operating: 1.17
   Modes: 1.10ff
   Operating awards: 1.15
   Public service: 1.18
   QRP (Low power operating): 1.16
   QSL cards: 1.15
   Resources: 1.21
   Rules and regulations: 1.3
   Satellites: 1.16
   Study guides: 1.5
   VHF, UHF, microwave: 1.17
Amateur Radio Emergency Data Network (AREDN): 15.31
Amateur Radio Emergency Service (ARES): 1.19
Amateur television: 1.12
Amateur television (ATV): 11.19ff
   Digital television: 11.20
   Remote sensing: 16.14
AMBE (vocoder): 15.30, 18.15
AMBE vocoders: 15.16, 15.30
American Radio Relay League (*see* ARRL)
Ammeter: 25.2
Ammeter, RF: 25.20, 25.55
Ampere (A): 2.2
Ampere-hours (Ah): 2.9

Amplification: 3.31
    Linear: 17.2
    Speech: 13.31
Amplifier: 3.31
    Bode plot: 3.33
    Buffer: 3.37, 4.43
    Class: 4.33, 5.16, 13.37, 17.2, 17.7ff, 17.32
    Common-emitter/base/collector: 4.35, 4.36
    Configuration: 4.33
    Cutoff (corner) frequency: 3.35
    Dynamic range: 3.32
    Emitter-follower (EF): 4.35
    Feedback: 5.17
    Field-effect transistor: 4.41
    Frequency response: 3.32
    Gain: 3.32
    Gain-bandwidth product (FT, GBW): 3.37
    Half-power frequency: 3.35
    High-frequency model: 4.33
    Input impedance: 4.35
    Large-signal model: 4.33
    Limiter: 3.36
    Linear power amplifier: 13.37, 17.2
    Load line: 4.36
    Log: 3.36
    Low-frequency model: 4.33
    Noise: 3.37
    Non-linear: 13.38
    Operating point: 4.36
    Output impedance: 4.35
    Quiescent (Q) point: 4.36
    Rise and fall time: 3.37
    Slew rate: 3.32
    Small-signal model: 4.33
    Stability: 3.35
    Summing: 3.35
    Transconductance: 3.32
    Vertical: 25.12
    Wideband: 25.29
Amplifier, RF power: 13.37, 17.1ff
    Automatic level control (ALC): 17.26
    Blower specifications: 17.20
    Broadband transformer: 17.31
    Cold tuning: 17.14
    Combiners and splitters: 17.34
    Common cathode: 17.6
    Comparison of solid state vs vacuum tube: 17.3
    Component ratings: 17.13ff
    Cooling methods: 17.19ff, 17.20
    DC blocking capacitor: 17.17
    Filament voltage: 17.18
    Grid bias: 17.19
    Grounded grid: 17.6
    Harmonic rejection: 17.10ff
    Impedance matching: 17.32ff
    Linear RF power: 17.2
    Mobile operation: 24.15
    MOSFET design: 17.27ff
    Neutralization: 17.22
    Overdrive (overshoot): 17.26
    Pallet modules: 17.36
    Parasitic oscillation: 17.24
    Parasitic suppressor: 17.25
    Pi network: 17.10
    Pi-L network: 17.11
    Plate voltage: 17.18
    Protection and control circuits: 17.41
    References: 17.53
    RF choke: 17.16
    Screen voltage: 17.19
    Sockets and chimneys: 17.20
    Solid state: 17.32ff
    Stabilization: 17.22ff, 17.35ff
    Surplus parts: 17.46
    Tank circuit: 17.9ff
    Tank circuit design methods: 17.10ff
    Transmission line transformer: 17.30
    Transmitter: 13.37
    Troubleshooting: 26.28ff
    Tuning procedure: 17.14
    VHF/UHF tank circuit: 17.14
Amplitude modulation (AM): 11.2ff
    Demodulation, detection: 12.43
    Double-sideband, full-carrier: 11.2
    Double-sideband, suppressed-carrier (DSB-SC): 11.4
    Modulation index: 11.4
    On-off keying (OOK): 11.5
    Overmodulation: 13.11
    Single-sideband, suppressed-carrier (SSB-SC): 11.4
    Transmitting: 13.20
Analog Filter Wizard by Analog Devices: 10.16
Analog switches and multiplexers: 4.54
Analog systems
    Analog signal: 3.31
    Buffering: 4.33
    Signal processing: 3.31
    Terminology: 3.31
Analog-digital conversion: 8.5
    Accuracy: 8.6
    ADC, DAC: 8.5
    Band-limiting: 8.7
    Binary coded decimal (BCD): 8.6
    Bipolar and unipolar: 8.6
    Choosing a converter: 8.11
    Code: 8.6
    Conversion rate (speed): 8.7
    Digitization: 8.6
    Full-scale (FS) value: 8.6
    Full-scale error: 8.6
    Jitter: 8.14
    Least significant bit (LSB): 8.6
    Linearity error: 8.6
    Noise: 8.12
    Noise shaping: 8.13
    Nonlinearity: 8.6
    Nyquist frequency: 8.7
    Nyquist rate: 8.7
    Nyquist Sampling Theorem: 8.7
    Offset: 8.6
    Over- and undersampling: 8.7, 8.13
    Percentage resolution: 8.6
    Pipelined architecture: 8.13
    Quantization code: 8.6
    Quantization error: 8.6
    Range: 8.6
    Resolution: 8.6
    Sample: 8.7
    SDR requirements: 8.12
    Signal-to-noise and distortion ratio (SINAD): 8.12
    Spurious-free dynamic range (SFDR): 8.13
    Step size: 8.6
    Total harmonic distortion plus noise (THD+N): 8.12
Analog-to-digital converter (ADC)
    Analog and digital ground: 8.10
    Delta-encoded converters: 8.8
    Dual-slope integrating converter: 8.8
    Flash (direct-conversion) converter: 8.7
    Input buffering and filtering: 8.9
    Sample-and-hold (S/H): 8.9
    Sigma-delta converter: 8.9, 8.13
    Single-ended and differential inputs: 8.9
    Successive-approximation converter (SAC): 8.8
Analytic signals: 11.14ff
Anderson Powerpole: 24.9
Angle
    Radians and degrees: 3.2
Angle modulation: 11.7ff
    AM noise and FM signals: 11.8
    Bandwidth: 11.7
    Bessel function: 11.8

Carson's rule:	11.8
Demodulation, detection:	12.46ff
Frequency response:	11.7
Modulators:	13.13
SDR modulators:	13.16
Transmitting:	13.23ff

Ansoft Designer SV2: 6.2
Antenna
Azimuth pattern:	21.4
Balun:	21.7, 21.35, 21.53
Bandwidth:	21.3
Conductor diameter:	21.3
Construction of wire antennas:	21.9ff
Construction, Yagi:	21.32ff
Current and voltage distribution:	21.2
Delta loop:	21.38
Dipole:	21.6ff
Dipole, multiband:	20.6
Dipole, sloping and vertical:	21.26ff
Directivity:	21.1
Driven array:	21.30
E- and H-field:	21.2
Elevation angle:	21.5
Elevation pattern:	21.4
End-effect:	21.2
End-fed half-wave (EFHW):	21.12
Far (near) field:	21.20
Feed point impedance:	21.3
Feeding, ground-plane:	21.22
Folded dipole:	21.14, 21.53
Front-to-back ratio:	21.3
Gain:	21.1, 21.4, 21.51
Glossary:	21.70
Ground losses:	21.20, 21.45
Ground plane:	21.20ff
Ground systems:	21.20
Height above ground:	21.3
HF mobile:	21.41ff
Impedance matching:	21.35, 21.46
Impedance matching at VHF/UHF:	21.52
Imperfect ground:	21.5
Installation:	28.19
Insulators:	21.9
Inverted-L:	21.25
Inverted-V:	21.12
Isotropic (radiator):	21.1
K factor:	21.4
Length-to-diameter (l/d) ratio:	21.4
Lightning arrestor:	28.13
Loading:	21.22, 21.42
Lobes and nulls:	21.4
Loop:	21.36ff
Loop and halyard:	28.15
Low-band delta loop antenna:	21.38
Magnet (mag) mount:	18.8
Mast material:	28.19
Mobile mounting:	21.46, 21.50
Modeling:	21.19
Multiband dipole:	21.14
National Electrical Code (NEC):	28.10
Parasitic array:	21.30
Pattern ratios (F/B, F/S, F/R):	21.5
Polarization:	21.1, 21.51
Portable operation:	24.21ff
Quad:	21.36ff
Radiation pattern:	21.4, 21.51
Radiation resistance:	21.2
Radio direction finding (RDF):	21.63
Re-radiation:	21.30
References:	21.71
Remotely tuned antennas:	21.44
Remotely-tuned antenna controllers:	21.47
Repeater operation (home station):	18.8
Safety:	28.14ff
Safety references:	28.23
Sense:	21.65
Stacking:	21.56
T antenna:	21.25
Temperature:	5.32
Through-the-glass (mobile):	18.8
Trap dipole:	21.15
Trap vertical:	21.24
Vertical:	21.20
VHF/UHF:	21.51ff
VHF/UHF mobile:	18.8
Whip:	21.41ff
Wire antenna supports:	21.12
Wire strength:	22.40
Yagi, optimized designs:	21.33ff
Yagi, Yagi-Uda:	21.29ff, 21.56ff
Zoning:	28.14

Antenna analyzer:	25.40ff
Broadcast interference:	26.35
Antenna coupler:	20.16

Antenna rotator (see Rotator)
Antenna systems
Measurements:	25.38ff
Troubleshooting:	26.34ff

Antenna tuner (ATU)
T configuration:	20.13

Antenna tuner (ATU, Antenna coupler, Matchbox, Transmatch): 20.16
Adjusting:	20.18
Location in the antenna system:	20.17
T configuration:	20.17
Unbalanced-to-balanced:	20.16

Antenna tuner (ATU, antenna coupler, matchbox, transmatch)
Balanced and unbalanced load:	20.16
Anticyclone:	19.26
APCO-25:	15.28
Apparent power:	3.22
Application-specific integrated circuit (ASIC):	4.34
APRS (Automatic Packet Reporting System):	1.12, 15.24
Automatic Identification System (AIS):	15.25
Beacon:	15.24
D-STAR and DPRS:	15.26
Email:	15.26
GPS:	15.24
Igate:	15.24
Near space tracker:	16.12
Position data:	16.10
Relay:	15.24
Secondary Station ID (SSID):	15.24
Software:	15.24
Tactical call:	15.24
Telemetry:	16.10
Tracker:	15.24, 16.2
Winlink:	15.26
Arbitrary waveform generator (AWG):	25.18
Arc-fault circuit interrupter (AFCI):	28.5
Arcing:	5.10
Arithmetic logic unit (ALU):	8.16
ARQ (Automatic repeat request):	15.2
ARRL:	1.1ff, 1.6
RF Safety Committee:	28.24
Section Manager (SM):	27.3
Technical Coordinator (TC):	27.3
Technical Information Service (TIS):	22.2

ARRL Lab
Receiver test procedure:	25.30ff
Transmitter test procedure:	25.36ff

ARRL Net Directory: 1.4
ARRL Radio Designer: 6.5
ASAPS: 19.22
ASK (*see* Amplitude-shift keying)
Astrotex (shock mounts):	24.12
Atmosphere:	19.6
Atmospheric noise:	12.1

Attenuation: 3.31
    Conversion between reflection coefficient, SWR,
        and return loss: 22.61
    Filter: 10.3
    Free space: 19.2
    Of transmission lines: 20.5
Attenuation constant (α): 20.9
Attenuator: 3.32, 25.28
    Microphone: 13.30
    Pi- and T-network values: 22.44
    Step: 25.56
ATV (*see* Amateur television)
Audio amplifier IC: 4.55
Audio equalization (transmitted): 13.28
Audio equipment RFI: 27.43
Audio frequency shift keying (AFSK)
    Audio levels: 13.30
Audio frequency-shift keying (AFSK): 11.12
Audio optimization (transmitted): 13.29
Audio oscillator: 25.53
Aurora: 19.14
Auroral E: 19.15
Authority having jurisdiction (AHJ): 28.2
AutoCAD: 6.3
Automatic gain control (AGC): 12.49
    Audio-derived: 12.51
    Pumping: 12.49
    Time constants: 12.49
Automatic level control (ALC): 13.39, 17.2, 17.26
    SDR: 14.3
Automatic link establishment (ALE): 15.17
    FSK: 15.17
    Link quality analysis (LQA): 15.17
    Scanning: 15.17
Automatic repeat request (ARQ): 15.18
Automotive RFI: 24.15, 27.46ff
    Alternator whine: 27.47
    Electric vehicle (EV): 27.49
    Hybrid-electric vehicle (HEV): 27.49
    Ignition noise: 27.48
Autoranging: 25.5
Autotransformer: 3.30, 4.17
Avalanche breakdown: 4.20

B

B2 Spice: 6.3
Back-voltage (back-EMF): 2.22
Background noise: 5.33
Backscatter: 19.19
Backwave: 13.19
Balanced modulator: 13.9, 13.21
Balloon, high-altitude
    APRS telemetry: 16.19
    BalloonSat: 16.3
    Batteries: 16.19
    Data platform: 16.15
    Environmental conditions: 16.16
    FAA requirement: 16.15
    Flight path prediction: 16.19
    Platform design: 16.18
Balun: 20.19ff, 21.7, 21.35, 21.53
    Bazooka: 20.20
    Bead: 20.24
    Broadband: 20.23
    Choke: 20.19ff
    Coiled coax: 20.23
    Combination ferrite and coiled coax: 20.26
    Current: 5.23, 20.22ff
    Current (ferrite bead) balun: 20.22
    Quarter-Three-Quarter Wave (Q3Q): 20.22
    Quarter-wave: 20.20
    Transmitting, ferrite: 20.25
    Voltage: 20.23
    Wound-coax ferrite choke: 20.26

Band plan
    Repeaters: 18.4
Band-pass filter: 3.35, 10.3
Band-stop (band-reject) filter: 10.3
Bandwidth
    Amplitude modulation: 11.4
    Angle modulation: 11.7
    Antenna: 21.3
    Complex signals: 3.8
    Digital signals: 11.25
    FCC definition: 3.8, 11.2
    FCC regulations: 13.1
    Filter: 10.3
    Resonant circuits: 3.25
    Rise and fall time: 3.38
Barkhausen criteria: 9.3
Battery
    Absorption Glass Mat (AGM): 7.36, 7.46
    Alkaline: 7.34ff
    Balloon, high-altitude: 16.19
    Battery Monitoring System (BMS): 24.14
    Cold-cranking amps (CCA): 7.45
    Deep-cycle: 7.36, 7.45
    Discharging methods: 7.42
    Electronic Load Detector (ELD): 24.14
    Handling guidelines: 7.43ff
    Lead acid: 7.34ff
    Lithium chemistries: 7.34ff
    Marine: 7.45
    NiCd: 7.34ff
    NiMH: 7.34ff
    Recycling: 7.45
    Reserve capacity (RC): 7.45
    Safety: 7.33
    Starter-lights-ignition (SLI): 7.36, 7.45
    Test and monitoring: 7.44
    Voltage regulation: 24.20
Battery charging: 7.37ff
    Chargers: 7.38
    From USB: 7.39
    Full charge detection: 7.40
    Lead acid: 7.39
    Lithium chemistries: 7.41
    NiCd: 7.40
    NiMH: 7.41
Battery Council Institute (BCI): 7.45
Battery Monitoring System (BMS): 24.14
Baud: 15.1
Baud (symbol rate): 11.6
Baudot: 15.2
Bazooka (balun): 20.20
Beacon (radio propagation): 19.21
Beam antenna: 21.29
Beat frequency oscillator (BFO): 12.14, 13.18
Bermuda high: 19.26
Bessel (filter): 10.6
Bessel function: 11.8
Beta (current gain): 4.23, 4.35
BFO (*see* Beat frequency oscillator)
Bias (amplifier): 4.19, 17.2
    Bias point: 4.19
    Quiescent (Q) point: 4.19
Bias (device), forward and reverse: 2.27
Bilateral diode switch (*see* Diac)
Bilateral networks: 5.26
Bill of Materials (BOM): 23.30
Binary coded decimal (BCD): 8.6
Bipolar junction transistor (BJT): 2.28, 4.23
    Active (linear) region: 4.23
    Breakdown region: 4.23
    Common-emitter/base/collector: 4.23, 4.33
    Comparison with FET: 4.26
    Current gain (β): 4.23
    Cutoff region: 4.23
    Dynamic emitter resistance, r_e: 4.35

Early effect:	4.23
Ebers-Moll model:	4.35
Emitter, collector, and base:	4.22
High-frequency models:	5.15
Hybrid-pi model:	4.35, 5.16
Operating parameters:	4.23
Phototransistor:	4.27
Saturation region:	4.23
Small-signal characteristics:	4.23
Specifications:	22.25
Birdies:	25.35
Bit error ratio (BER):	25.47
Bit rate:	15.1
Audio and video:	15.6
BJT (*see* Bipolar junction transistor)	
Bleeder resistor:	2.18, 7.13
High-voltage supplies:	7.30
Block codes:	15.15
Blocking dynamic range (BDR):	12.6, 25.31
SDR:	8.3
Blocking gain compression:	12.6
BNC connector:	24.10
Boat Anchor Manual Archive (BAMA):	26.14
Bode plot:	3.33
Bolometer:	25.20
Bonding:	28.6ff
Bus:	24.2, 28.7
Conductors:	28.11
Conductors - braid, strap, wire:	28.7
Radio frequency interference (RFI):	27.16
RF management:	28.8
Single-point ground panel (SPGP):	28.8
Station:	24.2
Boost converter:	7.23
BPL (Broadband over Power Lines):	27.8
BPSK (*see* Binary phase-shift keying)	
Brain, Charles G4GUO:	15.16
Branch (circuit):	2.5
Break-in (QSK):	13.20
Breakdown, dielectric:	5.10
Brick wall response (filter):	10.3
Bridge	
LCR:	25.18
Wheatstone:	25.3
Wien:	25.17
Broadband noise:	27.17
Broadband-Hamnet (BBHN):	15.31
Buck converter:	7.21
Critical inductance:	7.22
Buck-boost converter:	7.23
Buffer amplifier:	3.37
Cascode buffer:	4.44
Darlington pair:	4.43
Emitter-follower (EF):	4.43
Source-follower:	4.43
Burden voltage:	25.7
Butterworth (maximally flat) filter response:	10.5
Bypass capacitor (RFI):	27.30
Bypassing:	5.10
Paralleling capacitors:	5.11

C

C-rate:	7.34
C4FM:	15.30, 18.19
Cable TV, frequencies and leakage:	27.40ff
CadWeld (exothermic welding):	28.9
Calibration (sensors):	16.6
Call sign:	1.7
Capacitance (C):	2.14
Capacitor:	2.14
AC current and voltage:	3.10
AC-rated:	27.31
Axial and radial leads:	5.5, 22.6
Ceramic, disc and monolithic:	22.6
Charging and discharging:	2.17
Color codes, obsolete:	22.9
DC blocking:	17.17
Dielectric constant:	2.15
Dissipation factor (DF):	4.5
Effective series resistance (ESR):	4.5
Effects of construction:	4.7
Electrolytic, aluminum and tantalum:	22.7
Electrolytic, reforming:	26.37
Equivalent (effective) series inductance (ESL):	5.5
Film:	22.6
High-voltage:	7.30
IEC identification and marking:	22.10
Labeling:	22.8
Leakage resistance:	4.5
Loss angle or tangent (θ):	4.5
Oil-filled:	7.30
Parasitic inductance:	5.5
Parasitic inductance model:	5.5
Poly-chlorinated biphenyls (PCB):	7.30
Ratings:	4.5
Ratings, RF power amplifier:	17.16
RC time constant (τ):	2.17
Series and parallel:	2.16
Standard values:	22.6
Temperature characteristics:	22.7
Temperature coefficient (tempco):	4.5
Types of capacitors:	4.6
Voltage ratings:	22.9
Capacity (battery):	7.34
Capture effect:	11.9
Capture range (PLL):	9.32
Carabiner:	28.17
Cardioid microphone:	13.28
Carrier recovery:	11.13
Carrier squelch:	18.9
Carrier-current device:	27.8
Carson's rule:	11.8
Cascaded integrator comb (CIC) filter:	10.21
Cascading stages:	3.36
Cascode buffer:	4.40
CAT interface:	14.11
Cauer (elliptic function) filter:	10.6
Cavity resonator oscillator:	9.25
CCS (*see* Continuous Commercial Service)	
CDMA (*see* Code-division multiple access spread spectrum)	
Channel capacity:	11.26
Channel symbol:	15.15
Characteristic (surge) impedance (Z_0):	20.3
Characteristic curve:	4.18, 17.4ff
Chatter (comparator):	4.49
Chebyshev (equiripple) filter response:	10.5
Chinook wind:	19.27
Chip, chip rate:	11.22
Chip64 and Chip128 (*see* spread spectrum):	15.12
Chirp modulation:	11.22
Choke balun:	20.19ff
Choke, common-mode:	27.31, 27.33ff
Chordal hop:	19.17
CI-V Interface:	14.10
Circuit:	2.2
Branches and nodes:	2.5
Equivalent circuit:	2.7
Open (short) circuit:	2.2
Parallel (series) circuit:	2.2
Circuit breaker:	2.12, 7.2
Arc-fault circuit interrupter (AFCI)	28.5
Ground fault circuit interrupter (GFCI or GFI):	7.2, 28.5
Ratings:	2.12
Circuit simulation	
Component models and sources:	6.4
DC operating or bias point:	6.7
Electromagnetic:	6.13
Harmonic balance:	6.10, 6.13
Limitations at RF:	6.12

Scale factors: 6.3
Sources, voltage and current: 6.4
Switchmode power conversion: 7.28
Time and frequency domain: 6.8
Time step: 6.6
Transient: 6.8
Circular mil: 22.39
Clamping (*see* Clipping)
Class (amplifier): 13.37, 17.2, 17.7ff, 17.32
A, B, AB, C, D, E, F: 4.33, 5.16
Efficiency: 5.17
Clients, thick and thin (SDR): 14.9
Clipping: 3.35
Speech: 13.32
CLOVER: 15.21
Coder efficiency: 15.21
Modulation: 15.21
Phase-shift modulation (PSM): 15.21
CMOS: 2.31
Coaxial cable (coax): 20.1
75 Ω in 50 Ω systems: 20.7
Center insulator: 20.1
Dielectric: 20.2
Hardline: 20.1
Jacket: 20.1, 20.7
Shield: 20.1
Coaxial detector: 25.29
Code-division, multiple access (CDMA): 11.23
Codec: 8.2, 8.12, 15.4
Codec2 by VK5DGR: 15.16, 18.20
Coded squelch (repeater): 18.9
COFDM (*see* Coded orthogonal frequency-division multiplexing)
Cognitive radio: 8.2
Coil (*see* Inductor)
Cold Cranking Amps: 7.34
Color code
AC wiring: 28.4
Capacitor, obsolete: 22.9
Diode: 22.16
Inductor: 22.11
Resistor: 22.3
Transformer: 22.15
Colpitts oscillator
VFO: 9.5
Common-base (CB) amplifier: 4.35, 4.40
Current gain: 4.40
Input and output impedance: 4.40
Power gain: 4.40
Voltage gain: 4.40
Common-collector (CC) amplifier: 4.35
Input and output impedance: 4.39
Power gain: 4.39
Voltage gain: 4.39
Common-drain (CD) amplifier: 4.42
Input and output impedance: 4.42
Common-emitter (CE) amplifier: 4.36
AC performance: 4.38
Fixed-bias: 4.37
Input and output impedance: 4.38
Input impedance: 4.37
Power gain: 4.38
Self-bias: 4.37
Common-gate (CG) amplifier: 4.43
Input and output impedance: 4.40
Voltage gain: 4.43
Common-mode: 20.19, 27.13, 27.29, 27.31
Common-mode rejection ratio (CMRR): 4.46
Common-source (CS) amplifier: 4.41
AC performance: 4.42
Input and output impedance: 4.42
Self-bias: 4.42
Source bypass: 4.42
Source degeneration: 4.42
Voltage gain: 4.42

Comparator
Hysteresis: 4.49
Voltage: 4.44
Compensation
Frequency (op-amp): 4.46
Oscilloscope probe: 25.15
Complex frequency: 3.33
Complex loss coefficient (η): 20.9
Complex numbers: 11.14
Component measurements: 25.43
Composite noise (*see* Phase noise)
Compression (audio): 13.33
Compression (data): 15.4, 15.4ff
WSJT-X: 15.14
Compression (signal): 3.35
Computer-aided design (CAD) (*see* Circuit simulation)
Conductance (G): 2.4
Leakage: 5.3
Series and parallel: 2.7
Siemens (S): 2.4
Conducted emissions: 27.9, 27.20
Power inverters: 27.14
Conduction current: 5.5
Conductor: 2.1
Configuration and control interface
CAT: 14.11
CI-V (Icom): 14.10
SDR: 14.10
Connector: 24.12ff
Audio: 24.10
Avoiding poor quality RF connectors: 22.58
BNC: 22.47, 22.49
Coaxial, types: 22.50
Computer, pinouts: 22.44ff
Crimp: 24.9
Data: 24.11
F: 22.52
Identification guide: 22.53ff
N: 22.51
Powerpole, Anderson: 24.9
RF: 24.10
RJ: 24.11
Troubleshooting: 26.7
UHF: 22.46
Weatherproofing: 28.20
Constellation diagram: 11.12
Construction techniques
Circuit layout: 23.221ff
Common standard parts: 23.16
Component mounting: 23.17
Crimping tools: 23.6
Drill sizes: 23.5
Drilling: 23.40
Electrostatic discharge (ESD): 23.15
Enclosure fabrication: 23.40
Ground plane (dead-bug, ugly): 23.18
High-voltage: 23.26
Manhattan style: 23.19
Mechanical fabrication: 23.39
Metalworking: 23.39
Microwave: 23.37
Nibbling tool: 23.6
Painting: 23.40
Panel layout: 23.41
PCB fabrication services: 23.21
Perforated board: 23.19
Point-to-point: 23.18
Printed-circuit board (PCB): 23.21ff
Recommended tools: 23.4
Socket or chassis punch: 23.6
Soldering: 23.7ff
Solderless breadboard or prototype board: 23.20
Surface-mount technology (SMT): 23.11
Terminal and wire: 23.20
Tools: 23.3ff

Winding coils: 23.26ff
Wire-wrap: 23.20
Wired traces (lazy PC board): 23.19
Wiring: 23.26
Consumer Electronics Association (CEA): 27.24
Contestia (telemetry): 16.11
Contesting (radiosport): 1.13
Continuous Commercial Service (CCS) rating: 13.3
Continuous conduction mode (CCM): 7.22
Continuous tone-coded squelch system (CTCSS): 18.6ff
    Tone frequencies: 18.9
Continuous wave (CW): 9.2
    Bandwidth: 11.5
    Break-in (QSK): 13.20
    Envelope shaping: 13.18
    Key click: 13.2
    Key clicks: 11.5
    Keying waveform: 13.2
    Spectrum: 13.17
    Transmitting: 13.17
    Varicode: 11.6
    Words per minute (WPM): 11.6
    WPM: 13.18
Control wiring, low-voltage: 28.6
Conventional current: 2.2
Conversion
    Attenuation, SWR, return loss: 22.61
    Degrees and radians: 3.2
    Power and voltage: 22.60
Conversion loss
    Balanced mixer: 12.31
    Switching mixer: 12.30
Convolution: 3.36
    Digital filter: 10.17
Cooperative agreement, utilities: 27.28
Coordination (repeater): 18.9
Coplanar waveguide: 20.29
Corona discharge: 19.31, 27.28
Coronal hole: 19.12
Coronal mass ejection (CME): 19.12
Coulomb (C): 2.2
Counter, frequency: 25.10
Coupling (inductive): 2.23
Courage Kenny Handiham Program: 1.7
Courtesy tone: 18.5
CRC (Cyclical redundancy check): 15.2
Crimp connector: 24.10
Critical frequency: 19.8
Cross-reference, semiconductor: 4.19, 26.10
Crosspoint switch: 4.54
Crosstalk: 4.54
Crowbar overvoltage protection (OVP): 7.20
CRT (oscilloscope): 25.12
Crystal, quartz
    Characterization: 10.25
    Equivalent circuit: 9.19
    Holders: 22.38
    Oscillator: 9.17ff
CTCSS (see Continuous tone-coded squelch system)
CubeSats: 16.1
Current
    Conventional: 25.2
    Electronic: 25.2
Current (I): 2.1
    Ampere (A): 2.1
    Conventional current: 2.2
    Current source: 2.6
    Electronic current: 2.2
Current balun: 5.23
Current divider: 4.4
Current gain (β): 4.23
Current inrush: 7.11
Current shunt: 25.8
Current transfer ratio (CTR): 4.29
Cutoff (corner) frequency: 3.32, 10.3
Cutoff (semiconductor): 2.28
CW (Morse code)
    Modulation (On-Off Keying): 11.5
    Telemetry: 16.12

D

D layer propagation: 19.13
D'Arsonval meter movement: 25.2
d*Chat: 15.30
D-RATS: 15.30
D-STAR: 15.28, 15.30, 18.12ff
    Backbone: 15.29
    Call sign routing: 15.28
    d*Chat: 15.30
    D-RATS: 15.30
    D-STAR TV: 15.30
    Digital data (DD): 15.29
    Digital voice (DV): 15.29
    Dplus: 15.30, 18.14
    DPRS: 15.30
    DV Dongle: 15.30
    Ethernet bridge: 15.29
    Gateway: 15.29
    Hidden transmitter: 15.29
    JARL: 15.28
    Network overview: 18.13
    Repeater hardware: 18.14
    Station ID: 18.12
    Station routing: 18.12
    Texas Interconnect Team: 15.29
    Trust server: 15.28
Damping: 9.2
Darlington pair: 4.43, 7.16
    Pass transistor: 7.16
Data logger: 25.5
Data platforms: 16.3
    Buoy: 16.23
    Fixed: 16.23
    Navigation: 16.23
    Powering: 16.24
    Weather station: 16.23
Data sheet: 4.19
Datalogger: 16.2
dBd: 21.1
dBi: 21.1
dBm: 25.20
DC channel resistance, r_{DS}: 4.24
DC component: 25.1, 25.9
DC coupling
    Oscilloscope: 25.12
DCS (see Digital coded squelch)
Dead reckoning: 16.9
Decibel (dB): 3.32
Decimation: 8.21, 8.24, 12.23
Decoupling: 5.11
    Transmission line: 20.19
Deep-cycle battery: 7.45
Delta loop antenna: 21.38
    Bottom corner fed: 21.44
    Low band: 21.38
Delta match: 21.52
Demodulation: 12.43ff
Depletion region: 2.26
Design cycle: 6.2
Detection: 12.43ff
    AM and SSB: 12.44
Detector
    Diode: 25.20
    Thermocouple: 25.20
Deviation (frequency): 13.24
    Measurement: 25.38
Diac: 2.28
Diamagnetic: 2.19
Dielectric breakdown and arcing (strength): 5.10

Dielectric constant: 2.15
  Transmission line: 20.2, 20.11
Dielectric resonator oscillator: 9.26
Difference amplifier: 4.48
Differential amplifier: 4.48
Differential-mode (signal, current): 20.22, 27.13, 27.29, 27.31
Digipeater: 15.25, 18.4
Digital (signal): 3.31
Digital ATV: 11.20
Digital audio
  Audio formats: 15.3
  Bit depth: 15.3
  Bit rate: 15.4
  Codec: 15.4
  MIDI: 15.3
  MP3: 15.4
Digital audio format: 12.21, 13.29
Digital coded squelch (DCS): 18.9
Digital data (mode): 1.12, 15.1ff
  Automatic repeat request (ARQ): 15.2
  Baud: 15.1
  Baudot code: 15.2
  Bit, bit rate (bps): 15.1
  Bridge: 15.24
  Checksum: 15.2
  Code pages: 15.3
  Control characters: 15.3
  Cyclical redundancy check (CRC): 15.2
  Data rate: 15.1
  Dibit: 15.9
  Emission designator: 15.1
  Encryption: 15.6
  Error detection and correction: 15.2
  Error-correcting code (ECC): 15.2
  Forward error correction (FEC): 15.2
  FSK: 15.6
  Gray code: 15.10
  Gross and net bit rate: 15.1
  Hybrid ARQ: 15.2
  Networking modes: 15.18
  Parity: 15.2
  Sound card: 15.5
  Symbol, symbol rate: 15.1
  Table of modes: 15.32
  Throughput (bps): 15.2
  Unicode: 15.3
  Varicode: 15.2, 15.9
  Viterbi algorithm, coding: 15.9
  WSJT-X: 15.14
Digital downconverter (DDC): 8.5, 12.22
Digital filter
  Adaptive filter: 10.22
  Cascaded integrator comb (CIC): 10.21
  Convolution: 10.17
  Delay: 10.16
  Finite impulse response (FIR): 10.16
  Infinite Impulse Response (IIR): 10.20
  Tap: 10.16
  Windowing: 10.18
Digital image
  Color depth: 15.3
  High, true color: 15.3
  JPEG: 15.4
  Palette: 15.3
  Pixel: 15.3
  Raster: 15.3
  Vector: 15.3
Digital logic families: 22.31
Digital Mobile Radio (DMR): 15.31, 18.15ff
  Channels: 18.17
  Code plug: 18.18
  Simplex: 18.18
  Talk groups: 18.16
Digital modulation
  Audio levels: 13.30
  Bit error ratio (BER): 25.47
  Packet error ratio (PER): 25.47
  Test procedures: 25.47
Digital Radio Mondiale (DRM): 15.35
Digital sensor interfaces: 16.6
Digital signal processing (DSP): 8.1
  Arithmetic logic unit (ALU): 8.16
  Audio frequencies: 8.2
  Barrel shifter: 8.16
  Decimation and interpolation: 8.21, 8.24
  Direct memory access (DMA): 8.16
  Dithering: 8.23
  Embedded systems: 8.16
  Filters: 8.2
  Fixed and floating point: 8.16
  Graphics processing unit (GPU): 8.18
  Integrated development environment (IDE): 8.15
  Microprocessors: 8.15
  Multi-rate conversion: 8.21
  Multiplier-accumulator (MAC): 8.16
  Noise: 8.22
  Noise reduction: 12.55
  Notch filtering: 12.55
  Over- and undersampling: 8.22
  Pipeline: 8.16
  Processor manufacturers: 8.17
  Quantization error: 8.22
  Resampling: 8.21
  Zero-stuffing: 8.21
Digital upconverter (DUC): 8.5, 12.22
Digital video: 15.3
  Bit rate: 15.4
  Codec: 15.6
Digital voice
  AOR: 15.16
  D-STAR: 15.28
  DMR: 15.31
  FreeDV: 15.16
  FreeDV 2400A: 15.16
  P25: 15.30
  System Fusion: 15.30
Digital-to-analog converter (DAC): 8.5, 8.10
  Binary weighting: 8.10
  Current output DAC: 8.11
  Monotonicity: 8.10
  R-2R ladder DAC: 8.11
  Settling time: 8.10
  Summing: 8.10
  Zero-order hold: 8.20
Diode: 4.19, 22.15
  AC circuit model: 5.14
  Anode: 4.19
  At high frequencies: 5.14
  Cathode: 4.19
  Color code: 22.16
  Dynamic resistance: 5.14
  Fast-recovery: 4.20, 7.10
  Forward voltage: 4.20, 4.21
  Free-wheeling: 7.5, 7.22
  Kickback (flyback): 4.56
  Package dimensions: 22.17
  Peak Inverse Voltage (PIV, PRV): 4.20
  Photodiode: 4.27
  PIN: 4.21
  Point-contact: 4.21
  Ratings: 4.20
  Schottky: 4.21, 7.10
  Specifications: 22.16
  Switching time: 5.14
  Transient voltage suppressor (TVS): 4.22
  Vacuum tube: 17.4
  Varactor: 4.21
  Zener: 4.21
Diode detector: 25.20
Dip (grid dip) meter: 25.11, 25.60, 26.4

Diplexer by W4ENE:	10.11
Dipole:	21.6ff
Fan:	21.14
Folded:	21.14, 21.53
Half-wave vertical:	21.26
Inverted-V:	21.12
Multiband:	21.14
Near Vertical Incidence Skywave (NVIS):	21.15
Shortened:	21.13
Sloping:	21.12, 21.26ff
Table of dimensions:	21.11
Trap:	21.15
Vertical:	21.26ff
Direct analog synthesis (DAS):	9.28
Direct conversion (receiver):	12.12
Direct current (dc):	2.3
Direct digital synthesis (DDS):	9.28
Noise:	9.29
Sine-wave generator:	25.18
Direct memory access (DMA):	8.16
Direct-sequence (DSSS):	11.23
Direction finding:	1.18
Directional coupler:	25.29, 25.39
Directional wattmeter:	25.20
Directional wattmeter (*see also* Reflected power meter)	
Discharge (battery):	7.42
Discontinuous conduction mode (DCM):	7.22
Discrete time signals:	8.19
Displacement current:	5.5
Dissipation (power):	2.10
Distributed elements:	5.1
Dithering:	8.23
Diversity reception:	12.55
DMM (digital multimeter):	25.4
Autoranging:	25.5
DominoEX:	15.10
Telemetry:	16.12
Doppler shift:	21.69, 25.12
Mobile communication:	19.28
Double-balanced mixer:	12.30
AM modulator:	13.10
Phase detection:	12.32
Doubler (multiplier):	13.24
Downconversion	
Baseband:	8.3
Dplus:	15.30
DPRS:	15.30
DPSK (*see* Differential phase-shift keying)	
DQPSK (*see* Differential quadrature phase-shift keying)	
Drift velocity:	2.27
Driver array IC:	4.52
DSP (*see* Digital signal processing)	
DSP equipment troubleshooting:	26.15
DTMF (*see* Dual-tone multi-frequency)	
DTV, HDTV (*see* Digital television)	
Dual-tone multi-frequency (DTMF)	
Tone frequencies:	18.10
Ducting:	19.25ff
Dummy load:	25.28, 26.4
Duplexer:	18.5
Adjustment using spectrum analyzer:	25.24
DVD (Digital Video Disk) player RFI:	27.42
DXing:	1.13
Dynamic microphone:	13.27
Dynamic range:	3.32
Blocking (BDR):	12.6
Decimation:	12.24
Interference-free signal strength (IFSS):	12.10
Intermodulation distortion (IMD):	25.32
Receiver:	12.6ff
Receiver, SDR:	12.22
Reciprocal mixing:	12.10
SDR behavior:	25.34
Spectrum analyzer:	25.21
Spurious-free:	12.10
Superheterodyne receiver:	12.20
Superheterodyne vs SDR receiver metrics:	25.33
Third-order:	12.8
Dynamic resistance:	3.27, 5.14
Dynamics (speech):	13.27

E

E layer propagation (E skip):	19.13ff
E-field:	21.2
EAGLE (CAD software):	6.2
Earth-Moon-Earth (EME) communication:	19.31
WSJT-X:	15.15
Ebers-Moll transistor model:	5.15
EchoLink:	18.11
Eddy current:	2.22, 4.16
Education:	1.20
Effective moment (rotator):	21.71
Effective Radiated Power	
ERP, EIRP, ERPD:	3.9
Effective sunspot number (SSNe):	19.21
Efficiency (Eff, η):	2.10
EHF (frequency range classification):	3.39
Electret microphone:	13.28
Electric charge:	2.1
Coulombs (C):	2.2
Electric fence RFI:	27.19
Electric field	
Electromagnetic wave:	19.1
Electrostatic field:	2.14
RF exposure:	28.26
Electric vehicle (EV) RFI:	27.49
Electrical length (L_e, transmission line):	20.9
Electrical safety ground:	28.7
Electrical units:	2.2
Electroluminescence:	4.28
Electromagnetic	
Radiation:	19.1
Spectrum:	19.1
Wave:	19.1
Electromagnetic (EM) analysis:	6.16ff
Tools:	6.24
Electromagnetic (EM) simulation:	6.15ff
Electromagnetic compatibility (EMC):	27.1
Electromagnetic interference (EMI):	27.1
Electromotive force (EMF):	2.1
Voltage (V, E):	2.1
Electron:	2.1
Free electron:	2.1, 2.26
Mobility:	2.27
Electronic current:	2.2
Electronic design automation (EDA) (*see* Circuit simulation)	
Electronic Load Detector (ELD):	24.14
Electrostatic discharge (ESD):	4.26
Prevention:	23.15
Elliptic-function filter:	10.6
Elmer (mentor):	1.5
Elsie by W4ENE:	10.11
EME (Earth-Moon-Earth) communication:	1.17
Emergency communication:	1.18ff
Using repeaters:	18.3
Emission designators:	11.2
Emissions	
FCC regulations:	13.1
Occupied, necessary:	13.1
Emitter-follower (*see* Common-collector amplifier)	
Encryption:	15.6
End fed half wave (EFHW) antenna	
Radio frequency interference (RFI):	27.16
End-fed half-wave (EFHW) antenna:	21.7, 21.12
Energy and work:	2.2, 2.9
Ampere-hours (Ah):	2.9
Energy density:	2.10
Horsepower (hp):	2.9
Joule (J):	2.2

Potential energy:	2.14
Watt (W):	2.9
Watt-hour (Wh):	2.9
Equalization (microphone):	13.28
Equalization (transmit):	14.3
Equator, geomagnetic:	19.19
Equipment	
Arranging a station:	24.6
Interconnection:	24.8
Mobile mount:	24.12
Equivalent (effective) series inductance (ESL):	5.5
Equivalent (effective) series resistance (ESR)	
Capacitor:	4.5
Equivalent circuit:	2.7
Error detection and correction:	15.2
Error, measurement:	25.2
Ethernet	
RFI:	27.18
European Telecommunications Standards Institute (ETSI):	15.30
Excess noise ratio (ENR):	25.27
Excess temperature:	5.30
ExpressPCB (PCB vendor):	17.39, 23.28
Eye diagram:	11.28
EZNEC by W7EL:	21.19

F

F layer propagation:	19.16ff
Facsimile (Fax):	15.13
Formats:	15.13
Index of cooperation:	15.13
Fading	
Digital signals:	19.29
Ionospheric:	19.9
Selective:	11.11
Tropospheric:	19.27
FAI:	19.14
Fair-Rite Products Corp:	5.19
Fall (rise) time:	3.37
Farad (F):	2.15
Faraday rotation:	19.30
Faraday shield	
Toroid:	5.28
Fast Fourier Transform (FFT):	8.24, 15.10, 25.25
Fast Fourier transform (FFT):	6.18
Fast-scan television (FSTV) (*see* Amateur television)	
FCC:	1.3
Citation:	27.29
Emission designators:	11.2
Field Inspector:	27.29
Interference Handbook:	27.42
Notice of Apparent Liability (NAL):	27.29
RF Interference, cooperation with ARRL:	27.12
RFI:	27.6ff
FCC Part 15:	27.7ff
Absolute emission limits:	27.9
Certification:	27.11
Declaration of conformity:	27.11
Notification:	27.11
Operator requirements:	27.11
RFI rules and definitions:	27.10
FCC Part 18:	27.7
FCC Part 2 definitions:	27.8
FCC Part 97:	1.3, 27.6ff
Spurious emission limits:	27.7
FCC Regulations	
Repeaters:	18.4
FDTD:	6.16
FEC (Forward error correction):	15.2
Feed line (*see* Transmission line)	
Feed line radiation:	27.34
Feed point impedance:	20.9, 21.3
Feed-through termination:	25.29
Feedback:	3.35
Oscillator:	9.3

Feld-Hell:	15.13
FEM:	6.18
Ferri- and ferromagnetic:	2.18
Ferrite:	5.19
Bead:	5.20
Chokes:	5.23
Equivalent circuits:	5.19, 5.22
Permeability:	5.19
Permeability vs frequency:	5.21
Resonances of cores and chokes:	5.20
Toroid cores:	22.14
Type 31 material:	5.23
Type or mix:	5.19, 22.11
Use for EMI suppression:	5.23
Ferrite bead current balun:	20.27
FFT (*see* Fast Fourier transform)	
Fiber optics:	4.29
Field	
Electric (electrostatic):	2.14, 19.1
Magnetic:	2.18, 19.1
Field Day:	1.13
Stub filters:	20.12
Field programmable gate array (FPGA):	8.17
Field-aligned irregularities (FAI):	19.14
Field-effect transistor (FET):	2.29, 4.23
Breakdown region:	4.25
Channel:	2.29
CMOS, NMOS, PMOS:	2.31
Common-source/gate/drain:	4.25, 4.41
Comparison with BJT:	4.26
Cutoff region:	4.25
DC channel resistance, r_{DS}:	4.24
Depletion mode:	2.31
Enhancement mode:	2.31
Forward transconductance, g_m:	4.24
Gate leakage current, I_G:	4.24
High-frequency circuit model:	5.16
Junction breakpoint voltage:	4.24
Junction FET (JFET):	2.29
MOSFET:	2.30
N-channel, P-channel:	2.29
Ohmic region:	4.25
On resistance, $r_{DS(ON)}$:	2.30
Operating parameters:	4.25
Phototransistor:	4.27
Pinch-off:	2.30
Saturation region:	4.25
Small-signal model:	5.17
Source, drain, and gate:	2.30
Specifications:	22.24, 22.28
Field-strength meter (FSM):	25.38
Filter:	3.35
Active:	4.50
Active filter design tools:	10.16
Active RC:	10.11
All-pass:	3.35
Anti-aliasing:	8.4, 8.20
Band-pass:	3.35
Band-stop (band-reject):	10.3
Bandwidth:	10.3
Basic types and definitions:	10.3ff
Bessel (constant-delay):	10.6
Brick wall response:	10.3
Butterworth (maximally flat):	10.5
Capacitor- and inductor-input:	10.7
Cauer (elliptic function):	10.6
Center frequency:	10.8
Chebyshev (equiripple):	10.5
Combline:	10.33
Cutoff frequency:	10.3
Effect of component Q:	10.10
Effect of ripple:	10.10
Group delay:	10.6
Helical resonator:	10.30
High-, Low-, Band-pass:	10.3

High-pass:	3.35, 10.9
Insertion loss:	10.10
Ladder:	10.7
Low-pass:	3.35
Magnitude response:	10.3
Mid-band response:	3.35
Multiple-feedback:	10.15
Notch:	10.3
Notch filtering:	12.55
Nyquist:	11.26
Order:	10.4
Overshoot:	10.6
Passband:	3.35, 10.3
Passive, lumped-element (LC):	10.7
Phase response:	10.3
Quartz crystal:	10.23
Raised-cosine:	11.26
Receive and transmit:	10.2
Reconstruction:	8.20
Return loss (RL):	10.10
RFI:	27.29
Ringing:	10.6
Ripple:	10.4
Ripple bandwidth:	10.5
Ripple-VSWR-Return Loss table:	10.11
Roll-off:	3.35, 10.4
Sallen-Key:	10.15
Shape factor:	8.2
Specifications:	10.4
Stop band:	3.35, 10.3
Stop band depth and frequency:	10.5
Surface acoustic wave (SAW):	10.26
Switched-capacitor (SCAF):	10.12
Transformation, high-pass to band-stop:	10.9
Transformation, low-pass to band-pass:	10.8
Transient response:	10.6
Transition region:	10.4
Ultimate attenuation:	10.4
VHF and UHF:	10.11
Filter method (SSB generation):	11.17, 13.21
Filter, transmission line:	10.26
Band-pass:	10.27
Emulating LC filters:	10.29
Hairpin resonator:	10.28
Interdigital:	10.28
Microstrip:	10.26
Quarter-wave:	10.28
Stripline:	10.26
FilterPro by Texas Instruments:	10.16
Finite Impulse Response (FIR) filter:	10.16
Fire extinguisher:	24.8
Fixed and floating point:	8.16
Flat topping:	17.2
FLDIGI by W1HKJ:	15.5
Telemetry:	16.12
Flow graph:	14.11
Flyback converter:	7.23
Flyback (kickback) diode:	4.56
Flywheel effect:	17.9
FM and Repeaters	
Glossary:	18.21
References:	18.22
Foldback current limiting:	7.18
Forecast (propagation):	19.20ff
Tropospheric ducting:	19.27
Forward bias:	2.27
Forward converter:	7.25
Forward resistance:	2.27
Forward transconductance, gm:	4.24
Fourier transform:	6.18, 8.24
Inverse (IFT):	8.26
Non-periodic signals:	8.26
Spectral leakage:	8.26
Windows:	8.26
Franke, Steven K9AN:	15.15

Free space attenuation:	19.2
FreeDV by KDØEAG and VK5DGR:	15.16
Frequency:	3.2
Calibration:	25.12
Complex:	3.33
Counters:	25.10ff
Marker generators:	25.11
Measurement:	25.11, 25.15
Frequency accuracy, receiver:	25.35
Frequency coordination:	18.4
Frequency counter:	25.10
Use for troubleshooting:	26.6
Frequency Division Multiple Access (FDMA):	15.32, 18.15
Frequency domain:	3.4, 25.21
Frequency modulation (FM):	11.7ff
Demodulation:	12.46
Equipment, FM voice:	18.7
Limiter:	12.17
Modulators:	13.15
Ratio detector:	12.17
Frequency multiplier:	13.24
Frequency response:	3.32, 3.34
AC measurement:	25.10
Measurement with noise source:	25.28
Frequency shift keying (FSK):	11.10ff, 15.6
Audio FSK:	11.12
Binary FSK:	11.10
Gaussian minimum-shift keying (GMSK):	11.10
Multi-carrier FSK:	11.10
Multi-level FSK:	11.10
Selective fading:	11.11
Frequency stability, receiver:	25.35
Frequency standard stations:	25.12
Frequency synthesizer	
Analog:	9.44
Commercial ICs:	9.44
Direct analog (DAS) and digital synthesis (DDS):	9.27
Fractional-N:	9.40
Noise shaping:	9.41
Phase-locked loops (PLL):	9.27ff
Frequency-division, multiple access (FDMA):	11.24
Frequency-hopping (FHSS):	11.22
Friis formula:	5.31
Front-to-back ratio:	21.3
Yagi antenna:	21.30
FSK:	15.6
FSK441 (*see* MSK144)	
FSTV (*see* Amateur television)	
FT8:	1.12, 15.14ff
FTP:	15.24
Full-bridge converter:	7.25
Quasi-square wave:	7.25
Full-wave bridge, center-tap rectifier:	7.6
Function generator:	25.17ff
Fundamental (signal):	3.2
Fundamental diode equation:	2.27
Fundamental overload:	27.15
Fuse:	2.12, 7.2
Fuse holders:	2.12
High-voltage:	7.31
Ratings:	2.12

G

G-TOR:	15.21
Golay FEC:	15.21
Huffman A and B coding:	15.21
GaAs FET:	4.26
Gain	
Amplifier:	3.32
Antenna:	21.1, 21.51
Noise:	5.31
Voltage, current, and power:	3.32
Gain-bandwidth product (F_T, GBW):	4.46, 5.15

Galactic noise: 12.1
Gallium Arsenide (GaAs): 2.30
Gamma match: 21.35, 21.53
Gap noise circuit: 27.18
Gate leakage current, I_G: 4.24
Gateway (D-STAR): 18.12
Gauss (G): 2.19
Gaussian minimum-shift keying (GMSK): 11.10
GC Prevue (CAD software): 23.36
gEDA (CAD software): 6.2
Generator, function: 25.17
Generator, power: 24.17ff, 28.5
    Inverter: 24.18
    RF Noise: 24.19
    Safety: 24.19
Generator, signal: 25.26
Generator, tracking: 25.24
Generic array logic (GAL): 8.17
Geomagnetic equator: 19.19
Geomagnetic storm: 19.12
Gerbv: 23.36
Germanium (device): 2.27
Gilbert (Gb): 2.19
Gilbert cell mixer: 12.39
Gin-pole: 28.17
Global Positioning System (GPS): 25.12
Glossary
    AC theory and reactance: 3.12
    Amateur Radio, general terms: 1.22
    Analog devices and circuits: 4.57
    Antenna: 21.70
    Conductance and Resistance: 2.5
    DC and basic electricity: 2.3
    Digital modes: 15.34
    DSP and SDR: 8.27
    Filters: 10.42
    Modulation: 11.30
    Oscillators and Synthesizers: 9.51
    Power sources: 7.46
    Propagation: 19.33
    Radio frequency interference (RFI): 27.52
    Remote stations: 24.33
    Repeaters: 18.21
    RF techniques: 5.36
    Test equipment and measurements: 25.66
    Transmission lines: 20.33
GMSK (*see* Gaussian minimum-shift keying)
GNU Radio: 14.11ff
    Flow graph: 14.11
    GRC interface: 14.12
    UHD Universal Hardware Driver: 14.16
GPIB: 25.7, 25.17, 25.27
GPS: 16.2
    Receiver: 16.13
    Sentences (data): 16.9
Graphics processing unit (GPU): 8.18
Gray (grey) line propagation: 19.17
Gray code: 8.6, 15.10, 15.11
Grid (vacuum tube): 17.5
    Bias: 17.19
    Control: 17.5
    Screen: 17.5
    Suppressor: 17.5
Grid-dip meter (GDO): 25.11
    Measuring L and C: 25.18
Ground fault circuit interrupter (GFCI or GFI): 7.2, 28.5
    RFI: 27.45
Ground loop: 27.16
Ground rod: 28.9
Ground wave: 19.6
Ground-plane antenna: 21.20ff
    Feeding: 21.22
Grounded grid: 17.6
Grounding: 28.6ff
    AC (signal) ground: 4.33

Coax shields: 28.10
Concrete encased grounding electrode (GEGR): 28.8
Conductors: 28.9, 28.11
Dissimilar metals: 28.12
Earth ground: 28.8
Electrical safety ground: 28.7
Equipment ground: 28.7
Exothermic welding (CadWeld): 28.9
Galvanizing: 28.12
Generators: 24.20
Ground rod: 28.9
Inductance: 28.8
Lightning dissipation ground: 28.8
MIL-HDBK-419A: 28.6
National Electrical Code (NEC): 28.6
R56 Standards and Guidelines for Communications Sites: 28.6
Radio frequency interference (RFI): 27.15
Safety ground: 27.15
Single-point ground panel (SPGP): 28.8, 28.12
Soldering and brazing: 28.9
Station: 24.2
Ufer ground: 28.8
Group delay (filter): 10.6
Guanella transformer: 20.23
Gummel-Poon transistor model: 5.16
Guy wire, lengths to avoid: 22.40

H

H (hybrid) parameters: 5.15, 5.35
H-field: 21.2
Half-bridge converter: 7.25
Half-power frequency: 3.35
Half-wave rectifier: 7.5
    Output voltage: 7.5
    Voltage ratings: 7.6
Half-wave vertical dipole (HVD): 21.13
Ham Radio Deluxe digital communications software: 15.13
Hamfests: 1.8
HamWAN: 15.34
Handham (*see* Courage Kenny Handiham Program)
Hardware description language (HDL): 8.18
Harmful interference: 27.6
Harmonics: 3.2
    Measurement with spectrum analyzer: 25.22
    RFI: 27.7, 27.15
Hartley oscillator
    VFO: 9.6
Harvard architecture: 8.15
Heat management
    Forced-air and water cooling: 4.62
    Heat pipe cooling: 4.62
    Rectifiers: 4.62
    RF heating: 4.62
    RF power amplifier: 17.19ff
    Thermoelectric cooling: 4.62
    Transistor derating: 4.62
Heat sink: 4.60, 7.11
    Selection: 4.60
Height above Average Terrain (HAAT): 3.9
Helical by W4ENE: 10.31
Helical resonator: 10.30
    Coupling: 10.32
    Design nomograph: 10.30ff
    Insertion loss: 10.32
    Tuning: 10.32
Hellschreiber: 15.12
    Telemetry: 16.11
Henry (H): 2.22
Hertz (Hz): 3.2
Hertz, Heinrich: 6.15
Heterodyne (receiver): 12.11
Heterodyne (transmitter): 13.4ff
HF (frequency range classification): 3.39
h_{FE}, h_{fe}: 4.23

High-pass filter:	3.35, 10.3, 10.9
RFI:	27.30
High-Speed Multimedia (HSMM):	15.31
High-voltage power supply:	7.29
Bleeder resistor:	7.30
Capacitors:	7.30
Construction techniques:	7.31, 23.26
Equalizing resistors:	7.29
Fuses:	7.31
Grounding stick (hook):	7.32
Inductors:	7.30
Metering:	7.30
Safety:	7.29
Transformers:	7.30
Hilbert transformer:	11.16
Hipot test:	7.31
Horizon (radio):	19.24
Horsepower (hp):	2.9
Hot stick:	27.28
Hot, neutral, ground wiring:	7.2, 28.4
Hot-carrier diode (*see* Schottky diode)	
HP8640B generator:	25.27
HPIB:	25.7, 25.17
Huffman coding:	15.4
Humidity, relative (RH):	16.2
Hybrid combiner:	25.25, 25.59
Wilkinson:	25.30
Hybrid-electric vehicle (HEV)	
Automotive RFI:	27.49
Hybrid-pi transistor model:	4.35, 5.15
Hysteresis (comparator):	4.49
Hysteresis (magnetic):	2.21

I

I-V curves:	4.18
I/Q modulation:	11.13ff
AM modulation and demodulation:	11.18
FM modulation and demodulation:	11.19
Hilbert transformer:	11.16
I/Q demodulator:	8.3
I/Q signals:	3.3
Modulation and demodulation:	11.15ff
Single-sideband (SSB):	11.16
I2C:	16.7
ICAP4:	6.15
ICAS (*see* Intermittent Commercial and Amateur Service)	
IEC (International Electrotechnical Commission):	27.24
IEEE-488:	25.7, 25.17
IF rejection:	25.34
IFSS (*see* Interference-free Signal Strength)	
Ignition noise:	27.48
Image (GIF):	15.3
Image (receiver):	12.17
Image modulation:	11.19ff
Image rejection:	25.34
Image response:	5.32
Imaginary numbers:	11.14
IMD (*see* Intermodulation distortion)	
Immunity, RF:	27.6, 27.11
Impedance (Z):	3.17
Antenna:	21.2
Calculating from R and X:	3.20
Equivalent series and parallel circuits:	3.21
Graphical representation:	3.18
Mobile antenna:	21.46
Ohm's law for impedances:	3.21
Phase angle:	3.18
Polar and rectangular forms:	3.18
Polar-rectangular conversion:	3.19
Power factor:	3.23
Reactive power (VA):	3.22
Rectangular form:	3.18
Impedance inversion, pi networks:	5.26
Impedance matching:	5.24ff
Antenna to transmission line:	20.14
Antennas:	21.52
Conjugate matching:	20.12
L network:	5.24, 20.12ff
Network:	20.12
Pi network:	5.26, 17.10, 20.13
Pi-L network:	17.11
Quarter-wave (Q) section:	20.14
Resonating the antenna:	20.14
Series- and shunt-input circuits:	20.13
Solid-state amplifier:	17.32ff
T network:	5.26, 20.12ff, 20.17
Transformer:	20.15, 21.53
Transmission line:	20.12, 20.16
Twelfth-wave transformer:	20.15
Impedance matching unit (*see* Antenna Tuner)	
Impedance transformation	
Resonant circuits:	3.30
Impedance transformer	
Transmission line:	20.22ff
IMS (*see* Intermittent Mobile Service)	
In-circuit debugger (ICD):	8.15
In-circuit emulator (ICE):	8.15
In-circuit programmer (ICP):	8.15
Incidental emitters:	27.8
Inductance (L):	2.22
Air core formula:	4.9
Henry (H):	2.22
Induced voltage (back-voltage):	2.22
Mutual inductance (M):	2.23
Straight wires:	4.10
Inductance index (A_L):	4.12
Inductance tester:	25.51
Inductor:	2.18
AC current and voltage:	3.11
Air core:	4.9
Air gap:	2.22
At radio frequencies:	5.6
Color code:	22.11
Coupling:	2.23
Eddy current:	2.22
Effects of coupling:	5.7
Effects of shielded enclosures:	5.7
Energizing and de-energizing:	2.24
Ferrite toroid cores:	22.14
Ferrite toroidal:	4.13
High-voltage:	7.30
Inductance index (A_L):	4.12
Iron core:	4.11
Kick-back voltage, diode:	2.25
Laminations:	2.22
Machine-wound coil specifications:	22.42
Parasitic capacitance:	5.6
Powdered-iron toroid cores:	4.12, 22.12
Ratings, RF power amplifier:	17.16
RL time constant (τ):	2.23
Saturation:	2.21
Series and parallel:	2.24
Series resistance:	5.6
Slug-tuned:	4.12
Standard values:	22.11
Swinging choke:	7.14
Types of inductors:	4.8
Infinite Impulse Response (IIR) filter:	10.20
Insertion loss (filter):	10.10
Insertion loss (IL):	5.13
Instrumentation amplifier:	4.48
Insulated-gate FET (*see* MOSFET)	
Insulator	
Antenna:	21.9
Voltage (V, E):	2.1
Integrated circuit (IC):	22.18
Application-specific IC (ASIC):	4.34
Latch-up:	4.33
Parasitic SCR:	4.33
Programmable-gate arrays (PGA):	4.34

Integrated circuits (Linear): 4.30
    Hybrid circuits: 4.30
    Monolithic: 4.32
    Silicon-on-sapphire (SOS): 4.32
    Substrate: 4.32
Integrated development environment (IDE): 8.15
Intentional emitters: 27.8
Inter-symbol interference: 19.30
Intercept point: 12.8, 25.32
    Third-order (IP_3): 12.8
Interface
    Configuration and control (SDR): 14.10
Interface (analog-digital): 4.56
Interference (see Electromagnetic interference)
Interference-free signal strength (IFSS): 12.10
Intermittent Commercial and Amateur Service (ICAS) rating: 13.3
Intermittent Mobile Service (IMS) rating: 13.3
Intermodulation distortion (IMD): 11.26, 12.7, 13.2
    Identifying: 27.19
    Measurement: 25.32ff
    RFI: 27.15
    Spectrum analyzer: 25.22
Internal impedance
    Voltage and current sources: 2.7
International power standards: 28.4
Internet Radio Linking Project (IRLP): 18.11
Interpolation: 8.21
Intersymbol interference: 11.10, 11.26
Inverse Fourier transform (IFT): 8.26
Inversion: 19.25
Inverted-L antenna: 21.25
Inverted-V antenna: 21.12
Inverters, dc-ac: 7.45
    Sine-wave output: 7.45
    Square-wave output: 7.45
    Volt-ampere (VA) product, rating: 7.45
Inverting amplifier: 4.47
Ion: 2.1
IONCAP: 19.22
Ionogram: 19.8
Ionosonde: 19.8
Ionosphere: 19.7ff
Ionospheric
    Fading: 19.9
    Forward scatter: 19.2
    Refraction: 19.7
IR drop (see Voltage, Voltage drop)
ISM (Industrial, Scientific, Medical): 27.5
Isolation
    Summing amplifier: 3.35
    Toroid: 5.28
Isotropic (radiator): 21.1
Isotropic path loss: 5.33
ITU emission designators: 11.2

J

JESD204B protocol: 8.5
jjSmith: 20.9
Johnson, Johnson-Nyquist noise: 5.30
Joules (J): 2.2
JPEG compression: 15.4
JT4: 15.14ff
JT65: 15.14ff
    Earth-moon-earth (EME): 15.15
    Reed-Solomon code: 15.15
JT9: 15.14ff, 15.16
    Telemetry: 16.11
Junction FET (JFET): 2.30

K

K index: 19.13
Kelvin, Lord (see Thompson, Sir William)
Key click: 11.5, 13.2, 13.18, 26.18
Kicad (CAD software): 6.2

Kickback (flyback) diode: 4.56
Kirchoff's Current Law (KCL): 2.5
Kirchoff's Voltage Law (KVL): 2.6
Klystron: 9.27
Knife-edge diffraction: 19.3

L

L network: 5.24, 20.12ff
Ladder (filter): 10.7
Lagging (leading)
    Power factor: 3.23
Lamination: 2.22
Large-signal model: 4.34
Laser diode: 4.28
    Lasing current: 4.29
    Monochromatic light: 4.29
Latch-up: 4.33
Lead acid battery: 7.32ff
Leakage current: 7.30
Leakage flux: 4.15
    Toroid: 5.29
Leakage path: 5.10
Leakage reactance: 4.16
Leakage resistance
    Capacitor: 4.5
Least mean squares
    Filter: 10.23
Least significant bit (LSB): 8.6
LF (frequency range classification): 3.39
License: 1.5
    Classes: 1.5
    Examination: 1.5
Light-emitting diode (LED): 4.28
    Circuit design: 4.29
    Electroluminescence: 4.28
Lightning (source of noise): 19.32
Lightning dissipation ground: 28.8
Lightning protection: 24.2
    Lightning arrestor: 28.13
    Suppliers: 28.11
Limiter (amplifier): 3.36, 12.17
Limiting: 3.36
Line loss: 20.5
Line of sight propagation: 19.24
Linear (system): 3.31
Linear amplification: 13.37
Linear amplifier: 17.2
Lithium-ion (Li-ion) battery: 7.36
    Charging: 7.41
Litz wire: 4.9, 5.6
LNA (see Low-noise amplifier)
Load line (amplifier): 4.36
Loading (antenna): 21.22
Lock range (PLL): 9.32
Log (logarithmic) amplifier: 4.51
Log (on-air activity): 1.9
Logbook of The World (LoTW): 1.15
Logic analyzer: 25.47
Logic probe: 25.47, 25.50
Logic-gate oscillator: 9.23
Long-path propagation: 19.17
Loop antenna: 21.36ff
Loss
    Filter insertion loss: 5.13
Loss angle or tangent (θ): 4.5
Losses (radiative): 5.10
Lossless and lossy compression: 15.4
Low-noise amplifier (LNA): 12.3
Low-pass filter: 3.35, 10.3
    DC motors: 27.48
    RFI: 27.30
    Telephone RFI: 27.43
Lower sideband (LSB): 11.4, 13.21
Lowest usable frequency (LUF): 19.9

LTSpice by Linear Technologies: 6.2, 17.11
LUF: 19.9
Lumped elements: 5.1
LZW compression: 15.4

M

M-factor: 19.9
Macros: 15.5
Magnet wire: 20.16
Magnetic circuit analogies: 2.19
Magnetic field: 2.18
   Electromagnetic wave: 19.1
   Gauss (G): 2.19
   Hysteresis: 2.21
   Magnetic field strength (H): 2.19
   Magnetic flux: 2.19
   Magnetic flux density (ϕ): 2.19
   Magnetic flux linkage: 2.23
   Magnetomotive force (MMF, $\Im$): 2.19
   Mean magnetic path length: 2.19
   Oersted (Oe): 2.19
   Permeability (μ): 2.19
   RF exposure: 28.26
   Right-hand rule: 2.19
   Saturation: 2.21
   Tesla (T): 2.19
Magnetic flux
   Density: 2.19
   Maxwell (Mx): 2.19
   Weber (Wb): 2.19
Magnetism: 2.18
Magnetometer: 19.12
Magnetomotive force (MMF, $\Im$): 2.19
   Reluctance ($\Re$): 2.21
Magnetosphere: 19.6
Magnetron: 9.27
Magnitude response (filter): 10.3
Manuals, equipment: 26.14
Marine battery: 7.45
Marine layer: 19.27
Marker generator: 25.11
Mast, antenna: 24.21
MATCH by WØIYH: 20.13
Matchbox (*see* Antenna tuner)
Maunder minimum: 19.11
Maxim, Hiram Percy: 1.1
Maximum usable frequency (MUF): 19.8
   Prediction: 19.20ff
Maxwell (Mx): 2.19
Maxwell's equations: 6.15
Maxwell, James Clerk: 6.15
MDS (*see* Minimum detectable signal)
Megger: 7.31
MESFET: 4.26
Metal-oxide varistor (MOV)
   Specifications: 22.37
Meteor scatter: 19.15
Meteor shower: 19.16
Meter
   Digital panel (DPM): 25.8
   Internal resistance: 25.3
   Panel: 25.7
   Protection diodes: 25.8
   Resistance: 25.7
   Scales: 25.8
   Shunt: 25.5
MeterBasic by W4ENE: 17.51
Method of moments: 21.19
Metric units: 22.59
MF (frequency range classification): 3.39
MF propagation: 19.33
MFSK (*see* Multi-level FSK)
MICROCAP9: 6.15

Microphones: 13.27ff
   Attenuator: 13.30
   Pads: 13.30
   Placement: 13.28
Microstrip: 10.26, 20.29
Microwave band designations: 25.29
Microwave construction techniques: 23.37ff
   Capacitors: 23.38
   Lead lengths: 23.37
   PC board: 23.38
   Transmission lines: 23.38
   Tuning and no-tune designs: 23.39
   Waveguide metalworking: 23.37
Microwire: 16.7
MIL-HDBK-419A: 28.6
Military Auxiliary Radio Service (MARS): 1.19
Minimum discernible (detectable) signal (MDS): ... 12.4, 25.22, 25.30
Mirror scale, meter: 25.7
Mix (ferrite and powdered iron): 4.12, 5.19
Mix, Tom 1TS: 16.1
Mixer: 12.25ff
   Active: 12.32
   Amplitude modulator: 13.8
   Angle modulation: 13.14
   Distortion, distortion products: 12.25
   Double-balanced: 12.30
   Gilbert cell: 12.39
   Mixing products: 12.28
   Switching: 12.28
   Tayloe: 12.37
   Testing: 12.36
   Triple-balanced: 12.31
Mixing products: 12.28
MixW digital communications software: 15.12
Mobile
   Antenna efficiency: 21.48
   Antenna impedance matching: 21.46
   Antenna mounting: 21.46, 21.50
   Antennas (HF): 21.41ff
   Antennas (HF) - base loaded: 21.43
   Antennas (HF) - coil loaded: 21.42
   Antennas (HF) - radiation efficiency: 21.45
   Antennas (HF) - top loaded: 21.42
   Antennas (VHF/UHF): 21.50ff
   Ground losses: 21.45
   Impedance matching: 21.46
   Remotely tuned antennas: 21.44
   Remotely-tuned antenna controllers: 21.47
   SSB and CW antennas at VHF/UHF: 21.50
Mobile operation: 24.9ff
   Air bags: 24.16
   Amplifiers: 24.15
   Automotive interference: 24.15
   Cables and wiring: 24.12ff
   Mounts, control head: 24.12
   Operating techniques: 24.16
   RFI: 27.46ff
   Shock mounts: 24.12
   VHF/UHF propagation: 19.28ff
Modem: 15.18
Modes: 11.1ff
   Digital: 15.1ff
Modulation accuracy: 11.28
Modulation index
   Amplitude modulation: 11.4
   Angle modulation: 11.7
Modulation percentage
   Measurement: 25.38
Modulator
   AM: 13.8
   Balanced: 13.9
   Double-balanced mixer: 13.10
Molex connector: 24.9
MoM: 6.20

Monolithic microwave IC (MMIC)
   Specifications: 22.22
Monopole: 21.20
Monte Carlo analysis: 6.1
Moonbounce (see EME): 1.17
MOSFET: 2.30, 4.25
   Depletion mode: 4.25
   Electrostatic discharge (ESD): 4.26
   Enhancement mode: 4.25
   Pass transistor: 7.17
   Power: 4.26
MOSFET, RF Power
   Data sheet parameters and ratings: 17.29
   Gate structures: 17.27
   LDMOS vs VDMOS: 17.28
   RF power amplifier design: 17.27ff
   Thermal design: 17.29
   Transfer characteristics: 17.31
   Voltage ratings: 17.28
MP3 compression: 15.4
MSFK16: 15.9
   Convolution code: 15.10
   Fast Fourier Transform (FFT): 15.11
   Gray code: 15.10
   Hamming distance: 15.11
   Interleaver: 15.10
   Modulation: 15.11
   Quadbit, nibble: 15.10
MSK (see Minimum-shift keying)
MSK144: 15.16
   Low-density parity check (LDPC): 15.16
   Meteor scatter: 15.16
   Offset quadrature phase-shift keying (OQPSK): 15.16
MT63: 15.12
   Error-correction: 15.12
   Latency: 15.12
   Navy MARS: 15.12
   Noise immunity: 15.12
   Tuning error: 15.12
   Walsh function: 15.12
MUF (see Maximum usable frequency)
Multi-protocol controller (MPC): 15.18
Multi-rate conversion: 8.21
Multimeter: 25.3, 26.3
   Input impedance: 25.7
   Specifications: 25.5
   Use of: 25.5
   Used and surplus: 25.7
Multimode communications processor (MCP): 15.18
Multipath propagation: 19.29
Multiplier-accumulator (MAC): 8.16, 8.24
MultiPSK: 15.13
Mutual inductance (M): 2.23

N

N connector: 24.10
Narrowband noise: 27.17
National Bureau of Standards (NBS): 25.1
National Electrical Code (NEC): 28.2, 28.6
   Antennas: 28.3
National Institute of Standards and Technology (NIST): 25.1
National Recognized Testing Laboratories (NRTL): 28.2
National Traffic System (NTS): 1.20
Navigation data: 16.9
Near field: 25.38
Near-vertical incidence skywave (NVIS): 19.9, 21.15
NEC modeling engine: 21.19
Necessary bandwidth: 13.1
Necessary bandwidth (see Bandwidth)
Neper: 20.9
Netlist: 6.6, 23.29
Network analyzer: 25.25ff
Neutralization: 17.22
NiCd (NiCad) battery: 7.36
   Charging: 7.40

NiMH battery: 7.36
   Charging: 7.41
NIST traceable standard: 25.1
Node (circuit): 2.5
Noise: 3.37, 5.30ff
   AM noise and FM signals: 11.8
   Antenna layout: 13.26
   Background: 5.33
   Broadband: 27.17
   Cosmic: 19.32
   Factor, figure: 5.31
   Friis formula: 5.31
   From losses: 5.31
   Gain: 5.31
   Gap noise: 27.18
   Generator, used in transmission line measurements: 20.11
   Ignition: 27.48
   Image response: 5.32
   Johnson, Johnson-Nyquist: 5.30
   Man-made: 19.31
   Narrowband: 27.17
   Of cascaded amplifiers: 5.31
   Of preamplifiers: 5.32
   Power: 5.30
   Simulation: 5.17
   SINAD: 5.31
   Sources: 12.1
   Sun: 5.32
   Temperature: 5.30
   White: 5.30
Noise bandwidth: 25.31
Noise blanker: 12.53
Noise bridge: 25.40
Noise canceling: 12.54
Noise factor (F): 5.31
Noise figure (NF): 5.31, 12.3, 25.31
   Measuring: 25.27
   Preamplifier location: 12.3
   Relationship to noise temperature (Table): 22.43
Noise limiter: 12.53
Noise power ratio (NPR): 12.10
Noise reduction: 12.55
Noise source: 25.27
Noise source signature: 27.21
Noise temperature: 12.3
   Relationship to noise figure (Table): 22.43
Nominal value: 4.2, 22.2
Non-inverting amplifier: 4.47
Non-linear junction: 27.19
Northern California DX Foundation (NCDXF) beacons: 19.21
Norton equivalent circuit: 2.9
   Norton's Theorem: 2.8
Notch filter: 10.3
   DSP: 12.55
NTSC: 11.19
NVIS (see Near-vertical incidence skywave)
Nyquist
   Frequency: 8.7, 8.19
   Rate: 8.7, 8.19
Nyquist filter: 11.26
Nyquist sampling criterion: 8.19
Nyquist sampling theorem: 8.7

O

O wave: 19.9
Occupied bandwidth: 13.1
Octal: 8.6
Oersted (Oe): 2.19
OFDM (see Orthogonal frequency-division multiplexing)
Off-center fed (OCF) dipole: 21.7
Offset (repeater): 18.4
Ohm (Ω): 2.4
Ohm's law: 2.4
   Power formulas: 2.10
Ohmmeter: 25.3

Oil-filled capacitor: 7.30
Olivia: 15.12
  MFSK: 15.12
  Orthogonal tones: 15.12
  Telemetry: 16.11
On-off keying (OOK): 11.5
Open-collector output: 4.49
Open-wire line: 21.7
Operating
  Nets: 1.4
  Ragchewing: 1.4
Operational amplifier (op-amp): 4.46
  Active filter: 4.50
  Common-mode rejection ratio (CMRR): 4.46
  Comparator: 4.48
  Compensation (frequency): 4.46
  Difference amplifier: 4.48
  Differential amplifier: 4.48
  Gain: 4.46
  Gain-bandwidth product (F_T, GBW): 4.46
  Input and output impedance: 4.47
  Input bias current: 4.47
  Input offset voltage: 4.47
  Instrumentation amplifier: 4.48
  Inverting and non-inverting amplifier: 4.47
  Log amplifier: 4.51
  Open-loop gain: 4.47
  Peak detector: 4.50
  Power-supply rejection ratio (PSRR): 4.47
  Rail-to-rail: 4.47
  Rectifier circuit: 4.50
  Specifications: 22.32
  Summing amplifier: 4.48
  Summing junction: 4.47
  Transimpedance: 16.5
  Unity-gain buffer: 4.47
  Use of feedback: 4.48
  Virtual ground: 4.48
  Voltage-current converter: 4.51
  Voltage-follower circuit: 4.47, 4.48
Optoisolator: 4.29, 4.56
  AC load, driving: 4.56
  Circuit design: 4.29
  Current transfer ratio (CTR): 4.29
  Relay, driving: 4.56
Order (filter): 10.4
Orthogonal frequency-division multiplexing (OFDM): 11.11
Oscillation: 3.35
Oscillator
  Audio frequency: 25.17ff
  Cavity resonator oscillator: 9.25
  Colpitts: 9.5
  Crystal: 9.17ff
  Crystal circuits: 9.20ff
  Dielectric resonator oscillator: 9.26
  Disciplined: 25.12
  Feedback loop: 9.3
  Hartley: 9.6
  Logic-gate oscillator: 9.23
  Low-noise: 9.7ff, 9.22
  Phase noise: 9.45ff
  Pierce: 9.23
  Resonator: 9.3
  RF for circuit alignment: 25.59
  Start-up: 9.4
  Troubleshooting: 26.24
  Twin-T, audio: 25.17
  UHF and above: 9.24
  Variable crystal oscillator (VXO): 9.22
  VFO construction: 9.13ff
  VHF and UHF: 9.7
  Wien bridge: 25.17
  YIG-tuned oscillator: 9.26
Oscillators and Synthesizers
  Glossary: 9.51
  References: 9.52
Oscilloscope: 25.12ff
  AC measurement: 25.10
  Analog: 25.12
  Buying used: 25.17
  Digital: 25.14
  Dual-trace: 25.13
  Features and specifications: 25.16ff
  Probes: 25.15
  Rise time and bandwidth: 25.14
  Use for troubleshooting: 26.4
  Use of: 25.15ff
  X-Y mode: 25.14
OSI networking model: 15.18
  Layers: 15.18
  Protocol stack: 15.18
Out-of-band emissions: 27.6
Outlet strip: 28.1
  Safety: 28.2
Overmodulation: 13.11
Overshoot: 10.6
  CW keying: 13.2
Ozonosphere: 19.6

P

P25: 15.30
  APCO-25: 15.30
  Continuous 4-level FM (C4FM): 15.30
  Improved MultiBand Excitation (IMBE): 15.30
  Tetra: 15.30
Packet error ratio (PER): 25.47
Packet radio (AX.25): 15.24
  APRS: 15.25
  Cluster: 15.24
  Digipeater: 15.25
  FTP: 15.25
  KISS: 15.25
  Packet bulletin-board systems (PBBS): 15.24
  TCP/IP: 15.25
  TNC interface: 15.24
PACTOR
  Contact flow: 1.12, 15.19
  Link establishment: 15.19
  PACTOR-I, -II, -III, -IV: 15.19ff
  PACTOR-III link establishment: 15.20
  Speed comparison: 15.19
Pallet modules, RF amplifier: 17.36
Panadapter: 14.4, 25.25
  Architecture, SDR: 14.7
Parallel-bridge converter: 7.25
Paramagnetic: 2.19
Parasitic
  Oscillation: 17.24, 17.35
  Parasitic SCR: 4.33
Parasitic (stray): 5.1
  Capacitance (stray): 5.3, 5.5
  Capacitance of inductors: 5.6
  Effect on filter performance: 5.13
  Effect on Q: 5.8
  Effects of parasitic characteristics: 5.3
  General component model: 5.3
  Inductance: 5.3, 5.17
  Inductance of capacitors: 5.5
  Inductance of resistors: 5.4
  Inductance per inch of wire: 5.3
  Inter-electrode capacitance: 5.6
  Leakage conductance: 5.3
  Package capacitance: 5.6
  Radiative losses: 5.10
  Resistance: 5.3
  Self-resonance: 5.9
Parasitic suppressor: 17.25, 17.33
Parasitics (oscillation): 27.6, 27.15
Parity: 15.2

Part 15 devices: 27.5
Part 18 devices: 27.5
Part 2 definitions: 27.8
Passband (filter): 10.3
Payloads (data)
    HF: 16.15
    VHF/UHF/Microwave: 16.12
PC board construction: 23.21ff
PC board layout: 23.28ff
    Annotation, forward and backward: 23.30
    Annular ring: 23.30
    Auto-placement: 23.33
    Auto-router (autorouting): 23.33
    Bill of Materials (BOM): 23.30
    Board house: 23.31
    Component and solder sides: 23.30
    Component footprint: 23.29
    Copper fill: 23.35
    Design Rule Check (DRC): 23.36
    Double- and multi-layer: 23.30
    Drill file: 23.36
    Excellon file: 23.36
    Gerber file (RS-274X): 23.36
    Microwave techniques: 23.38
    Net: 23.29
    Netlist: 23.29
    Panelizing: 23.30
    Photoplotter: 23.36
    Plated-through hole: 23.30
    RF interference: 23.31
    Routing (traces): 23.33
    Silkscreen: 23.30
    Software: 23.28ff
    Solder mask: 23.30
    Surface-mount component: 23.30
    Symbol library: 23.29
    Through-hole component: 23.30
    Tin plating: 23.30
    Trace current limits: 23.35
PC board material (FR-4): 23.31
PC board transmission line: 20.29
PCB fabrication services: 23.31ff
Peak and peak-to-peak values: 3.6
Peak detector: 4.50
Peak envelope power (PEP): 3.8, 25.20
Peak envelope voltage (Value): 3.8
Peak inverse voltage (PIV, PRV): 4.20, 7.11
Peak power: 3.8
Peak surge current, I_{SURGE}: 7.11
Pedersen ray: 19.17
Peltier effect: 4.62
Pentode: 17.5
Performance requirements: 4.35, 6.2
Period: 3.2
Permeability (μ): 2.19
    Ferrite: 5.19
    Of magnetic materials: 2.19
Phase: 3.2
    Lag and lead: 3.3
    Phase shift: 3.32
    Polarity: 3.3
    Transmitted: 13.26
Phase angle (impedance): 3.18
Phase constant (β): 20.9
Phase detector: 9.29, 9.32
Phase modulation (PM): 11.7ff
    Demodulation: 12.46
Phase noise: 9.45ff, 12.1
    Effect on receiving: 12.4
    Frequency division: 12.5
    Frequency synthesizer: 9.41
    Measurement: 9.45
    Measurement, ARRL Lab: 9.49
    Reciprocal mixing: 9.46
    Transmitted: 9.47, 13.3
    Transmitter test procedure: 25.36

Phase response (filter): 10.3
Phase shift keying (PSK): 11.10ff
Phase-locked loops (PLL): 9.27ff
    Capture range: 9.32
    Charge pump: 9.34
    Dynamic stability: 9.30
    Frequency resolution (step size): 9.30
    Lock range: 9.32
    Loop bandwidth: 9.30, 9.32, 9.33
    Loop filter: 9.38, 9.39
    Measurement and troubleshooting: 9.43ff
    Noise: 9.33
    Phase detector: 9.29
    Phase noise: 9.48
    Prescaling: 9.36
    Reference frequency: 9.30
    Settling time: 9.30
    Voltage-controlled oscillator (VCO): 9.29
Phase-shift keying (PSK)
    BPSK modulator: 13.15
Phased array: 21.65
Phasing line: 20.14
Phasing method (SSB generation): 11.16, 13.22
Phasor: 3.3, 11.15
Photoconductivity: 4.27
Photoconductor: 2.26, 4.27
Photodiode: 4.27
Photoelectricity: 4.28
Photoisolator (*see* Optoisolator)
Photoresistor: 4.27
Phototransistor: 4.27
    Optoisolator: 4.29
Photovoltaic cell: 4.28
    Conversion efficiency: 4.28
    Open-circuit, V_{OC}, or terminal, V_T, voltage: 4.28
    Photovoltaic potential: 4.28
    Short-circuit current, I_{SC}: 4.28
    Solar panel: 4.28
Pi network: 5.26, 20.13
    Impedance inversion: 5.26
    RF power amplifier: 17.10
PI-EL by W4ENE: 17.10
Pi-L network
    135-degree phase shift: 17.13
    Component selection: 17.11
    Interactive tune and load, avoiding: 17.13
    RF power amplifier: 17.10
    Table of values: 17.12
Picket fencing: 19.29
Piezoelectric effect: 9.17
PIN diode: 4.21
Pinch-off: 2.30
Pinouts: 4.19
PL-259 connector: 24.10
Plasma frequency: 19.8
Plastic repair and restoration: 26.40
PN junction: 2.26
    Anode: 2.27
    Barrier (threshold) voltage: 2.27
    Cathode: 2.27
    Depletion region: 2.26
    Forward resistance: 2.27
    Forward voltage drop: 2.27
    Fundamental diode equation: 2.27
    Junction capacitance: 4.20
    Recombination: 2.26
    Response speed, recovery time: 4.20
    Reverse breakdown voltage: 4.20
    Reverse leakage current: 2.27, 4.20
    Reverse-bias saturation current, IS: 2.27, 4.20
PNPN Diode: 2.28
Point-contact diode: 4.21
Polar cap absorption (PCA): 19.12
Polarity: 2.1, 2.3, 3.3

Polarization
    Antenna: 21.1, 21.51
    Circular: 21.52
    Cross-polarization: 21.2
    Radio wave: 19.9
Pole (transfer function): 3.34
Port, electronic: 25.25
Portable operation: 24.17ff
    Antenna supports: 24.21
    Antennas: 24.21ff
    DC power sources: 24.21
    Power sources: 24.17ff
Potential: 2.1
Potentiometer: 4.4
    Digital: 8.11
    Taper (log, audio): 4.4
Powdered-iron core: 22.12
Power: 2.9
    Horsepower (hp): 2.9
    Joule (J): 2.2
    Station: 24.5
    Watt (W): 2.9
    Watt-hour (Wh): 2.9
Power density
    Spectral: 5.30
Power divider: 25.30
Power factor: 3.23
    AC measurement: 25.9
Power filtering
    Bleeder resistor: 7.12
    Capacitor-input: 7.13
    Choke inductor constant (A): 7.14
    Choke-input: 7.14
    Swinging choke: 7.14
Power inverters
    Conducted emission limits: 27.14
Power meter: 25.63
Power strip: 24.5
Power supply: 7.1ff
    Fault symptoms: 26.22
    Use for troubleshooting: 26.6
Power supply regulation: 7.12
    Crowbar OVP circuit: 7.20
    Foldback current limiting: 7.18
    Linear regulator: 7.16
    Load resistance: 7.12
    MOSFET: 7.17
    Over-voltage protection (OVP): 7.20
    Overcurrent protection: 7.17
    Pass transistor: 7.16
    Pass transistor power dissipation: 7.16
    Remote sensing: 7.16
    Series and shunt regulator: 7.15
    Three-terminal voltage regulator: 7.18
    Voltage regulation: 7.12
    Zener diode regulator: 7.15
Power-line noise: 27.2, 27.18, 27.25ff
    Cooperative agreement: 27.28
    Corona discharge: 27.28
    Noise-locating equipment: 27.26
    Signature or fingerprint: 27.26
    Ultrasonic location: 27.28
    Utility complaint: 27.25
Powerpole, Anderson: 24.9
Preamplifier: 12.3
    Microphone: 13.32
    Noise: 5.32
Precipitation static: 19.32
Precision (value): 4.2
Precision rectifier circuit: 4.51
Precision resistor: 4.2, 22.2
Prescaler: 9.36, 25.10
Preselector: 12.20
Primary battery: 7.33

Probe
    Logic: 25.47
    Oscilloscope: 25.15
    RF: 25.19
    Sniffer: 25.23
    Voltage: 25.23
Processing gain: 11.22
Processing, speech: 11.27, 13.31
Programmable array logic (PAL): 8.17
Programmable gate array (PGA): 4.33, 8.5, 8.17
    SDR: 14.17
Programmable logic array (PLA): 8.17
Programmable logic device (PLD): 8.17
    Manufacturers: 8.18
Programmable-gate array (PGA): 4.34
Propagation: 19.1ff
    Back- and sidescatter: 19.19
    Beacon: 19.21
    Below AM broadcast: 19.32
    Chart: 19.21
    D layer: 19.13
    E layer: 19.13ff
    Emerging theories: 19.20
    F layer: 19.16ff
    Forecast: 19.20ff
    Glossary: 19.33
    References: 19.35
    Sky wave: 19.6ff
    Software: 19.22
    Space communication: 19.30ff
    Summary by band: 19.4ff
    Tropospheric: 19.24ff
    VHF/UHF mobile: 19.28ff
Propagation delay: 3.38
PropLab Pro: 19.22
Protocol, digital
    APRS: 15.25
    Automatic repeat request (ARQ): 15.2, 15.18
    B2F: 15.27
    Broadcast: 15.18
    CLOVER: 15.21
    Connected and connectionless: 15.18
    D-STAR: 15.28
    G-TOR: 15.21
    Multicast: 15.18
    P25: 15.30
    Packet radio (AX.25): 15.24
    PACTOR: 15.18ff
    RMS: 15.27
    SMTP: 15.25
    Stack: 15.18
    TCP/IP: 15.18, 15.25
    TELNET: 15.25, 15.27
    Terminal node controller (TNC): 15.18
    UDP: 15.18
    Unicast (point to point): 15.18
    WINMOR: 15.23
PSK31: 1.12, 15.8
    BPSK, QPSK: 15.9
    Convolution code: 15.9
    Dibit: 15.9
    Envelope modulation: 15.9
    Phase-shift modulation: 15.9
    PSK63, PSK125: 15.9
    Telemetry: 16.12
    Varicode: 15.9
    Viterbi algorithm: 15.9
PSPICE: 6.14
PTT (*see* Push-to-Talk)
Public service: 1.18ff
Public-address equipment RFI: 27.44
Pull-up resistor: 4.49

Pulse modulation: 11.24ff
Nyquist frequency, criterion: 11.24
Pulse amplitude modulation (PAM): 11.24
Pulse position modulation (PPM): 11.24
Pulse width modulation (PWM): 11.24
Pulse-width modulation (PWM)
Switchmode power conversion: 7.22, 7.26
Push-to-talk (PTT): 13.36

Q

Q section: 20.14
QAM (*see* Quadrature amplitude modulation)
QRA64: 15.14ff
QRP (Low power operating): 1.16
QSL card: 1.15
Quad antenna: 21.36ff
QuadNet by W4ENE: 10.11
Quadrature: 3.3
Quadrature demodulators, detectors: 12.47
Quadrature modulation: 11.12ff
Quadrature amplitude modulation (QAM): 11.12
Quadrature phase-shift modulation (QPSK): 11.13
Quality factor (Q): 3.23
Amplifier tank circuit: 17.9
Loaded: 3.30
Loaded and unloaded: 5.13
Of components: 3.23
Unloaded: 3.25
Quantization
Amplitude: 8.21
Signal-to-noise ratio (SNR): 8.22
Time: 8.19
Quantization error: 8.22
Quantization noise: 8.22
Quieting (receiver): 11.9

R

R56 Standards and Guidelines for Communications Sites: 28.6
Radians: 3.2
Radiated emissions: 27.9, 27.20
Radiation
Ionizing and non-ionizing: 28.23
Radiation inversion: 19.25
Radiation pattern: 21.4, 21.51
Radiation resistance: 21.2
Radio Amateur Civil Emergency Service (RACES): 1.19
Radio astronomy: 16.1
Radio direction finding (RDF): 1.18, 21.63ff
Doppler shift: 21.69
Electronic antenna rotation: 21.66
Methods at VHF/UHF: 21.67
RFI: 27.24
Switched antennas: 21.68
Time of arrival: 21.68
Radio frequency (RF): 3.39
Radio frequency interference (RFI): 27.1ff
AC line (brute-force) filter: 27.24
AC-line filter: 27.14
Alternator whine: 27.47
Audio equipment: 27.43
Audio filter: 27.43
Automotive: 27.46ff
Bonding: 27.16
Breaker panel test: 27.3
Bypass capacitors: 27.30
Cable shield connections: 27.32
Choke placement: 27.36, 27.43
Common reported problems: 27.5
Common-mode: 27.13, 27.29
Common-mode choke: 27.31, 27.33ff
Computers and accessories: 27.44
Consumer Electronics Association (CEA): 27.24
Cooperative agreement: 27.28
Corona discharge: 27.28
Differential mode: 27.13, 27.29
Electric fence: 27.19
Electric vehicle (EV): 27.49
Electrical noise: 27.19
End-fed antennas: 27.16
FCC rules: 27.8
Fundamental overload: 27.15
Glossary: 27.52
Ground: 27.15
Ground loop: 27.16
Ground-fault circuit interrupters (GFCI): 27.45
Harmful interference: 27.6
High-pass filter: 27.30
Hybrid-electric vehicle (HEV): 27.49
Identifying: 27.17
Ignition noise: 27.48
Immunity: 27.6, 27.13
Intermodulation distortion (IMD): 27.4, 27.15
Keeping a log: 27.17
Locating source of: 27.20ff
Low-pass filter: 27.30
Non-linear junction: 27.19
Notch filter: 27.38
Part 15 devices: 27.7ff
Part 18 devices: 27.7
Part 2 definitions: 27.8
Path: 27.13
Power-line noise: 27.18, 27.25ff
Product review testing: 27.4
Public-address equipment: 27.44
References: 27.53
Repairing neighbor's equipment: 27.2
Source: 27.13
Speaker lead bypassing: 27.32
Speakers: 27.43
Survival kit: 27.36
Susceptibility: 27.2
Switching supplies: 27.45
Telephone: 27.42
Transmitters: 27.36
Troubleshooting: 27.35ff
Ultrasonic location: 27.28
Utility complaint: 27.25
Victim: 27.13
Working with neighbors: 27.2ff, 27.23
Radio horizon: 19.24
Radio propagation: 19.1ff
Radio spectrum: 3.39
Radio spectrum classifications: 3.39
Radiosport (contesting): 1.13
Radioteletype (RTTY): 1.12, 15.6
AFSK, FSK: 15.6
Baudot code: 15.6
Diddle character: 15.6
F1B *versus* F2B: 15.6
Fading: 15.8
Inverted or reverse shift: 15.6
Keyed AFSK: 15.6
Mark: 15.6
Minimal shift keyed (MSK): 15.8
Shift, LTRS and FIGS: 15.6
Shifts: 15.8
Space: 15.6
Spotting an RTTY signal: 15.6
Start and stop bit: 15.6
Telemetry: 16.11
Terminal Unit (TU): 15.6
Tone pair: 15.6
Unshift-on-space (USOS): 15.8
USB and LSB: 15.6
Ragchew: 1.4
Rain scatter: 19.25
Raised-cosine filter: 11.26
Random-wire antenna: 21.7
Rate of change (Δ): 2.23
Ratio detector: 12.17

Rayleigh fading: 19.28
RC time constant (τ): 2.17
Re-radiation: 21.30
Reactance (X): 3.10
  Capacitive (X_C): 3.10
  Chart *versus* frequency: 3.14
  Complex waveforms: 3.17
  Inductive (X_L): 3.12
  Ohm's law for reactance: 3.13
  Series and parallel: 3.13, 3.15
Reactive power (VA): 3.22
Reber, Grote W9GFZ: 16.1
Receiver
  Bandwidth: 12.14
  Blocking dynamic range (BDR): 12.6
  Blocking gain compression: 12.6
  Direct conversion: 12.12
  Dynamic range: 12.6ff
  Frequency accuracy: 25.35
  Frequency stability: 25.35
  Heterodyne: 12.11
  Intercept point: 12.8
  Intermodulation distortion (IMD): 12.7
  Mixer: 12.25ff
  Noise power ratio (NPR): 12.10
  Performance measurement: 12.1ff
  Phase noise: 12.4
  Preselector: 12.20
  Reciprocal mixing: 12.10
  Sensitivity: 12.1, 25.30
  Software defined radio (SDR): 12.21ff
  Superheterodyne: 12.13
  Troubleshooting: 26.25
Reciprocal mixing: 9.46, 12.10, 25.31
Recombination: 2.26
Reconstruction filter: 8.20
Rectification: 3.35, 7.4
Rectifier: 7.10
  Average dc current rating, I_0: 7.11
  Circuits: 4.22
  Current inrush: 7.11
  Equalizing resistors: 7.11
  Fast-recovery: 7.10
  Heat sinking: 7.12
  Inrush current limiting: 7.11
  Parallel diodes: 7.11
  Peak inverse voltage (PIV, PRV): 7.11
  Peak repetitive forward current, I_{REP}: 7.11
  Peak surge current, I_{SURGE}: 7.11
  Power dissipation: 7.11
  Ratings and protection: 7.11
  Reverse recovery time: 7.11
  Schottky diode: 7.10
  Semiconductor: 7.10
  Series diode strings: 7.11
  Switching speed: 7.11
  Thermal resistance (θ): 7.11
Reed-Solomon code: 15.15
Reference plane: 24.4
References
  Analog devices and circuits: 4.64
  Antenna: 21.71
  Antenna safety: 28.23
  Computer-Aided Circuit Design: 6.26
  Digital modes: 15.36
  DSP and SDR: 8.27
  Electrical safety: 28.14
  Filters: 10.42
  FM and Repeaters: 18.22
  Modulation: 11.32
  Oscillators and Synthesizers: 9.52
  PC-board layout: 23.36
  Power sources: 7.48
  Propagation: 19.35
  Radio frequency interference (RFI): 27.53
  Receiving: 12.56
  Remote stations: 24.34
  RF power amplifier: 17.53
  RF techniques: 5.37
  Telemetry and Navigation Data: 16.12
  Test equipment and measurements: 25.66
  Transmission lines: 20.34
  Transmitting: 13.42
  Troubleshooting: 26.41
Reflection: 19.3
Reflection coefficient (Γ,ρ): 5.36, 20.4
  Conversion between attenuation, SWR, return loss: 22.61
Refraction: 19.2
  Ionospheric: 19.7
  Tropospheric: 19.25
Refractive index: 19.2
Regeneration: 3.35
Regulator, voltage: 7.12
  Oscillators and Synthesizers: 9.14
Relay: 2.12
  Analog interface: 4.56
  Configurations: 2.12
  Construction: 2.12
  Optoisolator driver: 4.56
  Ratings: 2.13
  Types of relays: 2.13
Reluctance (ℜ): 2.21
Remote sensing: 16.2
Remote stations: 24.23ff
  Amplifiers: 24.29
  Antenna switching: 24.28
  Automation: 24.28ff
  Future enhancements: 24.32
  Glossary: 24.33
  Insurance: 24.32
  Internet requirements: 24.24ff, 24.32
  Latency: 24.25
  Licensing: 24.23
  Monitoring: 24.26, 24.29
  Networking: 24.23ff
  Power control: 24.29
  Power sources: 24.31
  Radio head: 24.28
  Radio interfaces: 24.30
  Receivers: 24.23
  Remote Ham Radio: 24.28
  RemoteHams: 24.28
  Resources: 24.34
  Rotators: 24.29
  Safety: 24.32
  Serial port servers: 24.30
  Site requirements: 24.31ff
  Smartphone apps: 24.32
  TCP server/client: 24.27
  VNC connection: 24.26
  VPN connection: 24.27
Repeater: 18.1ff
  AM and SSB: 18.2
  Amateur television (ATV): 18.2
  ATV: 18.4
  Band plan: 18.4
  Closed: 18.7
  Controller: 18.5
  Coordination: 18.2
  Crossband: 16.13
  D-STAR: 18.12ff
  D-STAR hardware: 18.14
  Digipeater: 18.4
  Digital: 18.2, 18.3
  Digital voice: 18.20
  DMR: 18.15ff
  Duplexer: 18.5
  FCC regulations: 18.4
  FM voice: 18.2, 18.4ff
  Frequency coordination: 18.4

Glossary: 18.21
History: 18.1
Internet linking: 18.11
Linking: 18.5, 18.10
Narrowbanding: 18.10
Offsets, standard: 18.10
Operation (FM voice): 18.5
P25: 18.20
Remote receiver: 18.6
Rules and regulations: 18.3
Simplex: 16.13
Standard offsets: 18.4
Timer: 18.5
Tone access: 18.7
Resampling: 8.21
Reserve capacity, battery (RC): 7.45
Resistance (R): 2.4
Bridge circuits: 25.3
Effect of temperature: 4.1
Equivalent resistance: 2.6
Four-wire resistance measurement: 25.5
Of wires: 4.1
Ohmmeter: 25.3
Resistivity (ρ): 2.4
Resistor: 2.4, 4.1
Bleeder: 7.13
Carbon composition (carbon comp): 22.2
Carbon film: 22.2
Color code: 22.3
Equalizing: 7.29
IEC identification and marking: 22.4
Metalized film: 22.2
Non-inductive: 5.4
Package dimensions: 22.3
Parasitic inductance: 5.4
Parasitic inductance model: 5.4
Power: 22.4
Precision: 4.2, 22.2, 25.3
Pull-up: 4.49
Resistor pack: 4.48
Series and parallel: 2.6
Standard values: 22.5
Temperature coefficient (tempco): 4.2
Thick-film power: 22.3
Thin-film resistor: 4.32
Types of resistors: 4.2
Wire-wound: 22.3
Resolution: 25.2
Resolution bandwidth (RBW): 25.22
Resonance: 3.16, 9.1
Of ferrite cores and chokes: 5.20
Resonant circuits: 3.24
Antiresonance: 3.27
Bandwidth: 3.25
Circulating current: 3.29
Impedance transformation: 3.30
Parallel: 3.26
Parallel, loaded Q: 3.30
Parallel, use for impedance matching: 3.30
Resonant frequency: 3.24
Selectivity: 3.25
Series: 3.24
Series and parallel: 3.16
Series, unloaded Q: 3.25
Resonant frequency: 3.24
Return loss (RL): 5.36, 10.10, 20.4
Converting between attenuation, reflection coefficient, and SWR: 22.61
Return loss bridge (RLB): 25.25
Reverse Beacon Network: 19.21
Reverse bias: 2.27
Reverse breakdown voltage: 4.20
Reverse leakage current: 2.27
RF ammeter: 25.20, 25.55

RF amplifier
Feedback: 5.17
Power amplifiers: 17.1ff
RF choke: 4.13, 17.16, 22.10
RF connectors: 22.46ff, 24.10
RF exposure and safety: 28.23ff
Cardiac pacemakers: 28.28
Environments, controlled and uncontrolled: 28.26
FCC exposure regulations: 28.28
Low-frequency fields: 28.30
Maximum permissible exposure (MPE): 28.25
MPE limits table: 28.28
Power density: 28.30
Power threshold table: 28.29
RF awareness guidelines: 28.31
RF Exposure and You: 28.31
RF safety standards: 28.27
Specific absorption rate (SAR): 28.25
Station evaluation: 28.29
Thermal and athermal effects: 28.25
RF ground plane: 24.4
RF heating: 4.62, 5.8
RF impedance measurements: 25.25
RF interference (RFI): 27.1ff
RF management: 24.3, 28.8
RF measurements: 25.19ff
RF power amplifier: 17.1ff
RF power measurements: 25.20, 25.63
RF power modules
Specifications: 22.31
RF power transistors (MOSFET)
Specifications: 22.28ff
RF probe: 25.19
RF sampler: 25.58
RF sniffer: 27.51
RF transformers: 5.27
Air-core resonant: 5.27
Binocular core: 5.29
Broadband ferrite: 5.28
RF voltmeter: 25.65
RFI (see RF interference)
Right-hand rule: 2.19
Ringing (filter): 10.6
Ripple: 7.4
Bandwidth (filter): 10.5
Filter: 10.4
Frequency: 7.13
Voltage: 7.13
Rise (fall) time: 3.37
Rise and fall time
Keying: 25.37
RJ connector: 24.11
RL time constant (τ): 2.23
Robotics: 16.3
Construction: 16.22
Data platform: 16.22
Subsystems: 16.22
Rocketry, amateur: 16.3
Construction: 16.21
Data platform: 16.21
Navigation: 16.21
Subsystems: 16.21
Roll-off: 3.35
Roll-off (filter): 10.4
Root-mean-square (RMS): 3.6, 25.9
Non-sinusoidal waveforms: 25.9
Rope: 28.17
Rotator (antenna): 21.70
Ratings: 21.70
Mounting: 21.71
Control unit: 21.72
Ring: 21.72
Position indicator: 21.72
Hy-Gain control unit: 21.73
Troubleshooting: 21.73

Rowe, David VK5DGR: 15.16
RS-274X: 23.36
RTL-SDR: 14.14
Run length encoding (RLE): 15.4
Ruthroff transformer: 20.23

S

S (scattering) parameters: 5.35
S parameters: 6.20
Safe operating area (SOA): 4.62, 7.17
Safety
    AC power: 24.2
    Antenna: 28.14ff
    Bleeder resistor: 7.30
    Chemical properties and hazards: 23.2
    Electrical: 28.1ff
    Electrical safety rules and guidelines: 26.1
    Generator: 24.19
    High voltage: 7.29
    Remote stations: 24.32
    RF exposure: 28.23ff
    Soldering: 23.10
    Workbench and shop: 23.1ff
Safety ground: 7.2
Safety, electrical: 28.1ff
    Back-feeding ac line: 28.5
    Class 1, 2, 3 wiring: 28.5
    Distribution box: 28.2
    Energized circuits: 28.13
    Lockout: 28.2
    National Electrical Code (NEC): 28.3
    Outlet strip: 28.2
    References: 28.14
    Solar panel: 28.13
    Uninterruptible power supply (UPS): 28.13
Safety, RF exposure: 28.23ff
Sample rate
    Digital audio: 12.21
Sampling, analog-digital conversion: 8.19
Satellite
    Amateur: 1.16
    Propagation: 19.31
    Space weather: 19.21
Saturation (magnetic): 2.21
Saturation (semiconductor): 2.28
Scalar network analyzer: 25.25
Scale, meter: 25.8
Scaling: 3.31
Scatter
    Rain: 19.25
    Tropospheric: 19.25
Scattering: 19.3
Scattering (S) parameters: 6.20, 25.25
Schematic capture
    Subcircuits: 6.6
Schematic capture software
    Eagle: 23.28
    Kicad: 23.28
Schematic diagram: 2.2
Schottky barrier: 4.21
Schottky diode: 4.21
Scintillation: 19.27, 19.30
SCR (*see* Silicon controlled rectifier)
Screen grid: 17.5
SDR (*see* Software defined radio)
Secondary (battery): 7.33
Secondary emission: 17.5
Section Manager (SM): 27.3
Selective fading: 13.18
Selectivity: 12.4
Self-discharge (battery): 7.33
Self-resonance: 5.9
Semiconductor
    Acceptor and donor impurities: 2.26

Compound: 2.26
Cross-reference: 26.10
Cutoff (semiconductor): 2.28
Depletion region: 2.26
Doping: 2.26
Extrinsic: 2.26
Free electron: 2.26
Hole: 2.26
Intrinsic: 2.26
Junction semiconductor: 2.27
Majority and minority carriers: 2.26
Monocrystalline: 2.26
N-type, P-type: 2.26
Photoconductor: 2.26
PN junction: 2.26
Polycrystalline: 2.26
Recombination: 2.26
Safe Operating Area (SOA): 4.62
Saturation: 2.28
Substitution: 26.11
Substrate: 2.29
Temperature effects: 4.62
Thermal runaway: 4.62
Sensitivity: 12.1
    Minimum discernible (detectable) signal (MDS): 12.4
Sensors: 16.4ff
    Calibration: 16.6
    Capacitance-based: 16.5
    Current-based: 16.4
    Digital interfaces: 16.6
    Powering: 16.8
    Remote sensing: 16.4
    Resistance-based: 16.4
    Voltage-based: 16.5
Serenade: 6.10
Serial Peripheral Interface (SPI): 16.7
Service monitor: 25.47
SFDR (*see* Spurious-free dynamic range)
Shack notebook: 26.6
Shannel-Hartley theorem: 11.26
Shannon, Claude: 11.26
SHF (frequency range classification): 3.39
Shield, RFI: 27.29
Shielding, oscillator: 9.16
Shock hazards and effects: 26.1, 28.13
Shock mounts: 24.12
Short skip: 19.13
Shortwave broadcast bands: 19.21
Shunt feed: 21.22
Sidescatter: 19.19
Siemens (S): 2.4, 3.11
Signal generator: 25.26
    Use for troubleshooting: 26.5
Signal injector
    Use for troubleshooting: 26.5
Signal source
    Use for troubleshooting: 26.5
Signal to noise ratio (SNR): 5.30
Signal tracing: 26.6
Signal tracing and injection: 26.15ff
Signal-to-noise and distortion ratio (*see* SINAD)
Silicon (device): 2.26
Silicon controlled rectifier (SCR): 2.29
    Anode gate: 2.29
    Cathode gate: 2.29
    Use in a crowbar circuit: 2.29
    Use in ac power control: 2.29
Simplex: 18.2
SINAD: 5.31, 8.12, 25.31
Sinc function: 8.20, 11.25
Sine wave: 3.1
Single sideband (SSB): 11.4ff
    Demodulation: 12.43
    Generating, filter method: 11.17
    Generating, phasing method: 11.16

Generating, Weaver method:	11.17
I/Q modulation:	11.16
Overmodulation:	13.11
SDR generator:	13.10
Transmitting:	13.20ff
Single-point ground panel (SPGP):	24.3, 28.8, 28.12
Skew path:	19.19
Skin effect:	5.6, 5.8, 20.1
Skin depth (δ):	5.8
Skip zone:	19.9
Sky wave propagation:	19.6ff
Slew rate:	3.32
Slow-scan television (SSTV):	1.12, 11.20, 15.13
Remote sensing:	16.13
Small-signal transistor model:	4.34, 5.16
BJT:	4.34
FET:	4.41
Smith chart software:	20.9
Sniffer probe:	25.23
Snubber network:	2.25

Software
4nec2 by Arie Voors:	21.19
Airmail:	15.27
Analog Filter Wizard by Analog Devices:	10.16
ASAPS:	19.22
Codec2 by VK5DGR:	15.16
d*Chat:	15.30
D-RATS:	15.30
Diplexer by W4ENE:	10.11
Dplus:	15.30, 18.14
DPRS:	15.30
Elsie by W4ENE:	10.11
ExpressPCB:	17.39
EZNEC by W7EL:	21.19
FilterPro by Texas Instruments:	10.16
FLDIGI by W1HKJ:	15.5
FreeDV by KDØEAG and VK5DGR:	15.16
GC Prevue:	23.36
Gerbv:	23.36
Helical by W4ENE:	10.31
IONCAP:	19.22
jjSmith:	20.9
LTSpice:	17.11
MATCH by WØIYH:	20.13
Meter by W4ENE:	17.51
MUF prediction:	19.22
MultiPSK:	15.13
PC-board layout:	23.28ff
PI-EL by W4ENE:	17.10
PropLab Pro:	19.22
QuadNet by W4ENE:	10.11
Smith chart:	20.9
SVC Filter by W4ENE:	10.11, 17.32
TLW by N6BV:	20.5
TubeCalculator:	17.7ff
VOACAP:	19.22
W6ELProp:	19.22
Webench by National Semiconductor:	10.16
WSJT-X:	15.14

Software (CAD)
Advanced Design System (ADS):	6.10
Ansoft Designer SV2:	6.2
ARRL Radio Designer:	6.5
AutoCAD:	6.3
B2 Spice:	6.3
EAGLE:	6.2
gEDA:	6.2
ICAP4:	6.15
Kicad:	6.2
LTSpice:	6.2
MICROCAP9:	6.15
OrCAD:	6.2
PSPICE:	6.14
RF-fluent:	6.9
Serenade:	6.10

Software-based test equipment:	25.38
Software defined radio (SDR):	8.2, 14.1ff
ALC:	14.3
Angle modulation:	13.16
Bandwidth:	14.2
Blocking dynamic range (BDR):	8.3
Buffering:	14.2
Cognitive radio:	8.2
Decimation:	12.23
Demodulation, detection:	12.43ff
Design tools:	14.11ff
Digitizing at IF:	12.21
Direct RF digitizing:	12.21
Direct sampling:	8.4
Down-, up-conversion:	12.22
Dynamic range:	8.3, 12.22
Dynamic range testing:	25.34
Equalization:	14.3
FPGA:	14.17
Panadapter display:	14.4
Phase noise:	12.25
Receiver:	12.21ff
Sample rate:	14.2
Signal chains, transmit and receive:	14.1
Signal loss:	14.2
SSB generator:	13.10
Third-order dynamic range (3IMD DR):	8.4
Transmitted:	13.6
Troubleshooting:	26.15
User interface:	14.4
Waterfall display:	14.8
Solar (Sunspot) Cycle 24:	19.11
Solar 27-day rotation:	19.12
Solar battery or cell (*see* Photovoltaic cell)	
Solar cycle:	19.10
Solar flare:	19.12
Solar flux:	19.10
Solar panel:	4.28
Solar wind:	19.6
Soldering:	23.7ff
Desoldering:	23.9
Irons and guns:	23.7
Lead-free:	23.8
Printed-circuit board (PCB):	23.22
Reduction of Hazardous Substances (RoHS):	23.8
Safety:	23.10
Solder types:	23.8
Surface-mount technology (SMT):	23.12ff
Surface-mount technology (SMT) tools:	23.7
Solenoid:	2.12
Solenoidal coil:	2.19
Sonnet:	6.22
Sound card:	15.5
Test equipment:	25.48
Source (voltage, current):	2.7
Source, RFI:	27.13
Source-follower (*see* Common-drain amplifier)	
Space weather:	19.23
Span, frequency:	25.22
Speakers	
RFI:	27.43
Twisted-pair cable:	27.43
Specific energy (battery):	7.34
Specific power (battery):	7.34
Spectral leakage:	8.26
Spectral power and voltage density:	5.30
Spectral purity	
Transmitter:	25.36
Spectrum analyzer:	25.21ff
Features and specifications:	25.24ff
Tracking generator:	25.24
Spectrum, frequency range classifications:	3.39
Speech processing:	11.27, 13.31
Spike (*see* Transient)	
Splatter:	11.27

Split operation: 18.2
Sporadic E propagation: 19.13
Spread spectrum (SS): 15.12
   Direct sequence (DSSS): 15.12
   Spreading: 15.12
Spread-spectrum modulation: 11.22ff
   Chip, chip rate: 11.22
   Chirp modulation: 11.22
   Code-division, multiple access: 11.23
   Direct-sequence (DSSS): 11.23
   Frequency-hopping (FHSS): 11.22
   Processing gain: 11.22
Spurious emission: 13.1, 27.6, 27.15
Spurious response
   Spectrum analyzer: 25.22
Spurious-free dynamic range (SFDR): 8.13, 12.10
Square-law detector: 12.44
Square-law device: 4.40
Squegging (squeeging): 9.7
Squelch: 18.9
   Sensitivity test: 25.35
SSB (*see* Single sideband)
SSNe: 19.21
SSTV (*see* Slow-scan television)
Standard cell (battery) sizes: 7.33
Standard frequency stations: 25.12
Standards
   Measurements: 25.1
   Traceability and transfer: 25.1
Standing-wave ratio (SWR, VSWR, ISWR): 20.4
   Conversion of attenuation, reflection coefficient,
      and return loss: 22.61
   Converting to return loss: 5.36
   Flat line: 20.4
   Myths about: 20.19
Static (precipitation): 19.32
Station
   Assembly: 24.1ff
   Documentation: 24.11
   Layout: 24.2ff
   Location: 24.1
   Power: 24.2
Stefan-Boltzmann's constant (k): 5.30, 5.33
Step attenuator: 25.56
Stethoscope
   Use for troubleshooting: 26.6
Stop band depth and frequency: 10.5
Stopband (filter): 10.3
Stratosphere: 19.6
Stray (parasitic): 5.1
Stripline: 10.26, 20.29
Stub (transmission line): 20.9
   As filters: 20.9
   Combinations: 20.11
   Connecting: 20.11
   Field Day stub filters: 20.12
   Measuring: 20.11
   Quarter- and half-wave: 20.9
Subaudible tone (*see also* CTCSS): 18.7, 18.9
Sudden ionospheric disturbance (SID): 19.12
Summing amplifier: 4.48
Sunspot: 19.10
Sunstone Circuits (PCB vendor): 23.28
Superheterodyne (receiver): 12.13
   AM and SSB: 12.14
   Bandwidth: 12.14
   Digital modulation: 12.15
   Down-, up-conversion: 12.18
   Dynamic range: 12.20
   Filters: 12.18
   FM: 12.15
   Image, image response: 12.17
   Mixer: 12.19
Superposition: 3.31
Suppression, carrier and sideband: 13.2

Suppression, sideband
   Measurement: 25.37
Surface acoustic wave (SAW) filter: 10.26
Surface Meshing
   Method of Moments (MoM): 6.20
Surface-mount technology (SMT): 22.2, 23.11
   Package types: 23.11
   Soldering: 23.12ff
Surge protector: 24.3
Susceptance (B): 3.11
   Capacitive (B_C): 3.11
   Inductive (B_L): 3.12
Susceptibility, RF: 27.2
SVC Filter by W4ENE: 10.11, 17.32
Sweep, oscilloscope: 25.13
Swinging choke: 7.14
Switch: 2.11
   Make and break: 2.12
   Poles and positions: 2.11
   Ratings: 2.11
   Types of switches: 2.11
Switch wafer repair: 26.30
Switched-capacitor filter (SCAF): 10.12
Switching circuit: 4.44
   Circuit design: 4.44
   High-side and low-side switching: 4.45
   Power dissipation: 4.44
   Reactive loads: 4.45
   Transistor selection: 4.46
Switching mixer: 12.28
Switching time: 5.14
Switchmode power conversion: 7.21
   Boost converter: 7.23
   Bridge converter: 7.25
   Buck converter: 7.21
   Buck-boost converter: 7.23
   Continuous conduction mode (CCM): 7.22
   Design aids and tools: 7.28
   Discontinuous conduction mode (DCM): 7.22
   Flyback converter: 7.23
   Forward converter: 7.25
   Pulse-width modulation: 7.22, 7.26
   RFI: 7.21, 27.18, 27.45
   Switching loss: 7.21
SWR meter: 25.39, 26.4
Symbol library (PCB layout): 23.29
Symbol, symbol rate: 15.1
Synchronous transformer: 20.14
System Fusion (Yaesu): 15.30, 18.19
   C4FM: 18.19
   Configuration: 18.20
   IMRS: 18.20
   Modes: 18.20
   Versions: 18.19
   WIRES-X: 18.20

T

T antenna: 21.25
T match: 21.35
T network: 5.26, 20.13
   Design: 20.17
Tank circuit: 9.1, 17.9ff
   Component ratings: 17.15ff
   Efficiency: 17.10
   Flywheel effect: 17.9
   Manual design methods: 17.12
Tayloe mixer: 12.37
TCP/IP: 15.24
Technical Coordinator (TC), ARRL: 26.2, 27.3
Technical Specialist (TS), ARRL: 26.2
Telemetry: 16.9ff
   Digital modes: 16.11
   Non-licensed: 16.11

Telephone
    RFI: 27.42
    RFI filter: 27.43
Television interference (TVI): 27.1, 27.36ff
    Analog TV: 27.39
    Cable TV: 27.39ff
    Digital TV: 27.39
    DVD and VCRs: 27.42
    Electrical noise: 27.39
    Fundamental overload: 27.37
    High-pass filter: 27.37
    Preamplifiers: 27.38
    Spurious emissions: 27.38
Temperature
    Antenna: 5.32
    Excess: 5.30
    Noise: 5.30
Temperature coefficient (tempco): 4.2, 22.2
Temperature compensated oscillator: 9.22
Temperature compensation: 4.63
    VFO: 9.15
Temperature inversion: 19.26
Temperature range
    Automotive: 16.2
    Commercial: 16.2
    Industrial: 16.2
    MIL-SPEC or MIL-STD: 16.2
Temperature sensor: 4.55
Terminal node controller (TNC): 15.18
    Modem: 15.18
    Multi-protocol controller (MPC): 15.18
    Multimode communications processor (MCP): 15.18
Terminations: 25.16, 25.29
Tesla (T): 2.19
Test equipment: 25.1ff, 26.3ff
Test probes: 26.4
    Adapters: 25.6
    Inductive pickup: 26.4
    Use for troubleshooting: 26.4
TETRA (protocol): 15.30
Tetrode: 17.5
Thermal conductivity (k): 4.59
Thermal noise: 12.1
Thermal resistance (θ): 4.59
    Rectifier: 7.11
Thermal runaway: 4.62
Thermionic emission: 17.4
Thermistors: 4.63
Thermocouple detector: 25.20
Thevenin equivalent circuit: 2.8
    Thevenin's Theorem: 2.8
Thin-film resistor: 4.32
Third-order dynamic range (3IMD DR): 25.32
    SDR: 8.4, 25.34
Third-order intercept point (IP$_3$): 25.32
Thompson, Sir William (Lord Kelvin: 25.1
Three-terminal voltage regulator: 7.18
    Adjustable: 7.19
    Current source: 7.20
    Increasing output current: 7.20
    Low dropout: 7.19
Throb: 15.12
Thrust bearing: 21.70
Thyristor: 2.29
Time base
    Frequency counter: 25.10ff
Time constant (τ)
    RC: 2.17
    RL: 2.23
Time division multiple access (TDMA): 15.31, 18.15
Time division, multiple access (TDMA): 11.24
Time domain: 3.4, 25.21
Time standard stations: 25.12
Time-domain reflectometry (TDR): 25.44
Time-invariant: 3.31

Timer (multivibrator) IC: 4.52
    Astable (free-running): 4.54
    Monostable (one-shot): 4.53
Tip-ring-sleeve (TRS) connector: 13.28
TLW by N6BV: 20.4
Tolerance: 4.2, 22.2
Tone, repeater access: 18.7
Tools
    Care of: 23.3
    Recommended for electronics: 23.4
Toroid
    Coupling: 5.29
    Isolation: 5.28
    Leakage flux: 5.29
    Magnet wire: 20.16
    Turns: 5.29
    Winding: 5.29
Total harmonic distortion + noise (THD+N): 8.12
Tower
    Base, concrete: 28.16
    Carabiner: 28.17
    Climbing harnesses and belts: 28.21
    Climbing safety: 28.21
    Crank-up: 28.11
    Erection and maintenance: 28.17
    Gin-pole: 28.17
    Ground crew: 28.23
    Guy wires, lengths to avoid: 22.40
    Guyed: 28.16
    Guying and guy wires: 28.18
    Legal considerations: 28.14
    Roof-mounted: 28.16
    Ropes: 28.17
    Safety references: 28.23
    Safety tips: 28.23
    Self-supporting: 28.16
    TIA-222: 28.15
    Wind load: 28.15
TR (see Transmit-Receive switch)
Tracker (see APRS)
Tracking generator: 25.24
Transceiver
    Handheld: 18.8
    Home station (FM voice): 18.8
    Mobile (FM voice): 18.8
    Troubleshooting: 26.28
Transconductance: 3.32
    Forward transconductance, g$_m$: 4.24
Transequatorial propagation (TE): 19.19
Transfer characteristics: 3.33
Transfer function: 3.33, 3.36
Transfer switch: 28.5
Transformer: 4.13
    50 Hz considerations: 7.3
    Broadband (RF): 17.32
    Color code: 22.15
    Evaluating: 7.3
    High-voltage: 7.30
    Impedance matching: 20.15, 21.53
    Impedance ratio: 4.15
    Interwinding capacitance: 4.16
    Isolation: 7.3
    Laminations: 4.14
    Leakage flux: 4.16
    Leakage reactance: 4.16
    Losses: 4.16
    Magnetizing inductance: 7.3
    Power: 7.3
    Power ratio: 4.15
    Primary and secondary: 4.13
    RF: 5.27
    Shielding: 4.16
    Step-up and step-down: 4.15
    Turns ratio: 4.14
    Volt-ampere rating: 7.3
    Voltage and current ratio: 4.14

Transient: 7.12
Transient protection
  Gas tube: 7.12
  Varistor: 7.12
  Zener diode: 7.12
Transient response
  Filter: 10.6
Transient suppressor diode (TVS): 4.22
Transimpedance amplifier: 16.5
Transistor
  Gain *versus* frequency: 5.16
  Switching circuits: 4.44
Transistor array IC: 4.52
Transistor tester: 25.49
  Use for troubleshooting: 26.6
Transition region (filter): 10.4
Transmatch (*see* Antenna tuner)
Transmission line: 20.1ff
  Attenuation (loss): 20.5
  Attenuation of two-conductor twisted pair: 22.41
  Balanced and unbalanced load: 20.20
  Balancing devices: 20.20
  Coaxial cable: 20.1
  Coplanar waveguide: 20.29
  Decoupling: 20.19
  Effects of loss: 20.6
  Glossary: 20.33
  Impedance of two-conductor twisted pair: 22.41
  Impedance transformation: 20.9
  Impedance transformer: 20.22ff
  Incident, forward, and reflected waves: 20.4
  Ladder line: 20.8
  Length per dB of loss: 20.6
  Load: 20.3
  Lumped-constant: 20.3
  Matched and mismatched: 20.3
  Matched- (ML) and mismatched-line loss: 20.5
  Measurements: 25.44
  Mechanical considerations: 20.7
  Microstrip: 10.26, 20.29
  Open-wire: 20.1
  Parallel-conductor (twin-lead): 20.1
  PC board: 20.29
  Phasing antennas: 20.14
  Quarter-wave (Q) section: 20.14
  Radiation cancellation in: 20.1
  Radiation from: 20.20
  References: 20.34
  Selecting type of line: 20.6
  Specifications: 22.48
  Stripline: 10.26, 20.29
  Stub placement: 20.10
  Stubs: 20.9
  Synchronous transformer: 20.14
  Termination: 20.3
  Transformer: 17.30
  Twin-lead: 20.1
  Velocity factor (VF): 20.1, 20.10
  VHF/UHF: 21.52
  Waveguide: 20.30ff
  Weatherproofing: 28.20
  Window line: 20.1
Transmit-Receive (TR) switch: 13.40
Transmitter
  Amplifier: 13.37
  Carrier and unwanted sideband suppression: 25.37
  CCS, ICAS, IMS rating: 13.3
  FCC regulations: 13.1
  Heterodyne, upconverting: 13.4
  Intermodulation distortion: 25.36
  Performance measurement: 13.2
  Phase noise: 13.3
  Phase noise test: 25.36
  SDR architecture: 13.6
  Speech processing: 13.31
  TR switch: 13.40
  Troubleshooting: 26.26
  Two-tone test: 25.36
Transmitter power output (TPO): 3.9
Transverse electromagnetic mode (TEM): 10.26
Trap (antenna): 21.15, 21.24
Traveling wave tube: 9.27
Triac: 2.29
Triggering, oscilloscope: 25.13, 25.17
Trimmer (potentiometer): 4.4
Triode: 17.5
Triple-balanced mixer: 12.31
Tripler (multiplier): 13.25
Triplexer: 20.10
Troposphere: 19.6
Tropospheric
  Bending: 19.27
  Ducting: 19.25ff
  Fading: 19.27
  Propagation: 19.24ff
  Refraction: 19.25
  Scatter: 19.25
Troubleshooting: 26.1ff
  Amplifier circuits: 26.23
  Amplifiers, power: 26.28ff
  Antenna systems: 26.34ff
  Assessing symptoms: 26.13
  Battery hazards: 26.8
  Circuit-level, analog: 26.18ff
  Circuit-level, digital: 26.20ff
  Completing repair: 26.21
  Component level: 26.7ff
  Connectors: 26.7
  DSP and SDR equipment: 26.15
  General symptoms: 26.26
  High-voltage supplies: 26.22
  Inspections: 26.14
  Microprocessor equipment: 26.17
  Newly constructed equipment: 26.14
  Oscillators: 26.24
  Power supplies: 26.22
  Professional repair: 26.22
  Radio frequency interference (RFI): 27.35ff
  Receivers: 26.25
  Recommended equipment: 26.3ff
  References: 26.41
  Rotators: 21.73
  Search engines: 26.2
  Semiconductors: 26.9ff
  Shack notebook: 26.6
  Signal tracing and injection: 26.15ff
  Systematic vs instinctive: 26.12
  Television interference (TVI): 27.36
  Transceiver: 26.28
  Transmit amplifier modules: 26.25
  Transmitters: 26.26
  Tube tester: 26.38
  Vacuum tubes: 26.12
Tube (*see* Vacuum tube)
Tube tester: 26.38
TubeCalculator software: 17.7ff
Tubing, aluminum: 21.31
Tuned circuit
  Single-tuned circuit: 5.13
Tuning procedure
  Amplifier, RF power: 17.14
Tuning tools: 23.7, 23.25
Turn-around time, transmitter: 25.37
Tuska, Clarence: 1.1
Twelfth-wave transformer: 20.15
Twisted-pair speaker cable: 27.43
Two-port network parameters: 5.34
Two-port parameters: 5.34
Two-tone audio generator: 25.53
Two-tone test: 11.27, 25.36

U

Uda (Yagi-Uda antenna): 21.29
Ufer ground: 28.8
UHF (frequency range classification): 3.39
UHF connector: 24.10
Ultimate attenuation (filter): 10.4
Ultraviolet radiation: 19.6
Unattended operation: 16.15
Underwriter Labs (UL): 28.1
Unicode: 15.3
Unintentional emitters: 27.8
Uninterruptible power supply (UPS): 28.13
Unipolar transistor (*see* Field-effect transistor)
Units
    Systems of measurement: 25.1
Units and conversion factors: 22.58
Unity-gain buffer: 4.47
Unmanned Aerial Vehicle (UAV): 16.3
    Data platform: 16.20
    Navigation: 16.20
    Powering: 16.21
    Subsystems: 16.21
Upper sideband (USB): 11.4, 13.21
USB battery charging: 7.39
User interface (SDR): 14.4
    Control interface: 14.9
    Panadapter display: 14.4
    Waterfall display: 14.8

V

Vackar oscillator: 9.9
Vacuum tube: 17.4ff
    Cathode: 17.4
    Construction: 17.6
    Cooling methods: 17.6
    Grid (control, screen, suppressor): 17.5
    Grid dissipation: 17.15
    Nomenclature: 17.5
    Operating parameters: 17.8ff
    Pentode: 17.5
    Plate (anode): 17.4
    Plate dissipation: 17.15
    Ratings: 17.15
    Screen dissipation: 17.15
    Secondary emission: 17.5
    Specifications: 22.34ff
    Tetrode: 17.5
    Thermionic emission: 17.4
    Triode: 17.5
    Troubleshooting: 26.12
Varactor diode: 4.21
    Specifications: 22.19
Variable crystal oscillator (VXO): 9.22
Variable frequency oscillator (VFO): 9.5ff
    Capacitor selection: 9.13
    Construction: 9.13
    Inductor selection: 9.13
    LC circuits: 9.5
    Shielding: 9.16
    Temperature compensation: 9.15
    Transistor selection: 9.14
Varicode: 11.6, 15.3, 15.8ff
Varistor: 7.12
VCR (videotape cassette recorder) RFI: 27.42
Vector network analyzer (VNA): 20.11, 25.25
    Low-frequency adapter: 25.65
Vectors: 3.3, 11.14
    Complex impedance: 3.18
Velocity (radio wave): 19.1
Velocity factor (VF): 20.1, 20.10, 25.46
Vertical amplifier: 25.12
Vertical antenna: 21.20ff
    Trap: 21.24
Vertical interval signaling (VIS): 11.21
VFO (*see* Oscillator)
VHF (frequency range classification): 3.39
VHF/UHF
    FM voice equipment: 18.8
    Home station antenna (for repeaters): 18.8
    Mobile antennas: 18.8
    Propagation (mobile): 19.28ff
Victim, RFI: 27.13
Video bandwidth: 25.22
Vintage equipment: 1.17
    Repair and restoration: 26.37ff
Virtual height: 19.7
VLF (frequency range classification): 3.39
VOACAP: 19.22
Vocoder: 15.4, 15.30
    AMBE: 18.16
    DMR: 18.16
Voice-operated transmit (VOX): 13.36
Volatile memory: 8.18
Volt-amp reactive (VAR): 3.22
Volt-ampere rating (transformer): 7.3
Voltage
    Potential difference: 25.2
Voltage (V, E): 2.1
    Voltage source: 2.6
    Volts (V): 2.1
Voltage divider: 4.3
Voltage multiplier: 7.7, 7.10
    Full-wave voltage doubler: 7.7, 7.8
    Half-wave voltage doubler: 7.7
    Voltage tripler and quadrupler: 7.8
Voltage probe: 25.23
Voltage reference IC: 4.52
Voltage regulation: 7.13
    Adjustable regulator: 7.19
    Dynamic and static regulation: 7.13
    Generator: 24.17
    Three-terminal voltage regulator: 7.18
Voltage regulator IC: 4.52, 22.17
    Specifications: 22.20
Voltage-controlled oscillator (VCO): 9.29, 9.35
    Noise: 9.48
Voltage-current converter: 4.51
Voltage-follower circuit: 4.47
Voltage-power conversion: 22.60
Voltmeter
    Digital multimeter (DMM): 25.4
    Multiplier resistor: 25.8
    RF: 25.65
    Sensitivity, ohms-per-volt: 25.3
    Vacuum-tube, VTVM: 25.3
Volume Meshing
    Finite difference time domain (FDTD): 6.16
    Finite element method (FEM): 6.18
    Transmission line method (TLM): 6.18
Volunteer Consulting Engineer (VCE), ARRL: 28.1
Volunteer Examiner (VE): 1.5
VOM (volt-ohm-meter): 25.3
Von Neumann architecture: 8.15
VOX (*see* Voice-operated transmit)
VSB, 8-VSB (*see* Vestigial sideband)

W

W1AW: 1.7
W6ELProp: 19.22
Waterfall display: 15.5. 14.8
Watt (W): 2.9
Watt-hour (Wh): 2.9
Wattmeter: 26.4
    Directional: 20.5, 25.20
    Reflectometer: 20.5
Wave cyclone: 19.26
Waveforms

Complex:	3.4
Ramp wave:	3.4
Sawtooth wave:	3.4
Sine wave:	3.1
Square wave:	3.5
Waveguide:	20.30ff
Coax-to-waveguide adapters:	25.29
Coupling to:	20.31
Cutoff frequency:	20.30
Dimensions:	20.32
Dominant mode:	20.31
Modes (TM, TE):	20.31
Practical application:	20.32
Termination:	20.31
Wavelength (λ):	3.40, 19.1
Wavemeter:	25.11
Waveshaping	
CW keying:	13.18
Weather station	
Data platform:	16.23
Weaver method (SSB generation):	11.17, 13.22
Webench by National Semiconductor:	10.16
Weber (Wb):	2.19
Weston, Edward:	25.3
Wheatstone bridge:	25.3
Whip antenna:	21.41ff
Loading:	21.42
White noise:	5.30
Whitten, David KDØEAG:	15.16
Wien bridge:	25.17
Oscillator:	25.53
Wilkinson hybrid combiner:	25.29
Wind Load (rotator):	21.70
Windowing (digital filter)	10.18
Winlink:	15.26ff
Airmail:	15.27
B2F:	15.27
Common Message Servers (CMS):	15.27
Paclink:	15.25
PACTOR:	15.25
PMBO:	15.27
Radio Message Server (RMS):	15.27
TELNET:	15.27
WINMOR:	1.12, 15.23
Comparison to PACTOR:	15.23
SCAMP:	15.23
Sound card:	15.23
TNC interface:	15.23
Wire	
Magnet wire:	20.16
Resistance:	4.1
Size (mobile installations):	24.13
Specifications:	22.39
WIRES-X (Yaesu):	18.20
Words per minute (WPM):	11.6
WSJT by K1JT:	1.12, 19.20
Meteor scatter:	19.16
WSJT-X:	15.14
Alphabet size:	15.15
Bandwidth:	15.15
Block codes:	15.15
Channel symbol:	15.15
Clock synchronization:	15.14
Fast modes:	15.15
Forward error correction (FEC):	15.14
Maidenhead grid locators:	15.14
Message compression:	15.14
Slow modes:	15.14
WSPR:	15.14ff
Telemetry:	16.11
WSPR (Weak Signal Propagation Reporter):	19.20
Wullenweber antenna:	21.66
WWV, WWVH:	19.22, 25.12
Propagation forecast:	19.10, 19.13

X

X wave:	19.9

Y

Y (admittance) parameters:	5.35
Yagi, Yagi-Uda antenna:	21.29ff
Director:	21.30
Parasitic excitation:	21.30
Reflector:	21.30
Stacking:	21.56
VHF/UHF:	21.56ff
YIG-tuned oscillator:	9.26

Z

Z (impedance) parameters:	5.35
Z-transform:	10.22
Zener diode:	4.21
Specifications:	22.18
Voltage regulator:	7.15
Zepp (antenna):	21.7
Zero (transfer function):	3.34
Zero bias:	17.2
Zero-order hold:	8.20
Zero-stuffing:	8.21

Project Index — Online indicates material available with the downloadable supplemental content.

Topic	Title	Page	Author
Amplifier, RF Power	10 GHz 2 W Amplifier	17.43	KB9MWR
	250 W Broadband Linear Amplifier	17.38	K4XU
	3CX1500D7 RF Linear Amplifier	17.48	K8RA
	6 Meter Kilowatt Amplifier	Online	K6GT
	All-Mode, 2 Meter, 80 W Linear Amp	17.41	W6PQL
	Amplifier Overshoot — Drive Protection	17.26	AD5X
	Everyham's Amplifier	17.44	K4ERO
	QSK Controllers for Amplifiers	Online	W7RY, W9AC
	2 Meter Power Amplifier	Online	N7ART
Antenna accessory	A Raspberry Pi Server/Client for Antenna Rotators	Online	W9KE
	Audible Antenna Bridge	Online	WA3ENK
	Eight-Channel Remote-Control Antenna Switch	Online	AC0HB
	External Automatic Antenna Switch for Use with Yaesu or ICOM Radios	Online	NJ1Q
	Legal-Limit Bias-Tee	Online	AD5X
	Low-cost Remote Antenna Switch	Online	KO4NR
	Microprocessor-controlled SWR Monitor	Online	K1QW
	Mounts for Remotely-Tuned Antennas	21.48	PA3VOS
	Transmitting Choke Baluns	20.23	ARRL, K9YC
Antenna tuner	160 and 80 Meter Matching Network for Your 43-Foot Vertical	Online	AD5X
	Switching the Matching Network for Your 43-Foot Vertical	Online	AD5X
	Z-match	Online	AD5X
Antenna, HF	75 and 10 meter dipole	Online	K8SYL
	40-15 Meter Dual-Band Dipole	21.16	K8CH
	All-Wire 30 Meter CVD	21.29	K8CH
	Compact Vertical Dipole (CVD)	21.28	K8CH
	Extended Double-Zepp for 17 Meters	Online	W5ZO
	Family of Computer-Optimized HF Yagis	21.34	N6BV
	Five-Band, Two-Element HF Quad	21.36	KC6T, W6NBH
	Half-Wave Vertical Dipole (HVD)	21.26	K8CH
	Low-band Quad and Delta Loops	21.37	ON4UN
	Multiband Center-Fed Dipole	21.16	ARRL
	Multiband Horizontal Loop Antenna	21.40	ARRL
	Retuning a CB Whip Antenna	21.48	ARRL
	Skeleton Slot for 14-30 MHz	Online	G2HCG
	Top-Loaded Low-Band Antenna	21.23	W9SR
	Triband dipole for 30, 17, and 12 meters	21.18	W1VT
	Triband Moxon Yagi Antenna	Online	K1LI
	Two Multiband, Coax-Trap Dipoles	21.17	W8NX
	Two-Band Loop for 30 and 40 Meters	21.39	NT4B
	Inverted-U Antenna	21.17	W4RNL
	The W4SSY Spudgun	Online	W4SSY
	Off-Center End-Fed Dipole for Portable Operation on 40 to 6 Meters	Online	KE4PT
Antenna, VHF/UHF	6 Meter Halo	Online	VE6AB
	New Spin on the Big Wheel for 2 Meters	Online	W4RNL
	Quick and Cheap Omni Antenna for 1296 MHz	Online	W1GHZ
	A Medium-Gain 2 Meter Yagi	21.57	W4RNL
	Cheap Yagis by WA5VJB	21.58	WA5VJB
	Fixed Moxons for Satellite Operation	21.61	W4RNL
	Homebrew Coaxial Dipole for VHF or UHF	21.54	W6NBC
	Simple, Portable Ground-Plane Antenna	21.54	W1VT
	Three and Five-Element Yagis for 6 Meters	21.56	N6BV
	Dual-band antenna for 146/446 MHz	Online	K3MF
	All-copper, 2 meter J-pole antenna	Online	KD8JB
Circuits and Components	Uses for Thermistors	Online	W0IYH
Computer interface	Simple Serial Interface	Online	N0XAS
	Trio of Transceiver/Computer Interfaces	Online	AA8DX
	USB Interfaces for Your Ham Gear	Online	N0XAS
CW Keyer	TiCK-4 -- A Tiny CMOS Keyer	Online	N2JGU, WB8YGG
	Universal Keying Adapter	Online	N0XAS
Filter, audio	Audio Intelligibility Enhancer	Online	N4GG
	Audio Waveshaping Filter for CW Reception	10.33	W4ENE
Filter, RF	Band-pass filter for 145 MHz	10.40	RSGB
	Broadcast-Band Reject Filter	10.35	ARRL
	Combline Filters for 50-432 MHz	10.33	W1GHZ
	Diplexer Filters	10.37	W0IYH
	Field Day Stub Assembly	20.10	W2VJN
	High-Performance, Low-Cost 1.8 to 54 MHz Low-Pass Filter	10.39	K8CU
	Optimized Harmonic Transmitting Filters	10.36	W4ENE
	Wave Trap for Broadcast Stations	10.35	ARRL
	Half-Lattice Single-Crystal Filter	Online	W0IYH
	Manually-Tuned Preselector	Online	W5OZF
	Software-Controlled Preselector	Online	M0WWA

Topic	Title	Page	Author
Oscillator	JFET Hartley VFO	9.11	W7ZOI, KA7EXM, W7EL
	Low-noise Differential Oscillator	9.10	K7HFD
	Modified Vackar VFO	9.9	N1UL
	VHF/UHF grounded-base oscillator	Online	N1UL
Power source	12-V, 15-A Power Supply	7.51	WA1TWX
	13.8-V, 5-A Regulated Power Supply	7.53	G4YNM
	Adjustable Resistive Load	7.55	G4YNM
	Adjustable Tracking Power Supply	7.61	KC0ZNG
	Automatic Sealed-Lead-Acid Battery Charger	Online	AA4PB
	Four-Output Switching Bench Supply	7.48	K3PTO
	High-Voltage Power Supply	7.57	W8ZR
	Inverting DC-DC Converter	7.55	Stewart, Jim
	Overvoltage Crowbar Circuit	7.63	ARRL
	Overvoltage Protection for AC Generators	7.62	ARRL
	Reverse-Polarity Protection Circuits	7.58	WA0ITP
	Simple Sealed Lead-Acid Battery Float Charger and Switch	7.59	K9JEB
Receiver	10 GHz Preamplifier	Online	W1VT
	430 MHz Preamplifier	Online	ARRL
	Configuring an RTL-SDR for Amateur Radio	Online	HA7ILM
	2 Meter Down-converter	Online	N1UL
	Dual-Band LNA for 2 Meters and 70 Centimeters	Online	AMSAT
	Micro R2 SSB or CW Receiver	Online	KK7B
	Rock-Bending Receiver for 7 MHz	Online	WI5W
	Binaural I-Q receiver	Online	KK7B
	High-Performance 45 MHz IF	Online	G3SBI
RF Interference	RF Sniffer	27.51	ARRL
	Active Attenuator	Online	PA0ZR
	Simple Seeker RFI Receiver	Online	W5IXM
Software defined radio (SDR)	SDR function source code	Online	KA9Q
	An Arduino-based Knob Box for SDR	Online	VE3EBR
Station accessory	Audio Interface Unit for Field Day and Contesting	Online	K0IZ
Test equipment	Bipolar Transistor Tester	25.49	N1AL
	Fixed-Frequency Audio Oscillator	25.53	ARRL
	Gate-Dip Oscillator	25.60	N1AL
	High-Power RF Samplers	25.58	W0IVJ
	Hybrid Combiners for Signal Generators	25.59	N6JF
	Inductance Tester	25.51	WA1PIO
	Logic Probe	25.50	N1AL
	Low-frequency VNA Adaptor	25.65	VE2AZX
	Return Loss Bridge	Online	N6JF
	RF Current Meter	25.55	W8JI
	RF Oscillators for Circuit Alignment	25.59	ARRL
	RF Power Meter	25.63	W7IEQ
	RF Step Attenuator	25.56	K7OWJ
	RF Voltmeter	25.65	K2QHE, GM4THU
	Tandem Match	Online	KI6WX
	Two-Tone Audio Generator	25.53	ARRL
	Test probe adaptors	25.6	W4QO, KG4VHV,
QRP ARCI			
	Wide-Range Audio Oscillator	25.53	Schultz, W9QB
Transceiver	A West Coast Lightwave Project	Online	VE7CA, VE7SL
	TAK-40 SSB/CW Transceiver	Online	WA2EUJ
Transmitter	VHF/UHF Beacon Transmitters	Online	WA3TTS
	MicroT2 Single-Band SSB Transmitter	Online	KK7B
	MkII Universal QRP Transmitter	Online	W7ZOI
	Tuna Tin 2	Online	W1FB
	Near-Space Tracker	16.12	KD4STH
	Pebble Crusher 7 MHz QRP CW Transmitter	Online	G3RJV
	VHF Signal Sources (50 and 144 MHz)	Online	KK7B
Transverter	A Microwave Transverter Controller	Online	OH2GAQ

Author Index — Online indicates material available with the downloadable supplemental content.

Author	Call	Topic	Section Ref	Page Ref
Adams, Chuck	K7QO	Measuring Crystal Parameters	Chapter 10	Online
		Making PC Boards With Printed Artwork	Chapter 25	Online
Allison, Bob	WB1GCM	ARRL phase noise measurement	9.7.7	9.48
		Transmitter testing	25.6.1	25.36ff
		Receiver testing	25.5.1	25.30ff
Applegate, Alan	KØBG	Mobile battery selection	7.13.9	7.45
		Mobile antennas	21.8	21.41ff
		Mobile stations	24.2	24.12ff
Apte, Anisha		Oscillator design	Chapter 9	Online
Audet, Jacques	VE2AZX	Low-frequency VNA Adaptor	25.9.16	25.65
Belrose, John	VE2CV	Sloping antennas	21.5.1	21.26
		Mobile ground losses	21.8.6	21.45
		Mobile antenna efficiency	21.8.6	21.45
Bloom, Alan	N1AL	DSP and SDR fundamentals	Chapter 8	8.1ff
		Digital filters	10.5	10.16ff
		Modulation	Chapter 11	11.1ff
		Digital mode table	15.6	15.32
		Test Equipment and Measurements	Chapter 25	25.1ff
		Test Instrument Bibliography	Chapter 25	Online
Botkin, Dale	NØXAS	Digital Basics	Supplement	Online
Bramwell, Denton	K7OWJ	RF Step Attenuator	25.9.9	25.56
Brenner, James	NT4B	Two-band Loop for 30 and 40 meters	21.7	21.39
Britain, Kent	WA5VJB	Cheap Yagi antennas	21.11	21.58
Brown, Bill	WB8ELK	Amateur Radio Data Platforms	Chapter 16	16.1ff
Brown, Glen	W6GJB	RF chokes for generator output	24.3.1	24.19
Brown, Jim	K9YC	Ferrite materials	5.5	5.19ff
		Noise, noise canceling, and diversity reception	12.7.4	12.54
		Noise performance, microphones and audio	13.7	13.26ff
		Placement of stubs used as harmonic filters	20.3.2	20.9
		Ferrite transmitting chokes	20.5.4	20.25ff
		RF chokes for generator output	24.3.1	24.19
		Antenna Analyzers, and Time-Domain Reflectometry	25.7	25.38ff
Buchmann, Isidor		Batteries and charging	7.13	7.33ff
Bunsold, Pat	WA6MHZ	Refurbishing Vintage Equipment	26.11.5	26.40
Burningham, John	W2XAB	Digital Mobile Radio (DMR)	15.5.17	15.31
		Introduction to DMR	18.5	18.15
Buxton, Al	W8NX	Multiband, coax-trap dipoles	21.2.11	21.17
Campbell, Jeremy	KC8FEI	Automotive RF interference	27.9	27.46ff
Campbell, Rick	KK7B	RF semiconductor design	Chapter 5	5.1ff
Cebik, LB	W4RNL	Inverted-U antenna	21.2.11	21.17
		Fixed Moxons for satellite operation	21.11	21.61
		Medium-gain 2 meter Yagi	21.11	21.57
Chen, Kok	W7AY	Unstructured digital modes	15.2	15.6ff
Clunn, Bob	W5BIG	Vector Impedance Analyzers	25.7	25.38ff
Cooknell, DA	G3DPM	Oscillator construction	9.3	9.13
Coval, Jeff	ACØSC	*FLDIGI*	15.1	15.5
Cowling, Scott	WA2DFI	FPGA data engines	14.4.2	14.17
Cutsogeorge, George	W2VJN	Transmission Lines	Chapter 20	20.1ff
Danzer, Paul	N1II	FM voice repeaters	Chapter 18	18.1ff
Daughters, George	K6GT	6 Meter Kilowatt Amplifier	Chapter 17	Online
Daso, Don	K4ZA	Tower and antenna safety	28.2	28.12ff
Dehaven, Jerry	WAØACF	Phase-locked loops	9.6	9.31ff
Demaw, Doug	W1FB	Wide-range VXO	9.4.5	9.22
Dodd, Peter	G3LDO	Skeleton Slot Antenna for 14-28 MHz	Chapter 21	Online
Doig, Al	W6NBH	Multiband quad antenna	21.7	21.36
Duffey, Jim	KK6MC	Construction techniques	Chapter 23	23.1ff
Eisenberg, Joe	KØNEB	Construction techniques	Chapter 23	23.1ff
Farson, Adam	VE7OJ/AB7OJ		Noise Power Ratio	12.1.4, 12.10
Fisher, Burns	W2BFJ	FOX-1 telemetry	Chapter 16	Online
Fitzsimmons, John	W3JN	Restoring vintage equipment	26.11	26.37ff
Fletcher, Terry	WAØITP	Reverse-polarity protection circuits	7.16.7	7.58
Ford, Steve	WB8IMY	Digital Communications	Supplement	Online
		Space Communications	Supplement	Online
Frey, Dick	K4XU	Solid-state linear amplifiers	17.9	17.27ff
		RF Transistor tables	Chapter 22	22.28ff
Gordon-Smith, Dave	G3UUR	Crystal filters	10.6	10.23ff

Author	Call	Topic	Section Ref	Page Ref
Grant, Doug	K1DG	DSP and SDR fundamentals	Chapter 8	8.1ff
		Digital filters	10.5	10.15ff
		SDR modulation	Chapter 11	11.1ff
		SDR receivers	Chapter 12	12.1ff
		SDR transmitters	Chapter 13	13.1ff
Grover, Dale	KD8KYZ	PC-board CAD	23.6	23.28ff
Gruber, Mike	W1MG	RF Interference	Chapter 27	27.1ff
Grumm, Linley	K7HFD	Low-noise oscillator	9.2.3	9.10
Hallas, Joel	W1ZR	Receivers	Chapter 12	12.1ff
		Transmitters	Chapter 13	13.1ff
		Annual Transceiver Survey	Supplement	Online
		Handbook History	Supplement	Online
		Receiver and Transmitter Architectural History	Supplement	Online
Halstead, Roger	K8RI	Surplus amplifier parts	17.12	17.46
	K8RI	Amplifier tuning	17.4	17.14
Harden, Paul	NA5N	Component data	Chapter 22	22.1ff
Hare, Ed	W1RFI	Construction techniques	Chapter 23	23.1ff
		Troubleshooting and Maintenance	Chapter 26	26.1ff
		RF Interference	Chapter 27	27.1ff
Hartnagel, Hans		The Dangers of Simple Usage of Microwave Software	Chapter 6	Online
Hass, Frank	KB4T	Locating RFI	27.5	27.20
Hayward, Wes	W7ZOI	RF semiconductor design	Chapter 5	5.1ff
		Oscillator temperature compensation	9.3.2	9.15
		Wide-range VXO	9.4.5	9.22
		Segment-tuned VCO	9.7.6	9.49
Henderson, Dan	N1ND	RFI management	27.2	27.4
Hicks, Steve	N5AC	SDR functions, effects of noise, and noise reduction	Chapter 12	12.1ff
		SDR functions and noise	Chapter 13	13.1ff
		SDR user interface and control interface	Chapter 14	14.1ff
Hilding, Rick	K6VVA	Remote stations	24.4	24.23ff
Hollingsworth, Riley	K4ZDH	RF Interference and the FCC	27.2	27.10
Holmes, Walter	K5WH	Digital voice	15.4.5	15.15
Honnaker, Scott	N7SS	Digital modes	Chapter 15	15.1ff
Hranac, Ron	NØIVN	HDTV modulation	11.7.1	11.20
		Cable and digital television	27.8.3-27.8.4	27.29ff
Humbertson, Ken	WØKAH	*FLDIGI*	15.1	15.5
Hutchinson, Chuck	K8CH	Antennas	Chapter 21	21.1ff
Jones, Bill	K8CU	Low-Pass Filter	10.11.6	10.39
Karlquist, Rick	N6RK	Mixers and demodulators	Chapter 12	12.1ff
		Mixers and modulators	Chapter 13	13.1ff
		Audio latency measurement system	24.4	24.25
Karn, Phil	KA9Q	Convolution digital filters	11.6.2	11.18
Kastigar, Matt	N9ES	Amplifier repair	26.9.4	26.28
Kay, Leonard	K1NU	RF Techniques	Chapter 5	5.1ff
Keuken, Jack	KE2QJ	Base-loading system for whip antennas	21.8.3	21.44
Kleinschmidt, Kirk	NTØZ	Generators	24.3	24.17
Klitzing, James	W6PQL	All-Mode, 2 Meter, 80 W Linear Amp	17.11	17.41
Lakhe, Rucha		Mathematical stability problems in simulation programs	Chapter 6	Online
Lampereur, Steve	KB9MWR	10 GHz 2 W Amplifier	17.11	17.43
Langton, Anthony	GM4THU	RF Voltmeter	25.9.15	25.65
Lapin, Greg	N9GL	RF safety	28.3	28.23ff
Larkin, Bob	W7PUA	RF semiconductor design	Chapter 5	5.1ff
Lau, Zack	W1VT	Triband dipole for 30, 17, and 12 meters	21.2	21.18
Luetzelschwab, Carl	K9LA	Propagation	Chapter 19	19.1ff
Lindquist, Rick	WW1ME	What Is Amateur Radio	Chapter 1	1.1ff
Loveall, Pete	AE5PL	D-STAR	15.5.14	15.28ff
		D-STAR repeaters	18.4	18.12
Lux, Jim	W6RMK	Electrical safety	28.1	28.1ff
Mack, Ray	W5IFS	SDR topics	Chapter 8	8.1ff
		Digital filters	10.5	10.16ff
		SDR functions	Chapter 12	12.1ff
		SDR functions	Chapter 13	13.1ff
Martin, Mike	K3RFI	Power-line RF noise	27.6	27.25ff
McClellan, Jim	N5MIJ	D-STAR repeaters	18.4	18.11
McCune, Earl	WA6SUH	DDS and analog synthesizers	9.6	9.27ff
Moell, Joe	KØOV	Radio direction-finding antennas	21.12	21.63ff
		Radio direction-finding techniques	Chapter 27	Online

Author	Call	Topic	Section Ref	Page Ref
Montgomery, Christine	KGØGN	Digital Basics	Supplement	Online
Morris, Steve	K7LXC	Tower and antenna safety	28.2	28.12ff
Mullett, Chuck	KR6R	CAD for power supplies	7.11	7.28
Newkirk, David	W9BRD	Computer-Aided Circuit Design	Chapter 6	6.1ff
		Mixers and Demodulators	Chapter 12	12.1ff
		Mixers and modulators	Chapter 13	13.1ff
Norris, Ken	KK9N	Remote stations	24.4	24.23ff
O'Hara, Tom	W6ORG	Amateur fast-scan television	Supplement	Online
Ott, Henry	WA2IRQ	Electromagnetic compatibility	Chapter 27	27.1ff
Pearce, Gary	KN4AQ	Repeaters	Chapter 18	18.1ff
Peterson, Larry	WA9TT	Slow-scan television	Supplement	Online
Petrich, John	W7FU	GNU radio and SDR design tools	14.4.1	14.11
Pittenger, Jerry	K8RA	3XC1500D7 RF Linear Amplifier	17.12	17.48
Pocock, Emil	W3EP	Propagation	Chapter 19	19.1ff
Poddar, Ajay	AC2KG	Low-noise VHF/UHF oscillators	9.2.2	9.7ff
Popiel, Glen	KW5GP	High-Speed Multimedia	15.5.18	15.31
Portune, John	W6NBC	Coaxial Dipole for VHF or UHF	Chapter 21	21.54
Rauch, Tom	W8JI	RF Current Meter	25.9.7	25.55
Rautio, Jim	AJ3K	Electromagnetic Simulation	6.4	6.15ff
Rogers, Robert	WA1PIO	Inductance Tester	25.9.3	25.51
Rohde, Ulrich	N1UL	Mathematical stability problems in simulation programs	Chapter 6	Online
		The Dangers of Simple Usage of Microwave Software	Chapter 6	Online
		Using Simulation at RF	Chapter 6	Online
		Simulation at RF	6.3	6.12ff
		Oscillator design	Chapter 9	Online
		Phase noise	Chapter 9	Online
		Low noise VHF/UHF oscillators	9.2.2	9.7ff
		Modified Vackar oscillator	9.2.3	9.9
		Crystal oscillators	9.4.4	9.19
		Testing and calculating intermodulation distortion	12.1.4	12.8
		Mixer performance capability	Chapter 12	Online
Rowe, David	VK5DGR	Digital voice - CODEC2	15.4.5	15.15
Sabin, Bill	WØIYH	Half-Lattice Single-Crystal Filter	Chapter 10	Online
		Diplexer Filter	10.10.5	10.37
		IF Speech Clipper	13.3.6	Online
		MATCH by W0IYH	20.4.2	Online
		Transmission-line transformers	20.5.2	20.22ff
Severns, Rudy	N6LF	Switchmode power conversion	7.11	7.21ff
Sherwood, Rob	NCØB	Receiver testing	12.1.4	12.11
		Papers on Receiver Testing and Performance	Online	25.30
Sickles, Cory	WA3UVV	System Fusion	15.5.16	15.30
		System Fusion repeaters	18.6	18.19
Silver, Ward	NØAX	Electrical Fundamentals	Chapter 2	2.1ff
		Radio Fundamentals	Chapter 3	3.1ff
		Circuits and Components	Chapter 4	4.1ff
		Filters	10.1-10.3	10.1ff
		Antennas	Chapter 21	21.1ff
		Amplifier maintenance	26.9.4	26.28
Siwiak, Kai	KE4PT	Discussion of Q	3.7	3.23
Stanley, John	K4ERO	Vacuum-tube amplifiers	17.1	17.1ff
		Optimum ground systems	21.3.1	21.21
Stearns, Steve	K6OIK	Effect of (antenna) conductor diameter	21.1.7	21.3
Steffka, Mark	WW8MS	Automotive RF Interference	27.9	27.46ff
Stein, William	KC6T	Multiband quad antenna	21.7	21.36
Stewart, Jim		Inverting DC-DC converter	7.16.5	7.55
Stockton, David	GM4ZNX	Poles and zeros	3.9.3	3.34
		Oscillators	9.1	9.1ff
		Fractional-n synthesizers	9.6.4	9.39
Stoddard, Patrick	WD9EWK	Satellite Communications	Supplement	Online
Straw, Dean	N6BV	Transmission Lines	Chapter 20	20.1ff
		Antenna modeling and design	Chapter 21	21.1ff
Stroud, Dick	W9SR	Top-loaded, low-band antenna	21.3.3	21.23
Stuart, Ken	W3VVN	Power sources	Chapter 7	7.1ff
Tayloe, Dan	N7VE	Active filter design process	10.4	Online
		Tayloe mixer	12.4.5	12.37
Taylor, Joe	K1JT	Noise	5.8	5.32ff
		WSJT-X modes	15.4	15.14
		Earth-Moon-Earth (EME) Communications	Supplement	Online

Author	Call	Topic	Section Ref	Page Ref
Telewski, Fred	WA7TZY	Poles and zeros	3.9.3	3.34
		Frequency synthesizers	9.6	9.28ff
Thompson, Chris	AC2CZ	Fox-1 telemetry	Chapter 16	Online
Thompson, Tom	WØIVJ	High-Power RF Samplers	25.9.10	25.58
Tonne, Jim	W4ENE	Filters and filter design software	Chapter 10	10.1ff
		Audio processing circuits	13.8.7	13.29ff
Ulbing, Sam	N4UAU	Surface-mount technology	Chapter 23	Online
Verhage, Paul	KD4STH	Amateur Radio Data Platforms	Chapter 16	16.1ff
Wade, Paul	W1GHZ	Noise	5.8	5.30ff
		Combline filters	10.11.2	10.33
		Waveguides	20.7	20.30ff
		Microwave construction techniques	23.7	23.37
		Antenna analyzer – alternative uses	Online	25.41
Wetherhold, Ed	W3NQN	Broadcast-band Reject Filter	10.10.3	10.35
Whitten, Mel	KØPFX	Digital voice	15.4.5	15.15
Winer, Ethan		Microphone conditioning circuits	13.8.7	13.30
Yoshida, Wayne	KH6WZ	Surface-mount device desoldering	Chapter 23	Online
Youngblood, Gerald	K5SDR	Tayloe mixer	12.4.5	12.37